S0-BRJ-880

Annotated Teacher's Edition

Life Science
A problem solving approach

Revised Edition

Joseph L. Carter
Howard P. Goodman
Danny D. Hunter
Leroy J. Schelske

Ginn and Company

Contents

Home Office: Lexington, Massachusetts 02173
0-663-35743-8

Introduction

General Philosophy of *Life Science: A Problem Solving Approach, Revised Edition*

This program was developed to teach life science concepts to children in such a way that they learn through their own experiences. This approach has been used successfully in science programs at all levels of instruction. Such activity-centered programs tend to keep student interest high, since the learners must take an active part in their own education. The teacher must provide the conditions in which pupils can work effectively in a laboratory environment. This calls for teaching skills different from those needed when pupils are kept at their desks at all times while information is dispensed to them. The suggestions found in this Teacher's Guide will hopefully help you to foster a classroom atmosphere that is conducive to individual student investigation.

The life science laboratory program has six major units. They are *Science—The Process of Organizing Information, The Cell—Building Block of Living Things, The Protists, Plant Structures and Functions, Animal Organs and Systems—The Frog,* and *Humans and Their Environment.* Each unit is divided into chapters. Each chapter consists of a brief introduction followed by specific problems to be investigated by the students in the laboratory. Content "bridges" appear between problems, tying them together as the students finish one problem and are about to start the next. The introductory material in each chapter pertains strictly to the problems that will be studied later in the laboratory investigations.

The problems are the heart of the teaching strategy of the program. The problems are much more than a set of instructions telling the students what to do. They are inquiry structures and include, in addition to specific procedural directions, a series of questions that compel the students to think about the purpose and meaning of the activity that they have just performed. These Guide Questions are worded to bring out the key ideas and concepts in the problem. This approach amounts to a form of self-instruction; the students discover facts and concepts for themselves as they proceed through the experiment. The more difficult ideas are reinforced by supplementary statements following some of the Guide Questions. The Guide Questions are to be answered by the students in their own notebooks. They form the main basis for discussion of the results of experiments by the class. Class discussion is always more meaningful to the learners when they have had a part in gathering the information being analyzed.

Each chapter is concluded with two sets of questions, which are used to test the understanding of basic concepts by the students. The first set of questions, entitled *Review Questions,* may all be answered from material given in the chapter introduction or problem contents. The more difficult questions are entitled *Check Your Understanding.* These questions call for a more sophisticated understanding of the concepts presented in the problems and generally may not be answered simply by looking up information in the text. You should consider the ability level of the group when making assignments from the *Check Your Understanding* questions.

Organization of Laboratory Teams

The experiments are best performed by teams of students. The number of students in a team may depend on the nature of the activity, the facilities available, and the ability of the pupils. It is usually recommended that teams consist of two to four students.

Equipment and Supplies

Equipment and supplies are an essential part of any laboratory program. The best way to proceed is to select the units, chapters, and problems your class will be working with and then arrange for the equipment and supplies that will be needed. When handled haphazardly, the obtaining of equipment and supplies can become such a headache that the teacher is tempted to avoid laboratory programs. However, most problems can be solved easily with a little advance preparation.

A comprehensive materials list is provided on pages 6-8 in this Teacher's Guide. This list gives a general picture of what equipment and supplies are needed to complete all the problems in the program. The problems were selected with equipment needs in mind, so the majority of them can be performed without great expense. Even so, starting and continuing a laboratory program is more expensive than a conventional "text-lecture-demonstration" science course. There are several methods of cutting equipment costs without sacrificing the quality of the program. For example, suppose you have thirty-six students in a class. If there are two students per team, you need 18 team "kits," but if there are four students in a team, you need only 9 team "kits"—a savings of 50 percent.

There is still another method of reducing supply needs. Suppose that in a chapter consisting of five problems, one experiment requires a special piece of equipment, such as a microscope. If every team in the class does the problems sequentially, you will need one microscope per team. But if the teams work on the problems in different orders, no more than two or three teams on a particular experiment at any one time, the equipment needs will be reduced considerably. Such a "revolving sequence approach" assumes that the experiments in any given section are nonsequential, that they can be performed in any order. This is usually the case in this book. Where a certain problem must precede a related problem, it is pointed out in the Teacher's Guide.

Housekeeping in the Laboratory

When thirty or more students are engaged in several lab activities at the same time, the amount of materials being used around the room is considerable. If the materials are not left in order at the end of a class period, it can create a major cleanup problem for the teacher. To avoid this situation, simply keep track of the time remaining in each period and announce cleanup time about five minutes before the period ends. This permits each team to return materials to the common supply table or to store their own part of the experiment until the next day.

Each team should be responsible for washing and drying all glassware before returning it to a common storage area. A pitcher of soap suds and a few brushes kept near the sinks will encourage the laboratory teams to wash their own dishes. The assignment of some kind of grade or point penalty might be considered as a reminder for teams that fail to clean up their work space at the end of a laboratory period.

In addition to the team cleanup effort, it is often helpful to assign several specific cleanup groups. These groups, consisting of perhaps five students from different laboratory teams, should be given the responsibility of maintaining the cleanliness of the supply table area, the sink areas, the balance areas, and the stockroom or storage area. A schedule of cleanup groups and specific responsibilities should be prepared and posted to remind students of their responsibilities.

Student Laboratory Notebook

It is essential in this kind of program for each student to keep a complete record of his or her work in the laboratory. Students will frequently need to refer to some previous activity or result for information. To promote good record keeping by the student, a laboratory notebook is a requirement for this course. The notebook serves as a permanent record of the student's observations, measurements, and conclusions. In addition, the answers to the numbered Guide Questions in each problem, including various charts and graphs, are to be recorded in the notebook.

The notebook should be the spiral-bound variety that lies completely flat when open so that the student can write in it easily while working. Students benefit most from the Guide Questions when they are required to answer them as they go along. If students cannot afford a spiral notebook, you could give them 25 sheets of lined paper stapled together, or allow them to use a section of their ring binder as a laboratory notebook.

The notebooks remain in the hands of the students as their own permanent records. They may be evaluated by you once or twice during each unit. This may be done as you move around the room supervising the work, or you may collect all notebooks for a more careful evaluation. The notebook should be assigned a significant part of the student's grade commensurate with the importance of the laboratory work in the program.

Laboratory results should be discussed frequently by the class as a whole or in smaller groups. This activity helps to unify the thinking of the group and to raise questions about results that seem doubtful. You may want to require individual laboratory report sheets for selected problems in which student results are desired right away. These report sheets may consist of lined notebook paper, plus graph paper if charts or graphs are called for in the problem. You may wish to prepare a laboratory report form that already has the Guide Question numbers listed on it. This adds some organization to the sheets but may tend to give the students the impression that they are doing a fill-in exercise.

In scoring the report sheets and laboratory notebook, each problem may be assigned ten points maximum credit, or it may be graded on the basis of one or more points for each acceptable answer to the Guide Questions. Even if a report is poor, it is probably good teaching psychology to give some credit for any laboratory report turned in. This encourages the student to continue his or her efforts, and recognizes the fact that the student has done more than the person who handed in nothing at all.

Science Terms

An alphabetical list of science terms appears at the end of each chapter in the student book. The list includes those words that have been introduced and defined in the chapter. The terms should be studied both for their meaning and for their correct spelling.

As the class proceeds through a chapter, each new science term should be written on the board along with its definition. A preliminary spelling test should be given shortly before the completion of the work in each chapter. Words not included in class assignments should be deleted from the list of science terms each student is responsible to know.

The following procedures could be used to help students improve their spelling.

1. Write each word on the board and pronounce it correctly several times for the class. Sound out each syllable distinctly. Point out troublesome word structures as in words that contain double letters, ei/ie parts, and Latin plural and singular endings.
2. Define each word by using it in the context of the chapter being studied.
3. Have students write each word three times in their notebooks. Have them pronounce the words correctly in unison or individually until the words are part of their working vocabulary.
4. Point out and define common prefixes, suffixes, and other word parts often used in science terms. (Some of these are provided for you below.)
5. Give students a spelling test on each set of science terms. Other words may be added if they have been used and defined as part of the lesson.

Common Word Parts

auto—self
bios—life
cent(i)—one hundred(th)
chroma—color
cide—killer of
co—together
di—two or twice
derm—skin
endo—inner
epi—upon
geo—earth
hypo—underneath
hyper—over
hydro—water
in—within, not, on
inter—between
meso—middle
micro—small
mill(i)—one thousand(th)
mono—single
meter—measure of
ology—study of
osis—condition or state

photo—light
phyll—leaf
phyte—plant
pod—foot
post—after
pro—for
sphere—round body
taxis—arrangement or motion
thermo—heat
trans—across
viab—life

Reading Skills

Most classes include a wide range of reading abilities, so some provision must be made for poor readers. This book requires reading with comprehension if the student is to perform the activities correctly and understand their significance.

It has been found helpful to assess the reading skill of each student at the beginning of the science program. This may be done in cooperation with the reading teacher or language arts department in the school. A simple test of reading ability may be available in your school.

A reading specialist also may be available to point out some ways of improving reading skills. You should enlist the help of the reading teachers in your school in working with those of your students who show serious weakness in reading. Provide the reading teacher with a copy of the text along with your schedule of lessons to be covered each week.

In the classroom you may want to have students read aloud from time to time. Good readers can help poor readers if they are allowed to work together. Poor readers can improve if they are encouraged to read in class and at home. A short quiz related to homework reading assignments motivates most students to read for comprehension.

You may enlist the aid of former students or teacher's aides to work with small groups of students who have severe reading problems. It is extremely difficult to teach much science to a student who cannot read and understand the instructions.

Reference Sources for the Teacher

Good reference sources for teaching life science abound. The following listing only begins to suggest what is available to you. Some of the titles listed are high school biology texts that will be helpful in providing more background information for class discussions. Some of the books are pictoral; you will want to have such as these available at times for students to see the vast differences that exist among organisms that have been classified as similar in taxonomic systems. And some of the titles will aid you in laboratory preparations, demonstrations, and techniques. You will find these and similar volumes extremely useful in teaching a lab-oriented program such as this one.

Biology. William Smallwood and Edna Green. Silver Burdett Company, Morristown, N.J. 1977.
Biology Teacher's Handbook. 3rd ed. (BSCS) Wm. V. Mayer, Ed. John Wiley and Sons, New York. 1978.
Biological Science: Molecules to Man. (BSCS Blue Version) Claude A. Welch, et al. Houghton Mifflin Co., Boston, Mass. 1973.
Culture Methods for Invertebrate Animals. James G. Needham. Dover Publications, New York. 1937.
The Mammals. Richard Carrington and The Editors of LIFE. Life Nature Library. Time, Inc., New York. 1963.
Modern Biology. James Otto and Albert Towle. Holt, Rinehart and Winston, New York. 1977.
The Plants. Fritz W. Went and The Editors of LIFE. Life Nature Library. Time, Inc., New York. 1963.
A Sourcebook for the Biological Sciences. 2nd ed. Morholt, et al. Harcourt Brace Jovanovich, Inc., New York. 1966.
Ward's Culture Leaflet Brochure. Ward's Natural Science Establishment, Inc., Monterey, California or Rochester, N.Y. 1978.

Features of this Annotated Teacher's Edition

This Annotated Teacher's Edition includes both the Teacher's Guide section and annotations on the pages of the student text. A brief description of the organization and features follows.

Annotated Section

Answers to all the Guide Questions appear as annotations within each problem. At the end of each chapter, answers to the Review Questions are also annotated.

Answers to Guide Questions. These questions are located at strategic intervals within each problem. The students answer these questions in their notebooks as they do the experiments. There is no better time for the students to write down what they observe and what they interpret it to mean than right after it happens. The answers in the annotated edition are those most likely to be given by the students if they work carefully, but a certain amount of variation in answers should be expected and accepted in some cases.

Answers to Review Questions. These are part of the end-of-chapter material. The Review Questions are usually easy and the answers may be recalled by the student or looked up in the chapter. Answers given in the annotations will usually not require much explanation to be understood.

Although most annotations are answers to specific questions, some teaching suggestions are included that have been found to be helpful in achieving the learning objectives of the problem. Included are suggestions for post-lab discussion, procedures that usually require additional clarification for some students, and precautions to be observed in maintaining a safe laboratory. Also, certain problems are annotated as appropriate for demonstration, and alternative materials are noted for some experiments. Additional teaching suggestions are found in the Teacher's Guide section.

Teacher's Guide Section

The Teacher's Guide is the supplementary section preceding the student text and printed on pages with a gray border. This guide contains brief summaries of the major concepts and activities in each unit and chapter. It also contains supplementary teaching suggestions for each problem, including an estimate of the time required to complete the problem. The answers to the *Check Your Understanding* questions are found here, as some of the more lengthy answers to Guide and Review Questions. The following are the major features of the Teacher's Guide.

Comprehensive Materials List. This is located on pages 6-8 and provides an overall picture of what is needed to complete all the problems in the text. Actual needs per problem, however, will depend on the size of the lab teams, the sequencing used, and so on. You will therefore want to refer to the specific problems and their materials list when you are planning ahead.

Introduction to the Unit. This consists of a brief summary of the chapters comprising the unit. The scope and sequence of the unit are discussed, along with a rationale for including the topics indicated. A few reference sources are included for the benefit of the teacher.

Chapter Introduction. The contents of the chapter and the relationship among the problems comprising the chapter are discussed. This section gives a quick overview of the development of the chapter and points out the topics receiving emphasis. Following the introduction, detailed instructions for presenting each of the problems in the chapter are given.

Time Requirements per Problem. An estimate of the number of class periods normally required to complete the problem precedes the Teaching Suggestions for each problem. A normal class period is considered to be 40 to 45 minutes in length. It has been the experience of the authors that the separate problems may be assigned over a longer period of time, such as a week, so that slower workers may still find time to finish.

Teaching Suggestions per Problem. This is perhaps one of the most helpful sections of the Teacher's Guide, since it anticipates teacher and student problems before they occur and suggests ways of minimizing them. This section includes not only timely hints about setting up the laboratory situation but also some suggestions for obtaining materials, giving pre-lab instructions, and points to be emphasized in the discussion following the laboratory work.

Suggested Answers to Check Your Understanding. These questions are more thought-provoking than the Review Questions. They are designed to test student understanding of concepts and principles presented in the chapter. Answers given in the Teacher's Guide will reflect the most likely responses based on the experience provided in the problems as well as on the background material in the text. Some variation in student responses to these questions should be expected.

Recommended Films and Filmstrips. Each chapter of the Teacher's Guide is concluded with some suggestions for films or filmstrips suitable as enrichment material for the chapter. (Filmstrips are specifically designated as such; all others are films.) Use discretion in showing these, so that no duplication of laboratory activities is presented in a film unless it is for review purposes. The films listed are intended to increase student understanding rather than to repeat what the students already know.

Achievement Test Questions. These are located on pages 61-87. In multiple-choice format, these questions may be used as end-of-chapter tests. You may want to supplement the suggested questions with some of your own, perhaps essay style or keyed to pre- or post-lab discussions that may have taken place.

Transparency Masters. These are located at the end of the Teacher's Guide section. Described on pages 87-89, the masters may be used to complement the laboratory activities and text.

Comprehensive Materials List

The following list summarizes the equipment and supplies required to complete all the problems in the program. The list is divided into four parts: *Laboratory Equipment, Foods and Biological Specimens, Chemicals and Other Special Materials,* and *Miscellaneous.* The introductory statement for each part defines whether the quantities are for individual lab teams or for bulk buying for the year.

The quantities noted should be used only as a general guideline. Actual quantities will depend on the care with which the items are dispensed and used, the size of the lab teams (recommended as two to four students), and the sequencing of activities. Also, certain problems have been noted in the Teacher's Guide and annotations as especially appropriate for demonstration if you wish to handle them as such. Refer to the specific problems and their materials lists when planning ahead.

Almost all the activities in this course require only common and relatively inexpensive equipment. If the budget prohibits the purchase of more expensive apparatus, such as the incubator, the activities in which such equipment is used may be eliminated.

Laboratory Equipment

The following equipment should be made available to each lab team.

beakers, 250-ml, 3
beakers, 400-ml, 2
beaker, 600-ml, 1
bottle, liter, 1
Bunsen burner, 1
cover glasses, 10
dialysis tubing, cellophane, 15 cm
dissecting kit, 1
dissecting pan, 1
dissecting pins, 10
filter paper, circles, 2
funnel, glass, or thistle tube, 1
forceps or tweezers, 1
graduated cylinder, 50-ml, 1
graduated cylinder, 100-ml, 1
inoculating loop, 1
jars, baby-food with lids, 2
jars, wide-mouth gallon, 3
lens paper, several sheets
magnifying glass or hand lens, 1
medicine droppers, 4
meter stick, 1
microscope, compound, 1
microscope slides, glass, 5
mortar and pestle, 1
pan, large, 1
petri dishes, 4

ring stand with ring and clamp, 1
ruler, flat transparent metric, 1
safety goggles, 1 pair per student
stirring rod, glass, 1
stopper, solid cork, 1
stopper, 1-hole rubber, 1
stopper, solid rubber, 1
test tubes, 18mm x 150mm, 4
test tubes, 22mm x 175mm, 4
test tube, 25mm x 200mm, 1
test-tube holder, 1
test-tube rack, for small test tubes, 1
test-tube rack, for large test tubes, 1
thermometer, Celsius, 1
tubing, glass, 40 cm
tubing, U-shaped glass, 2
tubing, rubber, 90 cm
wire gauze, 1
wooden splints, 12

The following items should be made available to the class as a whole. Each of these items is used in only one or two experiments; if the budget prohibits the purchase of any of these, the problems in which they are used may be skipped.

aquarium, small
balance
hot plate (or hot-water bath)
incubator (optional)
insulated ice chest
refrigerator with freezer compartment

Foods and Biological Specimens

Quantities given for foods and biological specimens are per lab team unless otherwise noted. Some of the specimens must be ordered from biological supply houses; others may be obtained from tropical-fish stores, florists, and supermarkets.

bacon, 1 piece
banana, 1
bread, stale, 1 piece
brine shrimp eggs, 1 small can per class (about 84 g)
butter, several dabs
cheese, 1 piece
clover, grass, or spinach leaf, 1
earthworm, live, 1
earthworm, preserved, 1
eggs, 2
elodea, 6-8 sprigs
fish, small aquarium, e.g., goldfish, 6
flowers, assorted perfect and imperfect, staminate and pistillate
frog, live, 1
frog, preserved, 1
fruits:
- apple, 1
- grapes, several
- orange, 1
- pear, 1

leaves, green, about 4 different species, several
peanuts, several
plants, green potted, 2
pond water culture
seedlings, corn, approx. 25
seeds:
- any variety, 15
- bean, 2
- corn, 2
- grass, 20
- pea, 40
- radish, 20
- tomato, 20

stem, leafy plant, 1
vegetables:
- beans in pod, 1
- carrot, 1 piece
- celery stalk, 1
- lettuce, 1 leaf
- onion, ¼
- peas in pod, 1
- potato, several pieces

yeast, dry, 1 package per class

Chemicals and Other Special Materials

Quantities given are approximations for each class as a whole unless otherwise noted. An average class is assumed to be 30 students.

alcohol, ethyl, 95%, 1 liter
agar medium, sterilized, 150 g
antiseptics, 3 types
Benedict's solution, 1.5 liters
chlorophyll solvent "A" (50 ml N-pentane, 15 ml acetone, 21 ml benzene)
chromatography solvent "B" (100 ml hep-

tane, 4 ml ethyl acetate, 1 ml benzene)
copper sulfate, approx. 5 g
distilled water, 4 liters
gibberellic acid solution, 1 liter
glucose solution, approx. 600 ml
hydrochloric acid, dilute, 300 ml
iodine solution, approx. 120 ml
limewater, 1 bottle
marble chips, 1 liter
methylene blue stain, 0.05%, 1 bottle
potassium permanganate, 4-oz bottle
PTC paper, 1 strip per student
sodium chloride, approx. 0.45 kg
sodium hydroxide pellets, 90
sodium hydroxide solution, concentrated, 1 small bottle
starch-water mixture, 1 liter
vermiculite, 2 liters

Miscellaneous

Students may be asked to bring many of these items to class. Unless otherwise noted, quantities given are for the class as a whole. An average class is assumed to be 30 students.

aluminum foil, 1 roll
bags, paper, 30
bags, plastic, 30
bottles, assorted shapes and sizes, 20 per team
cardboard, 10 cm x 30 cm, 1 per team
cardboard, thick, several pieces
cellophane tape, 1 roll
cloth, small pieces, 3
cloth, flannel, 1 sq yd
coat hangers, wire, 1 per team
cotton balls, 1 pkg
cotton thread, 1 spool
detergent, nonbiodegradable liquid, 1 bottle
flower pots, 4-inch, or half-gallon milk cartons, 2 per team
graph paper, 2 pkg
index cards, 3" x 5", lines on one side, 2 pkg
ink, permanent, 1 bottle
ink, red or blue washable, 1 bottle
jar, with twist-off cap, e.g., peanut butter, 1 per team
knife, kitchen, 1 per team
knitting needle, 1
masking tape, 1 roll
matches, wooden, 1 box
milk cartons, quart, 3 per team
newsprint, small, several selections
paper, brown wrapping, several sheets
paper, white, 8½" x 11", 1 pkg
paper clips, 1 box
paper punch, 1
paper towels, 2 rolls
pen, felt-tip, 1 per team
pencils or pens, 3 different colors per team
piano wire, 1 spool
plastic wrap, 1 roll
razor blades, new single-edged, several
rubber bands, 1 box
scissors, 1 per team
screening, plastic window, 8 cm x 8 cm, 1 per team
spoons, several
string, 1 roll
sugar, table, approx. 0.25 kg
toothpicks, flat, 1 pkg
toothpicks, rounded, 1 pkg
vegetable oil, 1 bottle
wire cutters, 1

Unit 1: Science — The Process of Organizing Information

This unit is designed to provide an introduction to some activities essential to gathering and organizing information. If the students are to be able to record and interpret the data they collect, they must be trained to organize and present it.

The unit starts with an activity that points out how much may be learned through senses other than the eyes. The use of tables and graphs is then presented as an aid to processing and interpreting data. The elements of good experimental design are also studied.

After a brief look at some of the similarities and differences between living and nonliving things, an introduction to classification systems is given. Reasons for classifying living and nonliving things are presented, along with some well-known examples of classification systems. The students begin by learning to classify nonliving objects. They then use a key to classify a group of mammals into different orders. The task of making up their own system of classification for a variety of leaves serves as a good test of their understanding of the design of a useful classification system.

Chapter 1: Gathering and Storing Information

It is recommended that you use demonstrations to introduce the students to the need for careful observation in the laboratory. Suggested demonstrations and follow-up activities are described before Problem 1-1 in this section. They will serve to instruct the students in how to observe and record meaningful data.

Problem 1-1 is designed to develop the powers of observation by using senses other than the eyes. The statements made by individual students form the basis for discussing the difference between an observation and an interpretation.

In Problem 1-2 the students use a meter stick to obtain measurements of the heights of students in the class. Besides familiarizing the students with the use of tables, this activity serves as an introduction to the metric system. Various methods of obtaining data are presented and used by each team of students. These data are then organized by the students into tables.

The importance of recalling data is pointed out before the students are introduced to retrieval methods. A "Knit-Pick" card system is used in Problem 1-3 to store data in a form that can be quickly retrieved. This system is compared with card files used in libraries and with computers used in many industries. The limitations of the Knit-Pick system are pointed out.

This introductory chapter concludes with a presentation of a controlled experiment in Problem 1-4. Each student is asked to study the factors that have been considered in the design of the experiment. The usefulness of the data obtained from this experiment is related to the design of the experiment. This introduction is used to challenge the students to design their own controlled experiment to solve a particular biological problem. Chapter 1 thus provides an introduction to several skills that will be used by the students throughout the remainder of the course.

Teacher Demonstration, First Day of Class

Good observation is an art. Good scientific observations are those that lead to provable conclusions. It requires concentration and practice to become a good scientific observer.

In order for students to be properly oriented in this course, they must be able to differentiate between observations and interpretations. Many people confuse the two, not only in science but also in their everyday lives.

Before performing the following demonstrations, you should inform the class as to what will be expected of them. The following instructions should be written on the chalkboard:

1. Observe all the activities very carefully.
2. Write a brief statement describing everything that is observed. (Observations are anything that can be seen, heard, smelled, touched, or tasted.)

At the end of the four demonstrations, give the class a questionnaire such as the one shown below (pages 10-11). Before performing the demonstrations, have all of the necessary materials prepared. While doing the demonstrations, work at a steady pace and make very few comments. Rinse and dry all glassware between classes. Do not let incoming students see how you prepare for the demonstrations.

Demonstration 1

Unroll about a meter of twine, cut it off with scissors, and tie the twine between any two points such as two rods or two ring stands. Take six or seven plant leaves, one at a time, from a sack and tape them to the twine. Use leaves of different colors and shapes. After a few minutes, untie the twine from both ends and put both twine and leaves into the sack.

Demonstration 2

Take out a large beaker of water into which you have previously put a cup of household ammonia. Place three small empty beakers on the table. Two should be completely empty and the third should have several drops of phenolphthalein indicator in it. The students should not know about the presence of the indicator. It may be wise to have the two empty beakers moist on the inside so that the indicator will not be noticed in the third beaker.

Now pick up a package of grape-flavored, powdered drink and pour about a teaspoonful of it into the first beaker. Half fill the beaker with the ammonia solution and hold it up so the students can see it. It will turn a purple color. Next add the ammonia solution to the second (empty) beaker. It will remain clear. Now pour ammonia solution into the third beaker (containing indicator). It should turn purple.

Allow the students time to complete their written observations, then pour the contents of all four beakers into the sink and *refill the large beaker from the tap.*

(Before the next class, prepare a fresh ammonia-water solution.)

Demonstration 3

Take out three water glasses and a milk carton. Have the carton wrapped with paper so that no printing can be seen. Half fill each of the three glasses with a white liquid from the carton. Set them aside.

Demonstration 4

Place two beakers on the table. One should be about half full of water and the other half full of denatured alcohol. Drop an ice cube into each one. The ice cube will float in the water and sink in the alcohol.

At the conclusion of the last demonstration, hand out a sheet of questions, which the students should answer by using the notes they took during the demonstrations. A suggested questionnaire on this material appears at the end of this section.

Allow the class about 5 minutes to complete the questionnaire. Then collect the papers and discuss the questions. Use an inquiry approach; that is, ask questions rather than simply telling the class the significance of each part of the demonstration.

In the discussion, try to bring out the difference between an observation and an interpretation. There are several opportunities for students to jump to unwarranted conclusions. In Demonstration 2, the clear liquid looks like water but has properties that differ from those of water. In Demonstration 3, the liquid looks like milk, but some students may have doubts after watching Demonstration 2, in which the "water" didn't behave like water in all three glasses.

The following is a sample questionnaire for the students to complete.

Questions About the Demonstrations

Name ________

Class period ________

1. How many observations did you make about the twine used in Demonstration 1?
2. How many observations did you write down about the leaves used in the first demonstration?
3. Did you use any numbers in your description of Demonstration 1?
4. How many glasses of water did you describe being poured in Demonstration 2?
5. How many glasses of powdered drink were present in Demonstration 2? How do you know?
6. What did you call the liquid in the large beaker?

7. How many glasses of white liquid were poured in Demonstration 3?
8. Did you call the liquid in Demonstration 3 "milk"? Why?
9. How did you describe the two liquids used in Demonstration 4?
10. Did you record that ice cubes were added to both glasses?
11. Could one of the liquids have been something other than water? Could one of the cubes have been something other than ice? How could you test either of the two possibilities just raised?
12. Did your notes help you recall the details of what you observed earlier?

You might allow a student or two to try out their ideas in Question 11 if it can be done safely and conveniently in the classroom. Question 12 illuminates the reason for taking notes on laboratory observations. This is a good time to tell students to bring a special notebook to class for recording their laboratory data.

The questionnaires should be returned to the students the next day with whatever comments, questions, or suggestions you have made. This might also be a good opportunity to announce the system that will be used in grading laboratory reports. Be sure that everyone who turns in anything at all on this first demonstration receives a respectable score.

Teaching Suggestions

Problem 1-1: What can you observe without using your eyes? *Pages 5-7*

Time Required: Two periods. Part of the first period can be used to explain the tasks, choose teams, and select station areas. Four stations can be visited the first day.

• The following are suggestions for observation stations. If time is short, you may eliminate some stations. You may want to supplement this list or substitute some of your own ideas. The important thing is for students to learn to make observations using senses other than sight. You may wish to duplicate the following instructions and give them to the Test Directors.

Station 1

Materials

shoe box containing:
life savers (several flavors)
clean petri dishes (3)

Procedure

A. Give each blindfolded student *a small piece of one flavor* life saver. Instruct the student to place it in his or her mouth. Do not allow other Observer Teams to see the contents of your box.
B. Ask the student to describe what he or she observes.
C. Record the actual flavor of the life saver given to each Observing Team as well as the description of the flavor given by the blindfolded person.
D. Change flavors as different Observing Teams visit your station.

Station 2

Materials

shoe box containing:
a small bottle of dilute household ammonia
a small bottle of dilute vinegar
a small bottle of colored water
(Each bottle is unlabeled except for the letters X, Y, and Z for the purpose of identification by the Testing Team.)

Procedure

A. Pass one open bottle of ammonia, vinegar, or water back and forth under the student's nose until he or she is able to smell the material. *Be sure that the bottle is at least 15 centimeters below the student's nose.*
B. Ask the student to describe what he or she observes.
C. Record the contents of the bottle used as well as the description of smell given by the blindfolded person.

Station 3

Materials

cardboard box containing:
electric motor
rubber band

Procedure

A. Bring either the electric motor or a vibrating rubber band close to the student's ear so that the sound can be heard.

B. Ask the student to describe what he or she observes.

C. Record the name of the item used in the test and the blindfolded person's response.

Station 4

Materials

cardboard box containing:
- milk carton
- tennis ball
- apple
- wooden block (square)

Procedure

A. Place tennis ball, apple, or wooden block in the empty milk carton. Tell the student to put one hand in the carton and feel the object. Change the object so that one student following another won't feel the same thing.

B. Ask the student to describe what he or she observes.

C. Record the item placed in the carton and the description of the object given by the blindfolded person.

Station 5

Materials

cardboard box containing:
- heat lamp
- switch, clock type

Procedure

A. Flip the switch and hold the heat lamp 15 centimeters from the back of the student's hand.

B. Change the procedure for another student by not turning on the heat lamp. Always flip the switch so that the sound is heard even if the lamp is not turned on.

C. Ask each student what he or she observes and ask what equipment may have been used in this test.

D. Record whether the lamp was on or off as well as the answers to each question asked the blindfolded person.

Station 6

Materials

cardboard box containing:
- electric fan

Procedure

A. Have the moving fan face one side of the student's head.

B. Change the procedure for another student by having the moving fan facing away from the student's head. Be sure to keep the fan the same distance from each student in both Steps A and B.

C. Ask the student to describe what he or she observes and to estimate the distance away the object is.

D. Record the direction the air is moving and the responses of the blindfolded person to the questions.

Station 7

Materials

shoe box containing:
- a small bottle of pine oil
- a small bottle of peppermint oil
- a small bottle of oil of wintergreen

(Each bottle is unlabeled except for the letters X, Y, and Z for the purpose of identification by the Testing Team.)

Procedure

A. Choose one of the three liquids and pass the bottle back and forth under the student's nose until he or she smells something. Be sure to keep the container at least 15 centimeters below the student's nose.

B. Ask the student to describe what he or she observes.

C. Record the type of oil used and the description of the stimulus given by the blindfolded person.

Station 8

Materials

shoe box containing:
- plastic bags (2)
- ice water
- hot water

Procedure

A. Place a plastic bag of either hot water (45°C) or ice water (about 0°C) on the back of a student's hand.

B. Ask the student to describe what he or she observes.

C. Record the temperature of water used and the blindfolded person's answers to the questions.

• Set the stations up before class, and cover them with newspapers so that students will not see them. Do not uncover the equipment until students are blindfolded. Except for certain items that can get stale (life savers, apples) or those that will not keep (ice water, ammonia), all materials can be kept for the following year.

• It is very important that the results of this activity be discussed in class; if they are not, the whole purpose of the activity is defeated. As the text directs, the discussion should be led by the Test Recorder for each station. You should interject comments and questions only when something important has been missed or left unsaid.

If the Test Recorders have difficulty starting the discussions, suggest that they, with the Test Directors' assistance, describe exactly what the tests consisted of. They should then read or summarize students' responses to the tests. Questions that might be asked are: Is this an observation or an interpretation? Is this observation accurate? Do all students' observations agree? What sense(s) is the student using? What could be concluded from these observations? Are these observations enough to positively identify the object causing the stimulus?

• You should check closely to make certain that students do not confuse observation with interpretation. From this activity, the student should come to recognize the need for careful observation and accurate description.

• Point out that a good interpretation should always be based on observation—not on "instinct" or "intuition." However, scientists must be open-minded and have imagination. They should be looking for and ready to accept new interpretations—provided they fit in with the observations.

Problem 1-2: How do you collect and record data? ***Pages 9-12***

Time Required: Two periods. Height measurements may be taken the first period and the remaining information gathered the second period.

• Have students copy Table 1-2 in their notebooks before class to save time.

• It may be a good idea to attach a fixed scale on a piece of paper to a wall to speed up measurements.

• If students are unfamiliar with the metric system and have never used meter sticks, you should supplement the description of this system that appears in the text. Emphasis should be placed on the decimal nature of the system, and the ease of converting from one unit to another. Explain that the prefixes deci-, centi-, and milli- mean one tenth, one one-hundredth, and one one-thousandth, respectively. Show students how to measure with a meter stick, pointing out all the divisions.

• One of the learning objectives of this activity is to familiarize students with tables and how they are used. For practice, you could have them organize the table of contents in their text into tabular form. (One column should be allocated for unit titles, one for chapter titles, and one for page numbers.)

Problem 1-3: How can you store information? ***Pages 13-18***

Time Required: Two periods. It will take a full period to prepare the cards before the questions are asked and answered.

• Enough index cards for each student should be on hand. Paper punches, scissors, and metric rulers should be available—the more of these there are in the classroom, the more rapidly the students will be able to prepare their data cards.

• Have students read the entire procedure before starting to work with the cards.

• Show a sample card or use an overhead projector to call attention to the details of a completed card.

• Point out the similarity between Knit-Pick cards and computer sorting systems. Most students are familiar with computer cards; explain that each hole in a computer card represents an answer to a yes-or-no question.

• If any time remains, allow students to use the Knit-Pick cards to answer questions other than those specified by the text. Keep the cards in your desk; the students can use them during free class time.

Problem 1-4: How is an experiment set up and interpreted? ***Pages 20-23***

Time Required: One period.

• This problem could be given as a homework assignment.

• A class discussion must follow to make certain that the students fully understand the example of scientific problem solving given. Among other things, discuss how this experiment fulfills the six requirements of a good experiment given on page 19 of the text.

• The following terms may be put on the chalkboard for emphasis: variable factors, control, experimental group, and control group. Make sure that students understand these terms, and how they apply to the experiment being discussed.

• Discuss why the pink seeds must be considered an experimental group rather than a control group. Some students may argue that pink is simply another shade of red.

• In discussing the problem, again point out the difference between interpretation and observation, especially in connection with Guide Question 6. Remind students that an observation is only something that they directly recognize by using one of the five senses. Anything else is an interpretation. For example, "Birds ate more red seeds than any other color" is an observation, whereas "Birds prefer red seeds" is an interpretation based on the observation. Emphasize that in order for an interpretation to be meaningful, it must be based on reliable observations. However, just because the observations are accurate, doesn't necessarily mean that an interpretation is the correct—or only—explanation of a particular phenomenon.

Suggested Answers to Check Your Understanding *Pages 23-24*

12. Hearing, smell, touch, and taste.
13. This was done so that the class preferences of certain flavors could be recorded without having an unmanageable list of flavors.
14. A series of questions would be formulated about the school clubs with "yes" or "no" answers. A Knit-Pick card system could then be constructed.
15. So that each number on the card referred to the same question for each student in the class.
16. The upper righthand corner was cut. This would permit the observer to see at a glance any card out of order.
17. An observation is an event recorded directly or by the use of instruments. An interpretation is the meaning attached to the data observed.
18. By having only one variable factor present, any change during an experiment may be attributed to the variable tested.

Recommended Films for Chapter 1

Aristotle and the Scientific Method (Coronet). 13 minutes, black and white. Aristotle made observations based on his experience, classified his data, performed experiments, and sought to arrive at a generalization or principle.

Scientific Method in Action (International Film Bureau). 19 minutes, color. Falling object experiments of Galileo serve as an introduction to scientific method. Actual historic motion pictures of experimental work by Jonas Salk and his research team on polio virus show application of scientific method to a complicated problem.

Chapter 2: Organizing and Interpreting Information

The purpose of this chapter is to provide direction and practice in organizing data. This organization is provided through the effective use of bar graphs, line graphs, and data tables. After a brief familiarization with the use of a data table, the student is shown how to prepare a line graph and a bar graph to plot data. The difference between the two kinds of graphs is explained briefly, and the type of data that should be presented in each kind of graph is pointed out. Finally, the student is shown how to read a graph: how to read individual points, how to read between plot points, and how to interpret trends, The student is instructed in the technique of estimating values beyond the plotted data.

Familiarity with tables and graphs will help the students to present and interpret data gathered from an experiment. Since the organization of data is so important in scientific investigation, these techniques must be emphasized and made meaningful to the students.

Teaching Suggestions

Problem 2-1: How may information be presented in tables and graphs? ***Pages 28-33***

Time Required: Two periods. The first period will be used to complete *Part One: Preparing a Data Table* and *Part Two: Preparing a Bar Graph.* The second period will be needed for *Part Three: Preparing a Line Graph.*

• This problem can be assigned to be read for homework. The Guide Questions and graphs, however, should be completed in class.

• Have the students draw the axes of the graphs into their notebooks in preparation for the actual plotting of the information during class time.

• Ask students to bring in sample graphs from newspapers and magazines. Analyze these graphs for kinds of information presented, variables, scales, etc.

• Discuss features common to all kinds of graphs (number scales, labeled axes, etc.).

• Post graphs on bulletin board to help students who have difficulty with graphing process. Label important features such as axes, line of best fit, plot points, etc.

• In class discussion, clarify terms "horizontal," "vertical," "axis," "slope," "scale," "dependent," and "independent."

• Most students will need help in identifying variables as dependent or independent. Explain that change in the independent variable is usually controlled or chosen by the scientist, while change in the dependent variable is determined by the independent variable.

• When line graphs are being constructed, encourage the use of two-dimensional plot points rather than dots; dots may be difficult to find when the lines are drawn.

• Explain that there is no hard-and-fast rule about when to use line graphs and when to use bar graphs. You should point out, however, that in the second graph in this problem (Figure 2-5) a line graph had to be used, since the daily changes in activity of three separate animals (i.e., three different sets of changes) were being graphed. If this information were to be presented in the form of a bar graph, three different graphs would be required, and the relationships between the activities of the three animals would not be seen so easily. Line graphs are usually used to show the relationships between changes in two or more sets of data.

If, on the other hand, the change in daily activity of only *one* organism were to be graphed, a bar graph could easily be used. In fact, it most likely *would* be used, since the relationship between the independent and dependent variable is not a proportional one. (The animal's activity does not regularly increase as time passes, nor does it regularly decrease. There is no pattern to its activity—one day it is relatively active, the next day it is inactive.)

The important learning objective in this chapter is not so much knowing *when* to use bar and line graphs, but *how* to present information on each kind and how to interpret graphs.

Problem 2-2: How may graphical information be interpreted and used? ***Pages 36-38***

Time Required: One period.

• Use a prepared chart or overhead transparency to discuss the results of both parts of the problem.

• Use graphs from newspapers and other sources to show how data may be read and predictions made from the graphs. Science and social studies textbooks are usually good sources of graphs.

• Show students how to extrapolate and interpolate values on graphs.

• Point out that a line graph could also be easily used for the Indianapolis 500 data. A definite trend is shown, and a line of best fit could easily be constructed. Emphasize that there is no definite rule about when to use each kind of graph.

Suggested Answers to Check Your Understanding *Pages 39-41*

11. Numerical variations related to a single object or phenomenon should be presented in a line graph. Bar graphs may be used to compare the results of many different objects being tested. Line graphs are customarily used when the changes in the independent variable are of a numerical nature; bar graphs are commonly used when the independent variable changes in a substantive rather than numerical manner. (For example, a line graph is used to show the relative activity of one hamster on succeeding days; a bar graph is used to show the relative activity of three different kinds of animals.) However, there is no hard-and-fast rule about the use of different kinds of graphs.
12. (a) 3; (b) 1; (c) 2.
13. An average of several measurements provides a better indication of the typical results than a single measurement alone.
14. It is necessary to keep them constant so that the variable factor being tested will be the only one responsible for the results observed.
15. The plot points represent the numerical relationships between the independent and dependent variables for different values of these variables.
16. Graph paper provides axial positions on which the data can be plotted. In order to correctly show relationships between quantitative data, it is important that the spaces be the same size.
17. Information may be predicted from graphs by observing the trends in the graphed data. Estimation, or extrapolation, of future data can then be made based on these trends.
18. (a) Five days. (b) Time in days. (c) The height in centimeters. (d) Five centimeters. (e) The growth on Day Number 1 was 5 centimeters. This is equal to the total growth on Days 2, 3, and 4. (f) The growth pattern shows no growth between Days 4 and 5. (g) The graph shows the growth pattern of a plant during a time of five days.
19. (a) The numbers should range from zero to twenty. (b) Two centimeters. (c) Plants C and E. (d) Plant B showed exactly one-half the growth of Plant D. (e) A bar graph was used since the growth of six different plants was being shown. It would not be appropriate to connect the data points in the form of a line graph since they refer to different plants.

Recommended Films for Chapter 2

The Language of Graphs (Coronet). 13 minutes, black and white. Presents types of graphs, their uses, and values. Bar, line, circle, and equation graphs are woven into a story.

Using Graphs (McGraw-Hill). Set #1, 405442 (*filmstrip*).

Chapter 3: Classifying Objects

This chapter introduces the important concept of classification. The student is shown the reasons for classifying objects, and some common examples of classification systems.

The student's first classification activity involves a number of geometric figures. The criteria of shape and color are used to arrange the figures into groups. This exercise shows that a given set of objects may be grouped in many different ways.

Further practice in classification is provided as the students are asked to classify a collection of bottles. Again the students see that there is considerable variety in the ways in which the objects may be grouped.

These simple classification activities are developed further in the next chapter when the student will learn about classification systems for living things.

Teaching Suggestions

Problem 3-1: In what ways may different objects be grouped? *Pages 46-49*

Time Required: One period.

• Have each student bring about 5 bottles. Each bottle should be different from the others. Only one should be a soft-drink bottle.

• Cardboard cartons that hold about 20 bottles can be cut down to proper height. This will eliminate loose bottles in the room and can also serve as storage bins if the bottles are to be saved. Label the boxes "Set 1," "Set 2," etc. Number the bottles in each set. A small piece of masking tape will serve as an adequate label.

• Try to get a few bottles that are unusual in some way and include one or more in each set of 20.

• The class should discuss the different ways in which the teams grouped the bottles. Have students defend their classification methods with logical reasons. If a grouping makes sense to the students then it is acceptable, as long as it can be clearly distinguished from other groupings. There cannot be hard-and-fast "correct" answers to this type of classification.

Problem 3-2: How are classification systems developed? ***Pages 50-52***

Time Required: One period.

• Put the three main requirements of a classification system given in Step A, Problem 3-1, on the board as a reminder to students.

• Have the students think of some common classification systems, and discuss how the three requirements of a good classification system apply. Possible examples include restaurant menus, classroom seating arrangements, mail-order catalogues, cookbooks, and calendars.

• Discuss various ways in which the students in the school are arranged into groups. Groupings include homerooms, classes, grades, programs of study, physical education groupings, and many others. Have students think of the reason behind each grouping, and the criteria used in forming each group.

• In this problem, students are asked to classify several different groups of objects. The answers provided in the annotations and here in the Teacher's Guide suggest some possible ways in which the various objects may be grouped. However, these are only some possible classification systems, and students will probably think of others. Accept any reasonable systems. Stimulate class discussion by asking why a certain object was placed with all the others or if it could be classified with another group.

• In Guide Question 2, students are asked to divide a group of living organisms into two groups. Division of the objects into plant and animal groups will be obvious to most students, although other groups, such as water organisms and land organisms, may be proposed. Again, accept any reasonable method for dividing the organisms into two groups.

Suggested Answers to Check Your Understanding ***Pages 52-53***

8. By alphabetical order, last names first.
9. By its construction, the address on a letter permits the letter to be sorted and directed to a particular state, city, street, house, and individual.
10. (a) They are all circular. (b) Student answers will vary depending on the groups identified. Most common number listed will be eight. Size—4 groups. Markings—3 marked, 1 clear. (c) Each individual group should show one characteristic that is different from other objects. Size or markings should be different for each group. (d) Grouping highlights the similarities and differences among objects. (e) The new object would require a separate group because it does not satisfy the requirements for any existing group.
11. Car characteristics may include manufacturer, year produced, body style, color, horsepower, etc. One characteristic is more useful than another only because it has more value in the sorting process. This, in turn, depends on the purpose of the classification.
12. (a) The purpose or use of the system must be clearly stated. (b) the groups must be clearly defined. (c) The classification system must be consistent or uniform throughout so that others may follow it.

Recommended Film for Chapter 3

Classifying Plants and Animals (Coronet). 11 minutes, color. Gives a short history of classification and introduces Linnaeus's system of binomial nomenclature. Traces classification of the common dog.

Chapter 4: Characteristics of Living Things

The unit is concluded with a chapter that introduces the student to some characteristics of living things. The students compare the activities of living and nonliving things by observing a fish and a mercury "ameba." They then discover that various life processes are used to distinguish between living and nonliving things.

The classification concepts used to group nonliving things in Chapter 3 are now extended to the classification of living things. In Problem 4-2, a number of animals belonging to the class Mammalia are presented to be grouped into their proper orders. This grouping is done on the basis of the characteristics listed for each order. The different mammals show the wide variety of characteristics that individuals within the same class may exhibit, thereby demonstrating the need for further subdivision.

The last problem in this unit calls for the students to prepare their own dichotomous classification key for sorting leaves. They have already used a dichotomous key to separate classes of vertebrates. From the observable features of leaves the students develop a key and determine the usefulness of their classification system. This understanding of dichotomous keys will be useful in future science courses and other activities that require identification of unknown objects.

Teaching Suggestions

Problem 4-1: What do living things do? *Pages 56-57*

Time Required: One period.

• The following demonstration forms the basis for this problem. You will need an overhead projector, and you should practice the demonstration before presenting it to the class. Do not show contents of either container to the class except when projecting with the overhead projector.

• Demonstration:

Container A—Mercury "ameba" in a petri dish. In one half of a glass petri dish pour 10-15 milliliters of dilute nitric acid (HNO_3). Other acids will not work. (To achieve the proper dilution, add 5 milliliters of concentrated nitric acid to 95 milliliters of distilled water.) Place one large drop of mercury (Hg) in the acid. Add one to three crystals of potassium dichromate ($K_2Cr_2O_7$). The mercury should move vigorously when it touches the potassium dichromate crystal. In time the crystal will appear to be "eaten" by the mercury. Actually a chemical reaction is taking place and mercuric oxide is formed. CAUTION: Do not allow students to handle the mercury or remove it from the work area. Mercury is poisonous if taken into the body through the mouth, skin, or as a vapor. Dispose of mercury by pouring it into a small container of powdered sulfur.

Container B—a live goldfish or other small fish in a transparent dish or finger bowl. During the demonstration, feed the fish with fish food, gently jar the dish, etc., so that students can note the fish's behavior.

• The purpose of the demonstration is to help students make subtle distinctions between the activities that are *always* carried out by living organisms and the activities that *may* be done at times by nonliving systems, such as the mercury "ameba." The students observe the activities of a goldfish and a mercury "ameba," and note similarities and differences between the two. The mercury "ameba" will seem to "eat" the potassium dichromate crystal and move in response to stimuli. With a minimum of help from you, the students should be able to point out that although the mercury seems to eat, it will not grow or use the food for energy as will the goldfish, and although it does move in response to environmental stimuli, the response is not coordinated, as a living organism's response would be.

Although the students cannot directly observe the goldfish growing and reproducing, they should realize that goldfish do perform these activities, whereas a mercury "ameba" does not. They should also know that the goldfish carries on respiration, but the mercury does not. The "ameba" lasts only a few minutes, and must be set up by the instructor; the goldfish, however, has a discrete life cycle, and reproduces its own kind.

While the demonstration is in progress, call attention to the activity in each dish. Ask questions such as, "Is it moving? Does it grow? Where did it come from?" Then finally ask, "Is it alive? How do you know?" Do not answer these questions yourself; allow the students to discuss their own ideas.

At the end of this demonstration and its follow-up discussion, students should realize that all living things move, carry on respiration, take in food (or make their own), use this food for energy and growth, and reproduce their own kind. Nonliving things may perform some of these activities, but no nonliving thing will perform all of them.

- You will need to prepare a fresh mercury "ameba" for each class.
- Some students may not understand what is meant by a response to a stimulus in the environment. Clarify this concept in class discussion.

Problem 4-2: How are characteristics used to group living things? ***Pages 58-60***

Time Required: One period.

- Rather than take a class period for doing this problem, it could be assigned as homework and then discussed in class.
- An overhead transparency of the animals shown in Figure 4-2 would be helpful when discussing the answers to the Guide Questions with the class.
- Class discussion might be directed to consider further subdivision of one of the better known orders of mammals, such as carnivores.

Problem 4-3: How can you make and use a dichotomous key to classify living things? ***Pages 62-64***

Time Required: One period.

- Request that leaves be brought in at least a day before they are needed. This will allow you time to sort the leaves into sets. Each assortment should contain 10 to 20 leaves with identifying numbers.
- Discard torn or broken leaves and plant parts that are not really leaves. A few unusual leaves add interest to the task of classification.
- Hand out leaf sets in large envelopes or shoe boxes.
- Alternate Procedure: Draw and duplicate a series of leaves found near your school. Make a complete set of 10-20 in number for each laboratory team. Put an identifying number on each kind of leaf but do not give the name.
- When the classes are through with the leaves, a good permanent display can be made by drying the leaves (pressing them between newspapers under weights) and mounting them on a large sheet of cardboard in the categories chosen. Label each subdivision to show what characteristics a leaf must have to be placed in that category.
- Discuss leaf characteristics that might change with the season, such as color and texture.
- Collect leaf sets after each class finishes with them. Most groups like to argue the merits of their own particular system, so the sets should be available again the next day.
- In Step B on page 64, leaves may be separated by shape (round, triangular, etc.), type of edge (toothed, smooth, lobed, branching, etc.), venation pattern, and so on. In describing the key in Guide Question 2, students should use the following single-letters/double-letter format, though they may have different groupings.

A Leaf is relatively round in shape.
AA Leaf is not round in shape.
B Leaf is smooth-edged.
BB Leaf is not smooth-edged.
C Leaf veins are netted.
CC Leaf veins are not netted.
D Leaf structure, simple.
DD Leaf structure, not simple (compound).
E Leaf is 8 cm or more wide.
EE Leaf is less than 8 cm wide.

Suggested Answers to Check Your Understanding *Page 65*

8. Living things differ from nonliving things in that they perform the processes of food-getting, movement, breathing, response, and reproduction.
9. A classification key provides an "either-or" system of classifying an object based on the characteristics it does or does not have.

10. Bats have all of the characteristics of mammals—they have hair on their bodies, they are warm-blooded, they nourish their young with milk, and they have a four-chambered heart. They do not have the characteristics necessary to be classified as birds.
11. Because the questions based on characteristics separate the object into one grouping or another. An object either possesses or does not possess the characteristic in question.
12. (a) All have three pairs of legs. All have two eyes and two antennae. All have three body regions (head, abdomen, thorax). (b) Not all the insects have wings. Those that have wings have one pair or two pairs. The legs of the insects pictured differ in size, shape, and function. Antennae are of different types. The insects pictured vary greatly in size. (c) Groups with or without wings. (1) Those with wings: those with one pair of wings, those with two pairs. (2) Those without wings: those with a slender abdomen or an enlarged abdomen. Other ways may include relative size, kind of antennae, type of legs, etc.
13. A sugar crystal gets larger as material comes out of solution and adds to the crystal. The crystal is not alive, since it does not respond to stimuli, move, take in food, use oxygen (respiration), or show any other true life processes.

Recommended Film for Chapter 4

What Is a Mammal? (Popular Science Publishing Company, Audio-Visual Division). Classification of mammals into various groups is developed using simple terminology. Shows special characteristics that make an animal a mammal. F.O.M. 187 (*filmstrip*).

Unit 2: The Cell—Building Block of Living Things

In this unit the students are introduced to the basic structural units of which living things are composed. They learn about the cells, tissues, organs, and systems that are characteristic of both plants and animals.

If they are to study fine structural detail, the students must be able to use a microscope. They learn about the compound microscope by using it to examine newsprint, hair, and other small objects. The field diameter of the microscope is measured in millimeters and then converted to microns. Based on this measurement, the students can then estimate the size of objects seen through the microscope.

Cells studied under the microscope include those found in onion skin, cheek epithelium, leaf epidermis, and cork. Stains are used to make the nucleus and other structures visible. Differences between plant cells and animal cells are conveyed in the Guide Questions.

The final chapter in the unit deals with the way cells are organized into more complex units. The students study characteristic tissues, organs, and organ systems in a representative plant and animal.

Chapter 5: The Microscope

By doing the problems in this chapter, students learn to use the compound microscope. By working with the instrument, they become familiar with the names and functions of each part. The students first prepare a wet mount slide of the printed letter "e" to learn the technique of focusing the microscope at both low and high magnifications. They discover that the position of the microscope image is reversed and inverted from the position of the object.

Next the students use a metric ruler to measure the diameter of the field of the microscope in millimeters. All measurements made in millimeters are then converted to microns. The students discover that the diameter of the field is greater at low magnification than at higher magnification.

Once the students have found the diameter of the field in microns, they are taught how to use this measurement to estimate the size of objects seen with the microscope. The students practice this technique by measuring such objects as string, wire, and cotton thread.

The microscope is frequently used for observation and measurement in the exercises contained in this book. The students must master the proper techniques for using the microscope, preparing wet mount slides, and measuring small objects if they are to have success in future problems.

Teaching Suggestions

Problem 5-1: How is the compound microscope used? *Pages 72-78*

Time Required: One to two periods.

• Since this problem will instruct students on the parts of the microscope and its proper use, it must be done before other problems using the microscope are studied.

• No two microscope models are exactly alike, although all have several features in common. Because of the differences in commercially available school microscopes, the text is purposely vague about certain features, notably number and magnifying power of objective lenses, and light-regulating devices. In class, you should point out and explain every feature of your kind of microscopes to students. If your microscopes differ in any way from the text description, you should point this out.

• If your microscopes differ radically from the text description (e.g., if they are Zoomscopes), you will need to supply your students with a description of their microscopes and instructions for how to use them. The answers to the Guide Questions might, in this instance, sometimes be different than those given in the page annotations; in some cases the questions themselves might have to be reworded or supplemented in order to be meaningful to the students.

• Impress upon students the necessity of knowing the parts of any new, expensive laboratory instrument that they are using for the first time.

• If students have never worked with microscopes before, demonstrate how to carry the microscope, clean its lenses, adjust the illumination, and focus it before letting students try these procedures.

• Emphasize that lens paper—not tissues or paper towels—should be used to clean microscope lenses. Show students how this is done.

Problem 5-2: How does the position of an object appear to change when viewed through a microscope? *Pages 79-80*

Time Required: Part of one class period.

• This problem must be preceded by Problem 5-1, since it depends on a knowledge of the use of the microscope.

• A few days before this activity is scheduled, direct students to obtain a word with the letter "e" from the want-ad section of the newspaper, since some of the smallest print in the newspaper appears there.

• All materials except the microscope may be made available in small boxes or envelopes to save time and steps for team members.

• Unless all students mounted the letter in the right-side-up position, the answers to Guide Question 1 will vary. Point out that following directions in an experiment is always important.

• A detailed discussion of lenses and optics is not needed here. Some students, however, may be curious about why the microscope reverses the image of the object being studied. You might give a very simple explanation of the lens system of your microscope, using lines to represent light rays. Some instrument companies will provide wall charts showing how light is focused in their microscope. This is a good time to call attention to the fact that lens systems in many microscopes and telescopes invert the image of the object being viewed.

Problem 5-3: How is the field of view of the microscope measured? ***Pages 81-82***

Time Required: One period.

• A useful activity for reinforcing the idea of measuring the field of view of a microscope is to use the overhead projector with a piece of paper having a 10-cm hole cut in the middle. The field of view can be measured by placing a transparent metric ruler across the hole. Discuss how the size of an object, such as the length of a toothpick, might be estimated by knowing the diameter of the hole in the paper.

• Before class, measure the field diameters of one or two microscopes. Different kinds of microscopes will have different field diameters; therefore, you should measure the field diameter of each model that the students are using. These measurements will give you an idea of the accuracy of the students' estimations of the field diameters.

• If students are not all using the same model microscope, it might be a good idea to number the microscopes and instruct the students to record the number of their microscopes in their notebooks. That way, once a student has calibrated the field diameters for a particular microscope, he or she can use the same microscope for all subsequent exercises.

• As this activity is in progress, check the students' microscopes to make sure that students are using the correct procedure and are reporting accurate values for field diameters.

• As a reminder, put an outline on the board of steps to be followed in handling and focusing a microscope. These directions are given in Problem 5-1.

• The text explains that for any microscope the field diameter is inversely proportional to the magnifying power of the objective lens (Step E, page 82). To clarify this, it may be a good idea to discuss the difference between direct and inverse proportionality. Many students need to review simple arithmetic relationships such as ratio and proportion.

Problem 5-4: How is the microscope used to measure small objects? ***Pages 83-85***

Time Required: One period.

• Have cotton thread, piano wire, and string precut and arranged in containers.

• Point out the importance of microscope measurement and its use in science.

• For the benefit of students who were absent or who had difficulty measuring the field diameters, write these values on the chalkboard.

• The thread will occupy only a small fraction of the field diameter under low-power magnification. Students will need some help in estimating its size. Using the overhead projector demonstration suggested in the first Teaching Suggestion for Problem 5-3, show students how to estimate the size of a pencil and other small objects. This will give them an idea of how to measure objects by comparing an object's size to the known diameter of the microscope field.

• Indicate that the values obtained for diameters of thread, etc., are only approximations and that everyone should not expect to get the same values.

• Students are asked to estimate the diameter of a thread using both low and high power. The two estimates may differ, simply because under high power the thread will occupy a much larger portion of the field of view than under low power, therefore making estimation much easier and probably more accurate. Discuss these results with students, making sure that they understand why the size estimates probably differ. Also make certain that they understand that the actual size of an object does not change when it is magnified—switching from low power to high power changes the size of the image, not the size of the object.

Suggested Answers to Check Your Understanding *Pages 86-87*

15. Lens paper can clean microscope lenses without scratching them because it does not contain dirt or other foreign matter.
16. 25X. (The total magnification of a compound microscope is determined by multiplying individual magnifications of the ocular and objective lenses. If the eyepiece is 10X, the objective lens must be 25X to give a total of 250X.)
17. Light must pass through an object to be viewed with a compound microscope. Thin objects will allow light to pass through them so the parts can be seen.
18. The water medium helps to sharpen the focus. It also keeps the material that is being examined from drying out. Dried-out material differs greatly from a fresh specimen.
19. An air bubble might be mistaken for a part of the specimen being examined. Air bubbles may also distort the image of the object being studied.
20. The micron allows you to measure and compare the size of very small objects.
21. An object is difficult to locate because high-power magnification examines only a small portion of the area viewed with low-power magnification. (This means that the chances of locating a small object under high power are small unless the object is first located under low power.)

Recommended Films for Chapter 5

The Microscope (McGraw-Hill Text Films). 11 minutes, color. Describes microscope as a compound series of magnifying lenses. Introduces students to the different parts and proper care of the microscope. Uses examples to show various levels of magnification.

Introduction to the Microscope (SVE). 42 frames. Explains functions of each part of the microscope. 448-1 (*filmstrip*).

The Microscope (Ealing Film-Loops). Explains slide preparation, light systems, lens system, focusing. No. 82-0159/1 (*filmstrip*).

Chapter 6: Cell Structures

The problems in this chapter all involve the study of cells. The students must know how to use a compound microscope before they try to do these problems. With the aid of the microscope, they examine onion skin to see the structures found in a typical nongreen plant cell. The human cheek cell, a representative animal cell, is studied and compared to the plant cell to determine the similarities and differences in the structures present. The cells are stained with methylene blue so that the transparent structures may be more easily seen. After the cells have been stained and the main structures identified, the size of the cells in microns is estimated by comparison to the diameter of the field, whose value was found earlier.

The students discover chloroplasts when they look at the cells of the green plant elodea. They observe the motion of the chloroplasts and are guided in forming an hypothesis that explains this movement. The function of chloroplasts is related to the process of photosynthesis.

As a final activity, the students observe cork cells. These cells are studied to determine what parts of a plant cell are living and what parts are nonliving.

This chapter introduces the cell and its component parts. The next chapter deals with the organization of these cells into tissues and organs.

Teaching Suggestions

Problem 6-1: What are the parts of an onion skin cell? *Pages 94-96*

Time Required: One period.

- Provide a 0.05% solution of methylene blue in several dropper bottles for easy use. Before class, check to see that the solution is neither too light nor too dark by viewing stained cells with the microscope.
- Each team will need about ¼ of an onion.

Remove brown outer layers before dispensing the pieces.

• Provide lens paper and encourage students to use it whenever lenses get dirty or smeared.

• Check the students' slides for proper staining. Advise them to start with only a small drop of stain. If more is needed, it may be added by placing a small drop at the edge of the cover glass; the stain will then spread by diffusion.

• During this and subsequent experiments involving the microscope, check to make sure that the students' microscopes are properly focused. Explain that a specimen may have more than one focal plane—this accounts for cells that appear to have more than one nucleus. The same cell may also have more than one focal plane, and the focus may have to be slightly altered when studying the different structures. Students should be encouraged to experiment with focusing, as long as they are very careful with the microscope.

• While the activity is in progress, check the students' drawings to make sure that they are reasonably accurate representations of what the students actually see with the microscope. Discourage students from copying cell illustrations from books.

• If the experiment takes a long time, it is a good idea occasionally to add a few drops of water at the edge of the cover glass to prevent the wet mounts from drying.

• Check students' slides to be sure that onion skin tissue is lying flat. Folding can lead to confusion, since layers of cells above and below the layer of focus will appear fuzzy, and cells may appear to have more than one nucleus.

• Suggest that, when estimating the size of the cells, the students move the slide so that one row of cells lies along the field diameter, and the end of one cell is at the edge of the field of view. A sketch on the board showing what this looks like may be helpful.

• When making observations, students may notice empty cells. There are dead cells that often occur in living tissue.

Problem 6-2: What are the parts of a human cheek cell? ***Pages 97-98***

Time Required: One period.

• Prepare a set of materials in a tray or small box for every three or four students. These sets should include everything needed except the microscope and light source.

• Make sure that students discard toothpicks in a wastebasket immediately after use. There should be no danger of transmitting germs into the mouth as long as clean toothpicks are used each time.

• Dropper bottles of 0.05% methylene blue should be made available for each team.

• Insist on slides and cover glasses being cleaned and dried after use.

• Remind students to clean lenses with lens paper if lenses appear dirty or images appear blurred.

• Make sure that all students are writing their responses to Guide Questions in their notebooks as they work in the laboratory. Raise questions or offer assistance where you see missing answers or answers that are obviously incorrect.

• Students sometimes overlook the cheek cells because of their small size. Remind students that they may be observing cells that are folded over each other. Many cells often remain hooked together when removed from the cheek.

Problem 6-3: What part of a green plant cell has the green coloring material in it? ***Pages 99-101***

Time Required: One period.

• Elodea (*Anacharis*) plants can be obtained from local tropical fish stores. Elodea may be kept alive and reproducing in the laboratory in aquaria or large jars.

• Prepare salt solution for plasmolysis of plant cells in Part Two by dissolving 37 grams of salt, NaCl, in 100 ml of water.

• Plants that have been stored in the dark and then placed in bright light usually show the most movement of chloroplasts.

• In post-lab discussion, indicate that the moving of the chloroplasts is accomplished by cytoplasmic streaming. Chloroplasts themselves have no means of locomotion.

• Remind students that chloroplasts may not move all the time. Encourage them to observe serveral different cells to find the most activity.

• Be sure that students do not get the idea that chloroplasts move through cell walls. This may appear to happen when cells from another layer are superimposed on the cell being observed.

• Remind students that when estimating the length of a cell, it is best to align the end of a cell with the edge of the field diameter. A sketch on the chalkboard or overhead projector would be helpful.

Problem 6-4: What structure or structures remain in a nonliving plant cell? ***Pages 102-103***

Time Required: Part of a class period.

• Sharp, single-edged razor blades must be used for this experiment. Demonstrate how to hold the razor blade and how to cut the cork.

• From this activity and the plasmolysis experiment, students should realize that the cell wall is a rigid structure. Discuss how this affects plants. Students may be able to point out that plant tissue, on the whole, is more rigid and less elastic than animal tissue.

• In post-lab discussion make certain students do not consider the air bubbles inside the cells as cells or cell structures. As a follow-up activity, discuss why only the outer boundary is present and why internal parts are missing in a nonliving plant cell.

• As a follow-up to this chapter, you might use the overhead projector to show photographs of various kinds of plant and animal cells. Ask the students to point out similarities and differences between the two kinds of cells. If students notice cell structures other than the ones discussed in the chapter, you might give a brief, simplified description of the function of these organelles.

Suggested Answers to Check Your Understanding *Page 106*

17. The cheek cells are positioned in flat, bricklike layers that form a uniform covering on the cheek. The flat surface cells protect the more sensitive cells beneath in much the same way that paper wrapping protects a package.
18. These cells might have similar shapes because they have similar functions. Both kinds of cells form a protective covering for underlying tissues.
19. The clear, colorless liquid found leaving living cells is probably water. It goes out of the cell through the cell membrane and the cell wall.
20. The movement of the cytoplasm within a cell causes the chlorplasts to move around. The chloroplasts cannot move by themselves.
21. Thin slices allow light to pass through so the material can be viewed through a microscope.

Recommended Film for Chapter 6

Photosynthesis and Respiration (Churchill Films). 14 minutes, color. Visualizes process both at microscopic level and molecular level. Shows how sugar molecules are formed from water and carbon dioxide, and indicates the complexity of the steps involved in this process. Explains process of releasing energy from food.

Chapter 7: Cells Work Together

The final chapter of this unit is designed to show how cells function together in multicellular organisms. The students observe the earthworm and the leaves of green plants in order to see how cells are organized into tissues, organs, and organ systems.

The students observe the structure and arrangement of cells in the epidermis of a leaf. The role of the stomata and guard cells in the processes of photosynthesis and respiration is discussed. The students count and compare the number of stomata per unit area in the upper and lower epidermis. The number of stomata and the structure of the leaf of a particular plant are shown to be related to the amount of moisture present in its environment.

The relationship of the structure and arrangement of specialized cells to the function they serve is explored further by preparing and examining a cross section of a leaf. The internal cells (mesophyll) are located and their function in photosynthesis is described. The conducting cells are observed, and their arrangement into vascular tissue is noted. The leaf serves as an example of how cells are arranged into tissues and organs.

The organs and organ systems of a living earthworm are studied. The students study the circulatory system by observing the blood flowing in the large blood vessels of the worm. The direction of blood flow and the pulse rate are determined. From these observations the students are able to understand the concept of a circulatory system composed of various organs.

Students learn about the muscular system of a worm as they observe the changes in body length and diameter when the earthworm moves. The two types of muscles responsible for locomotion are then related to the changes in shape and size of the worm.

The dissection of a preserved earthworm serves two purposes: the students learn the technique of dissection, and they observe the organization of the digestive system of the earthworm. The function of each individual organ is related to the total activity of the digestive system.

After this introduction to cells, tissues, organs, and organ systems, the student is ready to study the whole organism. The units and chapters that follow will build upon this introduction to the study of cells and their organization.

Teaching Suggestions

Problem 7-1: What different kinds of cells are found in the epidermis of leaves? *Pages 111-113*

Time Required: One period.

- Obtain leaves for class use the day they are needed to avoid their drying out. Privet hedge leaves work well, but several other different types of leaves should also be used.
- Supply lens paper for cleaning any microscope lenses that may be dirty.
- Make sure that all students are able to see guard cells in their own slides during the laboratory period.
- In Step D, page 112, students are asked to design a table. A sample table is shown here, though students may devise other forms for their tables. Accept any logical design.

Problem 7-2: What special cells and tissues may be found in a leaf cross section? *Pages 115-116*

Time Required: One period.

- Privet hedge leaves work well. Leaves of houseplants may be substituted if hedge leaves are not available. Be sure to examine leaves in advance to find the best species.
- Check students' slides to make sure that they are looking at the cross section of the leaf, not the epidermis.
- While the activity is in progress, circulate among the students, asking them to point out various leaf structures on their own slides. If a student has difficulty locating a particular structure, help him or her find it. This will encourage students to answer questions by examining their own specimens, rather than by looking at the illustrations in the text.
- A projected diagram or transparency of a cross section of a leaf will be helpful in the discussion following this activity.

Problem 7-3: What special structures are visible in the organ systems of an earthworm? *Pages 118-119*

Time Required: One period.

- Obtain live earthworms from supply houses or bait stores. Larger worms are best. It may be worthwhile to obtain large nightcrawlers in the warmer months and keep them in moist soil or sawdust until needed.
- Remind students to keep the worm on a damp surface except when observing it with the microscope.
- In post-lab discussion, point out the fact that the earthworm has no true heart. The aortic arches, which some of the students may have noticed, perform a pumping function similar to that of the heart in higher animals. The dorsal blood vessel also helps pump the blood.

Problem 7-4: What organs may be found in the digestive system of an earthworm? *Pages 120-122*

Time Required: One period.

- Preserved earthworms (one per team) are required for this problem. Large specimens are easier to work with.

• Demonstrate basic techniques of dissection, such as pinning the worm, and making the first longitudinal incision.

• In order to prevent damage to the earthworm's delicate internal structures, caution students to be careful not to cut too deep.

• You might set up a demonstration dissection using a live earthworm. The worm should be anaesthetized with a wad of cotton soaked in ether. Dissect the worm to reveal digestive tube and blood vessels, being careful not to tear any of the delicate tissues. If pins are used to hold back skin and muscles, great care should be taken; pins should not be inserted in the extreme anterior or posterior ends. The worm should stay alive for about ten minutes.

Suggested Answers to Check Your Understanding *Page 123*

12. A specialized cell is modified to perform some particular function. This modification may result in the loss of ability to perform other fundamental life processes. The specialized cell then depends on other specialized cells to supplement its own activity. (For example, a nerve cell is modified to respond to and to transmit stimuli; however, it depends on other tissues for its own food and oxygen supply, and the removal of its wastes.)
13. Bone cells would be likely to contain a material (calcium phosphate) that makes them hard and rigid and able to support the body.
14. To be called an organ, a leaf must contain different kinds of tissue. A leaf contains tissues for protection, epidermal tissue; tissues for conduction, xylem and phloem tissues; and tissues containing food-making cells, the mesophyll tissue.
15. Muscular movement helps force blood through the earthworm's body.
16. A cross section of an earthworm near the tail end would probably show the outside layers of protecting cells, muscle cells, blood vessels, the intestine, body cavity, and excretory tube. (For reference, see Figure 7-9 in student text, page 118.)

Recommended Films for Chapter 7

Earthworm—Anatomy and Dissection (Coronet). 11 minutes, color. Stresses correct laboratory techniques for dissection. Shows functioning of digestive, circulatory, excretory, nervous, and reproductive systems by extreme close-up photography, photomicrography, diagrams.

Leaves of Green (Stanton Films). 11 minutes, color. Describes and defines leaf structure and arrangement. Presents some of the more interesting leaf modifications. Shows biological and esthetic importance of leaves.

Unit 3: The Protists

The three chapters in this unit each deal with different kinds of protists. The laboratory exercises in these chapters involve observing and examining the structure and behavior of various microscopic organisms. Students gain additional skill in using the microscope and preparing specimens for microscopic examination.

In Chapter 8, the students examine the forms of life that exist in a drop of pond water. They learn the ways in which these microorganisms perform the activities that are characteristic of all living things—how they move, obtain their food, and reproduce. They discover that these organisms respond to stimuli in their environment, and they determine the nature of some of these tactic responses.

Yeasts and molds are studied in Chapter 9. Students learn the conditions that favor the growth of molds and bacteria, and also study substances, such as antiseptic solutions, that inhibit the growth of these organisms. Students go "microbe hunting" around the school as they try to answer the question, "Where can microorganisms be found?"

In Chapter 10, the same petri dish cultures grown for a problem in the previous chapter are examined for the presence of bacterial colonies. Students learn how to tell the difference between mold and bacterial colonies, and pure cultures of certain bacteria are grown. Students learn about the need to dispose of all mold and bacterial cultures in such a way that the microorganisms are killed, in order to prevent the dissemination of possible pathogens. They read about the effects of ultraviolet light upon the bacterium *Serratia marcescens.*

Chapter 8: Living Things in a Drop of Water

Students are always eager to learn more about microorganisms once they have seen the great activity that exists in a drop of pond water. Each team should prepare cultures in small jars several days before they are needed for the first problem in this chapter.

Students are shown the correct technique for obtaining samples from a jar of pond water. They then prepare wet mount slides and observe the organisms on the slides. Cotton fibers are used to restrict the motion of the organisms so that their various life processes may be observed. Students note the organisms' method of locomotion, means of obtaining food, and response to various stimuli. In a table in their notebooks, they record the activities of these organisms, and classify them as plants, animals, or protists.

Taxis responses are explored in the third problem in this chapter. The organism used for this study is the brine shrimp. Although brine shrimp are large enough to be seen with the naked eye, the microscope is used to observe their responses to stimuli in greater detail.

Teaching Suggestions

Problem 8-1: What kind of life may be found in pond water? ***Pages 133-135***

Time Required: The cultures prepared for this problem will be observed from time to time over a period of weeks.

- Pond water should be obtained a week or more in advance of when it is needed. This will permit organisms to multiply and will assure the class of adequate numbers of organisms.
- Invite students to bring in jars of pond water, including some material from the bottom and surface of the pond or ditch.
- Microorganisms grow best in moderate light, in neutral or slightly alkaline medium, and in glass containers that will admit some air. Add a few grains of rice and store in a cool place. Check pH with hydrion paper and if alkalinity is required, a drop or two of dilute NaOH solution may be added.
- Culture jars may be kept for many weeks. Subculturing may be done by pipetting a water sample from an old jar into jars of aquarium water in which plants and animals have been growing.
- You may assign students to copy tables into notebooks as a homework assignment. Or you

may want to duplicate sheets containing 5 data tables like Table 8-1 (page 134) to help organize the large amounts of data in this problem.

• Remind students to use dim illumination while finding and observing microorganisms with their microscopes.

Problem 8-2: What activities of pond water organisms can you observe? *Pages 137-139*

Time Required: One period.

• Pond water samples used in Problem 8-1 are to be used again for this problem.

• Remind students to use dim light when observing microorganisms with the microscope, and to add water to the edge of the cover glass periodically to prevent dryness.

• Discuss the different ways in which microorganisms obtain and ingest food. Briefly explain the process of phagocytosis to students. Some students, while examining their slides, may have noticed protists with both chlorophyll and a mouth. Explain that these organisms can be either autotrophic or heterotrophic, depending on environmental conditions.

• Discuss the different means of locomotion used by protists. Make sure that students understand the difference between cilia and flagella.

• Discuss the idea that specialized cell structures are needed to perform special cell activities. Compare specialized cell structures in protists to tissues, organs, and organ systems in higher organisms.

• As a follow-up to this activity, you might show the class drawings or photographs of various protists, identifying them by name. Have the class point out structures such as nuclei, vacuoles, cell membrane, cell wall, cilia, and flagella.

Problem 8-3: How do water animals react to stimuli? *Pages 140-145*

Time Required: Three periods.

• Do not begin this problem unless three consecutive days are available for observation and data collecting.

• Brine shrimp larvae can be produced in 48 hours from dried eggs, which are available in supply houses or tropical fish shops.

• Prepare brine shrimp hatching solution by dissolving 3.5 grams of NaCl per liter of distilled water (13 grams per gallon). You may prepare this solution in advance to save time. About half a liter per class will be required.

• Different groups may observe different responses to the same environmental stimulus. Caution students to make several trials and to compare results with other groups. Emphasize the importance of control groups in this experiment.

• Have ice cubes ready. Styrofoam buckets or chests will keep ice for several hours.

• Step P in Part Five, in which the students are asked to design experiments, could be answered by means of class discussion.

Suggested answer to Guide Question 10, page 145

Students may be expected to design several different kinds of experiments. Accept anything that fulfills the requirements of a good experiment listed on page 19 of the text. In particular, make sure that students introduce only one variable and have adequate controls. Some possible experiments:

Touch—you might observe the behavior of brine shrimp in a drop of solution when a toothpick is moved across the drop. The organism might respond by trying to attach itself to the toothpick, by moving away from the toothpick, or by completely ignoring the toothpick.

Electricity—you might observe the behavior of brine shrimp in a drop of solution when a weak electrical current from a 1½-volt dry cell is allowed to flow through the drop. Again the brine shrimp might move toward or away from either of the wires or not show any response to the electricity at all.

Chemicals—you might observe the behavior of brine shrimp in a drop of solution when a piece of thread soaked in any one of various chemicals is placed in the drop. Solutions such as vinegar, ammonia water, or sugar might be tested for brine shrimp response. A positive response would be shown by the brine shrimp collecting around the thread; a negative response would be shown by the brine shrimp avoiding the thread.

Suggested Answers to Check Your Understanding *Page 146*

9. A positive phototaxis is a positive response to the stimulus of light. An organism exhibiting positive phototaxis will move toward regions of greater illumination.
10. A many-celled organism is composed of more than one cell. A single-celled organism is made up of only one cell. The cells of a many-celled organism may be specialized and arranged in distinct structures.
11. Eight paramecia would be produced in three hours at this rate.
12. A paramecium moves by beating its cilia. It obtains food by swimming after it and taking food materials into its mouth and gullet.
13. The paramecia may have moved to the edge of the cover glass to avoid the bright light or its associated heat.
14. If fifty microorganisms were found in the sampled drop of water, an estimation of the total number may be obtained by figuring the number of drops in a small unit of volume (such as a milliliter) and multiplying by the capacity of the jar.

Recommended Films for Chapter 8

Life in a Drop of Water (Coronet). 10 minutes, color. Shows simplest plant and animal forms carrying on life processes in a drop of water. Shows how these lower forms meet the same problems that face higher forms in our larger world.

The Protist Kingdom (Film Associates of California). 14 minutes, color. Introduces the student to protists, describes and illustrates their characteristics, and defines the major groups of the protist kingdom.

Chapter 9: Yeasts and Molds

This chapter introduces students to another group of protists, the yeasts and molds. These organisms are quite plentiful around us and may be observed when cultured in the laboratory. The activities in this chapter point out the conditions that are most conducive to the growth of yeasts and molds, as well as the particular characteristics of each kind of these protists.

The first problem considers the best conditions for the growth of yeast cells. By measuring the amount of carbon dioxide produced by yeast cultures grown at different temperatures, the students obtain an indirect idea of the relative number and activity of the yeast cells present in each culture. If high-power magnification is available, reproduction by budding may be observed.

In Problem 9-2, the students learn the use of sterile techniques by growing a culture of bread mold. Various factors necessary for rapid growth of mold are identified. Mold spores as a reproductive form are observed and utilized in the experiment. Students learn to recognize a mold colony by the fuzzy appearance of its surface. Finally, the students make a subculture from a mixture of mold species to grow a pure culture.

In Problem 9-3, cellophane tape is used to collect microorganisms from various sources around the school, such as cafeteria tables, door knobs, and desk tops. The spores are then transferred by touching the tape to the agar medium in a petri dish that is then incubated. Among other things, the students should learn how to tell mold colonies from bacterial colonies.

The techniques and knowledge that the students acquire here will be used in the following chapter when they study bacteria.

Teaching Suggestions

Problem 9-1: How do temperature extremes affect the production of carbon dioxide gas by yeast? *Pages 152-157*

Time Required: Two periods.

- To save time (and to avoid some undue messiness in the classroom), you may prefer to do this problem as a demonstration.
- Obtain packets of dry yeast from a supermarket.
- Prepare the sugar solution in gallon lots if the students are doing the problem.

• In post-lab discussion, make certain that students understand that the volume of gas depends on (1) the number of yeast cells present and (2) the rate of activity of these cells. If one culture of yeast produces more gas than another, it can mean that there are more yeast cells present or that the yeast cells are more active—or both.

Problem 9-2: How does bread mold reproduce? ***Pages 159-162***

Time Required: A total of two periods or more. (Half a period to set up bread cultures, and a few minutes each day for the next few days to observe cultures. One period to observe mold and to transfer it to agar plates, and part of another class to observe subcultures.)

• Instruct students to bring in a slice of day-old bread (use Italian or bakery bread, since most other store-bought breads contain fungicides or other preservatives) and small glass jars for use in this problem.

• Each team will need one sterilized petri dish containing sterile nutrient agar. Disposable petri dishes containing sterile agar save time and eliminate breakage. These are obtainable from supply houses. If the budget does not permit this, prepare your own agar plates. One method follows.

Sterilize the petri dishes by steaming in a pressure cooker or autoclave for 15 minutes at 15 pounds pressure, or bake at 350°F for one hour in the oven.

Prepare nutrient agar. You may use the powdered nutrient agar or make your own. To do this, heat one liter of distilled water in a flask, and dissolve 15 grams of agar in it. When the agar has dissolved, add 5 grams peptone and 3 grams beef extract. Sterilize the flask containing the agar in a pressure cooker for 15 minutes at 15 pounds pressure (121°C). While the agar solution is still hot, pour it into the sterile petri dishes. After the agar has solidified, store the petri dishes in an upside-down position, to prevent condensed water droplets from falling onto the surface of the agar.

• Impress students with the need for sterile techniques when handling microorganisms. Warn them never to put contaminated equipment, such as forceps, down on the laboratory bench. They should realize that agar plates should never be left uncovered, either before or after inoculation. Students should wash their hands thoroughly before and after working with microorganisms.

• You may prefer to do Part Three (pages 161-162) as a demonstration. In either case, it is a good idea to demonstrate sterile techniques and the transferring of microorganisms from one dish to another.

• Provide containers of formalin or lysol solution for the disposal of old cultures. You may also have students empty cultures into a garbage pail containing a plastic garbage bag. At the end of the class, seal the bag carefully and have it incinerated.

Problem 9-3: Where can microorganisms be found? ***Pages 163-165***

Time Required: Two periods or more.

• Use disposable plastic petri dishes or prepare one sterile petri dish containing sterile nutrient agar for each team. Tape petri dishes shut and store in the refrigerator until students need them.

• At the completion of this problem, save and refrigerate the students' petri dishes for Problem 10-1.

• Students may use the fingers of their hands as one surface from which to take a sample. The class could be divided into thirds: one-third washing hands with soap, one-third rubbing hands with alcohol or other mild disinfectant, and one-third not cleaning their hands in any way. Students may dispense with the tape and just press their fingers gently onto the agar.

• To prevent the growth of pathogens, care should be taken to incubate the microorganism cultures at room temperature, not at body temperature.

• When the laboratory teams have obtained and recorded their results, display all of the cultures for class observation and discussion. Tape lids to petri dishes to prevent contamination.

Suggested Answers to Check Your Understanding *Page 166*

11. A hot pair of tweezers may destroy the substance being studied.
12. Bread mold spores travel in the air currents and fall on the bread. When conditions are right, the mold grows on the bread.
13. Athlete's foot and ringworm may be mentioned. They can be prevented by keeping the area dry. If an area becomes infected, prompt medical attention with fungicides will keep the growth from spreading.
14. Molds depend on their environment for food, moisture, oxygen, and an acceptable temperature.
15. Spores allow an organism to be distributed over a wide area in great numbers. They also protect the living material until conditions necessary for growth are present.
16. Yeast cells reproduce by budding and by producing spores. Under favorable conditions they reproduce in minutes. The spores can be moved around by wind, animals, or water droplets.

Recommended Film for Chapter 9

Life of the Molds (McGraw-Hill Text Films). 21 minutes, color. Reveals importance of molds in daily lives, their impact on history, and some of the beauty and mystery to be found in the study of these tiny protists.

Chapter 10: Bacteria

This chapter continues the study of the microorganisms grown in the petri dishes in Problem 9-3, but the emphasis here is on bacteria rather than molds. The organisms cultured in Problem 9-3 will be carefully examined to note such characteristics of bacterial colonies as color, shape, texture, and thickness, as well as differences between bacterial colonies and mold colonies. Conditions most favorable to the growth of bacteria are recognized. If high-power magnification (430X or greater) is available, students may recognize some of the characteristic shapes of individual bacteria that are described immediately following the problem in which the colonies are examined.

Problem 10-2 provides additional experience in the growing of pure cultures; these are used in testing the effectiveness of different antiseptics and germicides in killing or preventing the spread of bacteria on agar medium. Other environmental factors lethal to bacteria are also discussed.

Problem 10-3 is a reading activity that explores the effects of ultraviolet light on a nonpathogenic bacterium, *Serratia marcescens.* Using the data presented, the students prepare line graphs and interpret the experimental results.

Teaching Suggestions

Problem 10-1: What are some types of bacterial colonies? ***Pages 173-174***

Time Required: One period.

• Have petri dishes from Problem 9-3 ready for use in this problem.

• If you have a microscope available with a total magnification of 430X or greater, you may wish to make demonstration slides showing some of the bacteria from the students' cultures, or of *Serratia marcescens,* which is a large bacterium, easier to see, and readily available from supply houses.

To prepare a demonstration slide, use a sterile inoculating loop to obtain a sample from a bacterial colony. Spread this sample on a clean, dry slide. *Gently* heat-fix the bacteria by holding the slide, with forceps, high above a Bunsen burner flame for a few seconds. When the slide has cooled, stain with approximately 2% crystal violet solution or some other biological stain, allow to stand for a few seconds, then *gently* rinse the stain off with tap water. Allow to dry. The slide is now ready for observation. No cover glass is necessary. If you have an oil immersion objective, place the drop of oil directly on the slide.

As an alternative, obtain prepared slides of bacteria from a biological supply company.

• If the cultures from Problem 9-3 are overgrown with mold, make new cultures or obtain cultures of several kinds of bacteria from a biological supply house.

• Use an overhead projector to show the different types of colonies present in a petri dish.

• Emphasize that agar itself is not used to nourish bacteria, but to allow the development of colonies. The nutrients *added* to agar serve as food for the developing bacterial colonies.

• Provide a large container for the disposal of cultures. Have students scrape contents of the petri dishes into a collecting container in which a fungicide solution has been placed. A strong solution of hydrochloric acid and water works well. Other possible fungicides are strong formalin solution or a strong lysol solution.

After the contents have been removed, the petri dishes should be rinsed and then autoclaved. Autoclave contents of refuse beaker before discarding.

Disposable petri dishes should be dipped in fungicide before being thrown away.

Problem 10-2: What effect do antiseptics have on bacterial growth? *Pages 177-180*

Time Required: Two periods.

• Supply sterile petri dishes as well as sterile nutrient agar for each team; the agar should be warmed to about 100°C before pouring. Or, supply prepared agar plates.

• Instruct students to bring antiseptics and "germ killers" described in the text. Have at least three different types of antiseptics available.

• If dishes from Problem 9-3 are overgrown with mold, supply a commercially prepared pure culture of a bacterium.

• Compare the results of all groups within the class to obtain a detailed picture of the effects of antiseptics.

• Do not generalize about whether an antiseptic is good or bad, based on this one experiment. The effectiveness of an antiseptic must be judged by its use—obviously mouthwashes need not be as powerful as antibiotics.

Problem 10-3: What effect does ultraviolet light have on bacterium *Serratia marcescens*? *Pages 181-185*

Time Required: One period.

• You may want to assign this reading activity as homework.

• Class discussion should center around the experimental design described, the benefits of the serial dilution technique, and the interpretation of the results, showing that ultraviolet radiation will kill bacteria and may also cause mutations.

• Draw attention to the fact that exposure to X rays, chemicals, etc., has been associated with genetic mutations in humans.

Suggested Answers to Check Your Understanding *Pages 186-187*

9. A bacterium is a tiny, single-celled organism measuring less than two microns in diameter. Bacteria are known to have a cell membrane and a cell wall. Some have a protective layer of slime. Bacteria may have flagella for locomotion. Shapes of bacteria are coccus, bacillus, and spirillum.
10. When a bacterium lands on an area that has the conditions necessary for life, it divides again and again, forming a colony.
11. Bacterial colonies may differ in form, thickness, edge-shape, surface (texture), and color.
12. Mold colonies appear fuzzy—they have a mass of threadlike hyphae that are not found in bacterial colonies.
13. A pure culture makes results of testing more reliable by eliminating the chance of other organisms producing the results.
14. A serial dilution cuts down the concentration of organisms in an area. This is useful when individual colonies of bacteria are to be examined.
15. Yes. Bacteria are everywhere, including pond water. (School microscopes do not magnify pond water enough to allow the bacteria to be seen. Some students may wish to place a few drops of pond water on sterile nutrient agar to see what grows.)
16. Food, moisture, and a favorable temperature.
17. Milk is pasteurized by being heated to a temperature of 71°C (160°F) for 15 seconds or more, and then being cooled.
18. Fortunately, the favorable conditions necessary for bacterial growth do not exist for long. Disinfectants as well as other

organisms keep bacterial populations in check.

19. Ultraviolet light, chemical disinfectants, high temperatures, direct flaming, excessive amounts of sugar and salt, etc.
20. Washing removes bacteria. Any method of removing large numbers of bacteria is part of the aseptic technique.
21. You would incubate the cultures at 37°C (98.6°F), the temperature of the human body, since these bacteria grow in the human intestine. Bacteria usually grow best at a temperature that is close to that of their natural environment.
22. Ultraviolet light causes mutations in bacteria and may do the same to the cells in the human body. In addition, bacteria are killed by ultraviolet light by direct exposure. Since most bacterial infections in humans are not on the surface of the body, ultraviolet light would probably have little effect on the infectious bacteria.

Recommended Film for Chapter 10

Bacteria (Encyclopaedia Britannica Films). 19 minutes, color. Demonstrates basic characteristics, structures, manners of feeding, and reproductive processes of bacteria. Shows how bacteria are classified.

Unit 4: Plant Structures and Functions

This unit provides an introduction to the main processes carried on by green plants, from the germination of the seed to the production of seeds by the mature plant. Photosynthetic plants are ultimately responsible for producing all the food used by living organisms; it is important that the student understand the role of plants as food suppliers, and the key processes involved in this role.

If adequate herbarium facilities are available, this unit should be studied in the sequence in which it occurs in the text, since the concepts presented seem to fit most logically into this place. If, however, it is necessary to study this unit at a time when green plants are locally available, it is better to do so in the spring rather than the fall, since the activities and concepts presented here are based, to some extent, on knowledge and skills acquired in the earlier chapters.

The unit begins with a study of seeds in Chapter 11. Seed structures, germination, and the best conditions for growth are studied in separate experiments. The students discover that germinating seeds carry on respiration, using oxygen and producing carbon dioxide.

Chapter 12 deals with plant responses to stimuli. The students learn how plants respond to light and gravity. One of the problems in this chapter investigates the role of hormones in speeding up growth in certain portions of a plant.

Diffusion, osmosis, and transpiration are three important plant processes studied in Chapter 13. The effects of molecular motion and molecular concentration upon diffusion are emphasized. The movement of liquids into the roots and through the stem is observed and measured, and reasons are given to explain why the liquids move in the manner in which they do.

Chapter 14 consists of five problems dealing with various aspects of the process of photosynthesis. In the experiments, the emphasis is placed on testing different parts of green plants for glucose and starch resulting from the photosynthetic process. Conditions that favor the production of glucose are experimentally identified. In addition to glucose, the oxygen released during photosynthesis is measured. The student is introduced to the technique of paper chromatography, and learns how to separate different pigments found in leaves.

The unit is concluded with Chapter 15 on flowers and the purpose they serve in plants. The parts of a typical flower and fruit are identified as each is dissected. Each structure in the flower is related to its function in seed production. This chapter completes the study of plants.

The structure of the unit emphasizes the cyclical nature of plant growth, beginning with the development of the embryo within a seed and ending with a look at the plant organ responsible for producing more seeds. Students who complete this study of green plants should appreciate the vital importance of plants to all living things on earth.

Chapter 11: Seed Germination

The introductory chapter in this unit on plants explores the structure and germination of seeds. Corn kernels and beans, representative monocot and dicot seeds, are examined in Problem 11-1. The student identifies the embryonic leaves and roots within the soaked bean seed. Starch stored for use by the embryo plant after germination is identified in the seed by the iodine test, and the effect of water upon the seed coat is determined.

The concept of seed viability is introduced and studied in Problem 11-2. Each laboratory team observes the germination of seeds over a period of ten days; the seeds are kept moist and at room temperature. The students calculate the percentage of germination. In Problem 11-3, several varieties of seeds are germinated under different conditions of light and temperature. Factors that affect seed viability, such as age, temperature extremes, and broken seed coats, are considered in the text.

Carbon dioxide, the gaseous product of the respiration of pea seeds, is collected and measured in Problem 11-4 by means of water displacement. The students test the gas with limewater and a glowing splint, and observe that it has the properties of carbon dioxide. The fact that seeds carry on the process of respiration confirms the idea that the seed embryo is a living organism.

Teaching Suggestions

Problem 11-1: What are the main parts of corn and bean seeds? ***Pages 194-196***

Time Required: One period.

• Presoak a number of corn and bean seeds for 24 hours before this activity is begun. Each team will need one dry and one presoaked of each kind of seed.

• Display large charts or models of dissected seeds. Use these for post-lab discussion of the problem. Many transparencies of seed structures are available.

• Seeds of kinds other than those used in the experiment may be made available for teams that finish early or have extra time.

• Students should acquire the idea that the embryo within the seed is a living organism. Emphasize this point as students are doing the problem and in post-lab discussion.

• You might supply students with colored pencils to sketch the results of the starch test.

During class discussion, emphasize that the breaking of the seed coat is a necessary step in seed germination.

Problem 11-2: What is meant by seed viability? ***Pages 197-199***

Time Required: Approximately ten days will be required to give all seeds an opportunity to germinate. Only one period will be required to set up the original experiment. Students will need to inspect germination dishes daily.

• A storage area large enough to hold germination dishes for each team must be provided. It must be darkened and be at room temperature. Cabinets or shoe boxes work well for this purpose.

• Since a large quantity of seeds is required for this problem, you may want to purchase seeds from feed stores or garden supply houses. Seeds kept from a previous year may be compared to fresh seeds in this experiment. Bean and corn seeds can be purchased in large quantities and will keep for 2-3 years in a cool, dry environment. Viability usually decreases with the age of the seeds.

• Almost any variety of seed may be used. It is recommended that each class use a number of different kinds of seeds, to compare their different viabilities. If large seeds such as corn or bean seeds are used, they should be presoaked for 24 hours and treated with household bleach (full strength) or commercial fungicide solution just before starting the experiment.

• Do not store seeds in direct sunlight or extreme heat before use, since some seeds are sensitive to these conditions.

• Seed viability will probably vary somewhat from group to group since there are several variables present. The seeds may not all be the same age, some seeds may have received more water than others, etc. This would be a good topic for class discussion and would lead up to the next experiment.

• After setting up the experiment, students need only a few minutes each day to observe and record germination progress. The class should go on with other experiments in the meantime.

Problem 11-3: What effect do light and temperature have on seed germination? ***Pages 200-203***

Time Required: One day to set up experiment and a few minutes each day for the next two weeks.

• Seeds may be obtained in hardware stores and garden supply stores. Presoak the pea seeds for 24 hours in advance for each class. Treat with household bleach or commercial fungicide.

• Construct a light source for the refrigerator by running a lamp cord into the refrigerator through the hinged side of the door.

• You may want to duplicate a complete version of Table 11-2 and give to students for insertion in their notebooks. This will save them the time required to prepare such a detailed table for recording data.

• As a discussion topic, ask students to identify the control group, experimental group, dependent variable, and independent variable in each experiment.

• Seed viabilities often vary widely, and different lab teams may report different results. Answers given in annotations are those that have been found to be true in actual classroom experiments. If your students' results do not agree with these, it probably indicates that the seeds were initially in different conditions rather than that the laboratory technique was faulty. The important objective of this activity is not for students to memorize what kinds of seeds germinate best, but to learn that different kinds of seeds often have different viabilities, and that the viability of seeds is affected by environmental conditions.

Problem 11-4: How much gas do seeds release during germination? ***Pages 204-208***

Time Required: One and one-half periods on consecutive days.

• Assemble stopper and tubing before class. Use glycerine to lubricate ends of glass tubing.

• Limewater may be prepared by adding about 10 grams of calcium metal turnings to a liter of distilled water. Calcium reacts with water to produce lime, $Ca(OH)_2$, and hydrogen gas. The water becomes saturated with lime and the excess lime remains as a deposit at the bottom of the container. The solution should be prepared 24 hours in advance and the clear solution either siphoned or decanted into another clean jar, leaving the remaining lime behind. The limewater bottle should be stoppered to avoid reaction with carbon dioxide in the air.

• This experiment may also be done using different kinds of seeds, or the same kind of seeds under different temperature conditions. The latter, especially, would make a good demonstration; it shows, indirectly, how temperature change affects the rate of metabolism.

• To assure a positive test for carbon dioxide, you may wish to have half the groups test for oxygen and the balance test for carbon dioxide. This will eliminate the possibility of losing the carbon dioxide when the oxygen test is done.

• In post-lab discussion, remind students that they have only demonstrated that the gas they have isolated has two properties of carbon dioxide: it doesn't cause a glowing splint to ignite and it makes limewater cloudy. Emphasize that, ideally, an hypothesis needs as much experimental corroboration as possible.

Suggested Answers to Check Your Understanding *Pages 209-210*

9. Monocot seeds by definition have only one cotyledon; dicot seeds have two cotyledons.
10. The embryo would probably die due to lack of food.
11. Eighty percent.
12. At cooler temperatures, the seed embryo carries on respiration at a slower pace and consequently remains viable longer.
13. A thick seed coat would protect the embryo from being easily crushed or from drying out, and therefore it would be advantageous for seeds growing in arid regions or for seeds that are likely to undergo a lot of abrasion. A thick seed coat might be a disadvantage when the embryo starts to grow and attempts to break out of the seed coat.
14. Light seems to make some seeds, like the grasses, germinate faster, but seems to have no effect on most other seeds. (Increasing quantities of light may help end dormancy.)
15. Yes. Freezing would probably kill the embryo and prevent the seed from germinating.
16. The amount of heat given off by respiring seeds may be measured by placing the germinating seeds and water into an insulated container, such as a thermos bottle. The water temperature change could be determined with a thermometer.
17. There are many possible answers. Nongerminating seeds may be eaten by animals, collected by people, or decayed by bacteria and returned to the soil.
18. In view of answer to Question 17, the more seeds produced, the greater the chances of surviving to germinate.
19. Considerations should include the environment of the garden, e.g., its light and temperature conditions, and the requirements of the particular kind of seed being planted.
20. Some seeds have very thick seed coats. Soaking is necessary to aid the germinating seed in breaking through the coat.

Recommended Film for Chapter 11

Seed Germination BBS (Encyclopaedia Britannica Films). 14 minutes, color. Uses time-lapse photography to demonstrate a wide variety of experiments with germinating seeds. Explains that seed germination is one of the basic phenomena of the plant world, and discusses practical significance of seed and grain plants.

Chapter 12: Plant Responses to Stimuli

In Chapter 8, the students observed how motile organisms respond to stimuli, using brine shrimp as an example. In this chapter, they learn how plants respond to many of the same stimuli by observing the behavior of corn seedlings. Once a seed has germinated and the resulting plant has begun to grow, a number of stimuli may affect the growth of that plant. The investigation of the effects of various environmental conditions upon plants is an interesting and sometimes surprising activity for student and teacher alike.

The first problem consists of locating, on a corn seedling, the area of the root that grows most rapidly. The students place evenly spaced marks on the main (tap) root of the young corn plant and observe the spacings daily for several days. From the uneven spacing that results, the students infer that growth occurs more rapidly in certain areas of the root than in others. The fact that cells may multiply at varying rates in different parts of plants is the key to understanding the external manifestations of plant responses to stimuli. The experiments in this chapter show that cell division is responsible not only for the overall growth of the plant, but also for the relative movement and positioning of roots, stems, and other plant parts.

The students test the effects of various stimuli, including gravity, light, and gibberellic acid, on the growth of corn seedlings. From the text material, the students learn that plant cells contain hormones, or auxins, that are responsible for plant growth. They learn that varying concentrations of these hormones may alter the growth rate of the entire plant, or may cause different parts of the plant to grow at different rates. The presence of these chemicals is linked to the tropic responses of plants that the students have observed in the laboratory.

Corn seedlings in various stages of growth are required for all the experiments in this chapter. The seedlings must be started several days in advance; it would be a good idea to stagger the planting over a period of several days, so that seedlings of various sizes will be available.

All of the problems involve subjecting corn seedlings to various experimental conditions and observing these plants over a period of several days. All four experiments may be set up in two or three laboratory sessions. The subsequent daily observations will only take a few minutes, and the rest of the class time will then be free for discussion or further laboratory activity.

Teaching Suggestions

Problem 12-1: Where does growth take place in a root? *Pages 213-215*

Time Required: Half of one period the first day, then a few minutes each of the next few days.

- Cut plastic screen into squares approximately 8 cm on a side; one will be needed for each team.
- Plant corn seeds several days in advance so that each team can have a seedling two days old. Soak a handful of corn seeds for 24 hours, and then plant in vermiculite.
- India ink or permanent felt-pen ink should be used on the screens. If you use felt pens, test the ink beforehand to make sure that it is not water-soluble.
- Caution the students not to use too much ink, or it will fill in the spaces of the screen.
- Based on the knowledge that they acquire from this experiment, ask students to comment on similarities and differences between the growth patterns of plants and animals.

Problem 12-2: What effect does gravity have on plant growth? *Pages 216-218*

Time Required: One-half of the first period, then a few minutes of several subsequent periods. This problem may be set up at the same time as Problem 12-1 and the results of both experiments observed at the same time each day.

- Plant corn seeds several days in advance so that 5-cm seedlings are available for each team.
- Bring in several cardboard cartons to be cut up for cardboard backing mounts for the test tubes.
- Some students may have difficulty understanding that if a stem bends, the cells on one side must either be increasing or elongating. To clarify this, draw two lines to represent a bent stem on the chalkboard. Have students measure, with a tape measure, the lines representing the outside and inside of the bent portion. Let each centimeter (or inch) represent one cell. A comparison of the two measurements should show the students that there must

be more—or longer—cells on the side of the stem away from the direction in which the stem is bent.

• Point out, in class discussion, that no matter in what position *seeds* are placed, the stem seems to grow upward and the roots downward. Students should be able to relate this phenomenon to the geotropic responses that they have observed in this activity.

Problem 12-3: How do plants respond to light? ***Pages 220-224***

Time Required: One period to set up the experiment and a few minutes during each of the next several days to observe the growth of the seedlings.

• Enough corn seeds must be planted about one week in advance of this problem to provide at least three 5-cm seedlings for each laboratory team.

• Ask each student to bring in an empty half-pint or third-quart milk carton before the experiment is started. Cartons may also be obtained from the school cafeteria.

• Moist vermiculite is excellent for sustaining the growth of the seedlings for the short duration of this experiment. If this is not available, loose, sandy soil may be substituted with good results.

• Because of the size of the cardboard and graph, and for the sake of accuracy, the students will have to place their graphs in exactly the same position each time they measure the plants. Thus, the graph of the growth of the plant grown in the light (and possibly the one grown in total darkness) may be an almost vertical line. So that the growth trends can be seen more easily, have students mark plot points with colored pencils, using a different color for each day.

• Make sure that the students place the graph paper in exactly the same position each day. Instruct them to mark with a pencil the side of the carton in front of which they place the graph, so they will know which way to orient the graph paper each day. For the directed-light carton, the graph paper should be placed in front of one of the sides *adjacent* to the side with the opening, so that the resulting graph will show how the stem bends.

• Caution students to make sure that they replace the covers on the milk cartons each day. In the directed-light group, the light must come from one direction only; therefore the covers must be replaced in exactly the same way each time.

• Students should need no help in observing the differences between the plants kept in the dark and the ones exposed to light. Allow them to suggest possible explanations for the differences in the conditions of the plants.

Problem 12-4: What effect does gibberellic acid have on plant growth? ***Pages 225-229***

Time Required: One period to set up the experiment and several minutes daily for two weeks to observe and care for the plants.

• Have corn seedlings several days old ready for each laboratory team at the start of this experiment. Seedlings should show some visible stem after they are planted in the vermiculite.

• Prepare gibberellic acid solution by first dissolving 1 gram of gibberellic acid in 2 milliliters of ethyl alcohol, then adding the alcohol to 1 liter of distilled water.

• Establish the fact that scientists do not understand the effect of a great many chemical substances on living things. Through continuing research it is hoped that more information will be gathered to better understand some of these things.

• Plants should be placed under growing lamps or in an area where they will receive sunlight for part of the day.

Suggested Answers to Check Your Understanding *Page 230*

9. High concentrations of chemical salts may cause plant roots to show a negative chemotropism.
10. Periodically turn the plant so the side not facing the sun can obtain light.
11. Yes. A strong wind could easily control the direction of growing stem sections.
12. The plant grown in light will have fewer growth hormones, because light destroys these chemicals. Therefore, plants grown in the dark grow more rapidly. However, un-

less some light is present, the seedlings will soon die.

13. Vermiculite provides a material into which plant roots may anchor, yet the vermiculite does not add unwanted minerals.
14. An experiment might compare the growth of various plants in water containing minerals to the growth of plants in water containing no minerals (distilled).

Recommended Film for Chapter 12

Plant Tropism and Other Movements (Coronet). 11 minutes, color. Shows major types of plant movements, and also shows how they affect plant life and growth.

Chapter 13: Movement of Liquids in Plants

Plants require varying amounts of moisture in order to live. This chapter examines the role of water as a solvent; it also explores the movement of water to various parts of the plant, and how this movement is accomplished.

The importance of water as a solvent and a transporter of dissolved materials is shown in the first two problems in the chapter. The students observe a crystal of potassium permanganate dissolve in water, and note how the purple dye diffuses through the water until the concentration of the solution becomes uniform. The text points out that diffusion is accomplished by the movement of molecules in solution from an area of higher concentration to an area of lower concentration until equilibrium is achieved.

In Problem 13-2 the students observe selective diffusion through a semipermeable membrane. The results of this experiment instill the idea that molecules are of different sizes and that the pores in a semipermeable membrane are so small that only small-enough molecules can pass through.

The activity involving diffusion through a selectively permeable membrane serves as an introduction to Problem 13-3, which involves the study of osmosis in living cells. In an earlier chapter, the students observed the plasmolysis that occurred when an elodea leaf was placed in a salt solution; in this activity, they note the changes that occur in the texture and rigidity of potato slices placed in salt solutions of different concentrations. The Guide Questions help the students conclude that the movement of water molecules from inside the cell to the outside environment was responsible for the change in the potato slices.

In Problem 13-4, a reading activity, students use the data given to draw graphs and interpret results. They determine the rate of osmosis in a carrot root. Once again the osmotic movement can be related to the different solution concentrations inside and outside a membrane.

The movement of liquids through plant stems is studied in the final two problems in this chapter. In Problem 13-5, a celery stalk is placed in colored water and the movement of water through the stem is traced. After 24 hours the xylem tubes in the stem are easily visible. The student prepares a wet mount slide of a thin section of a xylem tube and notices that the structure of its component cells is specialized, enabling the cells to conduct water upward. Phloem cells are also described in the text, and their function is briefly summarized.

Water loss from leaves by transpiration is indirectly measured in Problem 13-6. A plant stem is connected to a length of glass tubing filled with water. Upward movement of water through the stem can be related to the rise of the water in the glass tubing. The text points out that some of the water is used in the metabolic activities of the plant cell, but that most of it is released into the air by the stomata in the leaves.

Teaching Suggestions

Problem 13-1: How do dissolved materials move in solution? *Pages 236-237*

Time Required: One period or less.

- This problem can be done effectively as a demonstration if you prefer.
- The beakers containing the water and potassium permanganate should not be moved

during this activity. Instruct students to make observations without touching the beakers.

- In post-lab discussion, review the difference between observation and interpretation, and analyze how it applies to this experiment. The students observe the dye spreading through the water, and interpret it to mean that the dye molecules are moving, or diffusing, among the water molecules.
- Students should understand that the process of diffusion can be *demonstrated* by the use of the dye potassium permanganate. Other dissolved particles are thought to diffuse in the same manner, even though the movement of the particles cannot be seen.
- An interesting demonstration of the same principle can be done by dropping a single large crystal of either potassium permanganate or copper sulfate into a tall cylinder of distilled water that is completely motionless. It is interesting to observe the spreading color as it diffuses slowly upward through the water. This system will continue to change for a week or more if left undisturbed.

Problem 13-2: What materials can diffuse through a semipermeable membrane? *Pages 238-241*

Time Required: Two consecutive class periods.

- Use soluble starch intended for iodometry. Household starch doesn't dissolve as well and may give a positive test for glucose. Soluble starch must be purchased from a biological supply house.
- Prepare a 2% solution of starch by heating 20 grams of starch in 200 milliliters of distilled water until it is dissolved, then pouring it into a one-liter container and adding enough water to make a liter of solution. This is enough starch solution for about 50 trials.
- Prepare glucose solution by dissolving 20 grams of glucose in one liter of distilled water. Do not substitute cane sugar (sucrose) for glucose, since it will not react with Benedict's solution. Sucrose may be broken down to produce glucose by the process of hydrolysis. This is accomplished by heating sucrose with dilute hydrochloric acid solution, then neutralizing the solution with concentrated sodium carbonate solution until all fizzing stops.
- Benedict's solution may be purchased from supply houses or you may prepare the solution yourself. To prepare the solution, dissolve 173 grams of crystalline sodium citrate, $C_6H_5Na_3O_7$, and 100 grams of anhydrous sodium carbonate, Na_2CO_3, in about 800 milliliters of water. Stir thoroughly and filter. Add to the filtered solution 17.3 grams copper sulfate, $CuSO_4{\cdot}5H_2O$, dissolved in 100 milliliters of water. Add distilled water until the volume of the solution is one liter.
- Cut cellophane tubing in 15-centimeter lengths and soak in a pan of water before use. Soaking makes the cellophane more flexible and easier to work with.
- Demonstrate proper method of heating a liquid in a test tube.
- Some states require students to wear safety goggles when heating liquids over a flame. Check the safety requirements in your particular state. Wearing goggles is a good idea, even if not required by law.

Problem 13-3: How does the concentration of a salt affect osmosis in a plant cell? *Pages 242-243*

Time Required: Half a period.

- Two or three potatoes will be needed for each class. A potato slicer works best to provide slices of uniform thickness.
- Prepare large quantities of salt solutions in advance to save time. For a 1% solution (approximate), add 10 grams of salt per liter of distilled water; for a 5% solution, add 50 grams of salt to 950 milliliters of distilled water.
- Discuss the concept of turgor as it relates to water content of cells and salt concentration outside cells.
- In post-lab discussion, have students relate the changes in the potato slices to the cellular changes that they observed when they studied plasmolysis in Problem 6-3.
- Put out waste containers to collect potato slices at the end of the experiment.

Problem 13-4: How may osmosis in a plant root be measured? *Pages 244-248*

Time Required: One period.

- You may want to assign this reading activity as homework.

• Class discussion should center around the experimental design and the interpretation of results.

Problem 13-5: Where is water transported in a celery plant? ***Pages 249-251***

Time Required: Two consecutive class periods.

• One branch of fresh celery with leaves is needed for each team.

• Washable inks work better than permanent inks. Food coloring may be substituted for ink.

• Most students will need to practice preparing the slides.

• Use sharp single-edged razor blades to cut out colored tubes found in the stalk.

Problem 13-6: How much water is lost to the air by a plant? ***Pages 253-255***

Time Required: One period and part of the next consecutive day's class period.

• You or one group of students may perform this experiment as a demonstration, rather than have each laboratory team do this activity.

• It is very important to cut off the end of the stem under water so that no air enters the xylem cells of the stem.

• In post-lab discussion, relate the amount of water lost through transpiration to daily humidity, wind conditions, etc.

• Another effective demonstration of water loss by transpiration in plants may be done as follows. Water a potted houseplant, then seal off all moisture in the pot and lower portion of the plant by lowering the pot carefully into a plastic bag and tying the top of the bag tight just above the top of the pot. Enclose the leaves of the plant in a second large, clean plastic bag and tie it. Set the plant in a sunny part of the room for 24-48 hours. Water lost from the leaves by transpiration will appear at tiny drops of condensed moisture on the inside of the bag.

A control pot could be a similar pot containing moist soil and a bare branch, wrapped with two plastic bags as before. Little or no moisture should appear in the upper bag if the soil moisture has been effectively sealed off.

Suggested Answers to Check Your Understanding *Pages 255-256*

11. Diffusion refers to the movement of molecules away from an area where they are highly concentrated until they are evenly distributed throughout the solution. The kinetic energy (motion) of the molecules is responsible for their spreading out to produce a uniform concentration.
12. Osmosis is a special kind of diffusion in which water passes through a membrane, eventually producing equal concentrations of water molecules on both sides of the membrane.
13. The living cell membrane acts to retain certain materials within the cell while permitting other materials to enter or leave.
14. No. The rate of osmosis depends on the differences in water concentration on the two sides of the membrane. If the concentrations are very close, the rate of osmosis will be slow. If there is a great difference in concentration, osmosis will occur at a rapid rate. Since water is used up at different rates, depending on the activity of the plant, the concentration of water will vary. Thus, the rate of osmosis will vary, too.
15. The concentrated salt solution causes water to leave the cell more rapidly than it enters the cell. This process, called plasmolysis, results in a shrinking of the cell contents, since the cell is largely composed of water.
16. A permeable membrane allows all dissolved materials to pass freely through it in both directions. A semipermeable membrane permits some molecules to pass through more rapidly than others and prohibits some from passing through at all.
17. Water enters the celery cells by osmosis, travels up the stem by capillary action, osmotic pressure, and cohesive forces, and into the leaf cells by osmosis.
18. Root hairs are extensions of root epidermal cells that provide greater surface area for sbsorbing water and minerals from the soil.
19. This procedure prevents the delicate root

hairs from being ripped off. It also prevents dehydration, which could occur if the root hairs were exposed to air.

20. The amount of water lost by plant leaves must be balanced by the amount of water entering the plant. If sufficient water is not available, the plant wilts and eventually dies.

Recommended Film for Chapter 13

Plant Life at Work (Moody Science Institute). 10 minutes, color. Shows how plants exhibit life processes that characterize all living things: use of energy for movement, growth, manufacture of food, and reproduction.

Chapter 14: Photosynthesis

Photosynthesis is extremely important, since it is the basic food-making process for all organisms. The series of chemical reactions that takes place during the photosynthetic process is highly complex; a simplified equation showing the overall reaction is given in the chapter introduction. The experiments in the chapter show what the products of photosynthesis are and how they are distributed. Students also determine the effects of some environmental conditions on the photosynthetic process.

The problems can be handled as student demonstration experiments. The class can be divided into four teams, each of which is responsible for conducting one demonstration for the class.

Problem 14-1 deals with the detection of glucose, one of the main products of photosynthesis, in various parts of green onions. The students observe that glucose is concentrated in the leaves, but is also found to some extent in the nongreen parts of the onion. They learn that diffusion and osmosis are the means by which photosynthetic products are distributed throughout the entire plant. The role of the conducting tissues is conveyed through appropriate Guide Questions.

The effect of light on starch production by plant leaves is studied in Problem 14-2. Following this, the student tests the effect of changing the amount of carbon dioxide available to plant leaves. Problem 14-4 is concerned with collecting, measuring, and testing the gas produced by green plants during photosynthesis. The experiment includes a comparison of plants kept in the light with those that have been kept in the dark.

The last problem consists of an introduction to chromatography. Pigments contained in the green leaves of a plant are separated; chlorophyll is identified. The importance of chlorophyll to the photosynthetic process is emphasized.

Teaching Suggestions

Problem 14-1: What is one kind of food produced by green plants? *Pages 261-262*

Time Required: One period.

• Have students bring in green onions (scallions) a day in advance. Only a few are required for each class.

• Point out that glucose is not the same as table sugar, but is the same sugar found in blood.

• When testing for glucose, remind students to heat the test tube and its contents slowly so that the sequence of color changes can be observed.

• Some states require students to wear safety goggles when heating liquids in a test tube. Check to see if your state requires it. It is a good practice to follow even if it is not required by law.

Problem 14-2: Where do plant leaves contain starch? *Pages 264-266*

Time Required: One period.

• If plants are not available in the classroom, have students bring in their own plants a day in advance. Each team needs two plants of the same variety in order to compare the effects of darkness and light on starch production.

• One group of plants must be kept in total darkness for 24 hours immediately preceding the experiment. Another group of the same kind of plants should be kept in light for a similar period. Growing lamps of some kind should be used.

• In post-lab discussion, check the understanding of your students by asking them the significance of the results of the chemical tests in this problem.

Problem 14-3: How does carbon dioxide affect the production of starch? *Pages 267-268*

Time Required: One period.

• This problem can be done effectively as a demonstration if you prefer.

• All plants used in this problem should be kept in the dark for 24 hours before use. This reduces the initial starch content of the leaves. During the experiment, light should be provided 24 hours a day, to increase the amount of glucose and starch produced.

• Tomato plants give good results; others may be tried out beforehand to determine their usefulness in this experiment.

• Plants should be well watered before starting the experiment.

• Provide aprons for all students handling the sodium hydroxide pellets or the hydrochloric acid solution. Caution students to be very careful when using these materials and to wash their hands immediately after using the chemicals.

• Review the procedure for testing for starch.

Problem 14-4: What is the effect of light on the production of oxygen by green plants? *Pages 270-272*

Time Required: One period.

• You may want to assign this reading activity as homework.

• Class discussion should center around the experimental design and the interpretation of results. Explain why the splint test is used to indicate the presence of oxygen.

Problem 14-5: How may the different pigments in leaves be separated? *Pages 273-275*

Time Required: One period.

• Chlorophyll solvent "A" should be prepared by mixing together 50 milliliters of N-pentane, 15 milliliters of acetone, and 21 milliliters of benzene.

• Chromatography solvent "B" should be prepared by mixing together 100 milliliters of heptane, 4 milliliters of ethyl acetate, and 1 milliliter of benzene. An alternative mixture for solvent "B" consists of 80 milliliters of butyl alcohol and 20 milliliters of distilled water.

• Many different kinds of green leaves will work for this experiment. Choose any that are readily available at the time the experiment is done. Frozen spinach leaves may be substituted if other kinds are not available.

• Solvents used in this experiment are very flammable and should not be used near an open flame.

• A waste jar with a lid should be provided for the solvent remaining in the test tubes at the end of the experiment. This will reduce odors and keep flammable materials out of the sink. The solvent may be discarded later in an unplanted area of the yard.

• A detailed explanation of the mechanisms involved in paper chromatography is not recommended here. Chromatography should be introduced as a separation technique useful for the observation of different pigments in leaves.

Suggested Answers to Check Your Understanding *Page 276*

14. The added weight came from materials produced in living plant cells by photosynthesis.
15. Photosynthesis traps light energy; this energy is stored in glucose molecules. In respiration, the glucose molecules combine with oxygen to release the stored energy. Also, oxygen is a reactant in respiration but a product in photosynthesis, and the reverse is true for carbon dioxide.
16. Plant pigments may be separated by the action of a solvent passing through the pigments. Certain pigments move along more rapidly with (dissolve faster in) the solvent than do other pigments.
17. The yellow or red pigments are actually present in the leaves at all times. However, only when cold weather and the reduced quantity of light destroy the chlorophyll can the other pigments be seen.
18. The chlorophyll has to be removed so that the blue-black color of a positive starch test can be seen.
19. All of the factors are essential for

photosynthesis. A wide range of answers should be expected and accepted here.

20. So the gas collected would be only that produced by the plant.

Recommended Film for Chapter 14

Photosynthesis BBS (Encyclopaedia Britannica Films). 21 minutes, color. Explains how green plants use light energy to make food by the process of photosynthesis. Laboratory demonstrations show how scientists study the process by which carbon dioxide and water—in the presence of light and chlorophyll—react to produce sugar and to release oxygen.

Chapter 15: Flowers, Seeds, and Fruits

This final chapter in Unit Four deals with the structures responsible for the reproduction of seed plants. The study of flowers, along with the seeds and fruits they produce, completes the cycle of inquiry about how plants grow from seeds, manufacture their own food, and finally produce seeds that give rise to the next generation of plants.

The first problem consists of the observation and dissection of a typical flower. Pollen from a flower stamen is observed under the microscope. The essential parts of the flower are located and their functions are conveyed by means of the text material and Guide Questions.

In Problem 15-2, the study of flowers is continued. The students investigate and learn the difference between perfect and imperfect flowers, and between self- and cross-pollination. The role of agents such as wind and insects in the pollination process is analyzed. The function of nectar and brightly colored flower petals is discussed, and the text helps the students think of factors that would be conducive to several different methods of pollination.

In Problem 15-3, a common fruit such as an apple or a pear is cut in half and examined for the remains of the flower from which it was formed. The remains of the ovary wall, dried sepals, and the enlarged base of the flower are identified as part of the fruit. The students examine peas or beans in pods, and learn why the pods are regarded as fruits. Examples are given of the ways in which fruits may aid in the distribution of seeds.

Teaching Suggestions

Problem 15-1: What are the parts of a flower? *Pages 284-286*

Time Required: One period.

- Ask students to bring in flowers. Make sure to have a wide variety of flowers for comparison. Perfect flowers (those containing both male and female structures) are necessary for this activity. Some desirable varieties include tulips, apple blossoms, petunias, nasturtiums, lilies, geraniums, etc.
- Commercial flower shops may donate certain types of flowers that are no longer marketable. They also may have suggestions for where to obtain the kinds of flowers that you need. Contact such sources well before the flowers are needed.
- Flowers may be grown in window boxes or interior planters if planted well in advance.
- Before class, check flowers to make sure that they are not damaged. While the activity is in progress, check to make sure that students are correctly identifying flower parts and recording the correct number of petals, sepals, etc.
- Review how to prepare wet mount slides and how to focus the microscope. Have students consult notebooks, Problem 5-3, for field diameter.
- Observe students' slides of pollen grains to make sure that students are making reasonable sketches and size estimates.
- Ask students to sketch the flowers that they observed and compare them with the typical flower shown in the text. Point out that flowers differ somewhat in appearance and structure, but they all serve the same general purpose of producing seeds.

Problem 15-2: How are flowers different? *Pages 288-289*

Time Required: One-half to one period.

• At least four different kinds of plant flowers are needed for this problem. These might include tulips, dandelions, iris, sweet peas, corn, cottonwood, nasturtiums, citrus flowers, and the flowers of grasses, such as buffalo grass and wheat.

• Make sure that you have at least one representative each of a staminate, pistillate, and perfect flower, so that the analogous structures may be observed and compared.

• Wind-pollinated flowers and insect-pollinated flowers must be available for comparison. Call a local florist if students are unable to bring in flowers for themselves.

• Plants and flowers may be pressed and saved for future use. This will provide a greater variety for study in the future.

• As an alternative or supplement to the use of live flowers, you may show color slides showing the structures of different kinds of flowers. If live flowers are unavailable, certain procedures, such as Step C, Question 8, will have to be omitted.

• If insects such as bees or flies are available, chloroform them and have students examine the insects' bodies and legs for structures useful for transporting pollen.

Problem 15-3: What are the different parts of a fruit? *Pages 291-292*

Time Required: One-half of a period.

• Ask one member of each team to bring in an apple or a pear for this experiment.

• Green peas and green beans in pods are needed, and can usually be purchased at the grocery store. If local stores are not likely to have these vegetables at the time you are doing this problem, you may freeze a supply of uncooked green beans and peas in the pod when they are available so that you will have them at this time.

• Do not permit fruit to be eaten after use in this problem since it will have been handled by several people.

• In post-lab discussion, compare the observations made by different teams. Discuss similarities and differences among different kinds of fruits, and, if possible, correlate structure to function.

• Commercial charts of flowers and fruits are helpful for comparison with the real fruits used in this problem.

Suggested Answers to Check Your Understanding *Page 293*

10. A fruit by definition is a ripened ovary. Many vegetables are ripened ovaries.
11. Answers will vary, but may mention wind, water, animals, people, etc. Examples: The seeds of dandelion have feathery attachments that enable them to be carried by the air. The seeds of coconut can be carried by water for long distances. The seeds of cockleburs have hooks that attach to the fur of animals.
12. When the pollen grain falls on the pistil, it starts to grow a tube down to the lower section of the pistil. When the pollen tube reaches the ovary, two sperm nuclei from the pollen grain move down the tube. One sperm nucleus combines with the egg cell to produce the embryo, and one sperm nucleus helps to form the endosperm (stored food).
13. Imperfect flowers, flower structures that interfere with self-pollination, or flower parts that ripen at different times could all prevent self-pollination in flowers. (Accept any two of these.)
14. An experiment testing self-pollination may be set up by keeping a flower covered, so that the pollen from no other flower could fertilize it. If seeds or fruit develop, the plant is capable of self-pollination.
15. The stamens and the pistil are necessary for seed production. These structures include the pollen, ovary, and ovules.

Recommended Films for Chapter 15

Flowers and Their Purpose (Cenco Educational Films). 15 minutes, color. Shows the various parts of flowers and tells their function; defines pollination, reproduction; shows examples of selective breeding and resulting hybrids.

Flowers at work, 2nd Ed. (Encyclopaedia Britannica Films). 11 minutes, color. Shows by animation, time-lapse photography, and close-up photography the processes of cross-pollination, self-pollination, and fertilization. Shows special devices of flowers that assure pollination and describes the part played by insects.

Flowers—Structure and Function (Coronet). 11 minutes, color. Specialized parts of a flower are seen in relation to their function of pollination and seed production. Iris, azalea, vetch, and mustard flowers illustrate complete flowers, while watermelon and pumpkin blossoms illustrate staminate and pistillate forms. Macroscopic and microscopic views show stamen, anther, pistil, stigma, ovaries, pollen, fruit. Pollination by insects and wind is illustrated. Shows growth of pollen tubes from pollen grains.

Fruits of Plants (Cenco Educational Films). 12 minutes, color. To botanists, a fruit is the ripened ovary of any kind of plant, grown to protect seeds. There is a great variation in appearance, although the function of all fruits is the same. The film shows edible and inedible fruits, dry fruits, capsule fruits, winged fruits, and fleshy fruits. It shows that through cross-pollination, grafting, and budding, people are constantly producing healthier, better-appearing, better-tasting fruits.

Unit 5: Animal Organs and Systems — The Frog

In this unit the students will have the opportunity to study the frog, a vertebrate animal having organ systems closely related to those of the human. In the course of this unit, the frog will be studied in both the living and the preserved states.

The first chapter in the unit consists of a series of observations of the living frog and the special body features that enable frogs to live both on land and in water. Sensory organs, modified leg and muscle structures that enable the frog to jump and swim, as well as the breathing process and the effect of external temperature on this process, are explored in this unit.

In Chapter 17, the students compare the anatomy of the frog with that of the human. They study various organs and systems of a preserved frog, and compare them to their human analogues. Because the students do the dissecting themselves, they should retain the knowledge that they acquire.

Chapter 16: Observing the Living Frog

The purpose of this chapter is to provide insight into the special body features that make the frog a successful animal in its environment. The students examine the external anatomy of the living frog. They observe how the frog's breathing rate changes as the environmental temperature varies.

The first problem calls attention to a number of special body features of the frog. The students observe structures used for jumping, and calculate the length of an average jump. They discover how the frog's body structures are adapted to living both in the water and on the land. The frog's oxygen supply is related to both the breathing of air and the absorption of dissolved oxygen from the water through the skin. Attention is called to the protective membrane that covers the eyes of the frog, keeping the eyes constantly moist and protecting them while the frog is under water.

In Problem 16-2, the student compares the breathing patterns of frog and human. Two different breathing movements of the frog—nostril movements and skin flap movements under the chin—are observed and counted. The breathing rate of a student is then calculated, and all the results are plotted on a graph for comparison. An organism's activity and its effect on breathing rate are analyzed.

The third problem seeks to determine the effect of a change in temperature on the breathing rate of a frog. Frogs are partially immersed in water baths of different temperatures, and the students count the number of times that the frogs' nostrils open and close. Changes in internal body temperature of each frog are measured by gently inserting a thermometer a few centimeters into the frog's mouth. These measurements reveal the ectothermic nature of the frog. A line graph is prepared to show the changes that take place in body temperature and nostril movement as the external temperature varies.

You may want to have students do Problem 16-3 first, when the frogs are fresh, or you may put a few frogs in reserve for this problem. You might also decide to perform Problem 16-3 as a demonstration, in which case, again, you will want to use a fresh frog for best results.

Teaching Suggestions

Problem 16-1: How is the frog adapted to live on land and in water? *Pages 302-304*

Time Required: One period.

- Live leopard frogs (*Rana pipiens*) may be obtained locally or through commercial suppliers.
- Leopard frogs may be stored in a refrigerator at temperatures between 4° and 7°C. A polyethylene pan containing water 3 centimeters deep makes a suitable container. Adding 100 milligrams of streptomycin sulfate per gallon of water will satisfactorily control the growth of many microorganisms injurious to frogs. Change the water daily.
- Students may need to prod the frogs gently in order to encourage jumping activity. Remind students not to prod the frogs with any sharp or pointed instruments. Do not permit mistreatment of the frogs.

Problem 16-2: How does a frog's method and rate of breathing differ from a person's? *Pages 306-308*

Time Required: One period.

- Data may be collected from the entire class and then assigned to one group for interpretation and discussion.
- Store frogs in an ice chest or the vegetable compartment of a refrigerator at about 4°-7°C. Add a pinch of streptomycin to prevent diseases. Change water daily, keeping the depth at about 3 centimeters.

Problem 16-3: How does a change in temperature affect the breathing rate and body temperature of a frog? *Pages 309-313*

Time Required: One period.

- This problem would make an effective demonstration if you prefer. Use a fresh frog for best results. If students do the problem, they also should use fresh frogs.
- Obtain three ice chests or aquaria for class use. Store the frogs in the ice chests or in the refrigerator at about 4°-7°C. Add a pinch of streptomycin to prevent fungus infection (red legs). Keep frogs in about 3 centimeters of water and change water daily.
- Prepare water in advance and have both warm and cold available at about the desired temperatures.
- In Step E, suggest to students that the thermometer be left in the frog's mouth as the frog is transferred to ice water. Use special care so that the students do not injure the frog or break the thermometer.
- In post-lab discussion, compare the frog's method of carrying on respiration to the human's. Explain how each organism's breathing method is adapted to its particular environment.

Suggested Answers to Check Your Understanding *Page 314*

11. To catch an insect, a frog extends its tongue in a whiplike fashion. The insect sticks to the sticky surface of the forked tongue and is pushed into the frog's mouth as the end of the tongue returns to the mouth.

12. Strong, muscular hind legs help the frog jump long distances. Webbing between the toes of the hind legs provides a pushing surface that is helpful in marshy areas. The front legs absorb the shock when the frog completes a jump.
13. Frogs swim by alternately extending and flexing their hind legs. The webs between the toes on the hind legs help push the frog through the water.
14. The frog's coloring, including the spots, provides it with a camouflage that keeps it from being easily seen. The brownish-green color of the frog helps it blend in with its pond environment.
15. A frog admits air to its mouth by lowering the flap of skin under the chin while the nostrils are open. It forces this trapped air into its lungs by closing the nostrils and raising the flap of skin.
16. The body temperature of a cold-blooded animal changes with the temperature of the environment.
17. A frog breathes through its skin when it hibernates. As a frog's activity is low during hibernation, its skin breathing is adequate for survival.
18. The frog's clear eyelid protects the frog's eye in the water and keeps the eye clean and moist while the frog is on land.
19. A frog feels cold to our touch because our body temperature is higher than the frog's body temperature.

Recommended Films for Chapter 16

Frog Heartbeat (Thorne Films). 7 minutes, color. Shows heartbeat of pithed frog through use of extreme closeup and slow-motion photography. ESEA Title II.

Frog Skeletal Muscle Response (Thorne Films). 4 minutes, color. Shows fundamental method for analysis of relationship between applied stimulus and response using gastrocnemius muscle of the frog. ESEA Title II.

Chapter 17: Comparing the Frog's Organ Systems to the Human's

In the previous chapter the students studied the living frog to become acquainted with the functions of various external structures. This chapter introduces the student to the internal structures of a preserved frog. Most students are interested in actually getting to dissect and examine the internal organs. The students are able to relate the structure and arrangement of organs in the frog to similar organs in the human.

The frog's mouth and associated structures are located and observed. The frog is then dissected. Each of the major organs is identified and associated with the body system to which it belongs. The heart of the frog is dissected, and the students learn the function of the various chambers and the path that blood takes as it travels through the heart. They complete the study of the preserved animal by examining the digestive system and locating its component organs.

In each of these activities the students compare the frog's organs and systems to those of humans by locating the same structures on a diagram of the human body. In this way they are able to appreciate the fact that vertebrate organisms perform many of the same functions in similar ways. They also learn about the different structures that two vertebrate animals use to carry out these activities.

After completing the activities in this chapter, the students should more clearly understand the organism in its entirety. They should realize that most living organisms are composed of many organs and systems, each of which contributes to the process of life.

Teaching Suggestions

Problem 17-1: How does the structure of your mouth compare with the structure of a frog's mouth? ***Pages 320-323***

Time Required: One period.

• Frogs preserved in formaldehyde should be rinsed in running water 1 hour before using to decrease the strength of the preservative. Frogs preserved in solutions other than formalin are available. Check various biological suppliers' catalogues for prices.

• If dissecting pans are not available, a piece of thick cardboard on top of a board may be substituted.

• Attaching a tag to each frog's leg will provide a place to record the names of each lab team. Use a pencil to avoid fading.

• It is desirable to keep frogs from each class in a separate container.

• Formalin solution may be saved to preserve other specimens.

• Students should use plastic gloves if they have cuts or sores on their hands.

• Spray deodorant, sprayed directly on the frog, is helpful in reducing the formalin odor.

• Hand lotion applied after handling the frog will help prevent cracking of the skin.

• Frogs preserved in formalin may be stored in water several days without danger of spoiling.

• If state law requires, have students wear goggles. They are a useful safety feature in many laboratory experiments.

Problem 17-2: What organs are found in the body cavities of frogs and humans? *Pages 325-328*

Time Required: One period.

• Make sure the scissors for dissecting have been sharpened and are in good working order.

• Demonstrate the technique recommended for opening the body cavity of the frog. This will save time for the students and produce better results.

• Wash the formalin out of the body cavity with running water. Spray deodorant will help control the formalin odor.

• Charts or models of human organs should be used for comparison with frog organs during this problem.

• While the activity is in progress, ask students to point out organs and systems in their dissected frogs, and to explain the relationship between various organs in a system. For example, students could be asked to trace the passage of food through the digestive system.

Problem 17-3: How is the human heart different from the frog's heart? *Pages 330-332*

Time Required: One period.

• A demonstration of recommended procedure for removing the heart will save student time and produce better results.

• Detailed diagrams and models of the human heart and circulatory system should be made available for comparison with the frog's heart and circulatory system.

• Ascertain that students understand the difference between arteries, capillaries, and veins. Discuss the function of each.

• Students may be assigned to do reports on subjects such as heart transplants, artificial hearts, and the effects of cigarette smoking on the heart and circulatory system.

Problem 17-4: How are the digestive systems of frogs and humans different? *Pages 334-336*

Time Required: One period.

• This is a good point at which to quiz students on their ability to identify the internal organs of the frog listed in Table 17-1 (page 328).

• Provide a waste jar for the disposal of the frog's body and internal organs when this problem is completed.

Suggested Answers to Check Your Understanding *Page 337*

12. A frog's body temperature varies with the temperature of the outside environment. As a result, its body activity slows down in cool weather and increases in warmer weather. Humans maintain a steady body temperature not greatly affected by the outside temperature. The frog must spend part of its life cycle in water; humans are not so restricted.
13. The large intestine of the human is useful largely for absorbing water from the food mass. Frogs are usually surrounded by water so it does not matter if most of the water in the food is not absorbed.
14. Internal nares and two special (vomerine) teeth.

15. The human heart has four chambers that keep oxygenated blood separated from deoxygenated blood. The frog heart, with only three chambers, allows mixing of the two.
16. The lungs help bring about the exchange of gases with the bloodstream. The circulatory system moves the oxygen from the lungs to the cells, and brings back carbon dioxide to the lungs.
17. The frog lacks teeth that can be used for grinding and chewing. In order for the food to be broken down so that it can be digested in the small intestine, it is necessary for the food to be ground in the frog's stomach.

Recommended Film for Chapter 17

Human Body—Circulatory System (Coronet). 14 minutes, color. Analyzes circulatory system. Explains in detail functions of heart, lungs, and kidneys; follows flow of blood through all parts of body; explains role of circulatory system in maintaining good health.

Experiments Using Pithed Frogs

If local and state laws permit, there are many interesting demonstrations that may be performed with pithed frogs. A pithed frog has had its brain destroyed and, although still carrying on some life processes and exhibiting certain simple reflex responses, it is for all practical purposes a dead animal.

It is not advisable to pith frogs in the presence of students, since frogs frequently squeal when the dissecting needle is first inserted and there are always some students who will be disturbed by this procedure. But once pithing is complete, the frog feels no pain, since its brain has been destroyed. Make certain that your students understand this, and explain to the class what the pithing procedure involves. Explain that pithed frogs, unlike preserved frogs, may be used to observe many life processes as they are occurring.

Instructions for Pithing a Frog

Obtain a live frog and rinse it with water.

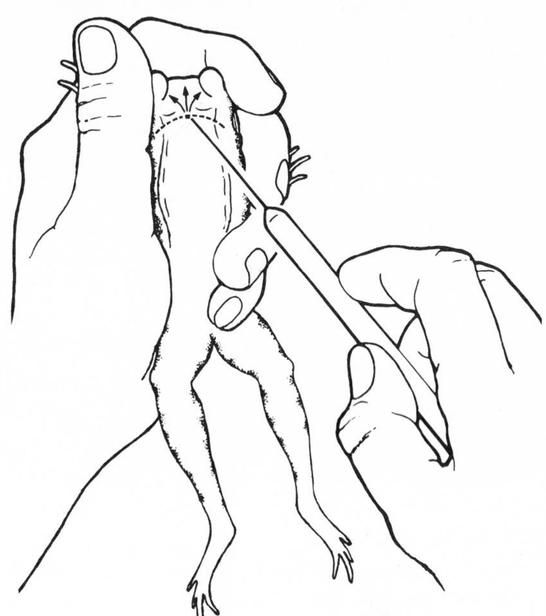

Bend the frog's head downward, locate the base of the skull, and insert the dissecting needle.

Hold the frog in the left hand so that the frog's body is in the palm of the left hand and its snout extends between the middle and the index fingers. (See illustration.) Bend the frog's head downward at a right angle to its body. Locate the cranial opening at the base of the skull by using your thumbnail or the blunt end of the dissecting needle. Place the point of the needle at the base of the skull and gently force the needle forward through the skin and into the brain cavity. Move the needle around inside the brain cavity until the brain is completely destroyed.

When the frog's brain is destroyed, the body becomes limp from shock, but this effect wears off after a few minutes. A frog that has been completely pithed will show no eyelid reflex in either eye—when the cornea is touched, the lower eyelid will *not* move. If the eyelids move, then the frog has not been completely pithed, and it will be necessary to reinsert the needle into the brain and repeat the pithing procedure.

The following problems may be performed by you as demonstrations, or they may be assigned to students. If students perform these dissections, they should be very closely supervised.

Demonstration 1: The Effects of Temperature Change on the Frog's Heartbeat Rate

You will need Ringer's solution for this problem. To prepare the solution, mix 6.5 grams of sodium chloride, 0.14 grams of potassium chloride, 0.12 grams of calcium chloride, and 0.2 grams of sodium bicarbonate with enough distilled water to make one liter of solution.

Open the body cavity of the pithed frog by cutting back the skin and making a longitudinal incision in the abdominal wall slightly to the right of the body midline. (This is to avoid severing the abdominal vein that runs along the body midline.) In order to expose the heart, you will have to cut through the sternum; when you do so, be very careful not to injure the heart.

After the longitudinal incision has been completed, make two transverse incisions to the right, one around the foreleg and one around the hind leg (see illustration). Pin back the abdominal wall.

Have available three test tubes of Ringer's solution, one heated to about 37°C, one at room temperature (approximately 22°C), and one cooled to about 5°C. Record the temperature of each test tube.

First flood the heart with Ringer's solution at room temperature. Count and record the number of heartbeats in a sixty-second period. Then repeat this procedure, first using the warm and then the cold Ringer's solution.

This demonstration should show a direct relationship between the temperature of the environment (Ringer's solution) and the heartbeat rate. Point out to the students that this is characteristic of all cold-blooded animals; the pulse rate of warm-blooded animals, however, is not significantly affected by the temperature of the environment.

As an additional supplementary activity, you may wish to assign students to graph the results of this demonstration.

Demonstration 2: Nerves and Muscles in a Pithed Frog

To expose the spinal nerves of the pithed frog, it will be necessary to remove the internal organs from the abdominal cavity. Open the ab-

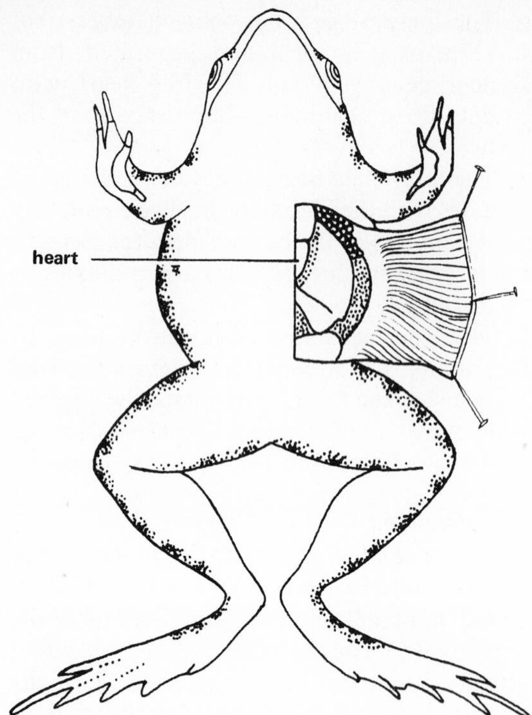

Exposed body cavity of a pithed frog.

dominal cavity (in this case, you do not need to avoid cutting the ventral abdominal vein) and remove the heart, the digestive system, and the kidneys. Be careful when removing the kidneys, since the spinal nerves are directly beneath them. After you have removed the internal organs, remove the skin from the lower legs. During the demonstration, keep the nerves and muscles moistened with Ringer's solution.

Using forceps, gently pinch one of the spinal nerves. This should cause one of the lower legs to twitch. If it does not, try stimulating another nerve.

Repeat the procedure, this time touching the nerve with two wires attached to the terminals of a six-volt battery. Dilute hydrochloric acid may also be used to stimulate the nerve.

Using the wires and the battery, stimulate various muscles in the lower legs, pointing out which muscles cause the limb to extend and which cause it to flex.

You may use this demonstration to show what stimuli cause nerves to respond, to show the relationship between nerves and muscles, and to demonstrate how muscles work by contracting.

Demonstration 3: The Action of the Cells Lining the Trachea

With dissecting scissors, cut through the jawbone at each corner of the mouth. Cut through the tissue on each side of the mouth until you can fold the lower jaw back to expose the glottis. Open the trachea by inserting small dissecting scissors into the glottis and cutting toward the front of the mouth. When you have exposed the interior walls of the trachea, use dissecting pins to keep the trachea open.

Place small bits of cork in the trachea. The cilia in the trachea should then cause the cork pieces to move in an anterior direction. Explain to students that the trachea is lined with hairlike cilia that act to remove particles from the respiratory system.

With a piece of rubber tubing, connect a pipette or bulb baster to a lighted cigarette. Draw smoke into the baster or pipette by squeezing, then releasing, the bulb. Then squeeze the bulb to blow the smoke over the trachea. Again place a small bit of cork on the trachea. The smoke will slow or stop the action of the cilia, so that the cork will be moved more slowly, if at all. Point out that cigarette smoke has the same effect on the cilia in the human respiratory tract.

Unit 6: Humans and Their Environment

This unit deals with the relationships that exist among living things. People's relationship to their environment is of primary importance, but there are many other relationships among plants, animals, and the environment that must also be understood. The first chapter considers some inherited human traits and how they vary within the population in the classroom. The "Knit-Pick" cards will again be used to store data for ready reference.

In Chapter 19 the students are given practice in sampling a community and measuring the biomass of the producers and consumers. The chapter introduces the concept of the balance that exists in nature, and makes the students aware of the possible consequences when any one single factor in the environment is changed.

After an introduction to the food relationships that exist between organisms within a community, the nutrients found in the human diet are considered. Tests for fats, proteins, carbohydrates, and vitamin C are performed. Students test orange juice for its vitamin C content both before and after heating and freezing the juice, to see the effect of temperature extremes on vitamin C.

The last chapter deals with a critical problem concerning our environment—pollution. Attention is called to several of the leading causes of pollution and to some of the ways in which pollution may be eliminated. Students are asked to investigate the battle against pollution that is going on in their own city or state. From this investigation, the student should get a better idea of the seriousness of the pollution problem, and how important it is to find acceptable solutions.

Chapter 18: Variations in a Human Population

This short chapter is intended as an introduction to the topic of hereditary variations that occur in the characteristics and traits in a population. The careful measurement of certain characteristics helps biologists identify distinct populations within larger groups of the same kind of organism.

The first problem involves the measurement of the hand span of each member of the class. Using the data, a special kind of bar graph called a histogram is prepared; it usually shows a normal distribution curve for this trait. Examination of three distribution curves for a given trait enables the students to recognize the presence of more than one population in the group that has been sampled.

The second problem in the chapter considers a number of hereditary traits that may or may not be present in an individual. These include such factors as color-blindness, tongue-rolling ability, and attached earlobes. To save time in determining the frequency with which any trait or combination of traits appears in the class population, the class is directed to prepare Knit-Pick cards as in Problem 1-3. This activity gives the students practice in using methods of sorting and retrieving information.

Teaching Suggestions

Problem 18-1: How do you measure the variation in one characteristic in a population? *Pages 345-349*

Time Required: One period.

• If necessary, review graphing techniques from Problem 2-1. Point out similarities and differences between histograms and bar graphs. If possible, show the class several examples of histograms, and discuss their features. Genetics texts usually are good sources of histograms.

• Demonstrate the correct procedure for measuring a hand span.

• To save time, Table 18-1 might be mimeographed beforehand and distributed to the students.

• You may wish to collect hand-span data from all of your classes to point out how a large sample more closely produces a normal distribution (bell-shaped) curve.

• Special reports dealing with the occurrence of certain inherited traits in populations could be assigned on a voluntary basis. Students might report on such topics as hemophilia, blood type, birth defects, and the relationship between heredity and environment in determining such things as intelligence and personality.

Problem 18-2: What traits are visible in a human population? *Pages 349-352*

Time Required: One period.

• Review the use of Knit-Pick cards as described in Problem 1-3, pages 13-18.

• Ask students to make suggestions of additional information they would like to process using the Knit-Pick system.

• P.T.C. is the abbreviation for phenylthiocarbamide. Two phenotypes occur—tasters and nontasters. Nontasters possess the recessive trait. The individual either tastes the chemical, which is somewhat bitter, or experiences no taste at all. You can make your own P.T.C. taste paper by cutting filter paper into 1-cm strips and soaking them in a solution of P.T.C. Gradually dissolve 500 mg of P.T.C. in 1 liter of water. At room temperature this will take about 24 hours. After soaking the filter paper, hang it up to dry. Store in an envelope or closed jar. Sterile conditions should be maintained during this procedure. P.T.C. paper can also be purchased directly from biological supply houses.

• During Step D, collect the Knit-Pick cards and have one student use the knitting needle to process the data. Results may be announced verbally and/or written on the chalk board.

Suggested Answers to Check Your Understanding *Pages 352-353*

11. By testing, recording, and analyzing P.T.C. tasting results in a large population.
12. Select the names of students from a hat and then question the students selected.
13. A random sample is representative of the total population. A random sampling is

used because it is not always convenient to survey the entire population. Ideally, a random sample should give a good indication of the characteristics of the total population.

14. Because they are recessive traits and would appear only when paired with the same recessive trait.
15. Three.
16. Somewhere in between. (Students' responses should include numerical data.)
17. First separate the cards for students having brown eyes and stack them. From those cards, insert the knitting needle into the hole for curly hair. Those that fall off the needle, indicating "yes" answers, have both brown eyes and curly hair.
18. Probably a dominant trait, but answers will depend on class data. *Note:* The relative number of phenotypes (in this case, the ability to roll the tongue) in a given population is actually determined not only by whether a given trait is dominant or recessive, but also by the frequency of the gene in the particular population. Example: Most Scandinavian people have blue eyes, although blue is recessive to brown. This is because the gene for brown eyes is rare in the Scandinavian population. The students, however, are not expected to understand this.
19. Weight, arm length, waist size, etc.
20. Grouped data may be more easily compared.
21. Height, weight, intelligence, etc.

Recommended Films for Chapter 18

Laws of Heredity, BBS (Encyclopaedia Britannica Films). 15 minutes, color. Explains mechanisms by which hereditary characteristics are transmitted from one generation to the next. Shows how understanding of mechanisms makes it possible to predict occurrence of inherited traits. Formulates basic laws of heredity and presents experimental evidence from which they were derived.

DNA—Molecule of Heredity (Encyclopaedia Britannica Films). 16 minutes, color. Explains why DNA is basis of growth and reproduction, and mechanism for transporting hereditary specifications from one generation to the next.

Chapter 19: Relationships Within a Community

In this chapter the students extend their study of populations into a broader context, the community. The primary activity in the last chapter was the sampling of traits within a population. In this chapter the students will be involved with sampling the number of populations within a community.

Problem 19-1 provides an opportunity for the students to sample a community by going out into the field and collecting the organisms included within the space of a coat hanger. The students count the number of each kind of organism in the sample and determine the number of representatives of each population. They separate the collected organisms into producers or consumers. Then they calculate the biomass of the total sample.

Problem 19-2 poses a hypothetical study of the ecological relationships between producers and consumers within a community. Students observe a graph showing the number of individuals in each of three different populations found in a food chain. The graph reveals the interdependence of one organism for another, especially in a closed community. The problem closes with a challenge to the student to predict the long-term effect on populations brought about by the unbalancing of a single factor in the environment.

Teaching Suggestions

Problem 19-1: How do you determine the number of different populations in a community? *Pages 358-360*

Time Required: One to two periods.

• The procedure should be discussed with the class to make sure that directions for field sampling are well understood.

• Not every student should collect and measure biomass of field samples. Data should be shared by all teams through post-lab discussion.

- Scientific names for some organisms may be found during this activity. This would be a good time to mention classification systems again, studied in Chapter 3.
- Distribute paper bags for collecting dry material and plastic bags for collecting wet material. Provide instruments for digging, such as trowels.
- Remind students to look for consumers (insects, worms, etc.) as well as producers. Remind students to include roots of plants.
- Select a vacant lot on or near the school grounds for sampling. If there are no such lots nearby, you might bring in one "coat-hanger sample" for the whole class to work with.
- Secure the owner's permission before taking samples. If possible, do not collect all samples from one area, to avoid depleting the lot. If it is necessary to take all samples from one lot, restrict samples to one or two per class.
- If you wish to save class time for weighing and identifying the organisms, you may assign students to bring in "coat-hanger samples" for homework. This procedure will also give a greater variety of samples.
- Provide taxonomic keys to aid students in identifying organisms.

Problem 19-2: How do different populations in a community affect each other? ***Pages 361-363***

Time Required: One period.

- You may want to assign this reading activity as homework.
- This problem presents a population study to be evaluated by the students. It will be much more meaningful if slides of some local pond area are shown and related to the textbook problem. An actual visit after discussing the problem would be even more effective for teaching the ecological relationships within a community.
- Another useful activity might be a visit to a local museum to observe the dioramas. These displays are professionally planned to show the actual plants and animals found in a natural community.
- Ask about food-chain relationships involving animals or plants other than the three mentioned here. Emphasize that if one link in the chain is broken or adversely affected, it can have disastrous results on the whole food chain.
- Explain that food chains frequently overlap; animals may be both carnivores and herbivores, and plants may be eaten by more than one kind of organism. Give students some idea of the complexity of food webs.
- Invite discussion about factors that might disturb the balance within a pond or other community—for example, water pollution, houses built nearby, etc. Ask students to point out how these things might upset the ecosystem.

Suggested Answers to Check Your Understanding *Page 364*

11. Accept any four of the following types of communities.

Community	*Populations*
Grassland	grass, insects, rodents, birds
Forest	trees, shrubs, insects, birds, carnivores
Polar	moss, fish, birds, carnivores
Pond	fish, algae, frogs, insects, grass
Desert	insects, hardy shrubs, birds

In each community, the consumers depend on the producers for food, and the producers depend on the consumers to keep their numbers in check. Accept any answer that indicates this interdependence.

12. Determine the biomass of a sample area, then multiply the biomass of the sample area by the number of such areas in the total pasture. (The sample area should ideally contain representatives of all kinds of organisms that are found in the pasture.)
13. The amount and quantity of fertilizer would affect the amount of grass produced in the area. This would affect the number of mice that could be supported by the area. Since owls feed on mice, the owl population would increase with an increasing mouse population.
14. Both producer and consumer organisms must be included. Green plants, fish, snails, and other organisms should be included. A

balanced aquarium would contain a fairly constant number of each kind of organism over a long period of time, i.e., the birth rate for each species would be approximately equal to the death rate.

Recommended Film for Chapter 19

Energy Relations AIBS (McGraw-Hill Text Films). 28 minutes, color. Explains transfer and loss of biomass and energy from primary producers to herbivores and to one or more levels of carnivores. Illustrates food chains, food webs, and explains productivity.

Chapter 20: The Food We Eat

Following the introduction to food chains and the interdependence of living things in the last chapter, we now turn our attention to the food eaten by people. Our diet must include a variety of nutrients, and students should find this topic quite interesting, since they are allowed to test foods to determine what nutrients they contain.

The first problem introduces the students to some chemical tests useful for identifying particular kinds of nutrients. The next problem calls for the students to use these tests to identify the nutrients present in several foods. The students should observe the relative amount of each nutrient that is present.

The importance of vitamins and minerals in the diet is discussed, and a simple test for the presence of vitamin C is presented. The students test several foods before and after heating to determine the effect improper cooking has on the vitamin C content of food.

The final problem in this chapter describes an experiment in which the energy value of food is measured by using a simple calorimeter to determine the energy released by a sunflower seed as it is burned. The students study the relationship between temperature change of water and the fuel value of the food as they calculate the calories released by the seed. This activity will help the students relate calories in the food they eat to the energy their bodies can release by the burning of those foods. The students should realize that if the energy is not used during body activity, a corresponding amount of energy will be converted to fat and stored in the body.

Teaching Suggestions

Problem 20-1: How do you identify different nutrients? ***Pages 368-369***

Time Required: One period.

• Prepare solutions of:

Starch—Dissolve 2 grams of starch (potato starch works well) into a small amount of cold water in a beaker to make a paste, then dissolve in one liter of hot water. Do not use laundry starch.

Glucose—A 10% solution by weight may be prepared by dissolving 10 grams in 90 milliliters of distilled water. Use dextrose as a substitute if necessary.

Sodium hydroxide—5 molar solution is needed. To make 200 milliliters, add 40 grams sodium hydroxide to 200 milliliters of distilled water. Caution: this solution is extremely corrosive (lye water). Wear apron and safety glasses when working with any caustic material.

Copper sulfate—Add 35 grams of copper sulfate, $CuSO_4 \cdot 5H_2O$, to 500 milliliters of distilled water.

• Neutralize acids with baking soda solution and dilute bases with water if spilled.

• Caution students about working with poisonous chemicals and the need for safety techniques. Students should wear safety goggles when heating liquids—and preferably for the entire lab.

• Caution students to use proper procedure for heating liquids in test tubes.

Problem 20-2: What foods contain carbohydrates, fats, and proteins? ***Pages 370-373***

Time Required: One period.

• Before this activity begins, review the chemical tests for the various nutrients.

• Have students bring small quantities of foods to test.

• An additional project might involve the

identification of nutrients in unknown food substances. Distribute unknowns in test tubes or baby-food jars; label them with numbers and record their contents. Use the term "Qualitative Analysis" to describe the activity, and give students some idea of its importance.

Problem 20-3: How can you test a food for the presence of vitamin C? ***Pages 374-376***

Time Required: One period.

- A refrigerator with freezing compartment is needed for this problem.
- Have fresh oranges and a juicer available. Other kinds of juice could be supplied or brought by the students to add additional interest to the problem.
- Freeze some of the freshly squeezed orange juice before class.
- Class discussion of this problem may lead to the construction of a bar graph that might be used to compare vitamin C content of fresh, frozen, and boiled orange juice.
- Discuss the relative merits of drinking orange juice that has been prepared by boiling, frozen orange juice, and fresh orange juice, keeping in mind the vitamin C content of each.

Problem 20-4: How do we measure the fuel value of a food? ***Pages 378-380***

Time Required: One period.

- You may wish to assign this reading activity as homework.
- Class discussion should center around the experimental design and the interpretation of the results.
- If you wish to prepare a calorimeter assembly, cut an equilateral triangle 4 centimeters on a side out of the base of the opened end of a 12-ounce can. Punch about fifteen equally spaced holes in the top of the closed end of the can around the outside edge. Punch a large hole (approximately 2 centimeters in diameter) in the *center* of the closed end to accommodate the test tube.

Note: To avoid the possibility of fire, you may wish to clamp a test-tube holder around the test tube to hold it in the can instead of taping the test tube to the can.

Suggested Answers to Check Your Understanding *Page 381*

9. The term *food* may be applied to anything we eat and obtain nourishment from. *Nutrients* are specific substances contained in foods from which the body derives nutrition. Some examples of nutrients are starches, sugars, proteins, and fats.
10. Proteins are used for growth and repair of cells and tissues; fats are used as stored energy; and carbohydrates are used to provide energy for immediate body use.
11. Sugar is chiefly used to supply energy for cell activity.
12. A balanced diet is one that includes all of the essential nutrients. It is obtained by eating a wide variety of foods containing these fats, carbohydrates, proteins, vitamins, minerals, and oils.
13. Vitamin C is heat sensitive. Boiling is very destructive to vitamin C while freezing seems to have little effect on it.
14. By eating foods from the four basic food groups, we should obtain the minimum daily requirements of vitamins necessary to maintain proper health. There are a wide variety of vitamins contained in the four basic groups of foods.
15. Deficiencies can occur in a diet if the variety of foods is greatly restricted. Large amounts of one type of food, although satisfying hunger, do not as a rule contain the vitamins, minerals, and nutrients necessary for a balanced diet. Feeling full is related to the bulk of food ingested, not to the food's nutritive value.
16. The number of calories absorbed by 100 grams of water is figured by multiplying the temperature change by the number of grams of water: 20° × 100 grams = 2,000 calories.

Recommended Film for Chapter 20

Understanding Vitamins (Encyclopaedia Britannica Films). 14 minutes, color. Explains what vitamins are, how they work, and why they are necessary for good health. Points out natural sources of important vitamins, and reveals effects on body tissues of a diet lacking in certain vitamins. Re-creates major events in discovery of vitamins and calls attention to present-day research.

Chapter 21: Pollution of the Environment

The final chapter calls attention to the critical problem of pollution of our environment. The discharging of liquid, solid, and gaseous wastes has developed into a problem that must be solved if our earth is to remain a healthy place in which to live. Attention is directed to some of the leading causes of pollution and what is being done to combat them. Mention is made of some substances, such as detergents and insecticides, that were originally thought safe and even beneficial but later turned out to be quite harmful when they became concentrated in the environment.

A class experiment is used to dramatize the effect of detergent as a pollutant in a fish tank. After observing the effects of the detergent on the fish, the students are asked to suggest a plan that would prevent this situation from occurring in nature.

The last problem calls attention to the pollution of our air and water resources. Through a series of pictures, the students are shown several forms of water and air pollution. By means of the Guide Questions, the students are made aware of the harmful effects such pollution may have on living things. The students are then directed to find out what pollution problems exist in their city, county, or state, and what efforts are being made locally to combat this problem. This will require the class to become more involved than when they simply read about the problems of environmental pollution. By understanding the complex problems of pollution, the students will be better prepared to take an active part in seeking solutions to these problems in their community.

Teaching Suggestions

Problem 21-1: How does detergent affect the activities of fish? *Pages 388-389*

Time Required: One-half of a period to set up, then ten to fifteen minutes of each successive class period up to ten days.

- Collect gallon jars from the cafeteria or other available source.
- During this activity, the fish's gills will increase in size and the fish may even die, depending on the amount and kind of detergent, the strength of the fish, and other factors. In class discussion, relate the observations that the students made during this activity to the results of pollution of rivers, lakes, and streams. Point out that nonbiodegradable detergents are not the only substances that harm fish and cause pollution.
- Materials that accumulate in the environment and cannot be chemically decomposed by microorganisms are serious pollutants. This idea should be brought out in class discussion.
- Literature about sewage treatment, the effects of detergents on living things, and other subjects related to pollution may be obtained from state and federal sources.
- You may wish to increase the amount of detergent added to each jar to emphasize the harmful effects on fish. You may also wish to do a comparative study, using different kinds of laundry products.
- In class discussion, have students make a list of the many different kinds of wastes and pollutants, and how they pose a threat to human health, property, wildlife, etc.
- Explain how certain insecticides and chemicals can accumulate in animal tissue, especially fatty tissue. Discuss how this can affect food chains.

Problem 21-2: How do people change the environment in which they live? *Pages 390-397*

Time Required: One period for answering Guide Questions; several weeks for collecting data on pollution control.

• A survey of government efforts to combat pollution should be started well in advance of this activity.

• Relate life support systems in spacecrafts to the necessity of purifying our environment. Emphasize that, although humans possess a great deal of adaptability, they can survive only in a relatively limited range of environmental conditions.

• Students should be encouraged to discuss the topics presented in this problem with their parents.

• Discuss the environmental aspects of using containers made of plastic and other materials that are not biodegradable. Ask students to suggest alternatives to such containers, or ways in which the containers might be recycled.

• Invite students to explore methods being used to conserve and recycle our natural resources.

• Emphasize that the most serious threat to the balance in nature is the human. Only people are able to manipulate and alter their environment to a great extent.

• Students should understand the role—and responsibility—of the individual in fighting pollution and caring for the environment. Point out that although large companies may cause pollution, it is the individual citizen who buys the products or services that the companies provide.

• Have students report on the causes, components, and hazards of smog.

• Identify the population explosion and its overall effect on the earth.

• Select a few students to make a survey of important natural resources that may be threatened, and efforts that are being made to conserve them.

Suggested Answers to Check Your Understanding *Page 398*

9. Pollution is an undesirable state of our environment. Its effects are far-reaching and often irreversible. Pollution can cause discomfort, illness, and sometimes even death.
10. Water pollution presents us with a serious problem because clean water is necessary for all living things. Polluted water can be purified, but the process is often slow and costly.
11. Water pollution may have harmful effects on all types of life. Polluted water may also be unfit for many industrial processes.
12. Air pollution cannot be easily controlled due to a large number of pollution sources. Automobiles, factories, mining operations, etc., all contribute to air pollution.
13. Water pollution.
14. The natural cycles that purify the air work slower than those that purify water.
15. Pollution can be prevented through strict adherence to control measures that regulate the release of potentially harmful materials into our environment.
16. Our environment directly or indirectly affects the food we eat, the shelter we need, and our daily activities. The more extreme the conditions of our environment, the more difficult is our daily fight for survival.
17. Individuals may do many things to fight pollution. They can use—or suggest that parents use—special products that contain few or no pollutants, such as low-phosphate detergents. Since power plants cause some pollution, individuals can cut down on their use of electricity, avoiding unnecessary appliances such as electric toothbrushes and can openers. They can walk or bicycle when possible, instead of traveling by car. They can purchase soft drinks in returnable bottles. By using such items as paper and aluminum foil effectively, they can make sure that they waste as few things as possible. A person can call attention to the pollution problem by talking to friends and writing letters to government officials.
18. The construction of a housing development on the shores of a lake would eliminate many producer organisms, such as trees, bushes, and shrubs. Besides this, it would destroy the habitat of many consumer organisms. If waste from the development were dumped into the lake, it could cause water pollution. If pesticides were used extensively in or around the development,

this, too, could cause pollution.

To protect the area, the builders of the houses could insure that few houses were built directly on the shores of the lake, and that as many trees and shrubs as possible were left standing among the houses. A sewage disposal plant could be constructed to prevent the pollution of the lake. Residents could strictly regulate the use of pesticides. They could also ban the use of high-phosphate detergents, which have been linked with excessive growth of algae.

19. Glass bottles could be sterilized and reused. Discarded glass could be ground, melted, and molded into new products. Paper could be reprocessed and used again, as could metal cans and aluminum foil.

Recommended Films for Chapter 21

It's Your Decision—Clean Water (Association Films, Inc.) 14½ minutes. How more people, prosperity, and products have resulted in a lack of usable water—and how secondary sewage treatment will help.

The River Must Live (Shell Oil Company, Film Library) 21 minutes. Effects of pollutants on a river, some manageable by the river, some not. Shows microscopic effect (microphotography). Demonstrates pollution abatement. Order 3-4 months in advance.

Troubled Waters (U.S. Senate Public Works Committee) 28 minutes. Description of pollution in the United States, using the example of the heavily polluted, industrialized Ohio River Valley. Order 3-6 months in advance.

Achievement Test Questions

Achievement test questions and their answers are provided here for all the chapters in the student text. The correct answers are boldfaced for your information. You will probably want to supplement these questions with some of your own in order to include essay questions or to test ideas that are brought out in pre- and post-lab discussions.

Chapter 1: Gathering and Storing Information

1. Science may be described as: **a. a process of gathering and organizing information.** b. the opinions of famous scientists. c. ideas collected from the past. d. information found only in textbooks.
2. Which of the following tasks might a scientist perform? a. observe results. b. interpret data. c. neither of these. **d. both of these.**
3. The microscope is a useful scientific tool because it: a. is used in most laboratories. b. gives people answers. **c. allows people to extend their sense of sight.** d. identifies the problem being studied.
4. The metric system of measurement is used for most scientific work because it: a. is more accurate than any other system. **b. is based on multiples of ten, and it is thus easy to convert from one unit to another.** c. is used in most of the countries of the world. d. was once used by a famous scientist.
5. The length of a meter stick is most nearly equal to: a. ten centimeters. **b. a yard.** c. ten millimeters. d. ten kilometers.
6. The metric unit of measure that is about equal to the thickness of a dime is a: a. kilometer. b. centimeter. **c. millimeter.** d. meter.
7. Experiments are usually performed to: a. find new problems. b. give scientists something to do. c. assemble new kinds of equipment. **d. find the answers to questions.**
8. A good experiment should contain all of the factors *except:* a. a clear statement of

the question to be answered. b. a definite procedure for finding the answer to a question. c. a control factor. **d. a definite idea beforehand as to what the results will be.**

9. In an experiment, the control group is necessary for: a. collecting information. **b. comparison with the experimental group.** c. gathering materials. d. publishing information learned.
10. The Knit-Pick information system could be used for which of the following questions? a. What kind of materials do birds use to make their nests? b. What color are your eyes? **c. Are there two children in your family?** d. What is your favorite book?
11. Information stored on Knit-Pick cards may be obtained quickly by: a. reading each card. b. alphabetizing the cards by first letter of the person's last name. **c. inserting a needle into a specific hole.** d. sorting only those cards with no holes punched.
12. Obtaining information by using the Knit-Pick system has an advantage over obtaining the same information written on filing cards because it: a. has more correct answers. **b. permits answers to be obtained quickly.** c. uses holes punched in cards. d. can be thrown away after use.
13. Problem 1-4 describes an experiment in which students colored sorghum seeds to see if birds choose the seeds they eat according to their color. A good title for the experiment would be: a. "What kind of seeds are eaten by birds?" **b. "Which color of seeds do birds prefer?"** c. "Can birds see different shapes of seeds?" d. "How many seeds can one bird eat?"
14. Which of the following statements would be correctly referred to as an observation? a. Pink seeds were most popular because they look like red sorghum seeds. **b. More red seeds were eaten than any other color.** c. Green seeds were the least popular because they were the same color as the ground below. d. The birds preferred the natural red-colored seeds because they were used to them.
15. Which of the following statements is an interpretation? a. 157 blue seeds were eaten. b. The greatest number of yellow seeds was eaten on Day 2. c. Fewer yellow seeds were eaten than other kinds. **d. Since so few yellow seeds were eaten, they must have been eaten only by accident.**
16. Sorghum seeds were used throughout the bird seed experiment because: a. "natural" sorghum seeds could be used as a control group. b. they could be dyed, thus permitting various colors to be tested. c. neither of these. **d. both of these.**

Read this paragraph before answering Questions 17, 18, and 19.

In 1954, the vaccine of Dr. Jonas Salk, after much testing with animals, was tested on humans. An experiment was devised to test a large number of students to see if the vaccine helped to prevent polio. 440,000 students were given a series of three Salk vaccine injections. Also, 210,000 students received "dummy" shots that contained a material having no affect. And 1,180,000 students received no injections at all. Records were kept on each student involved in the testing, to see how many students came down with polio.

17. A good problem title for the Salk vaccine experiment would be: a. "What causes polio?" **b. "Does the Salk vaccine help prevent polio?"** c. "Are 'dummy' shots important to science?" d. "Can records be kept on large numbers of students?"
18. The "experimental group" in this experiment can be identified as: **a. the group of students receiving the Salk injections.** b. the group of students receiving the "dummy" shots. c. the group of students receiving no injections at all. d. the total number of students on whom records were kept.
19. A "control group" in this experiment was: a. the group of students receiving the Salk injections. b. those students who came down with polio. **c. the group of students receiving the "dummy" shots.** d.

the total number of students on whom records were kept.

20. After a scientist gets an idea for an investigation, the next most likely step would be: a. to inform the local newspapers. b. to make observations. **c. to read about similar experiments done elsewhere.** d. all of these.

Chapter 2: Organizing and Interpreting Information

1. Information collected during an experiment is called: **a. data.** b. opinion. c. conclusion. d. interpretation.
2. Information tables are useful because they: a. are easy to prepare. b. are free of mistakes. **c. organize data.** d. interpret the data collected.
3. A graph represents: a. a mass of information. b. a straight line relationship. **c. data organized in picturelike form.** d. the answer to an experiment.
4. Graphs may be used to make predictions because graphs: a. always give good results. b. are easy to read. **c. show the trend of measured results.** d. explain the purpose of the experiment.
5. Experiments, tables, and graphs are all designed to: a. express the opinions of top scientists. b. agree with data collected earlier. c. make scientific instruments unnecessary. **d. explore and present relationships between variables.**
6. The result found by repeating an experiment several times does all of the following except: a. reduce the effect of personal error. **b. provide the only correct answer.** c. allow the scientist to estimate the answer to the experiment more accurately. d. provide more reliable data than a single measurement.
7. The "line of best fit" on a graph represents: **a. the general trend shown by the collected data.** b. a specific plot point. c. the independent variable. d. how the data were first collected.
8. The kind of graph that uses connected plot points (dots) to show relationships between variables is the: **a. line graph.** b. bar graph. c. both of these. d. neither of these.
9. The experimental variable that is changed and regulated by the experimenter is the: a. vertical axis. b. dependent variable. **c. independent variable.** d. axis line.
10. Temperature is the dependent variable in an experiment testing how long it takes an ice cube to cool a beaker of water. The independent variable would be the: a. amount of water. **b. time.** c. starting temperature of the water. d. size of the ice cube.
11. In an experiment to measure a person's weight change over a period of years, the number of years would be: **a. the independent variable.** b. the dependent variable. c. information that would not have to be recorded. d. plotted on the vertical axis.
12. A bar graph instead of a line graph would be used to compare the total weight of three different varieties of plants because: a. bar graphs are easy to prepare. **b. the weight of one plant is not related to another plant's weight.** c. a line graph cannot compare plant growth. d. none of these.
13. Which of the following information should best be shown in the form of a line graph rather than a bar graph? a. the average temperatures of eight different cities. b. the total body weight of five people. **c. the hourly temperature change in one city for a period of one day.** d. the population comparison of seven countries.

Use the graph that follows to answer Questions 14 through 20. (See page 64.)

14. Which letter in the graph identifies a plot point? a. (A) b. (B) c. (C) **d. (E)**
15. Which letter in the graph identifies the independent variable? a. (A) b. (B) c. (G) **d. (F)**

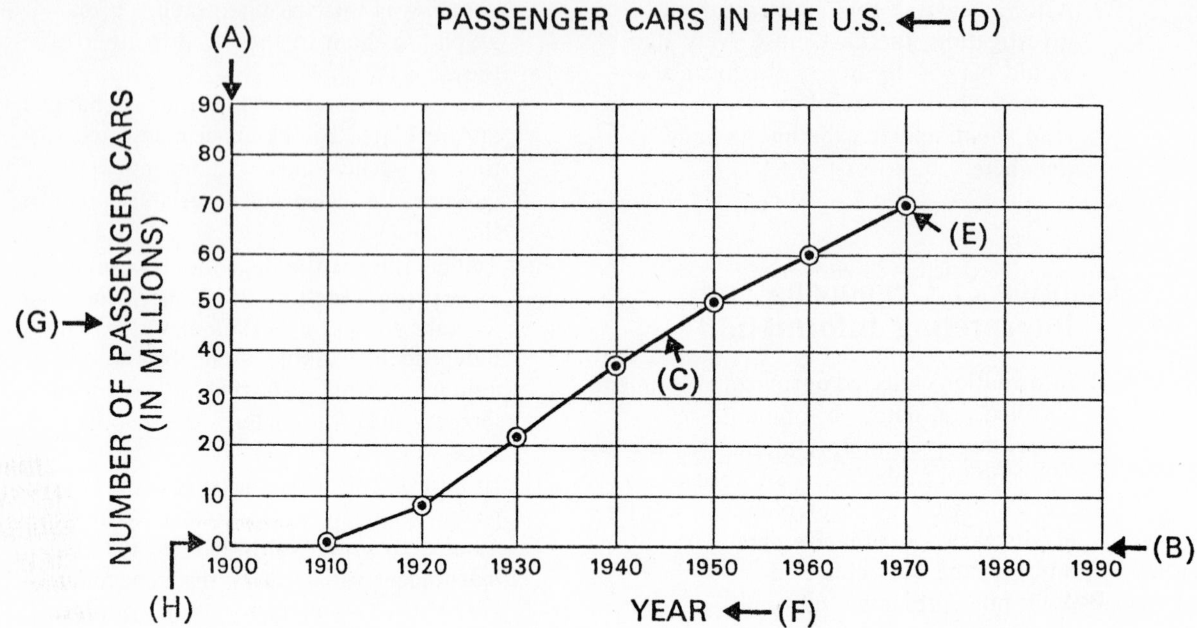

16. The vertical axis is labeled: **a. (A)** b. (B) c. (G) d. (F)
17. The slope line is labeled: a. (A) b. (B) **c. (C)** d. (E)
18. The number of passenger cars recorded in 1960 was closest to: a. 50 million. **b. 60 million.** c. 63 million. d. 58 million.
19. A reasonable prediction of the number of passenger cars expected in 1980 would be close to: a. 70 million. b. 75 million. **c. 80 million.** d. 100 million.
20. A trend shown by the graph is: a. a decrease in the number of passenger cars from 1900 to the present. **b. a steady increase in the number of passenger cars from 1900 to the present.** c. people walked more in 1900 than people do today. d. cars are able to travel farther on a gallon of gasoline today than they could in 1900.

Chapter 3: Classifying Objects

1. A classification system is often used in science because it: **a. allows similar objects to be grouped together.** b. can only be used by scientists. c. decides the answers for us. d. collects the necessary materials.
2. When arranging books on shelves, most librarians classify their books by topic or subject matter. This allows a book to be found: a. in the card catalog only. b. by librarians only. c. in alphabetical order. **d. in the same section in almost any library.**
3. When placing objects in groups, it is best to: a. name each object. b. look in the dictionary for help. c. make a chart. **d. look for similarities and differences among the objects.**

4. Classification systems are used to: a. select the best objects within a group. **b. show the relationship among similar and different objects.** c. describe the properties of one object. c. put all objects in the same group.
5. Which of the following characteristics would be *most* useful for classifying a collection of stamps from various countries? a. the age of the stamp. **b. the country that issued the stamp.** c. the city where the stamp was mailed. d. the shape of the stamp.
6. Before deciding upon the subgroups within a classification system, it is best to: a. name all the objects. **b. decide the purpose and use of the classification system.** c. sort out all the objects. d. all of these.
7. Canned goods in a supermarket would probably be arranged: a. according to alphabetical order of contents. **b. so that all of the same kinds of food are together.** c. by the color of the wrapping. d. according to the size of the cans.
8. The table of contents in the front of a textbook is arranged according to: a. alphabetical order. b. size of the chapters. **c. page numbers of the chapters.** d. all of these.
9. If you were sorting mail going to foreign countries, the part of the address you would look at first would be: a. the person's name. b. the street address. c. the city. **d. the country.**
10. Mail can be sorted more rapidly when it has a zip code because zip codes: **a. identify sections of the country by number.** b. are used instead of names of states. c. limit the size of the envelope. d. use alphabetical listings.
11. Which of these characteristics would be most useful in sorting out the many kinds of animals in the world? a. color. b. height. **c. body structure.** d. age.
12. By measuring the size, shape, and structure of an object, you have identified its: a. name. **b. characteristics.** c. family background. d. habitat.
13. Organization by classification is important to science mainly because: a. all science is organized. **b. groups with similar characteristics usually do things similarly.** c. classification does not change. d. information in science is important.
14. An assortment of twenty bottles may be grouped according to: a. height. b. weight. c. color. **d. all of these.**
15. A well-organized cupboard of dishes would be useful because it: a. looks good. b. cuts down food expenses. **c. makes dishes easier to find.** d. keeps dust away from dishes.
16. Someone picking the returnable pop bottles from an assortment of bottles illustrates: a. that there are a great many kinds of bottles. **b. classifying objects with a definite purpose in mind.** c. how bottles are made. d. none of these.
17. A good classification system must contain all of the following *except:* **a. at least six subgroups.** b. a well-thought-out purpose for the grouping. c. a clear, easily understood description of the categories. d. organization.

Use the following paragraph to answer Questions 18 through 21.

A school club planned to have a rummage sale and collected the following articles: 3 pairs of shoes, a can opener, 7 dresses, a raincoat, a scarf, 3 shirts, a set of dishes, 2 frying pans, an electric train set, a mixing bowl, a checkers game, 4 wool hats, 4 dolls, a set of doll clothes, an iron, and a vacuum cleaner. It was decided to sort these items into groups.

18. The most useful groupings would be: **a. clothing items and nonclothing items.** b. articles of clothing, dolls, and kitchen equipment. c. dresses, coats, and toys. d. doll clothing, household equipment, and toys.
19. All clothing items would *most* likely be sorted into which of the following groupings? a. woolen items and cotton items. b. shoes and all others. **c. clothing**

for males and clothing for females. d. hats and coats.

20. The purpose of the classification system used to sort rummage sale items would probably be to: a. separate large from small items. **b. separate items into categories for the benefit of shoppers.** c. show shoppers how to spend their money. d. persuade shoppers to buy damaged items.
21. The characteristic *most likely* to be used in sorting rummage sale items would be: a. size. **b. what it is used for.** c. color. d. structure.

Chapter 4: Characteristics of Living Things

1. One characteristic of living things is their ability to: a. reproduce. b. respond to stimuli. c. use food. **d. any of these.**
2. Most classification systems for grouping living things are based upon a knowledge of: **a. body structure.** b. where the plant or animal lives. c. size. d. none of these.
3. Which of the following is an example of a living organism? a. human hair cuttings b. a sea shell **c. a dandelion plant** d. a sugar crystal
4. In science, the classification of a living thing: a. is made up of only a single name. **b. is done according to related groups.** c. uses common names. d. cannot be determined.
5. Considering body structure humans are most closely related to which of the following? a. fish b. birds **c. bats** d. snakes
6. The order of mammals to which you belong is: a. Carnivora. **b. Primates.** c. Rodentia. d. Ungulata.
7. A kingdom is first subdivided into groups called: **a. phyla.** b. species. c. genera. d. families.
8. The smallest subdivision of a kingdom is called a: a. class. b. family. **c. species.** d. genus.
9. Which of the following groups includes the largest variety of different organisms? a. family b. species c. order **d. class**
10. Squirrels and beavers belong to the same order because they are similar in: a. the things they eat. **b. their body makeup.** c. their size. d. the place where they live.
11. One characteristic common to *only* animals in class Mammalia (mammals) is: a. they bear their young alive. b. they need water to live. c. they live on land. **d. they nourish their young with milk.**
12. A dichotomous key of classification successfully eliminates the sorting choices by: a. using alphabetical listings. **b. deciding on an either/or basis whether an object possesses a characteristic or does not.** c. asking new questions. d. all of these.

Use these sketches to answer Questions 13 through 20. (See page 67.)

With the help of the following key, identify by *letter* the leaf type represented by leaves 13 through 20:

1.	Leaf is simple	go to #2
	Leaf made up of many leaflets	go to #5
2.	Leaf with saw tooth edge	Leaf Type A
	Leaf with edge not saw toothed	go to #3
3.	Leaf with main veins originating more or less from one point and radiating out like fingers of a hand	Leaf Type B
	Leaf veins extending from a single mid-vein like a bird's feather	go to #4
4.	Leaf notched or cut out greatly	Leaf Type C
	Leaf not greatly cut out	Leaf Type D
5.	Leaflets extending from a single point	Leaf Type E
	Leaflets not extending from a single point	go to #6
6.	Leaflets numbering three or less in number	Leaf Type F

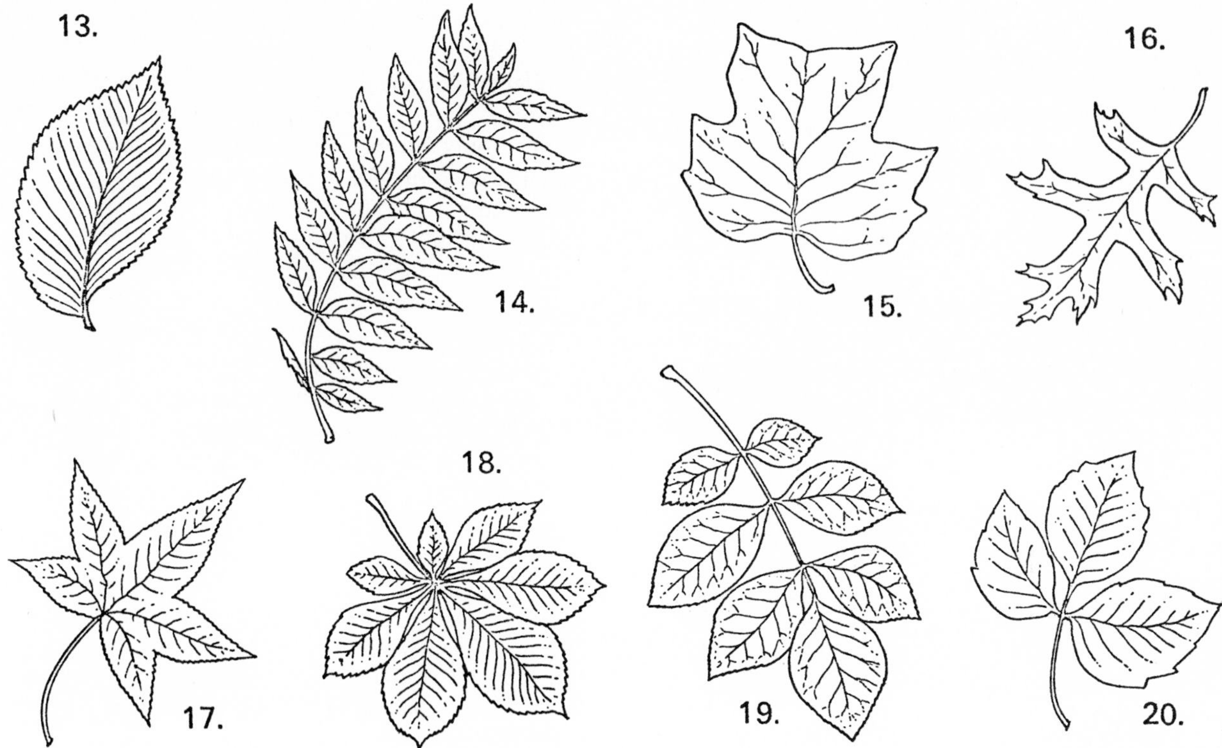

Leaflets numbering more than three	go to #7
7. Leaflets numbering five or less in number	Leaf Type G
Leaflets numbering more than five	Leaf Type H

13. Leaf Number 13 would be correctly identified as which leaf type? **a. Type A** b. Type B c. Type C d. Type D
14. Leaf Number 14 would be correctly identified as which leaf type? a. Type A b. Type C c. Type F **d. Type H**
15. Leaf Number 15 would be correctly identified as which leaf type? a. Type A b. Type B c. Type C **d. Type D**
16. Leaf Number 16 would be correctly identified as which leaf type? a. Type A b. Type B **c. Type C** d. Type D
17. Leaf Number 17 would be correctly identified as which leaf type? a. Type A **b. Type B** c. Type C d. Type D
18. Leaf Number 18 would be correctly identified as which leaf type? **a. Type E** b. Type F c. Type G d. Type H
19. Leaf Number 19 would be correctly identified as which leaf type? a. Type E b. Type F c. Type G **d. Type H**
20. Leaf Number 20 would be correctly identified as which leaf type? a. Type E **b. Type F** c. Type G d. Type H

Chapter 5: The Microscope

Use this drawing of a microscope to answer Questions 1 through 7. (See page 68.)

1. An objective lens is located by letter: a. A **b. F** c. H d. I
2. To bring an image into sharp focus it would be best to turn: a. B b. E c. F **d. D**

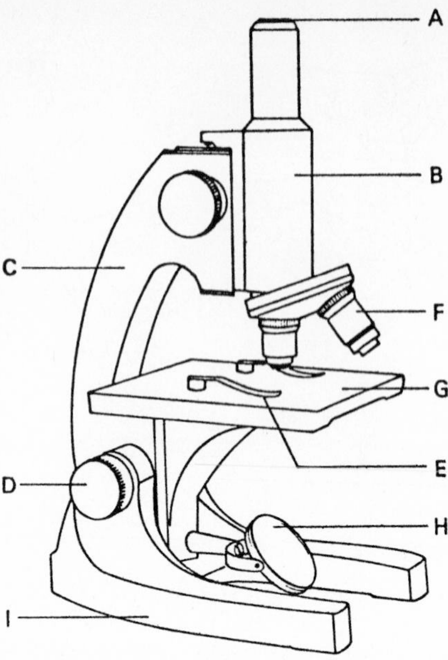

3. The part of this microscope that reflects light is shown by letter: a. A b. C **c. H** d. I
4. The part used to hold the slide in place is designated by letter: a. B b. G **c. E** d. I
5. Which parts would you use to carry this microscope correctly? a. A & H **b. C & I** c. B & D d. H & E
6. The stage of the microscope is identified by letter: a. B b. C **c. G** d. I
7. The letter "B" identifies the: a. base. **b. body tube.** c. stage clips. d. objective lens.
8. The total magnification of a compound microscope can be found by: a. looking through the eyepiece. b. adding more light. c. moving the slide forward. **d. multiplying the powers of the objective and eyepiece lenses being used.**
9. A compound microscope: a. was used by Leeuwenhoek to observe single-celled organisms. **b. uses a system of two or more lenses to magnify objects.** c. is limited to a magnifying power of about 10X. d. has a greater magnifying power than an electron microscope.
10. A student observed an object under a microscope at 50X magnification. If the magnification were changed to 200X, the student would see: a. a larger area or more of the object. b. the same area as before only sharper and brighter. **c. a smaller area or less of the object.** d. a larger area but out of focus.
11. A micron is: a. a type of musical instrument. **b. a unit of measurement.** c. a part of the microscope. d. a microscopic animal.
12. To measure the diameter of the field of view of a microscope, you should: a. measure the diameter of the objective lens. b. measure the diameter of the eyepiece. c. multiply the magnifying power of the objective times the magnifying power of the eyepiece. **d. none of these.**
13. The diameter of the field of view of a microscope measures three millimeters. A hair occupies approximately 1/6 of the field of view. Estimate the width of this hair in microns. **a. 500 μ** b. 1,000 μ c. 2,000 μ d. 3,000 μ
14. You wish to observe an entire object with a microscope, but find that you cannot see the whole thing. The object is too large for the field of view. You should: **a. decrease the magnification by switching to low power.** b. get a different object. c. increase the magnification by switching to high power. d. add a drop of water.
15. When a microscope slide is moved to the right across the stage, the image appears to: a. move to the right. b. not move at all. **c. move to the left.** d. become larger.
16. Objects sometimes appear blackened when viewed with a compound microscope. Which statement best explains the reason for this? a. There is too much light. b. The image is out of focus. c. The magnification is too great. **d. The section viewed is too thick.**
17. A "wet mount slide" is a slide that: a. should be dried before use. **b. uses water so materials may be seen more clearly.** c. is prepared by professional slide makers. d. shows a large object, such as a penny.

18. The letter "e" when viewed with the microscope will appear as: a. e b. ɘ c. ɕ **d. ə**
19. When making a wet mount slide, you should try to avoid trapping air bubbles because: a. they block out light. b. they make the microscope more difficult to focus. **c. they may interfere with the object being viewed.** d. they may dry out the wet mount.
20. The coarse adjustment knob should be used: **a. with the low power objective only.** b. to change objective lenses. c. with the high power objective only. d. with either the high or low power objective.

Chapter 6: Cell Structures

1. All living things that we know of are made up of one or more: a. muscles. **b. cells.** c. hearts. d. bones.
2. Scientists tell us a cell is: a. the basic structural unit in a living thing. b. made up of smaller parts. c. a complex living system. **d. all of these.**
3. Which of the following statements *best* sums up the ideas of the Cell Theory? **a. A cell is the basic unit of structure and function in a living organism, and must be produced by another cell.** b. Cells come from other cells, and are found in all parts of the earth. c. All cells are made up of a membrane, nucleus, and cytoplasm; some cells also have vacuoles. d. The cell is the unit of structure and function, and is basic to both plants and animals.
4. A cell was cut into two parts. One part died and the other lived. Which of the following structures was probably missing from the part that died? a. cytoplasm **b. nucleus** c. vacuole d. chloroplast
5. The green bodies found in some cells are: a. nuclei. b. cytoplasm. **c. chloroplasts.** d. green cell walls.
6. To better observe the nucleus of an onion skin cell you should: a. heat the slide. **b. add a drop of methylene blue solution.** c. add a drop of salt water. d. move the slide into the sunlight.
7. Which two structures are each found only in plant cells? a. nucleus and cell membrane **b. cell wall and chloroplasts** c. cytoplasm and nucleus d. cell wall and cell membrane
8. Cells of cork show: a. a nucleus and cytoplasm. b. a nucleus and a vacuole. **c. cell walls only.** d. chloroplasts and the cell wall.
9. A tiny, clear area found in both plant and animal cells that may be used to store food or wastes is the: a. nucleus. b. cytoplasm. c. chloroplast. **d. vacuole.**
10. Materials pass from the outside of the cell to the cytoplasm through the: **a. cell membrane.** b. nucleus. c. chloroplasts. d. chlorophyll.
11. The movement of chloroplasts in green plant cells is probably due to the: a. movement of other cells. **b. movement of the cytoplasm inside the cell.** c. chloroplasts swimming around. d. movement of the cell wall.
12. By using the electron microscope to study cells, scientists have been able to: a. cure cancer. **b. identify new cell parts.** c. see the nucleus. d. develop the Cell Theory.
13. The living part of the cell surrounding the nucleus is called the: a. cell wall. b. chloroplast. c. cellulose. **d. cytoplasm.**
14. When you looked at cork cells under the microscope, you knew that they were *not* alive because: a. the cells were not dividing, and all *living* cells reproduce. b. the cells were not moving. **c. the cells contained no nuclei or cytoplasm to perform life activities.** d. all of these.
15. The cell membrane is found in: a. animal cells only. b. bacterial cells only. **c. all living cells.** d. green plant cells only.
16. The nonliving material that makes up the cell walls in plants is called: **a. cellulose.** b. chlorophyll. c. chloroplasts. d. cell membrane.
17. If a living cell is put into water containing salt, the: a. nucleus will become darker and easier to see. **b. cell membranes may pull away from the cell wall as water leaves the cell.** c. chloroplasts will leave the

cell. d. cell will take in water and become larger.

18. In order to study cells with a microscope, the tissue containing the cells is cut into very thin slices. This is done to: a. make the cells easier to stain. b. help the cells grow faster. **c. allow light to pass through the slice.** d. all of these.
19. Which of these are the living parts of a cell? a. cell wall, chlorophyll, nucleus **b. cytoplasm, cell membrane, nucleus** c. vacuole, cell wall, cell membrane d. cell membrane, chlorophyll, vacuole
20. The word "structure" means the same as "part." The word "function" most nearly means the same as: a. environment. **b. use.** c. food. d. usefulness to humans.
21. A student measured a stack of 10 dimes and found it to be about 10 mm (1 cm). The thickness of a single dime expressed in microns would be: a. 1. b. 10. c. 100. **d. 1000.**

Chapter 7: Cells Work Together

1. Living organisms that are made up of only a single cell: a. have organ systems. b. must depend upon other single-celled organisms to maintain life. **c. carry on digestion within the cell.** d. all have a cell wall.
2. A cross section of a leaf viewed with a microscope under low power would show: a. no cells. b. only one cell. **c. different kinds of tissues.** d. cells that are all alike.
3. Sections cut at right angles to the length of an object (such as the thin slice of leaf that you examined in the laboratory) are called: a. length sections. b. cuttings. **c. cross sections.** d. slices.
4. A group of similar *cells* that work together in an organism is called: **a. a tissue.** b. an organ. c. a muscle. d. a system.
5. The human stomach wall is made up of three layers of different kinds of cells. The stomach is an example of: a. a tissue. **b. an organ.** c. a muscle. d. a system.
6. Which of the following *best* describes a kind of structural organization found within living things? **a. tissues grouped to form an organ** b. organs grouped to form a tissue c. cells grouped to form an organ d. systems grouped to form a tissue
7. As cells become specialized to do a specific task, the cells: a. increase in size. **b. depend more upon other cells.** c. live alone. d. increase in number.
8. Which of the following cells would most probably be able to live by itself without the help of other cells? a. a brain cell. b. a red blood cell. c. a muscle cell. **d. a bacterial cell.**
9. A new cell is produced when one cell: a. adds on parts of different cells. **b. divides its nucleus and cytoplasm.** c. separates the chloroplasts. d. receives the nucleus from another cell.
10. The earthworm moves by using: a. epithelial tissues. **b. longitudinal and circular muscles.** c. dorsal and ventral muscles. d. aortic arches.
11. A leaf is made up of many different kinds of tissues. This structure suggests that: **a. different kinds of tissues work together in the leaf.** b. all cells within this plant came from a single cell. c. the making of food takes place at a rapid rate in the leaf. d. all cells are surrounded by a cell membrane.
12. The main function of a leaf epidermal cell is to: a. make food. b. transport materials. **c. protect the cells below.** d. send information.
13. Specialized leaf cells called guard cells: a. support the leaf veins. b. collect water. c. store food produced in other parts of the plant. **d. regulate the gases passing into and out of a leaf.**
14. A student observing a palisade cell of a leaf under low power magnification would probably be able to see all of the following structures *except* the: a. chloroplasts. b. nucleus. **c. cell membrane.** d. cell wall.
15. Palisade cells in a leaf are usually found: a. loosely spaced. **b. tightly packed next to the upper surface.** c. linked together and flat. d. without chloroplasts.

16. Which group of cells is found only in plant leaves? a. mesophyll, epidermis, and muscle. **b. guard cells, phloem, and xylem.** c. guard cells, mesophyll, and arteries. d. epidermis, muscle, and nerve.
17. The esophagus of an earthworm is a part of which system? a. circulatory system. b. muscular system. **c. digestive system.** d. nervous system.
18. Blood is best described as a(n): a. organ system. b. organ. c. cell. **d. tissue.**
19. The organ located just in front of the earthworm's gizzard and used for temporary storage of food is the: a. mouth. b. esophagus. **c. crop.** d. intestine.
20. Tiny openings in certain leaves that are used for gas exchange are called: a. guard cells. **b. stomata.** c. mesophyll. d. upper epidermis.

Chapter 8: Living Things in a Drop of Water

1. The green scum found in pond water is most likely: a. a mold growth. **b. an alga.** c. a seaweed. d. a one-celled animal.
2. Microorganisms within a pond may be found: a. in the green scum. b. in the mud at the bottom. c. clinging to rocks. **d. in all these places.**
3. An examination of a pond water sample for several weeks would be likely to reveal: a. the same kinds of organisms always present. b. only one kind of organism. **c. different numbers and kinds of organisms as the culture grows older.** d. that certain organisms are always found in all pond water.
4. An experiment to determine the response of brine shrimp to an environmental stimulus must: **a. be able to be repeated by others.** b. use light as the stimulus. c. be performed in a laboratory. d. discover new information.
5. A jar containing pond water was placed in the dark for a week. Which of these organisms is *least* likely to survive? a. a goldfish. b. a single-celled animal. **c. a single-celled plant.** d. a snail.
6. Which one of the following organisms would be an example of a *protist*? a. a person **b. a paramecium.** c. a pine tree. d. an earthworm.
7. The green material called chlorophyll would most likely be found in: a. molds. **b. algae.** c. paramecia. d. all of these.
8. Pond water organisms move about by: a. flagella. b. cilia. c. extending the cytoplasm. **d. all of these.**
9. Brine shrimp may respond to an environmental stimulus by: a. moving toward it. b. moving away from it. **c. both a and b.** d. neither a nor b.
10. An experiment to test the response of an organism to a stimulus should include: a. more than one stimulus. b. only brine shrimp organisms. **c. a group of organisms to serve as a control.** d. none of these.
11. A food chain is: a. a daily requirement of vitamins. b. the basic foods. c. a balanced diet. **d. a food cycle in which some organisms eat others.**
12. To decide whether the cells in a cluster or colony of cells were one-celled organisms or belonged to a many-celled organism, it would be best to look for: a. a nucleus. **b. specialized cells.** c. the method of locomotion. d. chloroplasts.
13. Paramecia would most likely be found in: a. dust in the air. b. soil particles. c. tap water. **d. a mud puddle.**
14. Which of the following activities would a one-celled organism be unable to perform? a. reproduce. **b. think.** c. digest food. d. excrete wastes.
15. Cilia are: a. cysts. b. kinds of algae. c. brine shrimp movements. **d. none of these.**
16. Cotton fibers placed in pond water on a glass slide are used to: **a. slow down microorganisms.** b. identify the microorganisms present. c. provide food for microorganisms. d. help magnify animals present.
17. Under ideal conditions all protists are able to: a. form hard spore cases for

protection. **b. reproduce rapidly.** c. manufacture their own food. d. build many tissue layers.

18. The term "taxis" is used to describe: a. locomotion by one-celled protists. b. cell division of microorganisms. **c. response to a stimulus by an organism.** d. fission involving two or more cells.
19. Protists can be found: a. only in water. b. only on the top of lakes and ponds. c. in the air. **d. in almost any environment.**
20. Which of the following statements is *not* true of protists? a. They sometimes reduce water pollution. b. They serve as a food source for fish. **c. They have an internal organization of tissues, organs, and organ systems.** d. Many protists enclose themselves in cysts.
21. In an experiment to test the response of a certain protist to light, the protists were placed in a dropper partially covered with foil. When the dropper was exposed to light, most of the protists were found under the foil. This would be a: a. positive phototaxis. b. negative geotaxis. **c. negative phototaxis.** d. none of these.
22. In the experiment above, two medicine droppers were used. One dropper had foil wrapped around it. The second dropper had no covering. This second dropper served as a: a. "peephole." **b. control.** c. second experiment. d. reserve.

Chapter 9: Yeasts and Molds

1. The hairlike growth sometimes found on stale bread would most likely be: a. yeast. b. bacteria. **c. mold.** d. dirt.
2. Mold can be grown on a piece of moist bread because the bread: a. holds heat. **b. provides food.** c. remains cool. d. kills bacteria.
3. Molds reproduce by: **a. spores.** b. seeds. c. eggs. d. all of these.
4. Molds may be identified by: a. an examination of their structure. b. the type of food on which they live. c. comparisons with pure culture organisms. **d. all of these.**
5. Which of the following statements about molds is *not* true? a. Some molds may be eaten. **b. Molds produce their own food.** c. Some molds are used in medicines. d. Molds and their spores are found almost everywhere.
6. Conditions usually necessary for growing bread mold include: a. heat, light, and a food substance. **b. heat, darkness, and moisture.** c. heat, dryness, and a food substance. d. cold, dryness, and darkness.
7. A pure culture of bread mold: a. would contain many kinds of organisms. b. could not be grown in the laboratory. c. must be thrown away. **d. is useful for studying characteristics of a single organism.**
8. Mold spores are *usually* transported by: a. water. b. animals. c. birds. **d. air movement.**
9. Molds meet their food needs by means of: a. the chlorophyll they contain. **b. absorbing their food.** c. chewing actions. d. swimming movements.
10. Some molds grow well on bread while other molds do not. The most probable explanation for this would be that: a. some molds require warmer temperatures. b. some mold spores will not stick to bread. c. some molds require sunlight. **d. only certain kinds of mold can live upon the materials contained in bread.**
11. All molds: a. are parasites. b. have tissues. c. live off of dead material. **d. lack chlorophyll.**
12. Penicillin is produced by: a. trees. b. yeasts. **c. a blue-green mold.** d. mushrooms.
13. Carbon dioxide production by yeast: a. takes place only at night. b. cannot be measured. c. is most rapid after the yeast has been boiled. **d. decreases greatly if the yeast has been boiled.**
14. A fungicide is: a. a type of mold. **b. a chemical used to prevent mold growth.** c. food for molds. d. an insect spray.
15. Yeasts reproduce by: a. mitosis. b. spores. **c. budding.** d. all of these.

16. When yeast is used to make bread dough rise, a small amount of sugar must be added to the dough. This is to: **a. provide food for the yeast cells, so that they will produce carbon dioxide.** b. add flavor to the bread by providing food for the yeast cells. c. prevent the yeast cells from making the bread sour. d. all of these.
17. If an organism takes its nourishment from dead organic matter, it is: **a. some kind of saprophyte.** b. definitely a parasite. c. a colonial type of organism. d. probably a form of spore.
18. When yeast cells produce a great deal of gas: **a. they are active and healthy.** b. it is a sign that the cells are dying and disintegrating. c. the colony is no longer pure and must be thrown away. d. oxygen gas is being given off.
19. A parasite organism would most likely be found growing: a. on a dead tree trunk. **b. between a person's toes.** c. on dry sea shells. d. on bread.
20. A material often used to grow molds in the laboratory is: a. sugar. b. beef. **c. nutrient agar.** d. pond water.
21. A test used to check for the presence of carbon dioxide gas as a result of yeast activity is: **a. seeing if limewater turns cloudy.** b. seeing if the gas is cloudy. c. seeing if the gas appears colorless. d. methylene blue showing a color change.
22. The temperature must be carefully controlled when growing: a. yeasts. b. molds. c. bacteria. **d. all of these.**

Chapter 10: Bacteria

1. To make sure no microorganisms are present on the surface of a petri dish, a student should: a. wash it with soap and water. **b. heat it to a high temperature for 30 minutes.** c. rinse it with a mouthwash. d. dip it in alcohol.
2. If a serial dilution of a broth culture of bacteria is made, the number of bacteria in the *final* dilution will be: a. the same as in the original culture. **b. less than in the original culture.** c. zero. d. greater than in the original culture.
3. Pasteurizing milk kills harmful bacteria by means of: a. sound waves. b. low temperature. **c. heat.** d. chemicals.
4. Hospitals sterilize their instruments by: a. wiping them dry. b. scrubbing them with soap. **c. applying steam.** d. dipping them in acid.
5. A hot inoculating needle should be allowed to cool before it is used to transfer bacteria because: a. a hot needle will increase the number of bacteria. b. cooling the needle makes it safer to use. c. cooling prevents damage to the needle. **d. the high temperature would destroy bacteria.**
6. Spreading bacteria out in streaks on a sterile agar surface is a method of: a. identifying bacteria. **b. isolating individual bacterial cells.** c. destroying bacteria. d. treating bacteria.
7. "Round," "rod," and "spiral" are terms that are used to describe: a. food types. b. growth patterns of a bacterial colony. **c. the shapes of bacteria.** d. the structures making up molds.
8. Bacterial colonies are similar to mold colonies except that the bacterial colonies: a. are larger. b. produce spores. **c. have no threadlike structures.** d. cause disease.
9. Experiments in which bacteria are exposed to ultraviolet light have shown that: a. bacteria are unaffected by ultraviolet light. **b. mutations may be caused by ultraviolet light.** c. all organisms respond the same way to ultraviolet light. d. bacteria grow larger because of ultraviolet light.
10. Antiseptics differ from germicides in that antiseptics: **a. check or slow the growth of microorganisms without killing all of them.** b. kill great numbers of micro-organisms. c. affect certain kinds of microorganisms. d. kill bacteria in the mouth.
11. Disease-producing bacteria that affect people grow best: a. in dry places. b. where it is dark. c. at low tempera-

tures. **d. at a person's body temperature.**

12. Two petri dishes are inoculated with bacteria, and are then exposed to ultraviolet light. Dish A is exposed for 15 seconds, and dish B is exposed for 30 seconds. After incubation: a. dish A will probably show more mutations than dish B. **b. dish A will probably have more colonies than dish B.** c. dish A will have the most colonies and show the most mutations. d. the number of colonies should be about the same in each dish.
13. The effectiveness of an antiseptic may be tested by placing an antiseptic-soaked disc on a petri dish containing bacteria and seeing whether the antiseptic causes: a. mutations. b. the bacterial colonies to change color. c. the death of molds. **d. clear spaces on the petri dish.**
14. Bacteria need all of the following conditions in order to reproduce *except:* **a. a proper sterile environment.** b. proper temperature. c. sufficient food. d. sufficient moisture.
15. Bacteria obtain food by: a. mitosis. b. proper temperature. **c. taking nourishment from living and dead organisms.** d. taking food in through the roots.
16. Most of the bacteria in the world are: a. germs. b. beneficial. c. disease-producing. **d. harmless.**
17. The difference between sterilization and asepsis is: **a. sterilization kills all bacteria, asepsis does not.** b. asepsis kills all bacteria, sterilization does not. c. asepsis is a form of bacterial colony, while sterilization is a laboratory technique. d. sterilization cannot be done in a hospital.
18. Most of the antiseptics available in drugstores: a. can kill all bacteria. b. are not effective against common bacteria. c. do more harm to the skin than to the bacteria. **d. are able to slow the reproduction of many kinds of bacteria.**
19. Bacteria would probably grow best on which of the following foods? a. jelly or jam. b. raisins. c. dried beef. **d. cake.**
20. Rules for safely handling bacteria stress all the following *except:* a. keeping fingers and pencils out of your mouth. **b. immediately wiping up spilled bacteria with paper towels and placing the towels in the wastebasket.** c. keeping equipment sterile. d. not eating food or drinking liquid while handling bacteria cultures.

Chapter 11: Seed Germination

1. The resting period of the seed is known as: a. germination. b. viability. c. respiration. **d. dormancy.**
2. The part of a plant that appears first from a germinating seed is the: a. leaf. **b. root.** c. stem. d. fruit.
3. The embryo of a plant may best be described as: a. a root part. b. a seed. **c. an undeveloped young plant.** d. the area of food storage in a seed.
4. A thick seed coat might prove to be a *disadvantage* in that it might: a. protect the embryo from dryness. b. keep light from shining on the embryo. c. allow the seed to float. **d. keep the embryo from emerging.**
5. The function of the cotyledon is to: a. supply water. b. protect the root. **c. supply food.** d. store carbon dioxide gas.
6. The size of the seed is related most closely to the size of its: a. seed coat. **b. cotyledon.** c. embryo. d. root.
7. Low temperature and bright light may affect the germination of seeds by: a. increasing the percentage that germinate. b. decreasing the percentage that germinate. **c. killing all of the embryos within the seeds.** d. none of these.
8. Two conditions that are most necessary for seeds to germinate are: a. light and moisture. b. moisture and soil. **c. moisture and the right temperature.** d. light and the right temperature.
9. Respiration in living plants is: a. not carried on during the day. **b. a term applied to the energy-releasing process in the plant's cells.** c. the same as germination. d. carried on only during the day.
10. Several different materials were placed in

test tubes and covered with water. The next day, one tube showed a gas being produced. After collecting some gas in a test tube, a student tested it with limewater. The limewater turned cloudy. Which of these materials might have produced this gas? a. salt. **b. radishes.** c. dead leaves. d. all of these.

11. Testing seeds with iodine may be used to identify the presence of: a. protein. b. the embryo. **c. starch.** d. the seed coat.
12. Viability is: a. a period of seed inactivity. **b. the ability of seeds to germinate.** c. the sprouting of a seed. d. the same as respiration.
13. The viability of a seed may be affected by: a. how long it has been stored. b. the temperature at which it has been stored. c. a broken or cracked seed coat. **d. all of these factors.**
14. Seeds stored in a freezer died. The best explanation for this is that: a. the seed coat became frozen. b. the cotyledon was used up. **c. the embryo was killed by the cold.** d. the viability of seeds tested was poor.
15. Which test could be used to identify a gas as oxygen? a. limewater turning cloudy. **b. a glowing splint igniting.** c. a burning splint causing an explosion. d. iodine solution turning blue-black.
16. The part of the seed that contains stored food is the: a. seed coat. b. embryo. **c. endosperm.** d. all of these.
17. The *embryo* of a dicotyledon contains: **a. starch.** b. two leaves. c. seed coat. d. one leaf.
18. If 22 seeds out of a total of 30 germinate, what is the percentage of germination? a. 66% b. 80% **c. 73%** d. 78%
19. If you wished to plant a lawn and wanted the grass to germinate quickly, before planting you might: a. keep the seeds in the refrigerator for a week. b. place the seeds in the sun to dry for a day. **c. soak the seeds in water for a few hours.** d. warm the seeds in the oven for an hour.
20. Since germination conditions are not the same from place to place: a. different kinds of plants grow in different areas. b. the same kinds of plants are not found everywhere. c. various techniques are followed to grow certain ones successfully. **d. all of these.**
21. Some examples of dicotyledon plants are: a. grasses, corn, and orchids. b. grasses, peas, and corn. **c. beans, peas, and sunflowers.** d. all of these.
22. Certain seeds have such a thick seed coat that they have difficulty germinating. Before planting the seed coat is mechanically scratched in a process called: **a. scarifying.** b. soaking. c. aerating. d. heating.

Chapter 12: Plant Responses to Stimuli

1. Plants usually respond to stimuli by changes in: a. vein pattern. **b. growth pattern.** c. number of leaves. d. root hairs.
2. Which region of a root would probably show the most rapid cell growth? a. section closest to the stem. b. middle section. **c. tip.** d. root hairs.
3. Growth of the root is due to: a. gravity. **b. cell division.** c. gibberellic acid. d. root hair growth.
4. A root grows downward into the soil: a. looking for food. b. because it needs minerals. **c. in response to gravity.** d. to get away from the light.
5. Plant growth toward a water source is called: a. positive hydrotaxis. **b. positive hydrotropism.** c. negative geotropism. d. positive geotropism.
6. The growth of a stem toward light is called: a. positive geotropism. b. negative geotaxis. **c. positive phototropism.** d. negative phototropism.
7. Trees grow straight up rather than along the ground in response to the stimulus of: a. light. b. gravity. c. plant hormones. **d. all of these.**
8. When seeds are planted upside down, the

roots never grow up through the soil. This is probably a result of: a. light. b. temperature. **c. gravity.** d. the soil.

9. Hormones are produced in response to environmental stimuli. Which of these is *not* an environmental stimulus? a. gravity. b. water. c. sunlight. **d. snails.**
10. Auxins are: a. leaf types. **b. chemicals produced by plant cells.** c. materials in soil. d. a group of tropisms.
11. Gibberellic acid affects the growth of seedlings by: a. killing them. b. slowing seedling growth. **c. making seedlings taller than normal.** d. producing no effect.

Use this paragraph to answer Questions 12, 13, and 14.

A scientist wished to determine the effect of different lighting conditions on the growth of seedlings. Seedling A was grown in total darkness and seedling B in sunlight. Each seedling was 2 cm tall at the start of the experiment. After 2 days, seedling A was 5 cm tall and seedling B was 3 cm tall.

12. From the results of the experiment described above, it might be concluded that: a. light did not affect the plants tested. **b. the plant kept in darkness grew taller.** c. darkness had no effect on plant growth. d. light affects plants by making them grow taller.
13. If the experiment above were to be extended for two more days, the results would probably show: **a. the same pattern.** b. both plants at the same height. c. the plant kept in the light taller than the one kept in the dark. d. that the plant in darkness had lost all of its leaves.
14. The variable factor for this experiment was: a. seedling A. b. seedling B. **c. light.** d. water.
15. When a house plant is placed on a sunny windowsill, the leaves will turn toward the light. This is best explained by the fact that: a. the windowsill is warm and unshaded. b. auxin is present in large amounts on the *sunny* side of the stems. **c. auxin is present in large amounts on the *dark* side of the stems.** d. ultraviolet light in sunlight kills disease-causing organisms that can destroy young leaves.
16. Which one of the following situations is an example of a negative chemotropic response? a. roots growing toward water. b. stem growing away from the dark. **c. roots growing away from soil poisons.** d. a stem growing straight up from the ground.
17. The growth of three plants was measured and recorded for one week. One plant grew 4.44 mm; a second plant grew 3.25 mm; a third grew 5.96 mm. What was the average growth of these plants? **a. 4.55 mm.** b. 4.44 mm. c. 4.00 mm. d. 4.25 mm.
18. Most plant responses are very slow. Organisms that do not move from place to place but do slowly respond to stimuli are said to show: a. taxis. b. control. **c. tropism.** d. all of these.
19. A plant grown in the dark does not produce: a. auxins. **b. chlorophyll.** c. growth. d. root hairs.
20. The three major factors that help determine where a root will grow in the soil are: a. light, water, gravity. b. food, gravity, light. **c. gravity, water, chemicals.** c. chemicals, light, air.

Chapter 13: Movement of Liquids in Plants

1. Plants get the water and minerals they need through their: a. leaves. **b. roots.** c. bark. d. flowers.
2. Root hairs are important to the plant because: a. they anchor the plant. **b. they provide greater surface for absorption of dissolved materials.** c. they are centers of cell division and growth. d. all of these.
3. Water moves upward primarily through the: **a. xylem.** b. phloem. c. bark. d. auxin.
4. Foods move downward in a stem through the: a. xylem. **b. phloem.** c. bark. d. auxin.

5. The experiment in which the crystal of the pink-purple dye potassium permanganate was dropped into a beaker of water showed: a. how materials are absorbed in cells. b. what materials are transported in cells. c. what foods are needed by plants. **d. how materials spread out in solution.**
6. Water and molasses separated by a semi-permeable membrane will: a. mix evenly. **b. show the water moving more rapidly through the membrane into the molasses.** c. show the molasses moving more rapidly through the membrane into the water. d. show no liquid movement.
7. Sugar molecules diffuse through a semi-permeable membrane more rapidly than starch molecules. One possible interpretation of this is that starch particles: **a. are larger than glucose molecules.** b. are smaller than glucose molecules. c. are the same size as glucose molecules. d. do not dissolve in water.
8. Materials entering a cell through the cell membrane must be: **a. in solution.** b. heated first. c. in solid form. d. can be all of these.
9. Wilted celery becomes crisp when placed in water because it: a. loses water. **b. takes in water.** c. loses minerals. d. takes in minerals.
10. The experiment in which the bottom portion of a celery stalk is placed in water containing a colored dye was performed to show: a. how plants make food. b. how leaves get their color. **c. where water moves in plants.** d. where temperature affects plants.
11. The process by which water creeps up the sides of extremely narrow tubes is: **a. capillary action.** b. cohesion. c. transpiration pull. d. root pressure.
12. A slice of potato becomes soft in salt water because the cells: a. absorb water. b. absorb salt. **c. lose water.** d. lose minerals.
13. When a molasses solution is placed inside a hollowed-out carrot surrounded by water: a. water diffuses out of the carrot. **b. water diffuses into the carrot.** c. no liquid movement occurs. d. rapid cell growth occurs.
14. Over a period of a day, the rate of osmosis into a root: **a. varies greatly from one hour to the next.** b. increases steadily from one hour to the next. c. cannot be determined. d. is not related to the rate of water lost at the leaves.
15. Benedict's solution was used to show the presence of: a. starch. b. protein. **c. sugar.** d. all of these.
16. When compared to the total amount of water absorbed, the amount of water lost to the air by a plant is: a. much less. b. much greater. **c. slightly less.** d. exactly the same.
17. The loss of water by a plant is dependent upon which of the following factors? a. the amount of water the plant takes in. b. the temperature of the air. c. the humidity of the air. **d. all of these.**
18. Xylem and phloem tissues in plants are most important in the process of: a. photosynthesis. **b. liquid movement.** c. root growth. d. respiration.
19. Water performs which of the following functions in a plant? a. dissolves substances essential for plant growth. b. transports essential substances throughout the plant. c. gives rigidity and support to the plant. **d. all of these.**
20. The loss of water vapor from a plant through the leaves is called: a. respiration. **b. transpiration.** c. evaporation. d. vaporization.
21. When a sugar cube is placed in a cup of water, the sugar dissolves and spreads out evenly throughout the cup. This process of spreading out (moving from an area of high concentration to an area of low concentration) is called: **a. diffusion.** b. osmosis. c. permeability. d. all of these.

Chapter 14: Photosynthesis

1. Photosynthesis is the process by which: a. green plants burn food. **b. green plants**

make food. c. green plants respond to stimuli. d. bacteria multiply.

2. Green plants manufacture most of their food in their: a. roots. b. stems. **c. leaves.** d. flowers.
3. In order for plants to manufacture their own food, they must: **a. contain chlorophyll.** b. produce seeds. c. produce starch. d. take in oxygen.
4. In the process of photosynthesis, plants use: a. water and oxygen. b. nitrogen. c. sugar and carbon dioxide. **d. carbon dioxide and water.**
5. Energy for photosynthesis is supplied by: a. sound. b. heat. **c. light.** d. food.
6. The gas that green plants need to make food and that animals exhale from their lungs is: a. oxygen. b. nitrogen. c. hydrogen. **d. carbon dioxide.**
7. When plants make food, they give off: **a. oxygen.** b. carbon dioxide. c. nitrogen. d. hydrogen.
8. All of these are necessary for photosynthesis *except:* a. carbon dioxide. b. sunlight. c. water. **d. oxygen.**
9. The food made *directly* by photosynthesis is: **a. glucose.** b. fat. c. starch. d. all of these.
10. Starch found in leaf cells indicates that: a. plants are good to eat. **b. photosynthesis has taken place.** c. respiration is going on. d. chlorophyll is important to plants.
11. The amounts of sugar and starch found in leaves would probably be lowest at: a. 10 AM. b. 2 PM. c. 7 PM. **d. 6 AM.**
12. In an experiment to test the effect of sunlight on green plants, the control plants should be treated just like the experimental plants except for the amount of: a. wind. b. water. c. heat. **d. sunlight.**
13. Tomato plants were kept in the classroom a week and they lost most of their green color. The loss of color was probably because these plants *lacked:* a. moisture. **b. light.** c. warmth. d. carbon dioxide.
14. Gas bubbles coming from a water plant in sunlight can be proved to be oxygen by the use of: **a. the glowing splint test.** b. the limewater test. c. the reaction with iodine. d. the reaction with Benedict's solution.
15. During the fall, leaf pigments other than chlorophyll may be seen because: a. leaves turn color in the fall. **b. chlorophyll is no longer produced.** c. photosynthesis is taking place. d. the fall is usually a period of dryness.
16. Chromatography may be used to: a. identify the presence of starch. b. show patterns of leaf growth. **c. separate materials making up plant pigments.** d. all of these.
17. Before testing a leaf for the presence of starch, it is necessary to remove the: a. water. **b. chlorophyll.** c. sugar. d. phloem.
18. Plants store glucose by converting it to: **a. starch.** b. fat. c. oxygen. d. water.
19. The leaf of a plant grown in the dark for 48 hours would probably show a lack of: a. water. b. minerals. **c. starch.** d. color.
20. The carrot, potato, or onion that you eat is the part of the plant where food is stored. They all taste different because: a. the color of each is different. b. they are harvested during different seasons of the year. c. of differing amounts of chlorophyll in the plants. **d. different chemicals are found in the stored food of each plant.**
21. Van Helmont's experiment, in which he grew a tree in a pre-weighed, dried quantity of soil, definitely proved that: a. chlorophyll is necessary for photosynthesis. b. plants manufacture food by the process of photosynthesis. **c. plants do not grow by taking materials from soil.** d. all of these.
22. Plants are useful to us because: a. they serve as food. b. they release oxygen into the atmosphere. c. they are useful for decoration, building, etc. **d. all of these.**

Chapter 15: Flowers, Seeds, and Fruits

1. A plant organ specialized for seed

production is the: a. stem. b. root. c. leaf. **d. flower.**

2. Pollen is produced in the flower structure called the: **a. stamen.** b. pistil. c. sepal. d. fruit.
3. Seeds are produced in the structure called the: a. sepal. **b. ovary.** c. anther. d. filament.
4. A flower part that is not directly involved in reproduction is the: a. pistil. b. stamen. **c. petal.** d. anther.
5. Transfer of pollen from the stamen of a plant to the pistil of a plant of the same variety is called: **a. pollination.** b. fertilization. c. germination. d. seed formation.
6. Self-pollination occurs: **a. within a single flower.** b. between two flowers. c. among many flowers. d. in all flowers.
7. Fertilization is accomplished when: a. a pollen grain attaches to the stigma. b. two sperm nuclei join. **c. a sperm nucleus joins with an egg nucleus.** d. pollen is moved from the stamen to the pistil.
8. A complete flower would have: a. stamens and a pistil. b. stamens, a pistil, and sepals. **c. stamens, a pistil, petals, and sepals.** d. pollen and insects.
9. Flowers that have both nectar and perfume are usually pollinated by: a. wind. **b. insects.** c. water. d. birds.
10. An imperfect flower could not be: a. wind pollinated. b. insect pollinated. **c. self-pollinated.** d. cross-pollinated.
11. Petals would probably be missing in flowers pollinated by: a. bees. **b. wind.** c. moths. d. birds.
12. The ripened ovary of a flower is called a: **a. fruit.** b. seed. c. ovule. d. stamen.
13. The function of a fruit is to: a. feed animals. b. feed birds. c. store food. **d. contain seeds.**
14. The main function of plant flowers is to: a. make bouquets and wreaths. b. provide the perfume industry with sweet aromas. c. manufacture food for bees, butterflies, and birds. **d. produce the seeds for the next generation.**
15. The essential parts of a flower include: a. roots and root hairs. b. petals and sepals. **c. stamens and pistils.** d. all of these.
16. Pollen grains must be able to stick to the surface of the: a. style. **b. stigma.** c. ovary. d. anther.
17. Besides the embryo, a seed contains stored food called the: a. ovary. b. stigma. **c. endosperm.** d. sperm nucleus.
18. Pollen in flowers is produced in the: a. pistil. **b. anther.** c. sepal. d. stigma.
19. The female part of the flower that produces the egg cells is the: **a. pistil.** b. anther. c. sepal. d. stigma.
20. When the pollen grains from one flower land on the pistil of another flower, the process is known as: a. self-pollination. b. fertilization. **c. cross- pollination.** d. grafting.
21. An example of a perfect flower is a: **a. rose.** b. plum. c. date palm. d. pussy willow.

Chapter 16: Observing the Living Frog

1. An animal that is not active during the winter could be in a condition known as: a. amphibian. **b. hibernation.** c. habitat. d. metamorphosis.
2. A frog carries on respiration mostly by using its: a. tongue and lungs. **b. lungs and skin.** c. skin and tongue. d. lungs alone.
3. The blood of cold-blooded animals: **a. is about the same temperature as the outside environment.** b. is generally a great deal warmer than the outside environment. c. is usually much colder than the outside environment. d. circulates very slowly because it is too cold to move fast.
4. The transparent eyelid of a frog: a. helps to shade its eyes and so prevents damage by the bright sun. b. protects the eyes against cold and hot water. **c. covers the eyes but allows the frog to see while under water.** d. has no practical use to the frog.

5. Camouflage is helpful to a frog because it: a. enables the frog to feed under water. **b. permits the frog to blend with its environment.** c. helps to regulate the frog's body temperature. d. makes the environment suitable for laying eggs.
6. While a frog is floating on the surface of a pond: a. its nostrils are tightly closed. b. the frog is hibernating. **c. breathing is carried out through the frog's nostrils.** d. the hearing mechanisms are under the surface of the water.
7. The breathing rate of a frog: a. is about the same as a person's. b. is dependent on the time of day. **c. is generally much more rapid than a person's breathing rate.** d. is more rapid in water than on land.
8. When a frog is in water: a. the temperature does not affect the frog's breathing rate. **b. the colder the temperature, the slower is the breathing rate.** c. the higher the temperature, the slower is the breathing rate. d. the frog does not breathe at all until it is on land again.
9. The internal body temperature of a frog: a. depends on the breathing rate. **b. is about the same as the outside temperature.** c. cannot be measured because the frog is a cold-blooded animal. d. is much lower than the external environmental temperature.
10. Amphibians are animals that: a. live in the desert. b. live in the ocean. c. live in the air and on the ground. **d. live both in the water and on the land.**
11. The variation in the coloration of the frog's ventral and dorsal surfaces enables the frog to: a. float in the water with its eyes above the surface. **b. blend with the environment when it is floating in the water.** c. blend with the air when it is on land. d. swim when it is in a water environment.
12. When an organism hibernates, its body functions: a. remain the same. b. greatly speed up. **c. slow down considerably.** d. completely stop.
13. If a frog were placed in ice water, its internal temperature would: a. remain constant regardless of environmental temperature. **b. change to approximate that of the outside environment.** c. become warmer than the outside environment. d. go up and down rapidly as long as the frog was in ice water.
14. Which statement best describes the way the frog's forelegs are adapted? **a. short to absorb impact when landing.** b. large and powerful for quick extensions. c. large and powerful with webs between the toes. d. short and powerful to enable the frog to jump long distances.
15. Which statement best describes the relationship between nostril counts and chin movements in the frog's breathing pattern? a. both the same. b. nostril counts higher. **c. nostril counts lower.** d. varies with activity of the frog.
16. If a frog is moved from a cold temperature environment to a warm environment, its breathing rate will probably: a. remain the same. **b. increase.** c. decrease. d. cannot predict.
17. If a person moves from a cold environment to a warm one, his or her breathing rate will probably: **a. remain the same.** b. increase. c. decrease. d. cannot predict.
18. Which statement best describes what happens to the internal temperature of a warm-blooded animal when it is moved from a warm to a cold temperature? **a. remains the same.** b. increases. c. decreases. d. cannot predict.
19. The change in body form that occurs during the development of a frog is called: a. tadpole. **b. metamorphosis.** c. hibernation. d. amphibian.
20. Which statement best describes how a frog is adapted to catch insects? a. strong and powerful hind legs. b. clear covering over the eyes. **c. large mouth and sticky tongue.** d. nostrils and eyes above water when floating.
21. A man named Vesalius was dissatisfied with the ancient anatomy books that were taken for granted by the people of his day. He experimented and wrote a book that corrected over 200 errors. He taught us to: a. study several different reference

sources, and then make a conclusion. **b. search for evidence rather than rely on written information.** c. write a book of your own based on what other scientists have reported. d. have a good family doctor.

22. Frogs are able to absorb oxygen dissolved in water through their skin. This is possible due to: a. pores in the skin. b. the frog's cold-blooded nature. **c. the presence of many tiny blood vessels just under the skin.** d. the coloration for camouflage.

Chapter 17: Comparing the Frog's Organ Systems to Those of Humans

1. The anterior part of a frog: a. is the area to the rear of the middle. **b. contains the vital organs of the brain, eyes, and tongue.** c. is the entire undersurface. d. aids in jumping because it is the location of the powerful leg muscles.
2. In the frog the eustachian tube: a. carries air from mouth to lungs. b. connects the nostrils to the mouth. **c. is a connection between the ear and mouth.** d. controls the swallowing movements.
3. The word that refers to the total body processes of an organism is: a. metamorphosis. b. hibernation. c. digestion. **d. metabolism.**
4. The chemicals that are produced by the body to aid in the process of digestion are: **a. called enzymes.** b. made in the circulatory system. c. also involved in respiration. d. called simple sugars.
5. The order in which parts of the frog's digestive system are found is: a. mouth, esophagus, intestine, stomach. b. mouth, stomach, esophagus, intestine. **c. mouth, esophagus, stomach, intestine.** d. mouth, intestine, stomach, esophagus.
6. One of the major reasons why humans can live in almost any environment is that: a. they walk upright on two legs. **b. they have a constant internal temperature.** c. they are able to chew food with teeth. d. they do not breathe through their skin.
7. The teeth of the human mouth are designed to perform certain functions. Which of the following combinations is correct? a. incisor — grind. b. molar — tear. **c. incisor — bite.** d. canine — bite.
8. If food went down the "wrong pipe" when we swallowed it, it probably meant that: **a. the glottis wasn't covered by the epiglottis.** b. the food wasn't chewed properly. c. the eustachian tube was plugged up. d. the epiglottis was tightly covered by the glottis.
9. The frog's teeth are mainly used: a. to chew food before it is swallowed. **b. to hold food before it is swallowed.** c. to bite its prey in order to kill it. d. to crush insects before swallowing them.
10. In both frogs and humans, blood vessels carry blood through the body. Which of the following combinations properly identifies the type of blood vessel and its function? a. carries blood away from the heart — capillary. b. carries blood to the heart — artery. c. exchanges digested food, oxygen, and wastes through a thin wall — vein. **d. carries blood to the heart — vein.**
11. The lower, triangular section of the heart in both frogs and humans is the: a. atrium. **b. ventricle.** c. aorta. d. valve.
12. Animals that live on a diet of plants require an intestine that is: **a. longer than that of meat-eating animals.** b. shorter than that of meat-eating animals. c. the same length as that of meat-eating animals. d. more curled and narrower than that of meat-eating animals.
13. The organs in frogs and humans that produce chemicals that help to digest food are the: a. heart and lungs. b. large intestine and liver. c. pancreas and esophagus. **d. pancreas and liver.**
14. Bile is produced by the: a. pancreas. b. gall bladder. **c. liver.** d. small intestine.
15. Which statement best describes the process of digestion in an organism? a. Food is placed in the mouth. b. Food moves down the digestive tract. **c. Food is broken up mechanically and by enzymes.** d. Food

passes out of the digestive tract.

16. When comparing the lengths of the large intestines of frogs and humans, which statement best describes the relationship? a. The large intestines of frogs and humans are of equal size. b. The relative length of the large intestine of humans is shorter. **c. The relative length of the large intestine of frogs is shorter.** d. The length of the large intestine of the frog is greater because of the animal's smaller size.
17. Which of the following best describes the path of blood through the human heart? a. left atrium, right ventricle, to lungs, to right atrium, to left atrium, to the body. b. right atrium, left atrium to lungs, to left ventricle, to right ventricle, to the body. **c. right atrium, right ventricle to lungs, to left atrium, to left ventricle, to the body.** d. left atrium to ventricle, to lungs, to ventricle, to the body.
18. Which series of organs is all part of the digestive system? a. anus, gall bladder, pancreas, arteries. **b. esophagus, liver, pancreas, gall bladder.** c. mouth, sternum, vein, ventricle. d. cloaca, gullet, eustachian tube, pharynx.
19. Which of the following is *not* a function of the circulatory system? a. exchange gases with lungs and cells. b. transport digested food materials to the cells from the intestines. **c. manufacture enzymes.** d. remove wastes from the cells.
20. What set of terms best describes the location of the frog's tongue? a. anterior and dorsal to the nostrils. b. anterior and ventral to the lower jaw. **c. posterior and ventral to the nostrils.** d. posterior and dorsal to the eyes.
21. If you were asked by your teacher to examine the ventral side of the frog, you would be working with which side? a. upper. b. rear. c. front. **d. lower.**
22. In the frog, the process of digestion starts as the food enters the: a. mouth. b. intestine. **c. stomach.** d. glottis.

Chapter 18: Variations in a Human Population

1. When examining a group of scores showing a normal distribution curve, you would probably find most of the scores: a. at the left side of the curve. b. at the right side of the curve. c. evenly distributed through the entire curve. **d. in the middle of the curve.**
2. A characteristic that could be inherited by a human is: a. ability to swim. **b. color of hair.** c. extent of vocabulary. d. education.
3. A trait that can be hidden by another trait is said to be: **a. recessive.** b. dominant. c. inherited. d. sex-linked.
4. One characteristic that is sex-linked is: a. detached earlobes. b. curly hair. **c. color-blindness.** d. ability to roll the tongue.
5. The term "population" could be used to describe: a. all the people in a city or state. b. the students in your class or school. **c. both a and b are correct.** d. neither a nor b is correct.
6. To study how physical and mental characteristics vary among individuals, a person would have to have some knowledge of: a. the populations of large cities. **b. genetics and heredity.** c. a histogram. d. a normal distribution curve.
7. If a child inherits a dominant gene for a particular trait from the mother and a recessive gene for the same trait from the father, the child will show: a. the recessive trait. **b. the dominant trait.** c. a trait somewhere between the recessive and dominant trait. d. cannot tell.
8. A good way to take a random sample would be: a. counting all the people who have the particular characteristic in which you are interested. b. *not* counting any of the people who have the particular characteristic in which you are in-

terested. **c. counting everyone in a sample chosen by chance and noting those who have the particular characteristic.** d. having people with the characteristic visit you and tell you about it.

9. Which of the following probably describes the histogram of a characteristic shown by two distinct populations? **a. two separate curves.** b. two overlapping curves. c. one curve. d. two curves that are hard to separate.
10. Which statement probably describes the variation in *a single characteristic* measured within a given population? a. All members are exactly the same. b. All members are different from each other. **c. Some members are like other members.** d. Most members have some likeness with other members.
11. Which statement best describes the procedure used to number the vertical axis when preparing a histogram? **a. using a range of numbers large enough to cover all of the measurements made.** b. using only odd numbers in the scale to cover all measurements. c. using only even numbers. d. using a range of numbers to cover the first and last measurements made.
12. Which of the following structures contains the units that transmit hereditary characteristics? a. cytoplasm. **b. chromosomes.** c. cell membrane. d. chloroplasts.
13. What chemical in the cell is responsible for duplication of hereditary material? a. STP. b. ATP. **c. DNA.** d. RNA.
14. Each inherited characteristic is the result of genes from: a. the mother and her parents only. b. the father and his parents only. **c. the father and mother.** d. the mother only.
15. A recessive characteristic cannot be inherited when: a. both parents show the recessive trait. b. recessive genes are received from both parents. **c. only one parent possesses recessive genes.** d. impossible to tell.
16. When using the term "population," you must specify: a. the type of individual included. b. the area that is included. c. the given time in which it was considered. **d. all of these.**
17. A histogram is a: **a. special kind of graph.** b. special sample of a population. c. special type of laboratory equipment. d. all of these.
18. A scientist cross-pollinated pea plants that had tall stems and green seeds with pea plants that had short stems and yellow seeds. The offspring plants resulting from this cross *all* had tall stems and yellow seeds. The *recessive* traits were: **a. short stems and green seeds.** b. tall stems and yellow seeds. c. tall stems and green seeds. d. short stems and yellow seeds.
19. When using Knit-Pick cards to measure some traits among your classmates, which of the following examples could you *not* use? a. straight or curly hair. **b. vanilla, strawberry, or chocolate ice cream preference.** c. play football or do not play football. d. take typing or do not take typing.
20. When you measure your classmates for comparison of hand spans, you would measure from: a. the inside tip of the thumb to the inside tip of the little finger. b. the outside tip of the thumb to the inside tip of the little finger. **c. the outside tip of the thumb to the outside tip of the little finger.** d. the inside tip of the thumb to the outside tip of the little finger.

Chapter 19: Relationships within a Community

1. Which one of the following is a producer? a. community. **b. wheat.** c. grasshopper. d. food chain.
2. The limiting factor to the number of consumers in a community would most likely be: **a. number of producers.** b. size of the community. c. rainfall during a particular week. d. number of bacteria.
3. When living things depend on each other they: a. are independent. b. eat the same type of food. **c. are interdependent.** d.

live in the same community.

4. A biomass could be described as: a. all the rocks and soil in a community. b. all the rocks, soil, and food in a community. c. the mass of all the producers in a community. **d. the mass of all the consumers and producers in a community.**
5. Which one of the following would *not* be considered a part of the natural environment? a. water supply. **b. fire hazards.** c. food supply. d. temperature.
6. A food chain could be described as: **a. the relationship between producers and consumers and their dependence on each other.** b. the number of producers in a community. c. the number and kind of consumers in a community. d. the total mass of producers and consumers in a measured area multiplied by the total of that area.
7. The number of consumers in an area is limited by: a. the number of producers. b. the kind of producers. **c. both a and b.** d. neither a nor b.
8. Which of the following groups are all consumers? a. grasshoppers, grass, trees. **b. mouse, deer, eagle.** c. grass, wheat, dandelion. d. deer, wheat, eagle.
9. Which of the following would *most* likely be a closed community? a. a prairie. b. an ocean. c. a forest. **d. a pond.**
10. Ecology can be defined as: **a. the interrelationships of populations of organisms with each other and their environments.** b. the influence of one population on another population. c. how one plant is capable of surviving in a community. d. all of these.
11. The total biomass of a given area is determined by: a. the number of consumers. b. the number of producers. **c. the limiting factors of the environment.** d. the sampling technique used.
12. Which would be the best method of taking a sample to determine biomass of an area? a. Select an area with the most plants. b. Select an area with the most animals. c. Select an area with the fewest plants and animals. **d. Select an area that represents the entire community.**
13. If the number of producers in a community decreases: **a. the number of consumers will decrease.** b. the number of consumers will remain the same. c. the number of consumers will increase. d. the food chain will not be affected.
14. What can be done to increase the number of consumers in a closed community? a. Remove all disease-causing organisms. b. Continually add fertilizers to the soil to increase producers. c. Decrease the death rate of consumers. **d. all of these.**
15. Which of the following is a community? a. one population from a given area. b. several populations from different areas. c. the populations you are studying in a given area. **d. all of the populations in a given area.**
16. An open community is represented by: a. an aquarium. b. a pond. **c. an ocean.** d. a fish bowl.
17. Which of the following is *not* an ecological community? **a. a heard of cattle.** b. a river. c. a prairie. d. a pine forest.
18. If the biomass of a sample area of one square meter is known, what must be done to find the biomass of the entire field from which the sample was made? a. Take more samples of the area. **b. Multiply the biomass of the sample area by the area, in square meters, of the entire field.** c. Measure the mass of the plants found in the entire field. d. Look up the biomass of other similar areas and average the total.
19. Grass, weeds, ants, earthworms, molds, and bacteria are living organisms most likely to be found in a: a. group called producers. b. group called consumers. **c. lawn community.** d. pond community.
20. Some birds feed heavily on earthworms. If weather conditions bring heavy rains and flooding, the earthworm population decreases. We might expect the bird population to: a. increase in number. **b. decrease in number.** c. remain about the same in number. d. look for another source of food.

Chapter 20: The Food We Eat

1. Which nutrient does the body usually use to produce energy? **a. carbohydrate.** b. protein. c. calcium. d. starch.
2. What color indicates the presence of starch when the material is tested with iodine solution? a. green. b. orange-red. c. yellow. **d. blue-black.**
3. Which of the following is used to test for sugar? a. iodine solution. **b. Benedict's test solution.** c. sodium hydroxide solution. d. all of these.
4. When fats or oils are rubbed on brown paper: a. the paper gets black. **b. light is then able to show through the paper.** c. the paper turns a blue-green color. d. iodine is then dropped on the grease spot to test for fat.
5. The most plentiful nutrient found when testing bread is: a. protein. b. fat. c. sugar. **d. starch.**
6. Which type of nutrient should be eaten daily by young people to insure proper growth? **a. protein.** b. fat. c. sugar. d. starch.
7. Beriberi and scurvy are two deficiency diseases caused by a lack of: a. carbohydrates. b. proteins. c. minerals. **d. vitamins.**
8. What happens to vitamin C content when fruit juice is boiled? a. The vitamin is concentrated. **b. The vitamin is destroyed.** c. The vitamin remains unchanged. d. The strength of the vitamin increases.
9. When carbohydrates are oxidized or burned: a. vitamin C is destroyed. b. fats are stored in the body. **c. energy is released.** d. sugars are formed.
10. The amount of heat needed to raise the temperature of one gram of water one degree Celsius is known as: a. calorimeter. b. a gram-degree. c. energy. **d. a calorie.**
11. Which one of the following does *not* influence the number of calories you need? **a. part of the city where you live.** b. your age. c. the activities you perform. d. how well your body burns food.
12. If a person is overweight, his or her calorie intake is probably: a. less than the number of calories used. **b. more than the number of calories used.** c. about the same as the number of calories used. d. unrelated to his or her excess weight.
13. When measuring the number of calories in a nutmeat, a student found that 20 milliliters of water in a test tube warmed up 30 degrees Celsius as the nut was burned. The number of calories added to the water was: a. 60. b. 30. c. 200. **d. 600.**
14. Of the choices given here, the most balanced diet for your breakfast would consist of: a. juice and doughnut. **b. bacon, egg, toast, orange juice.** c. orange juice and cinnamon toast. d. All of these would be balanced breakfasts.
15. How many small calories are contained in a large Calorie? a. 1. b. 10. c. 100. **d. 1,000.**
16. Which type of food would probably contain the *least* amount of vitamins? a. raw carrots. b. cooked fresh carrots. c. frozen carrots. **d. cooked frozen carrots.**
17. What food material should be in your daily diet? a. milk-meat group. b. bread-cereal group. c. vegetable-fruit group. **d. all of these.**
18. What chemical is used to test for vitamin C? a. Benedict's solution. **b. starch and iodine solutions.** c. starch and Benedict's solutions. d. iodine.
19. White rats are used in nutritional experiments concerning human diets because: a. the rats are easy to raise. b. the rats will not eat the wrong kind of diet. **c. the rats may be fed many of the same foods that humans eat.** d. the rats reproduce rapidly.

Chapter 21: Pollution of the Environment

1. Which of these does not contribute to the air pollution problem? **a. the gases**

produced by green plants. b. exhaust from automobiles. c. burning of hard coal. d. oil furnace fumes.

2. The problem of detergent pollution of water supplies was partially solved when: a. detergents were chemically changed so that they cleaned clothes better. b. enzymes were added to detergents. **c. detergents were chemically changed so that they could be broken down by bacteria.** d. detergents were removed from markets.
3. The balance of nature can be upset most violently by: a. planting trees and building bridges. **b. people interfering with nature.** c. daylight saving time. d. poor diets.
4. Decaying organic wastes in streams and lakes cause death of fish because: a. the decay process uses food needed by the fish. **b. the oxygen needed by fish is used by the decaying organic matter.** c. organic wastes in the water take up space that fish need. d. the smell of decaying organic wastes is not good for fish.
5. The more green algae living in a stream or lake: a. the more fish can live there because of the increased food supply. **b. the fewer fish can live there because of the shortage of oxygen.** c. there is no effect on the number of fish that can live there. d. the healthier the environment.
6. The hydrosphere consists of: **a. the water supply of the earth.** b. the oxygen supply of the earth. c. the hydrogen supply of the earth. d. the supply of water, oxygen, and hydrogen of the earth.
7. The care of the environment and the prevention of pollution is *mainly* the responsibility of: **a. each individual citizen.** b. industry. c. the government. d. conservation clubs.
8. Putting fish in water containing detergents: a. allows them to live cleaner, healthier lives. **b. causes them to get sick and die.** c. has no effect on them. d. increases the rate at which they multiply.
9. The single largest source of air pollution in cities is: **a. automobiles.** b. factories. c. burning trash. d. all of these.
10. The atmosphere consists of: a. the water supply of the earth. **b. the gases surrounding the earth.** c. the oxygen supply of the earth. d. all of these.
11. Smog consists of: a. the moisture in the atmosphere. b. the smoke found in the atmosphere. **c. a mixture of various air pollutants reacting due to ultraviolet radiation.** d. smoke, carbon dioxide, and carbon monoxide released by car engines.
12. The widespread use of the pesticide DDT resulted in: a. killing disease-carrying insects. b. killing birds that feed on insects. c. killing fish that live in rivers. **d. all of these.**
13. Which of these probably represents the *best* way to deal with a disease-carrying insect pest? a. Use chemicals to kill the pest. **b. Use an organism that is a natural enemy of the insect and let it feed upon the pest.** c. Do nothing about the pest. d. Poison the food supply of the pest.
14. Before a new chemical substance is released for use by the public: **a. extensive tests of its long-range effect on the environment should be made.** b. only the effectiveness of the substance should be determined. c. it should be released without any testing because of the cost involved in testing. d. limited testing should be done on some experimental animals.
15. The most critical factor about water pollutants in the environment is: a. they often remain in harmful form for long periods of time. **b. some organisms tend to concentrate the substances in their bodies.** c. they are often changed to other substances. d. they are easy to recognize as harmful.
16. Which of the following examples best illustrates the concept know as the balance of nature? a. a green plant living in a field. b. a pet mouse in a cage. **c. a herd of deer eating grass in a meadow.** d. people building a freeway.
17. A detergent is a material used by people to: a. kill insects. b. kill plants. **c. remove dirt.** d. prevent pollution.

18. Ways you might try to help avoid pollution of the environment would *not* include: a. saving paper for paper drives and eventual recycling. b. collecting bottles for recycling. **c. buying synthetic detergents noted for their cleaning power.** d. using more dead leaves and similar compost with less emphasis on commercial fertilizers.
19. Atomic fuel promises clean air and cheap electricity. However, even here there are forseeable problems. Which of the following is *not* a possible side effect? a. storing radioactive wastes in the environment. b. prolonging the growing season of some plants due to releasing millions of liters of warm water into nearby water, thus producing a thick mat of algae. c. warm water may affect the growing cycle of fish. **d. radiation burn from standing too close to the nuclear power plant.**
20. During an experiment to find the effects of detergents on fish in a jar, which symptoms would probably *not* be exhibited by an affected fish? a. swimming high in the jar. b. rapid gill motion. **c. smooth, graceful swimming motion.** d. gill covers wide open and enlarged.

Transparency Masters

These transparency masters are designed as teaching aids to complement the material covered in the text and in the laboratory. They are especially useful as review material, and for introducing certain topics.

Depending on the equipment available, projection transparencies may be made either by carefully removing the masters from the book and processing them, or by processing them while they are still bound in the book. If the masters are removed from the book, they may be stored in a folder or envelope and used again.

The following are specific suggestions for using each transparency, plus answers to the questions that are found on each transparency. The transparency masters themselves immediately follow this section.

1. Use any time during Problem 2-1 to show how data from a chart can be used to prepare a graph. Indicate how much easier it is to read and interpret the graph than the table. **Responses:** (a) By month, consecutively. (b) You can see at a glance the highest and lowest figures. (c) June. (d) Horizontal.

2. This may be shown at any convenient "break" during Problem 2-2, but not before the experiment is started. Each of the four different kinds of graphs is used to present a certain type of information. **Responses:** (a) From 8:00—10:00 A.M. or from 10:00—12:00 A.M. (b) 1920, 54.1; 1950, 68.2; 1970, 71.0. (c) Iowa, Illinois, and Indiana. (d) Insects.

3. Use at the end of Chapter 4. Set up for a class demonstration. Ask students to set up a dichotomous key. **Responses:** (a) Dichotomous refers to a paired or branched arrangement. As a dichotomous system is developed, the grouping is arranged so that there is an either/or choice for each characteristic. (b) By subdividing the large group into two smaller groups. Each smaller group is then subdivided into two more subgroups, etc. (c) The first step would be to find a characteristic that can be used to separate the large group into two smaller groups (such as "laboratory glassware" or "not laboratory glassware"). (d) Not necessarily; the outcome of any grouping is based on the purpose or need established.

4. Use this transparency as a follow-up to Transparency 3. **Responses:** (a) Different purposes and desired outcomes will lead to different classification systems. (b) Examine the characteristics of the medicine dropper bottle and then place it in the group in which it belongs.

5. Use at the end of Problem 5-1 or at the end of Chapter 5. **Responses:** (a) 1—eyepiece or ocular lens; 2—coarse-adjustment knob; 3—body tube; 4—fine-adjustment knob; 5—arm; 6—objective lens; 7—stage clips; 8—stage; 9—mirror; 10—base. (b) Parts 1 and 6. (c) The coarse-adjustment knob, number 2. (d) Parts 5 and 10, arm and base.

6. Use during Problem 5-3 or at the end of Chapter 5. **Responses:** (a) As the magnification is increased, the field diameter decreases. (b) 0.3 millimeters; 300 microns. (c) 100X.

7. Use after the completion of problems on plant and animal cells. A review of cell structures and functions could be included at the same time. **Responses:** (a) *Similar*—unit of structure of living things, both contain nucleus, cytoplasm, mitochondria, cell membrane, and vacuole; *different*—only plant cells have cell walls and chloroplasts. (b) Nucleus. (c) Cell wall.

8. Use after the completion of Problem 7-2 on leaf structure. Incorporate a review of cell types found in a leaf and discuss the function of each type of cell. **Responses:** (a) A—palisade cells; B—vascular tissue (xylem); C—vascular tissue (phloem); D—lower epidermis; E—guard cell; F—stoma; G—air space; H—spongy cells; I—upper epidermis. (b) E and F—guard cells and stomata. (c) Upper and lower epidermis. (d) Palisade and spongy cells (mesophyll).

9. Use after problems on earthworms (7-3, 7-4). Review structures students should have found, as well as the function of each structure. **Responses:** (a) *Live:* setae, dorsal blood vessel; *preserved:* circular muscles, longitudinal muscles, ventral nerve cord, brain, pharynx, esophagus, aortic arch, reproductive organs, crop, gizzard, intestine. (b) *Dorsal blood vessel* returns blood to heart. *Setae* (bristles) anchor worm for locomotion and protection. *Circular muscles* help in locomotion and lengthen worm. *Longitudinal muscles* help in locomotion and shorten worm. *Ventral blood vessel* carries blood away from the heart. *Ventral nerve cord* coordinates activities of various segments of the worm. *Brain* controls activity of whole organism. *Pharynx* ingests food. *Esophagus* helps digest food; grinding action. *Aortic arches* collect and pump blood. *Reproductive organs* produce and store sex cells. *Crop* provides storage area for food. *Gizzard* is a grinding structure to digest food. *Intestine* provides area for absorption of digested foods.

10. Use after the completion of Problem 8-3 on brine shrimp. Review tactic responses and reaction of brine shrimp to various environmental stimuli. **Responses:** (a) Toward the surface; negative geotaxis. (b) Away from the ice; positive thermotaxis. (c) Away from the dark covered area; positive phototaxis.

11. Use after completion of Problem 10-2 on antiseptics as a review of substances that affect bacterial growth. Point out that only certain bacteria are affected by mouthwashes. **Responses:** (a) There are clear areas surrounding some substances on the petri dish. (b) Mouthwash, penicillin, and soap inhibit the growth and reproduction of bacteria. Vinegar does not affect the growth and reproduction of bacteria. (c) Antiseptics. (d) It would be inhibited or killed.

12. Use after Problem 10-3 for review of radiation effects. **Responses:** (a) The 15-second exposure produced color changes. These are called mutations. (b) 30 seconds. (c) No. The dish exposed for 2 minutes still contained a colored colony. (d) The control dish showed the normal appearance of bacteria that have not been irradiated.

All of the Following Transparencies Can Be Utilized in End of Chapter Reviews

13. For use after Problem 12-2. **Responses:** (a) Plant stems and leaves show negative geotropic response (grow away from the earth). (b) Plant roots display positive geotropism (grow downward). (c) Both stem and leaves as well as roots will probably be growing parallel to the floor.

14. For use after Problem 12-4. **Responses:** (a) Speeds it up and causes greater growth than the plant would normally achieve. (b) About 40 mm. (c) It would have been steeper. By the 10th day the plant could have been 50 mm or more high. (d) No. It could be an abnormal plant. Two large groups of plants should be used, one group treated with gibberellic acid and the other untreated.

15. Use after Problem 13-2. **Responses:** (a) B. (b) A. (c) There may be fewer "A" molecules in the beaker; the "B" molecules might be more evenly distributed between the dialysis bag and the beaker. (d) It acts as a semipermeable membrane that allows particles of only a certain size to pass through.

16. Use after Problem 13-4. **Responses:** (a) It is a constant and even rise. (b) Lower; the volume of the liquid would be the same. (c) It would either rise only a short distance or not rise at all. Syrup in the beaker due to the leak would neutralize any osmotic pressure. (d) The syrup-water would rise as far as its osmotic pressure is able to compress the air in the closed tube, then it would probably stop.

17. For use after Problem 15-1. **Responses:** (a) A—stigma; B—anther; C—style; D—ovary; E—sepal; F—ovules; G—petals; H—stamen. (b) *Male:* B, H; *female:* A, C, D, F. (c) B—anther. (d) F—ovules.

18. Use after completion of Problem 17-1. May be used as a review of structures found in the mouth of a frog. **Responses:** (a) A—maxillary teeth; **B**—special (vomerine) teeth; **C**—internal nares; **D**—eye bulges; **E**—opening to eustachian tube; **F**—gullet; **G**—glottis; **H**—tongue. (b) Tongue, vomerine teeth, and eye bulges. (c) Glottis. (d) Gullet. (e) Eustachian tubes.

19. Use after completion of Problem 17-3. **Responses:** (a) Frog has 3 chambers, human has 4 chambers. (b) *Frog:* Blood enters right atrium—to ventricle, to lungs, to left atrium, to ventricle, to the major arteries of the body, to capillary beds, to veins, to great veins, to right atrium. *Human:* Blood enters right atrium—to right ventricle, to lungs, to left atrium, to left ventricle, to the major arteries of the body, to capillary beds, to veins, to great veins, to right atrium.

20. Use after completion of problems on the internal organs of frog and human. As a review and comparison of the organs found in the body cavity of frog and human. **Responses:** (a) *Frog:* **A**—esophagus; **B**—liver; **C**—stomach; **D**—large intestine; **E**—small intestine. *Human:* **A**—esophagus; **B**—liver; **C**—stomach; **D**—large intestine; **E**—small intestine. (b) *Esophagus*—pass food from mouth to stomach; *stomach*—to digest food with enzymes and grinding action; *liver*—production of bile; *small intestine*—absorb digested food, help digestive process; *large intestine*—absorb water, remove waste from body. (c) Longer esophagus in human and longer large intestine in human. The other organs are very similar with the exception of the internal ridges of the frog's stomach, and differences in the gross structure of the liver.

21. Use after Problem 19-2. **Responses:** (a) 1955, corresponding to increase in mouse population. (b) Owl predators, disease, presence of insecticides or other pollutants. (c) Other predators, disease, availability of food.

AVERAGE MONTHLY RAINFALL IN CHICAGO

TABLE

Month	Inches
Jan	1.9
Feb	1.6
Mar	2.6
Apr	3.0
May	3.7
June	4.0
July	3.4
Aug	2.6
Sept	2.1
Oct	2.3
Nov	1.6
Dec	1.4

GRAPH

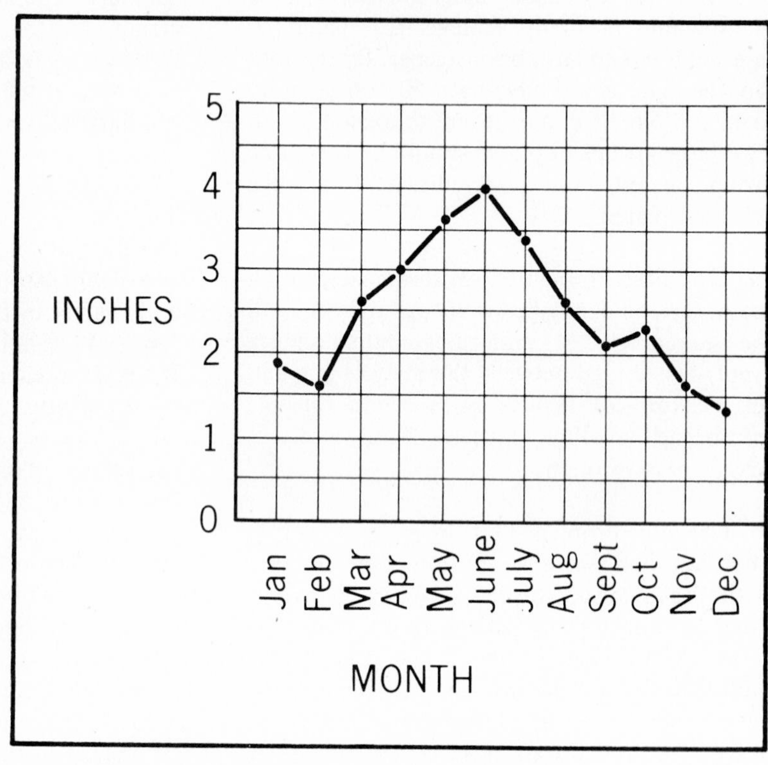

PRESENTING INFORMATION ON A GRAPH

(a) How have the rainfall data been grouped in the table?

(b) How does the graph make information more clear?

(c) On the average, in which month does the most rain fall in Chicago?

(d) Which axis (side) of the graph is called the independent variable?

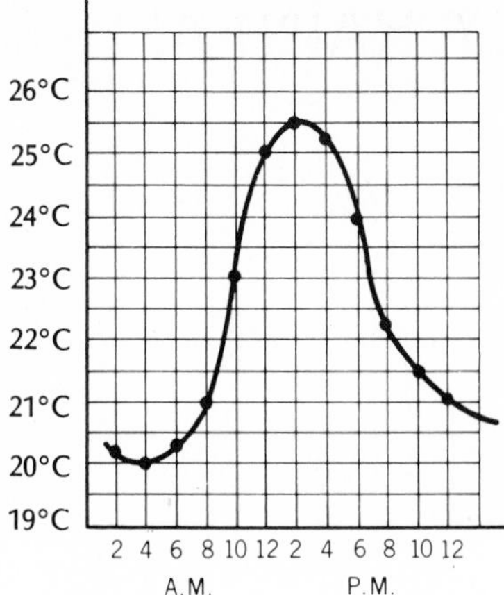

Figure A, Line Graph
Air Temperature Change
During a 24-hour Period

Birth Year	Life Expectancy, Years
1920	54.1
1930	59.7
1940	62.9
1950	68.2
1960	69.7
1970	71.0

Figure B, Bar Graph
Life Expectancy, 1920 to 1970

	State	Annual Corn Production
9.0	Iowa	0 0 0 0 0 0 0 0 0
9.0	Illinois	0 0 0 0 0 0 0 0 0
4.2	Indiana	0 0 0 0 0
3.6	Minnesota	0 0 0 0
3.0	Nebraska	0 0 0
2.4	Missouri	0 0 0

Figure C, Pictograph
Corn Production in Six Leading States
(ear of corn/100 million bushels)

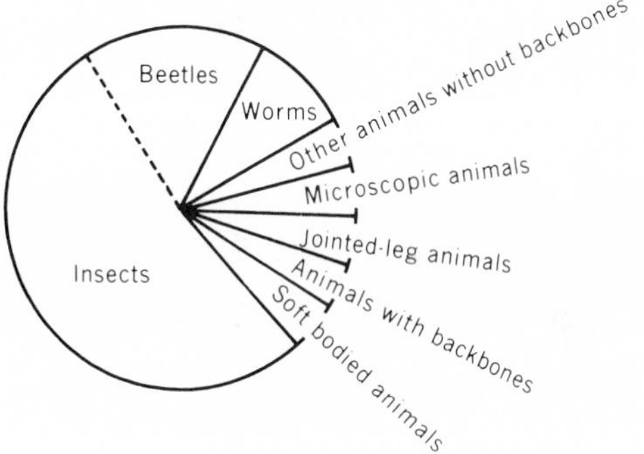

Figure D, Circle Graph
Abundance of Animals on Earth

READING INFORMATION FROM GRAPHS

(a) In Figure A, which 2 hour period showed the greatest temperature change?

(b) Read the life expectancy for a person born in 1920; 1950; 1970.

(c) What are the three leading states in corn production?

(d) What kind of animals are most abundant on earth?

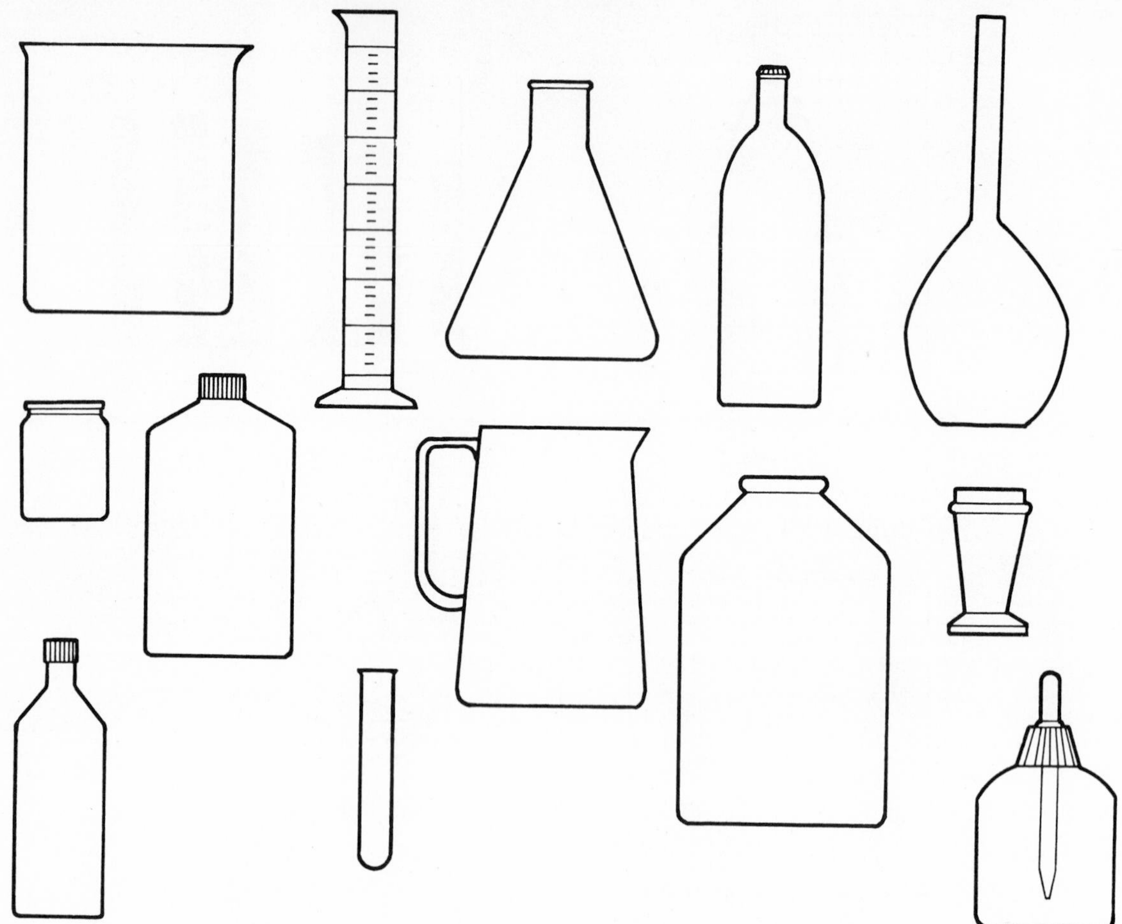

CONSTRUCTING A DICHOTOMOUS KEY

(a) What does the word dichotomous mean?

(b) How would you prepare a dichotomous key for sorting these pieces of glassware?

(c) What is the first step in separating the bottles into two groups?

(d) Will each person choose the same system for grouping the bottles?

Transparency Master # 4

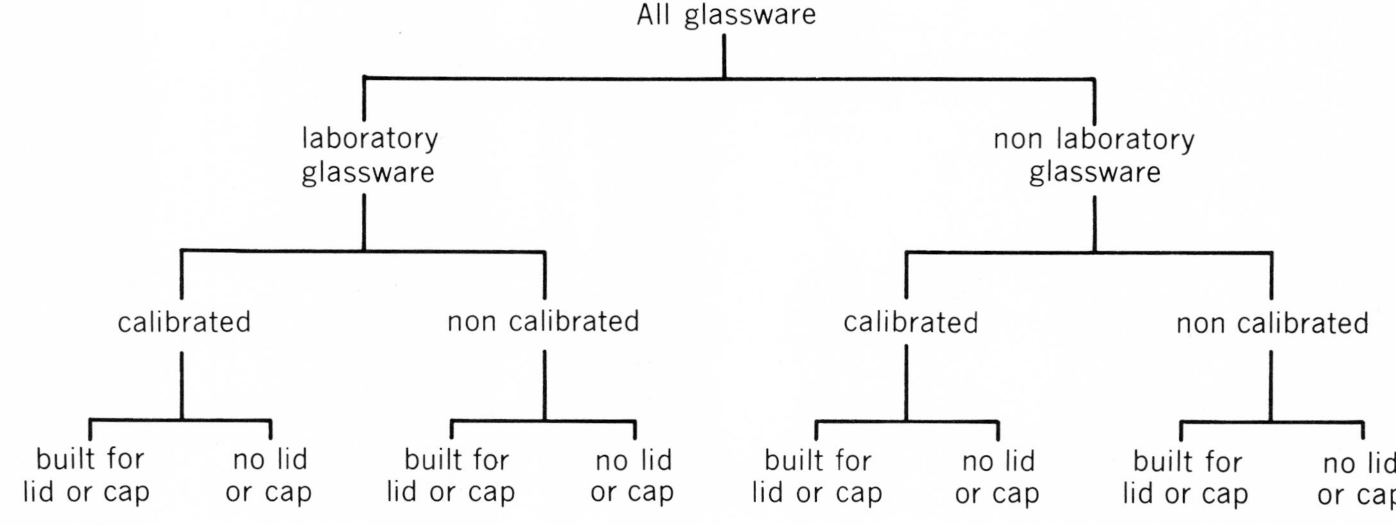

A SAMPLE KEY FOR CLASSIFYING BOTTLES

(a) How may your classification key be different from this one? Does this make yours wrong? Explain.

(b) How could you classify a piece of glassware such as a medicine dropper bottle?

Transparency Master # 5

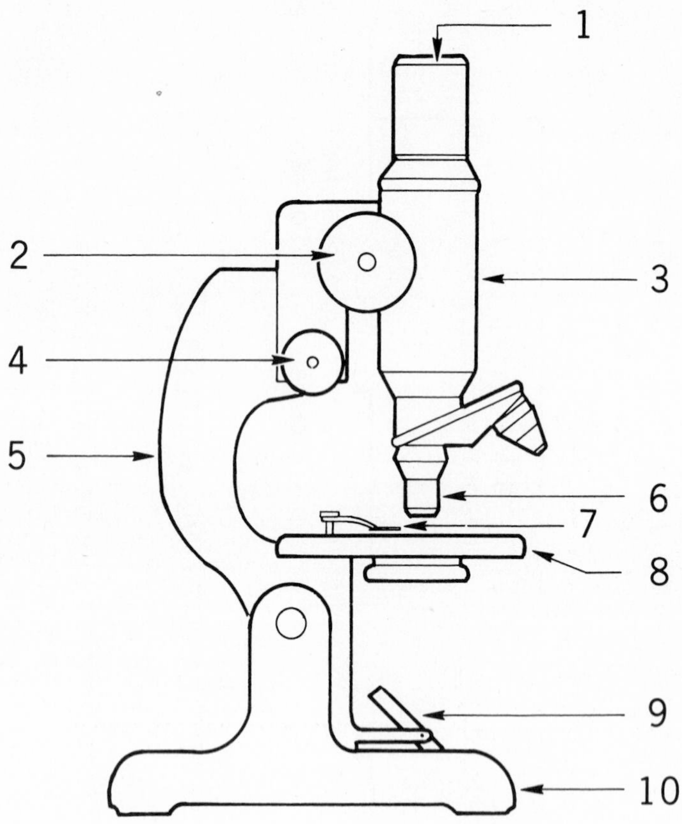

PARTS OF A COMPOUND MICROSCOPE

(a) What is the name of each numbered part of the microscope?

(b) Which parts focus light rays?

(c) Which knob should be turned first when focusing the microscope on an object?

(d) Which part(s) of the microscope should be held or supported when moving the microscope?

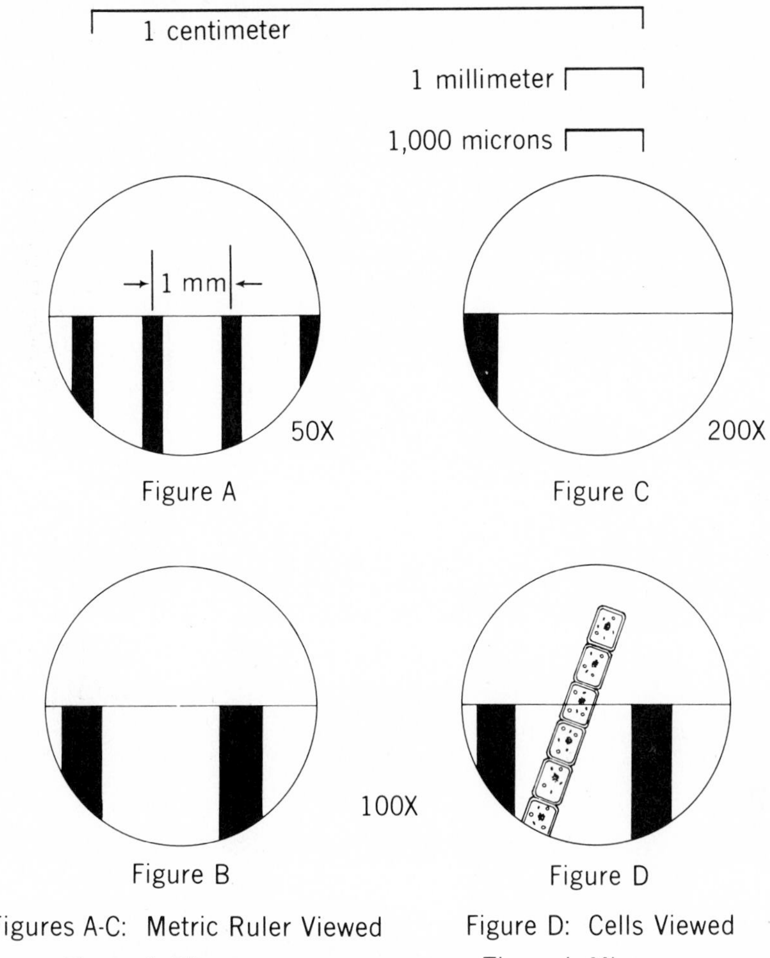

Figures A-C: Metric Ruler Viewed Through Microscope

Figure D: Cells Viewed Through Microscope

MEASURING WITH THE MICROSCOPE

(a) How does the field diameter of the microscope change as the magnification is increased, Figure A to Figure C?

(b) Estimate the diameter of the cells in Figure D in millimeters; in microns.

(c) What magnification power is shown in Figure D?

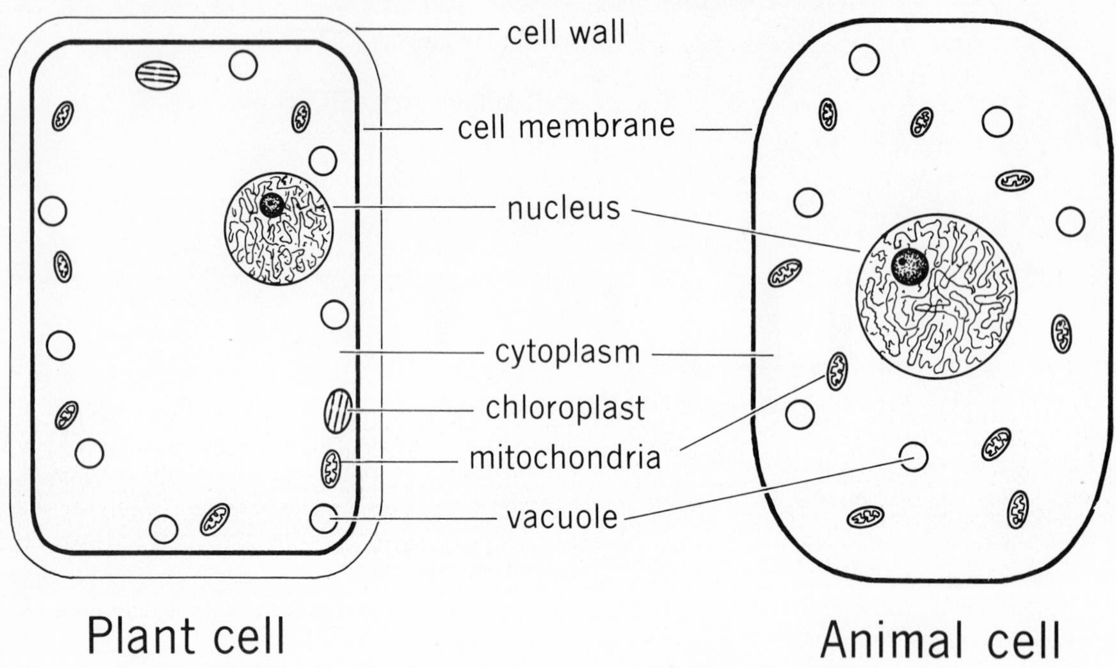

COMPARING PLANT AND ANIMAL CELLS

(a) How are plant and animal cells similar? How are they different?

(b) What structure controls all cell activities in both kinds of cells?

(c) Which of the labeled structures are non living matter?

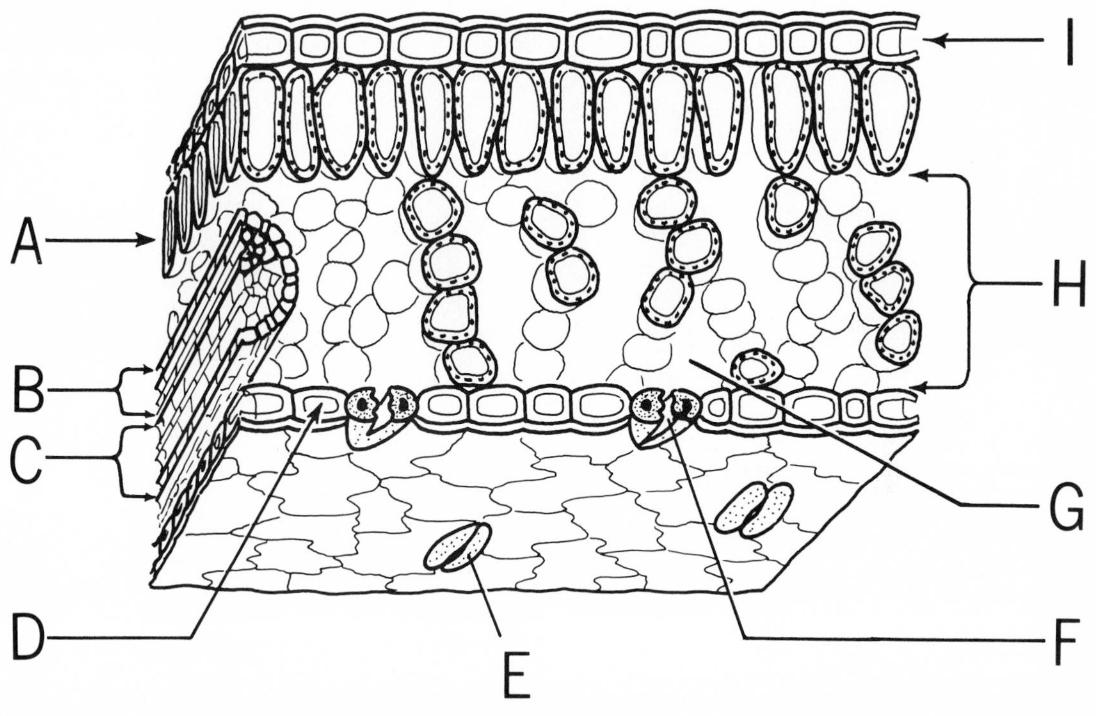

LEAF CROSS SECTION

(a) Name the structures identified by the letters in the leaf cross section.

(b) Which structures admit carbon dioxide to the interior of the leaf?

(c) Which structures protect the interior of the leaf?

(d) Which cells contain the most chlorophyll?

Transparency Master # 9

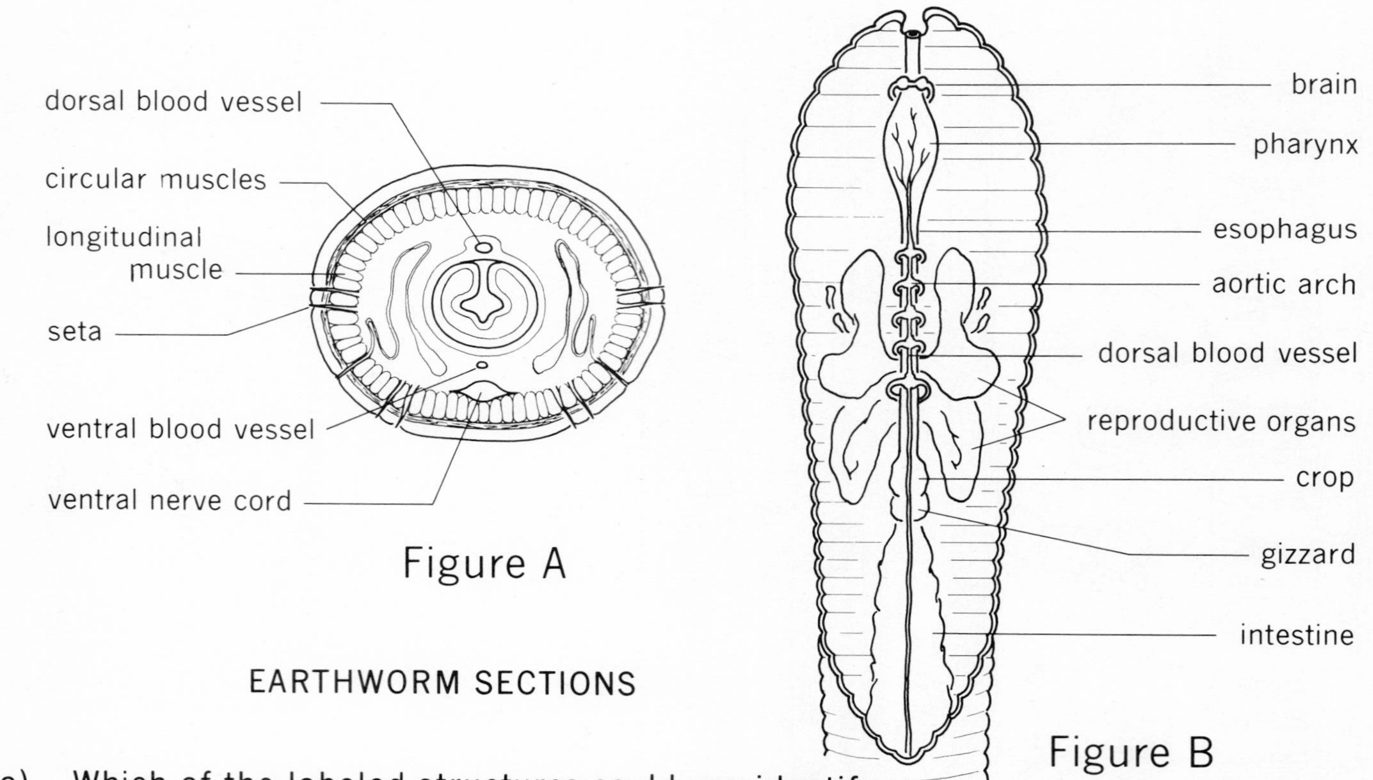

Figure A

Figure B

EARTHWORM SECTIONS

(a) Which of the labeled structures could you identify on the living earthworm? on the preserved earthworm?

(b) What function do each of the labeled parts of the earthworm perform?

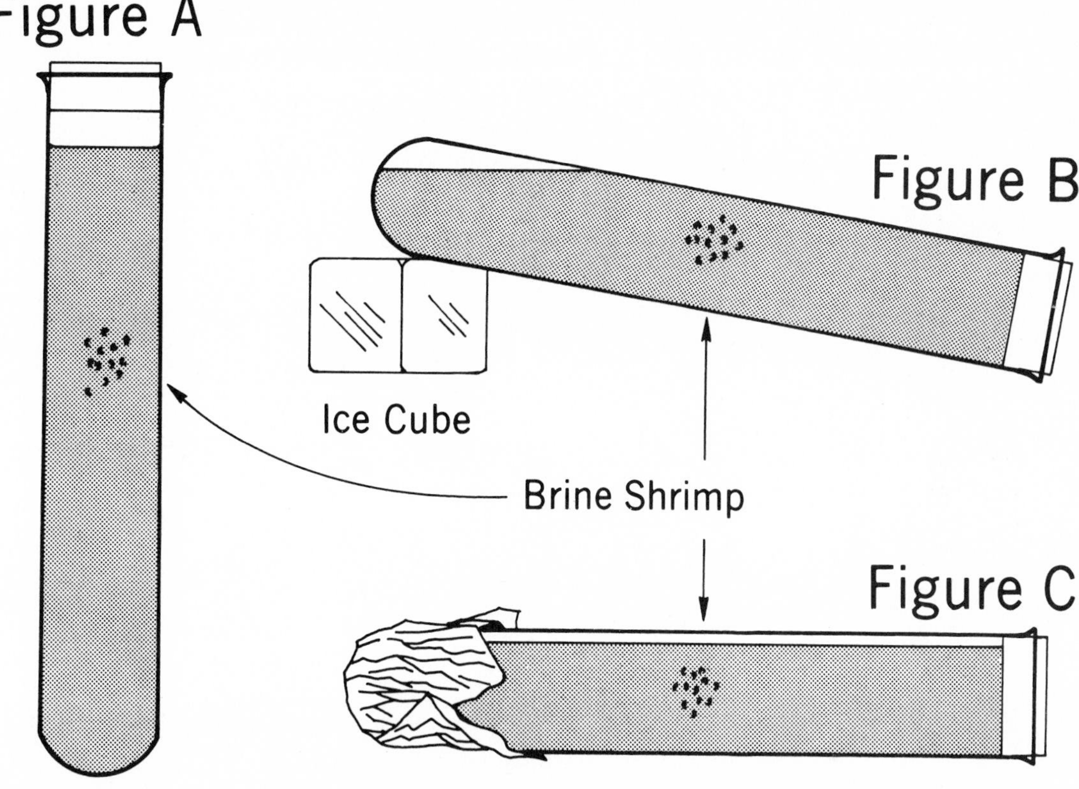

BRINE SHRIMP RESPONSES

(a) In what direction would brine shrimp be expected to move in Figure A? What is this type of response called?

(b) In what direction would brine shrimp be expected to move in Figure B? What is this type of response called?

(c) In what direction would brine shrimp be expected to move in Figure C? What is this type of response called?

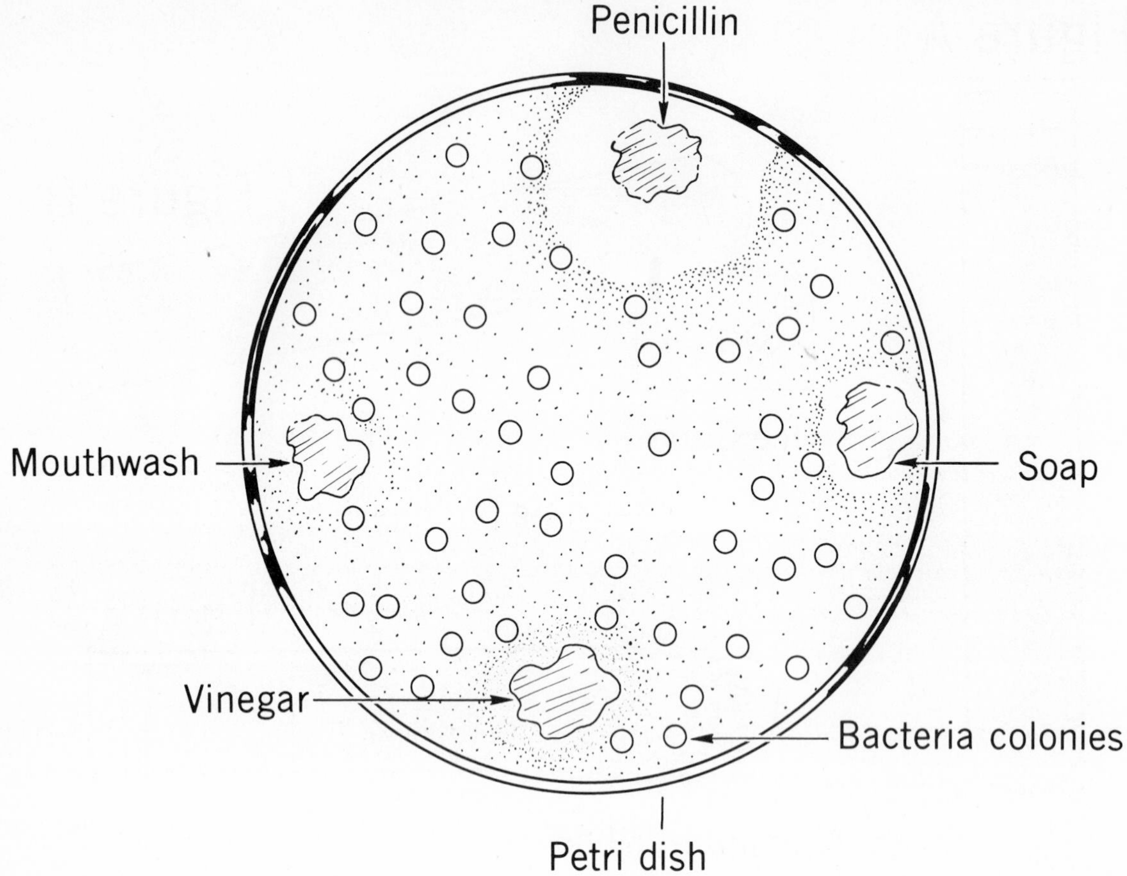

BACTERIA FIGHTERS

(a) What <u>observations</u> can you make of the petri dish culture above?

(b) What <u>interpretations</u> can you make?

(c) What general name is often used to describe substances that prevent the growth of bacteria?

(d) What would probably happen to a bacterium that landed near the area soaked with penicillin?

Bacteria Colonies Exposed to Ultraviolet Radiation

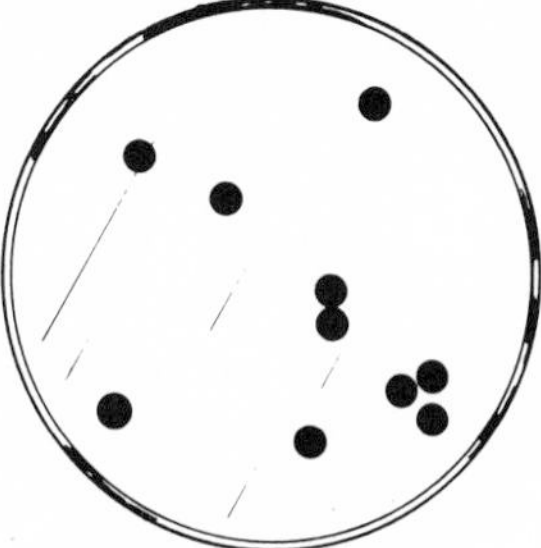

Figure A
Control - no radiation

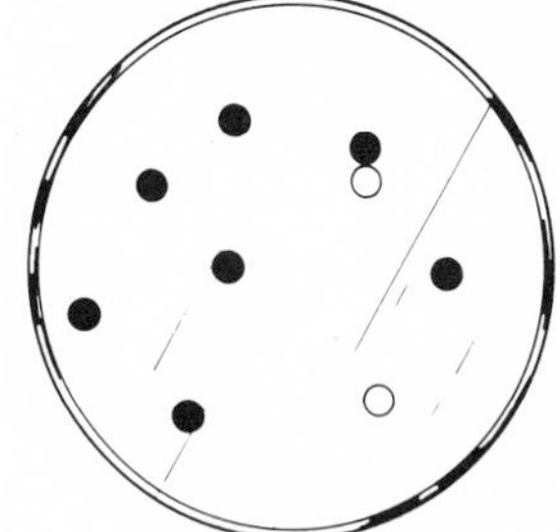

Figure B
Radiation - 15 second exposure

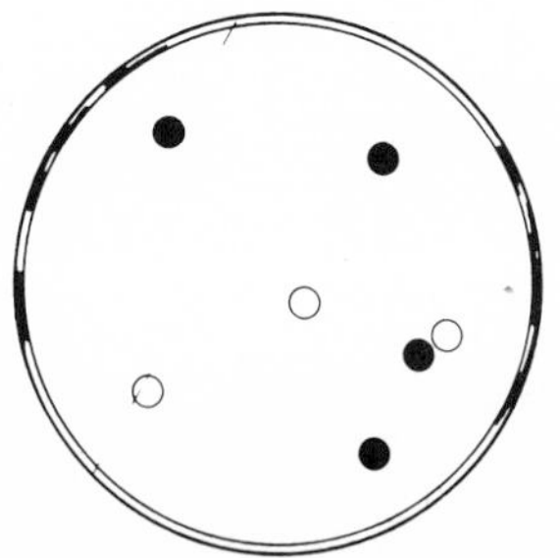

Figure C
Radiation - 30 second exposure

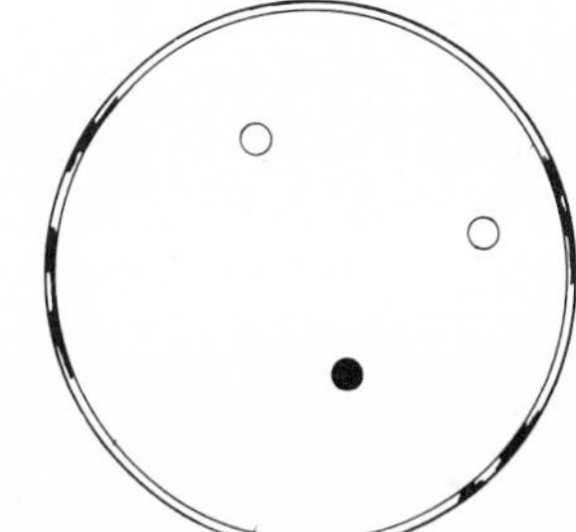

Figure D
Radiation - 2 minute exposure

RADIATION EFFECTS ON BACTERIA

(a) What exposure time was enough to produce colorless colonies but not kill bacteria? What are such permanent changes in an organism called?

(b) What exposure time was required to produce both a decrease in number of colonies and colorless colonies?

(c) Does a longer exposure time necessarily produce only colorless colonies? Explain.

(d) What was the purpose of the control dish in this experiment?

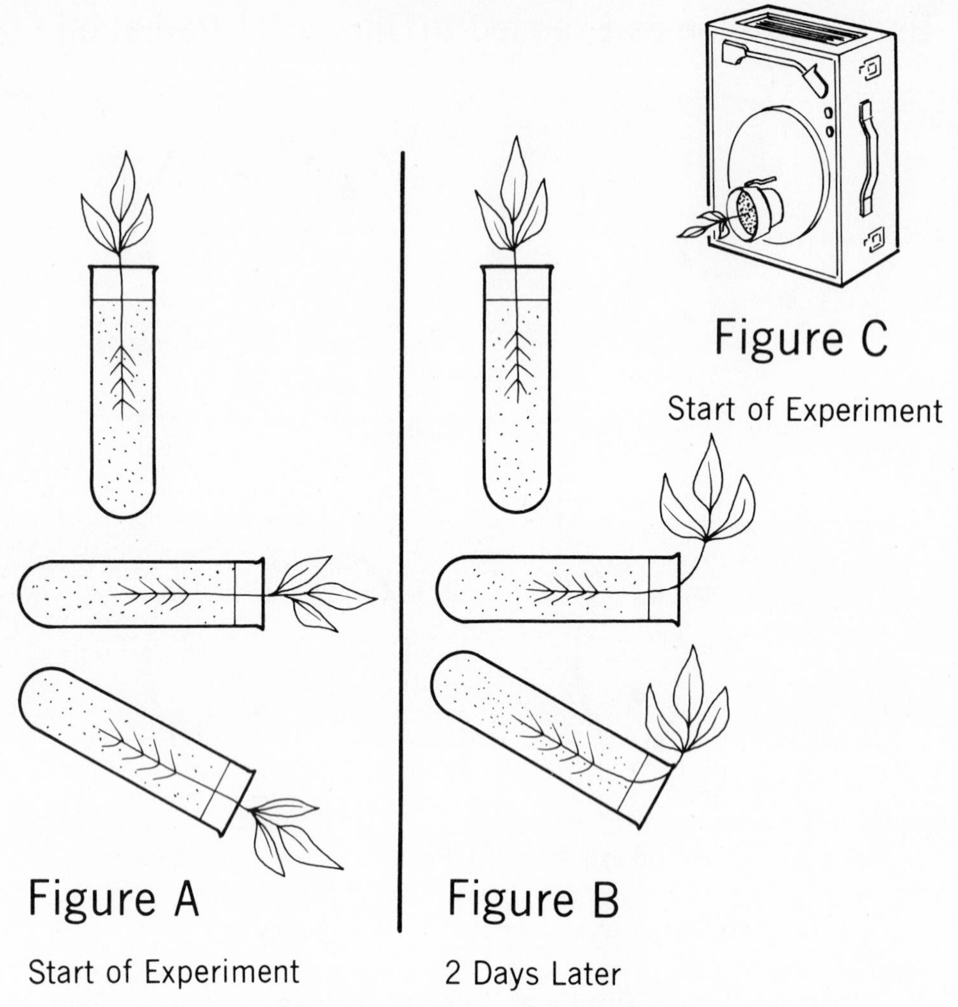

Figure C

Start of Experiment

Figure A

Start of Experiment

Figure B

2 Days Later

GRAVITY EFFECTS UPON PLANTS

(a) How do plant stems and leaves respond to gravity?

(b) How do plant roots respond to gravity?

(c) In what direction would you predict the stem and leaves of the plant in Figure C (on moving record player turntable) would move during a two day period? Would the roots move in the same direction?

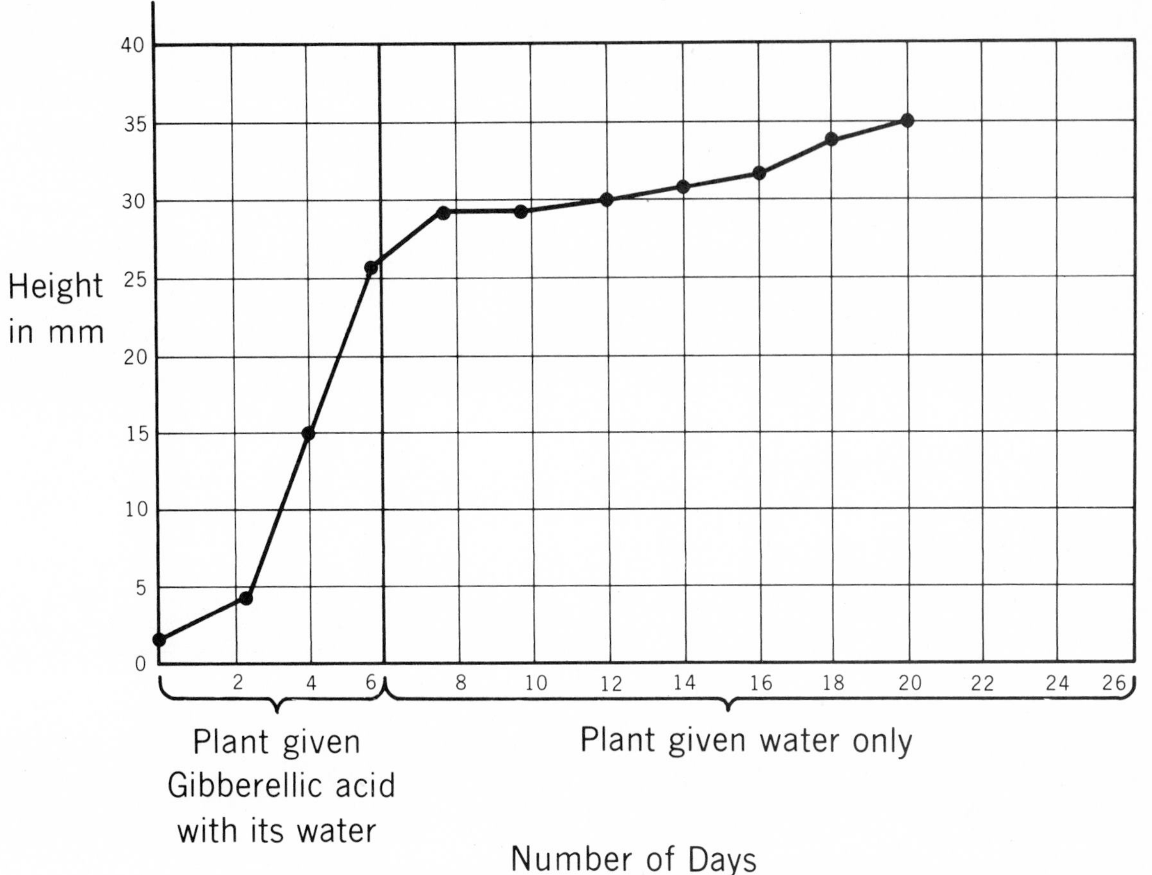

PLANT GROWTH HORMONES

(a) How does gibberellic acid affect the rate of plant growth?

(b) How tall do you think the plant will be in 26 days if it continues to grow at the rate shown here?

(c) If the addition of gibberellic acid solution had been continued beyond the 6th day, how might the growth curve have been affected?

(d) Should conclusions from growth experiment results be based upon the growth of a single plant? Explain.

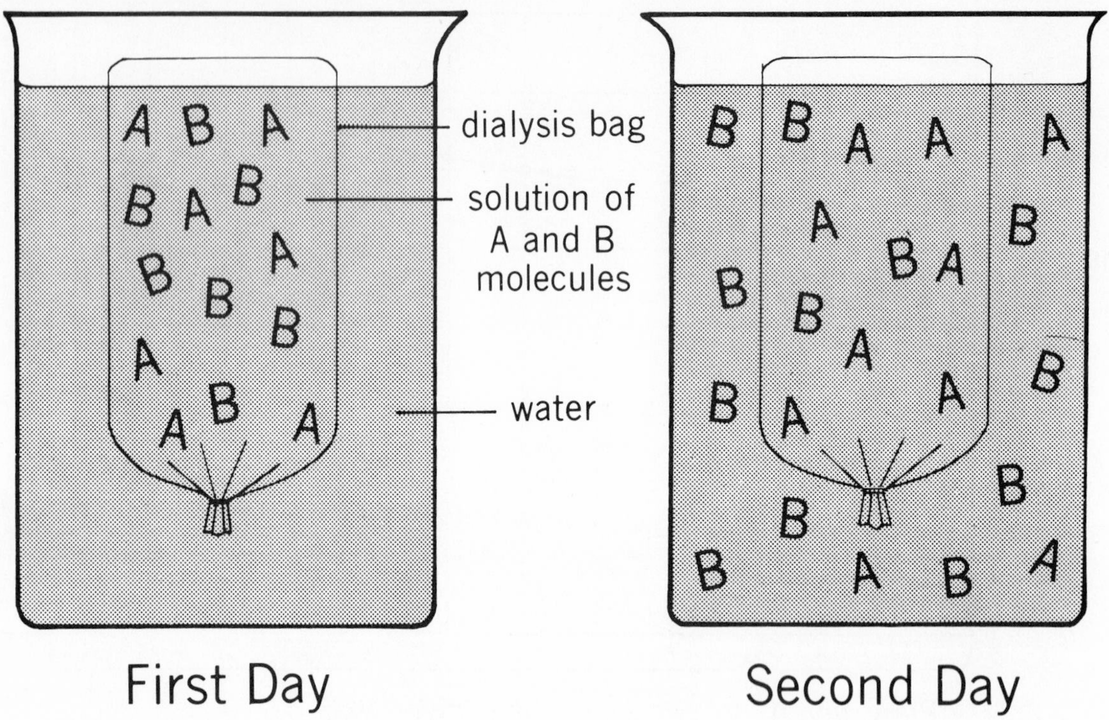

First Day

Second Day

MEMBRANES AND MOLECULES

(a) Which kind of molecules , A or B, move through the dialysis bag more readily?

(b) Which molecules are probably larger?

(c) What changes in the location of the A and B molecules might be expected on the third day?

(d) What is the function of the dialysis bag?

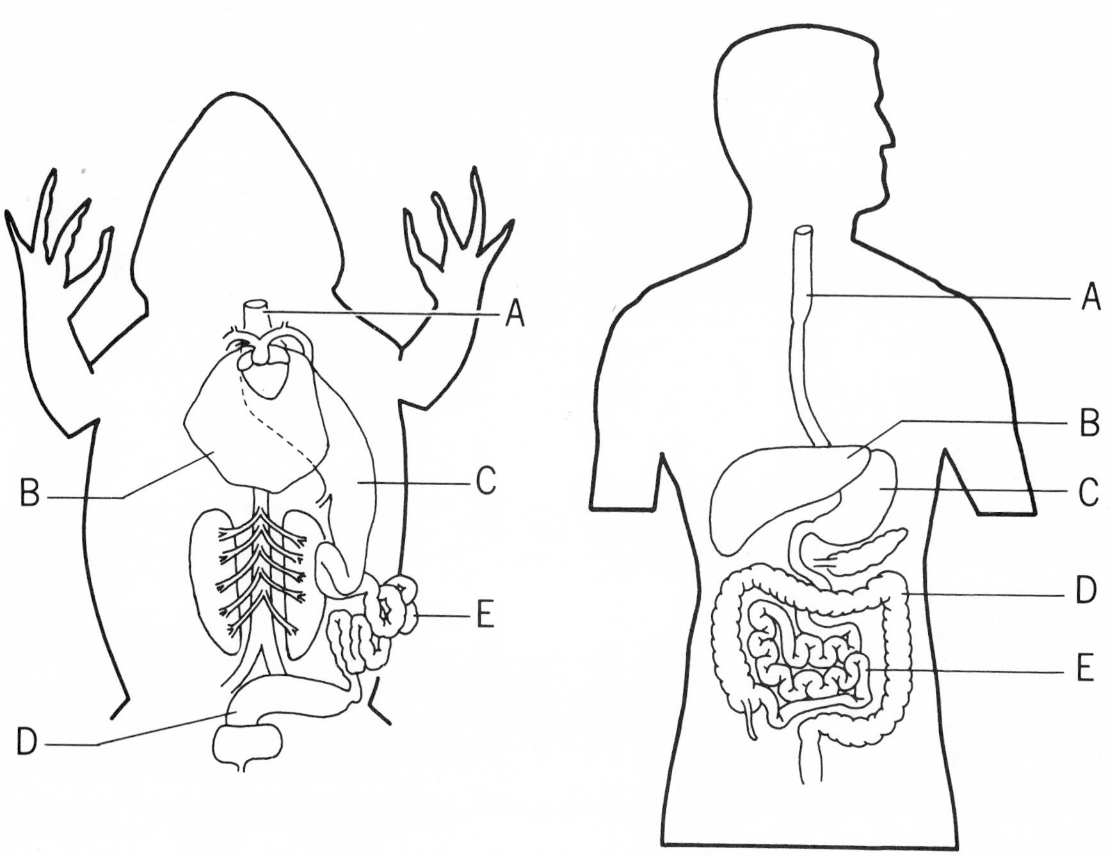

COMPARING THE DIGESTIVE SYSTEMS OF FROG AND HUMAN

(a) What organs are indicated in each diagram?

(b) What is the function of each organ shown in the diagrams?

(c) What are the main differences between the two digestive systems?

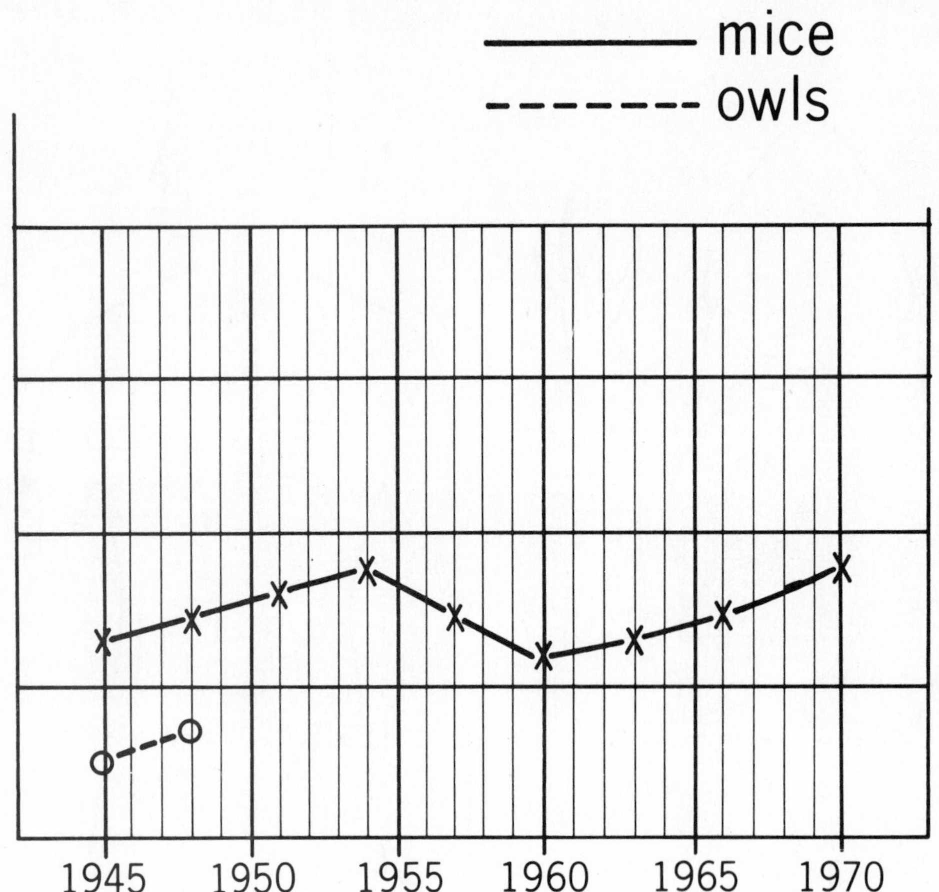

FOOD SUPPLY AND POPULATION

(a) If owls feed on mice, which years would the owl population be expected to be greatest? Why?

(b) What factors other than mouse population could affect the number of owls in the community?

(c) What factors might cause the mouse population to change?

Life Science
A problem solving approach

Revised Edition

Joseph L. Carter
Howard P. Goodman
Danny D. Hunter
Leroy J. Schelske

Ginn and Company

Joseph L. Carter, senior author of the group that developed this project, teaches science and is District Science Specialist in the Anaheim Union High School District in Anaheim, California.

Howard P. Goodman has written for television and radio, and presently teaches science at Sycamore Junior High School in Anaheim, California.

Danny D. Hunter teaches science at the Oxford Junior High School in Cypress, California.

Leroy J. Schelske has taught science in junior high school, and is now teaching biology at Loara High School in Anaheim, California.

Credits

Design and Production: Designworks, Inc.

Illustrations: Graphics; Les Morrill; Richard Spencer

Photographs: Wally Aaron, 269 (trees), 359 (mullein); American Society for Microbiology, 168 (tetanus); Armed Forces Institute of Pathology, negative no. 66-1836-1, 89 (microscope); Armstrong Cork Company, 89 (bottom); Bausch & Lomb, 70, 74; Robert Bendick, 301 (tadpole); Dennis Brokaw/National Audubon Society, 234; Burndy Library, 89 (top cork cells); Burpee Seeds, 277, 287 (morning glories); Karen Collidge/Taurus Photos, 219; Michael Collier/STOCK, Boston, 104; Steve Croy, 357 (desert), 359 (Queen Anne's lace); The DeLaval Separator Company, 170; Diamond Crystal Salt Company, 141; John H. Durrell, U.S. Public Health Service, 158; Walker English/Photo Researchers, 128; Ron Everhart, 301 (leopard frog); Sam Falk/Monkmeyer, 397 (top); W.B. Finch/STOCK, Boston, 338; Fleischmann Laboratories, Standard Brands, Incorporated, 157; Owen Franken/STOCK, Boston, 341, 357 (tropics); General Electric Company, 185; Eric V. Grave/Photo Researchers, 91 (paramecium); Nelson Groffman/Franklin Photo, 278 (fruits); A. Grotell/Peter Arnold, 357 (marine); Gerhard Gscheidle/Peter Arnold, 397 (bottom); Dr. William H. Harlow/Photo Researchers, 192; Jim Harrison, 43; Grant Heilman, 231; Ellis Herwig/STOCK, Boston, 391; W.H. Hodge/Peter Arnold, 150 (top, middle); Paul Johnson, 365; A.S. Joyce/Photo Researchers, 147; Manfred Kage/Peter Arnold, 88, 124, 126 (spirogyra, stentor), 167, 172 (left, right), 188; S.J. Krasemann/Peter Arnold, 148 (yellow coral mushroom); Harold M. Lambert, 287 (rose); Frederic Lewis, 394 (cars); Eli Lilly and Co., 168 (coccus); Stephen Maka, 54, 278 (water lily), 287 (lady's slippers), 294, 297, 298 (frog, toad), 300 (eggs, toad), 301 (eggs), 354; Massachusetts Audubon Society, 385; Massachusetts Division of Fisheries and Game, 392; Dan McCoy/Rainbow, 383; Peter Menzel/STOCK, Boston, 69; Merck & Co., Inc., 366; C.E. Mohr/Photo Researchers, 282 (witch hazel); NASA, viii; National Air Pollution Control Administration, 384; National Audubon Society/Photo Researchers, 305; National Peach Council, 289 (peach half); New York Academy of Medicine Library, 71 (portrait), 90 (left, right), 176; Winton Patnode/Photo Researchers, 126 (single-celled algae); Peace River Films, 298 (salamander); Norman Prince, 13; Norman Prince, courtesy of the University of California, 25; Joan Rahn, 279; Herbert Randle, 3, 8, 71 (top); Rapho Guillumette Pictures, 386; Arthur Richmond, 29, 73, 77, (left, right), 91 (plant cells), 148 (oyster mushrooms, bracket fungi), 159, 190, 284; H. Armstrong Roberts, 291; M.F. Roberts, 304; Runk/Schoenberger from Grant Heilman, 169; Meredith Rutter, 300 (marsh); Sargent-Welch Scientific Company, 269 (spectrum); SCALA/Editorial Photocolor Archives, 116; photo by Nathan Sharon, originally published in *Scientific American*, 168 (diplococcus); Hugh Spencer, 160, 290; E.R. Squibb & Sons, 373 (left, right); David M. Stone, 211, 278 (cactus), 282 (milkweed, burdock), 287 (dahlia), 298 (eggs), 359 (tansy, pokeweed, thistle); Karl H. Switak/Photo Researchers, 315; Ronald F. Thomas, 149; Unitron Instruments, Inc., 70; University Museum, University of Utrecht, 71 (microscope); U.S.D.A., 359 (ragweed), 393; Fred Ward/Black Star, 394 (plane); Ward's Natural Science Establishment, 289 (pit halves); T. Eliot Weier, 105, 263; James N. Westwater, 257, 382, 394 (industrial smoke); Cary Wolinsky/STOCK, Boston, 42

Home Office: Lexington, Massachusetts 02173
0-663-35740-3

Preface

The methods of teaching science have undergone a great deal of careful study, evaluation, and change in recent years. One of the most fundamental changes that have taken place is the increased emphasis on student involvement in the learning process. The student must be a participant in the discovery of science concepts rather than merely a receiver of information.

This movement has been spearheaded on the secondary level especially by courses preparing students for college science programs. The elementary school science curriculum also has a number of fine programs that encourage participation by the learners. This text provides an activity-oriented program designed to offer a working experience in life science for students at the intermediate level with a wide range of interests and abilities.

The authors realize that the learner must be involved in the learning process if the activity is to have meaning. For this reason, learning experiences needed to be designed that would be interesting and at the same time teach the concepts essential for a sound understanding of science. The emphasis on student performance of relevant experiments requires the treatment of less subject material but in a more useful and meaningful context.

One of the basic goals of this program is an understanding of the processes by which information about science is gained. Too often science books tell only what information has been learned after dozens of scientists have researched the particular problem. Our approach, however, encourages students to make their own observations and to draw their own conclusions. If a student is wrong, others in the class will be quick to raise questions. They too have "done some science" and have a stake in the results of the laboratory activity. This exchange of ideas between students and teacher results in a more meaningful learning experience.

The emphasis on basic science concepts makes this program of maximum benefit to the student who will go on to more advanced laboratory science work. The practical nature of the activities also makes the material interesting and relevant to students who have not been attracted to previous science courses. The major emphasis of this program is on the *how* and *why* of science, rather than on the what.

Different students learn at different rates. Teachers are now more than ever aware that good learning programs must accommodate these differences in ability. With this in mind, we designed our program to be flexible. The material in this book is arranged in specific experiments, or problems. Some students may perform more of the activities than other students who require more time to understand the concepts being taught.

The main objectives of each laboratory problem are stated at the end of each experiment. These objectives, entitled "You Should Now Be Able To . . ." state what skills and understandings the learning activity is designed to develop. This enables the student to see what the learning activity is supposed to accomplish. This particular feature also helps the teacher evaluate results of the program in terms of the objectives that the activities were designed to achieve.

The objectives usually begin with action words such as "observe", "describe", "measure", or "predict", rather than "memorize." Such directions, being different in that they emphasize activity rather than content, require a special kind of evaluation. The teacher must seek evidence that the learner has reached the stated goals, or else supplement the objectives and change the approach of the lesson.

The authors would like to thank the Anaheim Union High School District (grades 7-12) for permitting the use of the preliminary versions of this program in the district. The criticisms and constructive suggestions of the many teachers who have used the materials have been especially helpful. Their experience in using the preliminary materials with more than 3,000 students has helped us immensely in making improvements. The suggestions of many other science teachers are also gratefully acknowledged. We also appreciate the encouragement of Dr. Richard Merrill, Consultant in Secondary Curriculum at Mt. Diablo Unified District in California.

Contents

To the student

There are many different ways to learn about a subject. You may read books, see films, take lecture notes, or do a number of other things. These activities are valuable, but they are also limited, because they are the thoughts and experiences of others.

This book, *Life Science: A Problem Solving Approach,* lets you take a more active part in the learning process. The work you will do in the laboratory is the most important part of this program. Instead of merely reading or being told the answers to problems, you will perform many experiments to help you decide what the answers are. We believe this problem solving approach to science will be the most exciting method of learning you have experienced.

For many of you this will be the first chance to set up and carry out an experiment of any kind. The laboratory is not just a place where you mix things together to see what happens. For the results to be meaningful, activities in the laboratory must be carefully planned and carefully carried out.

Each chapter in this book begins with a brief introductory section. The introduction is important for you to read, as it starts you thinking about the topics you will be investigating in the laboratory.

Each laboratory activity starts with a question to be answered. So it is called a *Problem*. The aims of each problem are listed next as the *Purpose*. Next follows a list of *Materials*, if any are needed. Then comes the *Procedure,* which lists the steps that will help you solve the stated problem.

It is most important that you read and follow the steps in the procedures exactly. Read the directions carefully. Don't be afraid to ask for help, but first be sure you have read everything you were supposed to read. The use of special equipment will be explained before you are asked to work with it. Use all lab equipment with care, so that you do not damage it.

You will find a series of numbered questions in the procedure of each problem. These questions will help you focus on the main ideas in the experiment. Try to answer the questions as you go along. There may be some that you can't answer with certainty. Don't be afraid to write down what you *think* is the answer. But always try to say *why* you respond as you do.

Your teacher will probably have you keep a record of your work in a notebook. The notebook will be your record of results and observations for future study when you need it.

Each problem ends with a section called "You Should Now Be Able To. . . ." It gives a list of things you should be able to do after completing the problem. You should read this section even before you start the problem. Then you will know just what you should be able to do when you have finished.

A special point should be made about safety in the lab. You will not be asked to work with any materials that could be harmful unless the precautions are emphasized in the directions. This means that you have to *read all the directions* before working with any materials. A list of general safety measures to be observed at all times is given below. Your safety, as well as the safety of those around you, depends very much on you.

1. Follow directions exactly as written, unless modified by your teacher.
2. Unauthorized experimentation will not be tolerated. Perform *only* those experiments approved by your teacher.
3. Take care to protect your clothing. Wear an apron when directed by your teacher.
4. Wear safety glasses when directed.
5. Keep your work area clean and well organized.
6. In case of an accident, report to your teacher at once.

As you progress in the course, you will become more familiar with the materials and methods of life science. We hope that you will find out that science can be both enjoyable and important.

Unit-opening photo shows scientist-astronaut Harrison H. Schmitt collecting rock samples with a "lunar rake."

Unit 1

Science — The process of organizing information

Science could be described as a body of organized knowledge. This general definition could include the body of knowledge about any kind of subject. Unit One is an introduction to life science. You will obtain and organize information about living things to solve problems.

A good example of problem solving may be found in the conquest of polio. Polio is a crippling disease caused by a virus that attacks the nerves. Since the nerves control muscle movement, the victim may be crippled or even die.

In 1955 nearly 29,000 people in the United States caught this dreaded disease. Over 1,000 of them died. Twelve years later, only 47 cases were reported in the United States. What took place in those twelve years is a tribute to the skill of many scientists in organizing information.

Many scientists gathered as much information about the disease as they could. They studied the work that others before them had carried out. They organized all the data into meaningful notes. They eliminated those experiments that had not given positive results. Then they conducted their own experiments. These were eventually successful in determining the cause of polio and how to prevent it.

Certain substances from the blood of polio victims were injected into monkeys. This and other experiments helped prove that polio was caused by a virus. The virus was then killed with chemicals, and this vaccine was injected into test animals. The animals that received the dead virus were found to be immune to polio when exposed to the living virus.

The experiment was then carried a step further. The vaccine was tested in humans! Over 400,000 children were inoculated. Half were inoculated with the vaccine. The other half received a harmless material. At the end of the year, it was clear that the group that received the vaccine suffered far fewer cases of polio than the group that received the harmless material. Scientists had solved a problem that had plagued people for centuries.

This solution to an old problem was possible for several reasons. First of all, the tools needed for researching the problem were available. Information recorded by many scientists over a period of years was gathered. Above all, the most important factor was the use of proper techniques in problem solving. The scientists who worked on the polio vaccine planned their work carefully. They followed a procedure that led them step by step to the discovery of a life-saving vaccine.

All the problem titles in this book are in the form of questions. On page 5, for instance, Problem 1-1 is titled, "What can you observe without using your eyes?" You will perform experiments to answer the questions posed in the problem headings. While you work, try to take notes on all the things you observe taking place. The information you gather will be used to answer questions based on your experimental results.

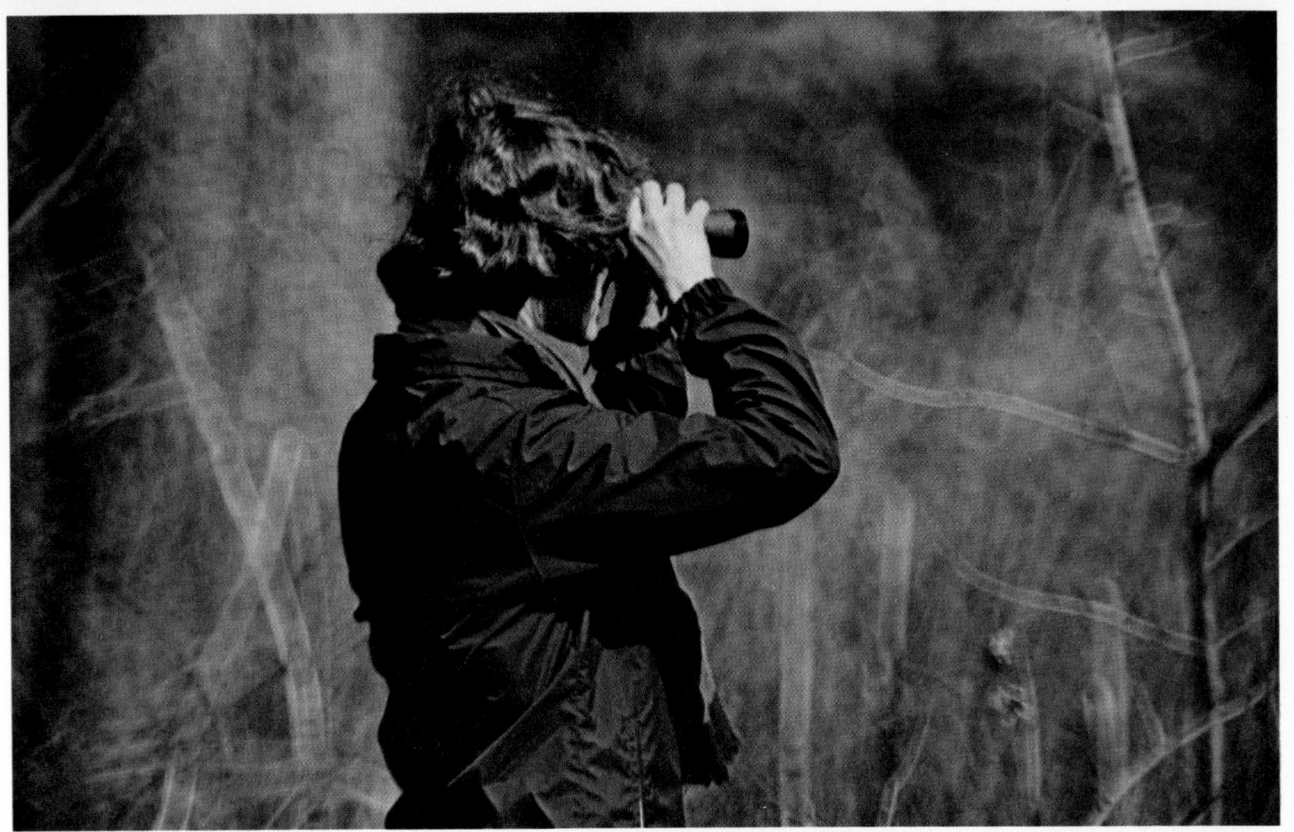

Chapter 1 Gathering and storing information

For suggestions for demonstrations on the first day of class, see Teacher's Guide section.

Chapter-opening photo illustrates the concept of visual observation. Problem 1-1 deals with observations that can be made *without* using the eyes.

"There is none so blind as they that won't see." So said Jonathan Swift, the author of *Gulliver's Travels*. He was referring to people who refuse to see, perhaps because of prejudice or ignorance. Sometimes we really want to see but may look at something and be unaware of its importance. When a movie is shown in class, some students will observe things that other students don't. Different students remember different things. Each student decides which things are important or worth remembering and which are not.

The same thing happens when eyewitnesses to an accident are asked to describe what they saw. Very different accounts of the same accident are often given. Different people see the same things and then unconsciously decide what to remember. Some people attach so little importance to what they see that they remember very little unless they are told exactly what to look for.

You should not confuse an observation with an interpretation. An **observation** is the careful inspection of some object or event. Most often observations are made with the eyes. You will use your other senses to test your powers of observation in Problem 1-1. Observation may give information about *who, when, where,* or *what* happened.

When you try to answer *why* something happened, then you are making an **interpretation.** Suppose you see a clear liquid turn purple when it is poured into a clean container. That is an observation. If you tried to explain why it changed to purple, that would be an interpretation.

If you think something you have seen is really important, you will want to write it down. If you saw the license number of a car in a hit-and-run accident, you would try to write it down before you forgot it. In science experiments certain information is going to be important. Problem 1-2 deals with collecting and recording such information.

Be sure to keep a notebook and pencil handy during all lab sessions. Your notebook becomes your record of all the observations you make during each experiment.

In long research projects, many scientists may work on a single experiment. They each keep notes. The notes are then stored in a computer. When people want to know the results of any part of the experiment, they get them from the computer.

Another way to store information is microfilm. Photographs are made of the written records using a special camera and film. Each roll of film is smaller than a dime, yet it can hold dozens of pictures. A special projector is used to enlarge each frame of the film for easy viewing.

You will not use a computer or microfilm to store information. You will, however, see how a simple data storage-and-retrieval system works. You will construct one in Problem 1-3 using an index card.

In the final problem in this chapter you will read about an experiment that you might wish to conduct on your own. It involves finding out if birds prefer certain colors of seeds. Pay close attention to the steps that lead to setting up a good experiment. These same procedures will help you to understand all the experiments that you work on throughout the year.

Problem 1-1 What can you observe without using your eyes?

Purpose To use all of your senses except sight to obtain information about objects and events. To learn the difference between observation and interpretation.

Procedure

See Teacher's Guide section for directions for setting up observation stations.

A. The class will be divided in half. One half of the class members will form "testing teams" of two persons each. The other half will form "observing teams" of two persons each.

The testing teams will be assigned to different testing stations. They will remain at these stations throughout the experiment. Each testing team will be made up of a Test Director and a Test Recorder.

The observing teams will also have two students each. One will be blindfolded. The other will serve as a guide for the blindfolded student. The observing teams will visit each of the testing stations. At each station the blindfolded student will make observations and answer questions without help from the guide or anyone else.

B. Each Test Director will be in charge of getting the test materials ready at his or her station and giving each blindfolded student the test.

1-1. Tests determine the observation powers of the blindfolded students.

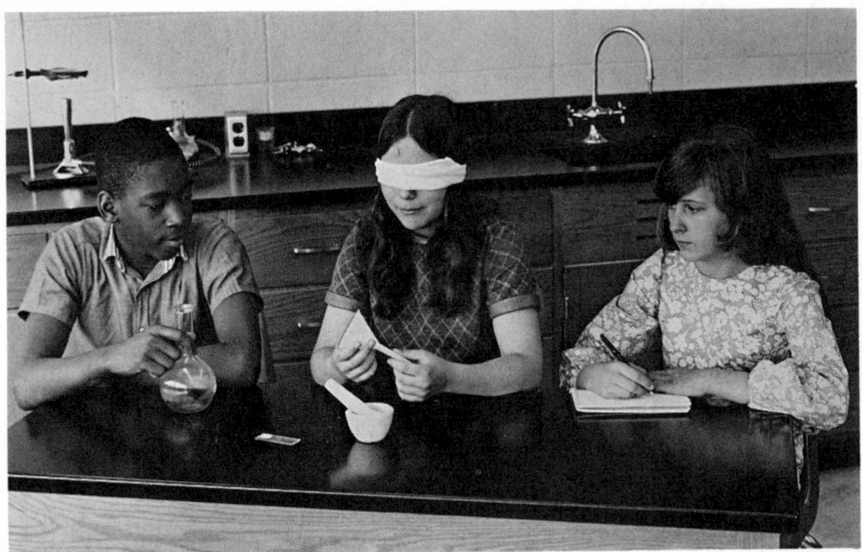

Douglas R. Pens

1. For the sake of consistency.

1. Why should the same person give the test each time?

C. The Test Recorder will write a description of all the responses made by each subject tested at his or her station. The responses should be organized in a chart in the recorder's notebook. (See Table 1-1.)

D. The guide will help the blindfolded student move from station to station. The guide will also be sure that the subject is always blindfolded.

Do not ask for or acknowledge attempts to identify the object by name. An accurate description of what the stimulus sounds, smells, tastes, or feels like is preferable.

E. The blindfolded student will be moved from station to station as time permits. At each station a different test will determine what the students can sense without using their eyes. The subjects must be as exact as possible in describing the stimulus they receive, or what happens to them, at each station. These stimuli may involve the ears, nose, tongue, fingers, or skin. The stimuli will not be harmful in any way. The blindfolded students are to

TABLE 1-1 RECORDED OBSERVATIONS OF BLINDFOLDED STUDENTS
This is a sample table. Copy this table in your notebook. Do not write in this textbook.

Station No. ________

Test Recorders are responsible for completing this chart. The responses will vary, depending on the materials used at the Recorder's station.

Observing Team	*Materials Used*	*Responses Given*
A		
B		
C		
D		
E		
F		
G		
H		

Discussions should be led by Test Recorders. The emphasis is thus on the students' interpretations rather than on the teacher's comments or evaluations.

tell the recorder what they sense from the stimuli. They are to answer all questions asked by the Test Directors as best they can.

F. The information obtained from the blindfolded students will be discussed in class the day after the experiment. The Test Recorders and Test Directors must have their notebook tables complete and ready to discuss.

You should now be able to

Use your ears, hands, nose, and tongue to help you gather information about objects.

Describe certain objects or events without seeing them.

Distinguish between observations and interpretations when making statements about events.

Evaluate observations made by several observers.

Becoming a good observer

While participating in Problem 1-1 you must have realized the importance of sight. You use your eyes not only to see but also to help your other senses. Sounds are heard by the ears. But many times the object making the sound is located by the eyes. And with only the sense of touch, it can be impossible to tell whether an object is hot or cold. Seeing the object often helps you determine its temperature. Your eyes tell you the difference between an ice cube and steam. You *expect* one to be cold and the other to be hot.

To be a good observer, you must use all your senses. You must observe carefully to notice any changes in shape, color, or size. You may be directed to use your senses of touch and smell to determine special information.

When you are directed to smell an unknown chemical, fan the gases toward your nose as shown in Figure 1-2. *Never* put your nose directly over a chemical and inhale. Gases from some chemicals could harm the membranes inside your nose. Tasting an unknown substance can also be dangerous. *Never* do so unless you get specific instructions from your teacher.

Whatever observations you make through any of your senses, you should write them down in a precise manner. These observations will be used to answer questions in the experiments. All the problems in

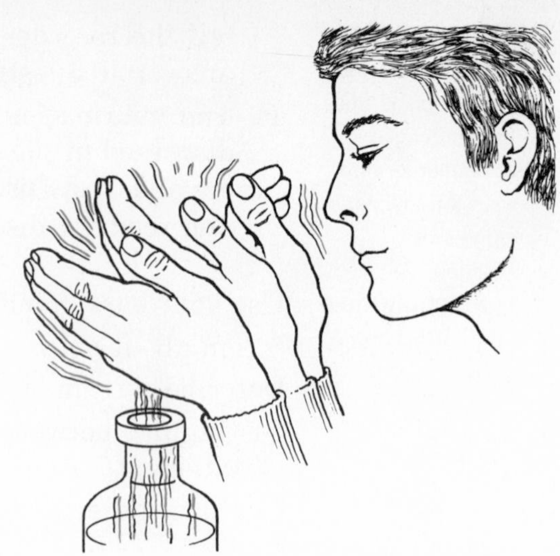

1-2. Never put your face directly over a chemical and inhale. Fan the gas toward you instead.

this book raise questions that you are exepected to answer. The answers to these questions also should be recorded in your notebook. A neat, well-bound set of notes may be used to recall results of previous experiments when you study for tests. You may also use them in future science courses.

Develop a questioning mind. Do not accept the first results you get as a final answer. Ask yourself *why* things happen, *how* they happen, and *how often* they happen. The questions you ask yourself will affect how useful the resulting information will be to you.

1-3. In the metric system a length of one meter (m) equals 100 centimeters (cm). Each centimeter is divided into 10 millimeters (mm).

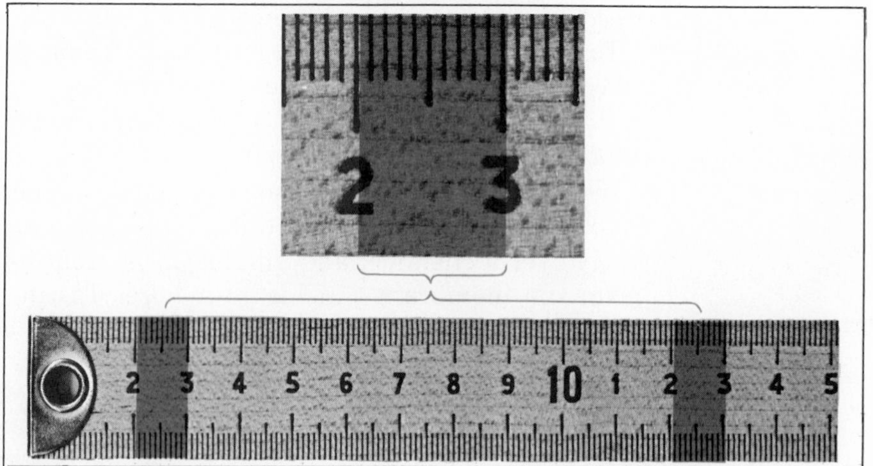

Compare the metric system to the English system of feet, inches, etc. Students should see how much more simple and practical the metric system is.

In the next problem you are going to measure lengths using a meter stick. In the last part of the problem you can record the preferences of your classmates for their favorite flavor of ice cream.

A word about using the meter stick. A **meter** is the basic unit of length in the metric system. A meter is a few inches longer than a yard. The **metric system** of measure is used by most other countries of the world and by most scientists. One of the reasons this system is so widely used is that all its units are related to each other in multiples of ten.

The metric units of length that you will use in Problem 1-2 are the **meter,** the **centimeter,** and the **millimeter.** The prefix *centi-* means "one-hundredth", and the prefix *milli-* means "one-thousandth." Here's how these units relate to each other —

1 meter (m) = 100 centimeters (cm)
1 centimeter = 10 millimeters (mm)
1 meter = 1,000 millimeters

Problem 1-2 How do you collect and record data?

Purpose To use different methods of collecting data and to compare the usefulness of each of the methods.

Materials meter stick

Procedure

To make data available to whole class, draw table on board and have each student fill in his or her name and height.

A. Use a meter stick to measure the height of all the boys or all the girls in your class.

B. In your notebook draw a table like Table 1-2 (page 10) to organize the height measurements.

C. Record the height of each student in your table. *Do not record any data in the tables in this textbook.*

1. What method of collecting data did you use to obtain the heights of the students?

1. Direct measurement with meter stick.

The table that students design in Step D should be similar to Table 1-2, but instead of the column for height, there should be 12 columns for the months of the year.

D. Design a table to record the month in which each student in your class was born. Draw the table in your notebook.

E. Have one student collect information on the month in which each student was born. Record the information in your table.

2. How many categories should you provide to record everyone's birthday?

2. Twelve—one for each month.

3. What advantage do you see in providing several categories for recording information rather than listing each item separately?

3. Information is grouped and easier to interpret.

4. Answers will vary among classes.

5. Answers will vary among classes.

6. Grouping data makes it easier to interpret. One can see at a glance the approximate heights of the tallest and shortest students, and the height ranges into which the majority of students fall. The average height can be inferred.

Emphasize to students that they should copy tables in their notebooks and never write in the textbook.

F. Look again at your table of height measurements (Steps A, B, and C). You can get a better picture of the distribution of those heights by putting them in categories. Table 1-3 shows how this might be done. Copy Table 1-3 into your notebook.

G. Record each individual height in the correct range in the table with a tally mark (x). Three persons in one height range would be shown with three tally marks (xxx).

4. Which height range has the greatest number of students in it?
5. What three height ranges contain the greatest number of individuals?
6. What advantage do you see in recording data in the form of Table 1-3 rather than Table 1-2?

TABLE 1-2 HEIGHT OF STUDENTS MEASURED IN CENTIMETERS

Student	*Height in Centimeters*

If you think your students have a good understanding by now of designing tables for data collection, you may want to skip Steps H and I.

Draw table for Step H on board so students can pool information. For meaningful interpretation of grouping, it is recommended that no more than four flavors be listed for selection.

TABLE 1-3: HEIGHT DISTRIBUTION TABLE

Height Range (Centimeters)	*Number in Range (use a tally mark (x) to record each individual's height)*
more than 179	
175–179	
170–174	
165–169	
160–164	
155–159	
150–154	
145–149	
140–144	
135–139	
130–134	
125–129	
120–124	
less than 120	

7. Answers will vary, but 4 are recommended.
8. Answers will vary.
9. If "yes," there should have been a column labeled "other."
10. Distribution of tally marks would have been broader, with fewer in the most popular columns.
11. *Height:* direct measurement. *Birthday:* questions and answers based on facts. *Ice cream:* questions and answers based on preferences.

H. Design a table to record the favorite ice cream flavor of each student in the class. Use your own judgment to restrict the choices of flavors that can be named.

I. Have one class member collect information on the flavor of ice cream preferred by each member of your class. Record the flavor choices in the table in your notebook.

7. How many ice cream flavors did you use in your table?
8. Which flavor was preferred by the most students?
9. Did you allow for recording the preference of students who liked unusual flavors best? If so, how?
10. If the number of flavor choices used had been greater, how could this have affected the results of your survey?
11. What different methods were used to obtain information on an individual's height, birthday, and ice cream preference?

You should now be able to

Use a measuring device to obtain data directly.
Obtain data by observation.
Organize the data collected in the form of a table.
Ask questions that give useful data.

Storing information

A lot of information was collected in the last problem. You measured heights and recorded birthdays. And you surveyed individual preferences for something most people like — ice cream. The reason for all that was to get experience in collecting data and recording it in an organized way. Such data might be useful if you wished to compare heights in one class to those in another. Or you might use the data on ice cream choices to advise ice cream makers which flavors to make more of.

Information noted in the laboratory must be recorded and stored in a useful manner. It should be easy to find when needed. Sometimes the stored information is in large quantities and must be retrieved or recalled quickly. Card catalogs and microfilm are systems used to store and locate data quickly.

The most rapid means of storing data and retrieving it on demand is by the use of electronic computers. Many businesses make daily

1-4. You can find a book in a library by looking in the card catalog for either the book title or the author's name on the cards.

1-5. The electronic computer can store thousands of bits of information. Whenever data are needed, they can be sorted by the computer, printed on a tape, and read by the operator.

use of computers. They depend heavily on them for storing a vast amount of information that may be needed later.

In the next problem you will prepare an information storage card. You will use it to store the answers to ten questions. The information storage cards will be able to store only yes-or-no answers. So the questions have been carefully phrased. Perhaps you know of a business that could use this simple, but useful, approach to storing information.

Problem 1-3 How can you store information?

Purpose To use a sorting method to store and retrieve information.

Materials

index cards, 3″ × 5″, lined on one side	scissors	paper punch
	ruler	knitting needle

Procedure Each student in the class must prepare the lined side of identical index cards in the same way. Any mistake in the preparation of a card will make it useless for this experiment.

A. With the red line of the index card at the top, locate the upper right-hand corner of the card. From the corner, measure a length of 1 centimeter along each edge. (See Figure 1-6.) Make a pencil mark at both points and connect them with a straight line as shown. Cut off the corner.

This is done so that when the cards are put together in a pack the cut edges can be lined up. Then all the cards will be right side up and facing the same direction.

Instruct students to hold the paper punch so that the hole in the punch is above the card. This permits them to see the card and to punch the holes in the proper places.

B. Look at the card in Figure 1-7. As shown there, draw a vertical line 1 cm in from both the left and the right edges of your card. Then punch a hole as shown, in the space between the red line and the first blue line. Try to punch this and all the holes so that one edge of the hole is on the 1-cm line. The punched holes should be centered between the printed lines on the card.

Skip a space, then punch another hole between the next two lines. Repeat the punching procedure until you have five holes on each side of the card. (See Figure 1-8.)

C. As shown in Figure 1-8, label the holes on the left-hand side from top to bottom 1, 2, 3, 4, 5. Label the holes under the cut edge 6, 7, 8, 9, 10. In the space above the red line, print your name, class period, and the title "Series A." The next card you may make, with different questions, would be "Series B." As the caption for Figure 1-8 tells you, you have made a *Knit-Pick* card.

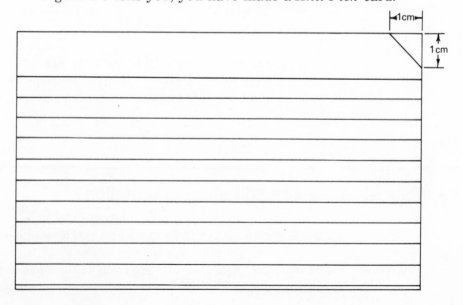

1-6. Measure in from the edge, then remove the upper right corner from the marked index card.

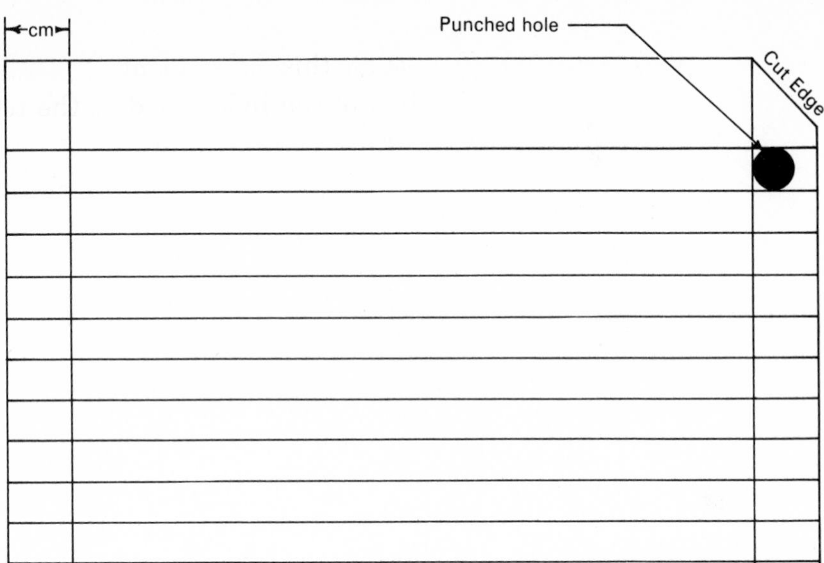

1-7. Punch out a hole on every other line.

1-8. A completed Knit-Pick card.

D. The Knit-Pick system you are making is useful only when yes-or-no questions are asked. In Step E, you will be answering such questions. And you will store your answers on the card you have just made.

To store a "yes" answer, you will use scissors to cut from the edge of the card to the top and bottom of the hole next to the question. (See Figure 1-9.) If your answer to a question is "no", you will leave the hole unchanged. All the cards with "yes" answers to a particular question can then be found easily. Simply insert a

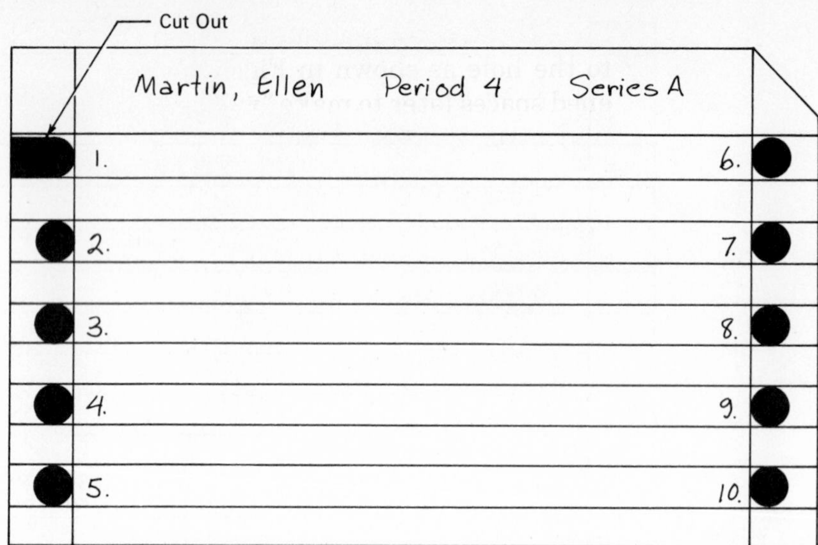

1-9. If the answer to a question is "yes", open the punched hole to the edge of the card.

1. They will stay in the pack and not fall off the needle.

2. They will fall off the needle and out of the pack.

3. Its information would not correspond to the other cards in the pack. It would be "misfiled."

knitting needle through the hole next to that question and lift the pack of cards with the needle. (See Figure 1-10.)

1. What will happen to the cards in which the answer to a particular question is "no"?
2. What will happen to the cards in which the answer is "yes"?

Arranging the cards by the cut corners ensures that the same hole numbers line up for each card in the stack.

3. What could happen in the sorting process if a punched card was turned the opposite way from the other cards in the stack?

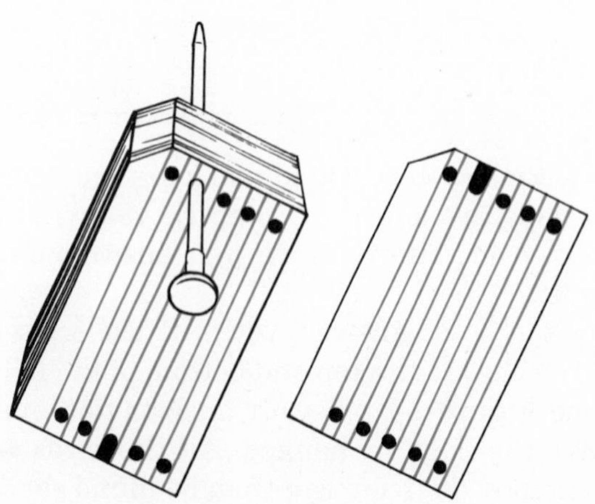

1-10. Sorting the Knit-Pick cards with a knitting needle.

E. Answer the following numbered questions on your Knit-Pick card. If you answer a question "yes", darken the outer space next to the hole as shown in Figure 1-11. You will cut out the darkened spaces later to make "yes" answers. If you answer a question "no", do not put a mark on the card.

Remind students that only questions requiring yes-or-no answers may be used in this kind of system.

1. Are you 13 years old or older?
2. Do you have light blonde hair?
3. Are you a female?
4. Do you always walk to school?
5. Are your eyes brown?
6. Are you enrolled in a speech or drama class?
7. Do you live within 4 blocks of the school?
8. Do you like liver and onions?
9. Do you like to read?
10. Would you like to do a science project?

1-11. Marking the Knit-Pick card.

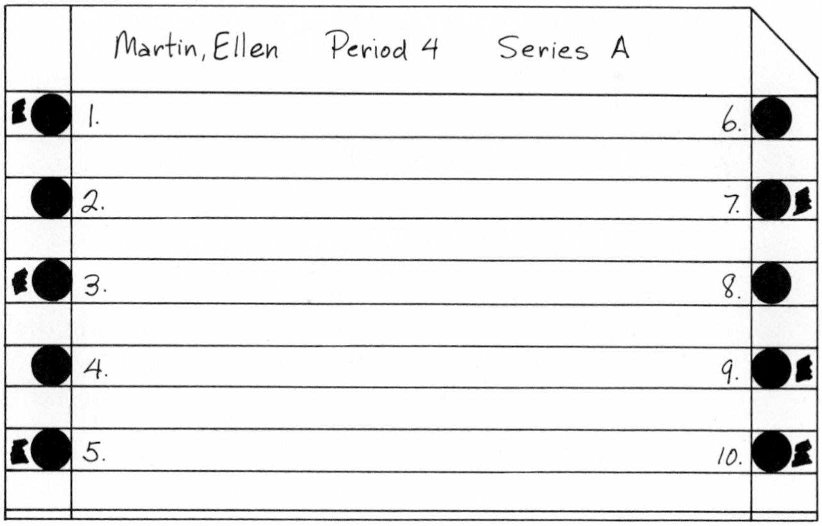

F. You should now have marked all your "yes" answers by darkening the spaces next to the holes. Cut through to these holes as described in Step D.

Have one student handle the cards and have another student list the number of "yes" answers to each question on the board.

G. The cards will be collected from all class members. One person will then use a knitting needle to retrieve information for the whole class.

4. Answer should be the number of cards that dropped off the needle for Question 8.
6. The cards of students who do not like liver.
7. Answers will vary among classes.
8. By putting needle into Hole 5, and allowing the "yes" cards to drop out of the pack.
9. Take the cards with "yes" answers to Hole 5, stack them together, and insert needle into Hole 8. Those that fall off have brown eyes *and* like liver and onions.

H. Use your knowledge of the Knit-Pick system and the information from Step G to answer the following questions.

4. How many members of your class like liver and onions?
5. Into which hole would you insert the knitting needle to get the answer to question 4? 5. Into Hole 8.
6. What cards remain on the needle after the sorting process?
7. How many people in your class have brown eyes?
8. How did you get the answer to question 7? Explain.
9. How would you use the Knit-Pick system to find out how many people have brown eyes and also like liver and onions?

One of the most important things to remember about the Knit-Pick system is the type of question that must be asked.

10. What type of answer is required when asking a question for this system? 10. Yes or no.
11. Write in your notebook several sample questions that could be used in a system such as this.

You should now be able to

Construct Knit-Pick cards to store information in an organized way.
Retrieve information that has been stored on Knit-Pick cards.
Organize questions to get only yes-or-no answers.

---

11. Appropriate questions will be those having yes-or-no answers.

Experimental design

Experiments are conducted to find the answers to questions. When cooks change recipes to see if better-tasting dishes result, they are conducting experiments. What determines the results of a cooking experiment? The response of the people who eat the food, of course. If they like the new recipe better, the change is an improvement and will be accepted.

If most of these people leave the food on their plates, then the change is a failure and will have to be discarded. Notice that we did not say that the *experiment* was a failure. It was successful in answering the question of whether the changed recipe would produce a better-tasting dish.

This example can be used to point out some essential features of a good experiment. One essential feature is a clear statement of the question to be answered. In the example given, the question is clearly whether a change in the recipe will inprove the taste of the dish.

Next a plan must be made to find the answer to that question. The cook changes something about the recipe in order to change the resulting flavor. What should the new dish be compared to? It should be compared to the dish made from the original recipe. The original, or unchanged, part of an experiment is called the **control**.

How are the two dishes to be compared? The standards for comparison might be their appearance, aroma, or, much more meaningfully, their taste. Should the cook accept the reaction of just one or two people? Probably not. The reactions of a large number of people should be obtained. Then the cook will be more certain that the response represents the reaction of most people who might sample his or her cooking.

The cook should also make sure that only one ingredient or direction has changed from the original recipe. Then the final dish will be different in only one way from the original. This way, the cook can be sure of just what caused the flavor to change.

Suppose the changed recipe is an improvement How can the cook be sure to prepare that dish the same way the next time? By recording exactly how the recipe was changed. And the cook must also be able to find the new recipe again when it is needed. What if other cooks wish to use the new recipe? Should they expect to get the same results as the original cook did? Yes, they should if they follow directions carefully.

The "ingredients" of a good experiment, then, may be summarized as follows:

It is very important that students understand these basic requirements of experimental design. Discuss Problem 1-4 in terms of these 6 steps. You may wish to design several hypothetical experiments with the class, seeing that the six requirements are fulfilled.

1. State exactly what the problem is that must be solved.
2. Use any previous knowledge that is available to help solve the problem.
3. Design the experiment to change only one thing at a time in order to determine the effect.
4. Keep all parts of one experiment unchanged to serve as a control.
5. Analyze the results of the experiment with an open mind. Do not insist that every experiment turn out just the way you thought it would.
6. Keep an accurate record of what you did and what the results were. Make notes throughout the experiment. This will allow both you and others to check your results when the experiment is repeated.

In Problem 1-4 you will be given information about an experiment designed to test the food preferences of birds. Keep in mind the "ingredients" of a good experiment. See how many of them you can recognize in the next problem.

Problem 1-4 How is an experiment set up and interpreted?

Purpose To recognize the essential steps that should be followed when setting up an experiment. To learn the difference between an observation and an interpretation.

Procedure

A. A group of students wanted to know if birds choose the seeds they eat strictly by the color. The students knew that birds like to eat small, red, round sorghum seeds. They decided to use this type of seed in an experiment to find out which color birds would choose if they had several choices.

B. The students attached a cupcake pan to a platform on the end of a long pole. They set up the pole at the end of a field near some trees. In one of the sections of the cupcake pan, they placed twenty-five natural red sorghum seeds. They then used some odorless and tasteless food coloring to color separate batches of sorghum seeds yellow, blue, pink, and green.

Twenty-five seeds of each color were placed in separate sections of the pan atop the pole. Each day for two weeks the students counted how many seeds remained in each section of the pan. Each day they recorded the number of seeds missing (eaten). And each day they replaced the missing seeds so there would again be twenty-five seeds of each color in the pan. Table 1-4 shows the record of seeds eaten during the two-week period.

1. Whether birds choose seeds according to color.

1. What problem were the students trying to solve in this experiment?

1-12. Each day the cupcake pan started out with 25 seeds of each color.

TABLE 1-4 NUMBER OF SEEDS EATEN

Seed Color	*Day of Experiment*														*Total*
	1	2	3	4	5	6	7	8	9	10	11	12	13	14	
Natural (Red)	23	24	23	24	22	20	20	23	23	24	25	23	22	24	320
Blue	18	21	12	11	12	14	8	11	15	7	9	12	10	7	157
Green	10	12	14	7	9	1	0	0	4	2	11	20	7	1	98
Pink	22	21	19	20	22	23	22	23	23	19	22	20	22	21	299
Yellow	5	15	7	2	4	6	5	8	4	1	2	7	5	4	75

C. To compare results, two related experiments are usually done at the same time. One group has a single factor that is changed. This is the **experimental group.**

2. Which part of the seed experiment could be called the experimental group or groups?

2. The pink, blue, green, and yellow seeds. (The pink seeds are almost like the red, but they must still be considered experimental, since they are not the natural color.)

Another part of the experiment keeps everything unchanged or as natural as possible. This is the **control group.**

3. Which part of the seed experiment was left unchanged as a control group?

3. Natural red seeds.

The single factor that is changed between the experimental and control groups is called the **variable factor.** The other factors are kept the same for both groups. They are called **control factors.** You can analyze the results of an experiment by comparing the experimental group with the control group.

4. What was the variable factor in the seed experiment?
5. What were some factors that were kept the same (control factors) for both the experimental and the control groups?

4. Seed color.

5. Number and type of seeds; containers; location.

D. One **observation** of the results of the experiment would be that the favorite color of seed in the experimental group was pink.

6. What are two other observations of the experimental results that you could make?

6. Birds ate more red seeds than any other kind. Birds ate fewer yellow seeds than any other color. (Check to be sure that answers are observations and not interpretations.)

One **interpretation** of the results might be that the reason pink seeds were the most popular is that they looked most like the natural color of the red sorghum seeds.

7. Which of the three statements that follow could be classed as an interpretation?
   a. Fewer yellow seeds were eaten on the average than any other experimental seed color.
   b. Birds eat yellow seeds only by accident, since so few were eaten.
   c. Birds must like the color red and dislike the color yellow, since they ate a lot of red seeds but very few yellow seeds.

7. Statements b and c.

E. Sometimes the results of an experiment raise other questions. One such question that could be raised about this experiment is, "Do birds always prefer pink or red seeds over other colors?"

8. Explain how you could set up a similar experiment to answer the above question, this time using seeds such as corn seeds.
9. How could you change the original experiment to restrict the size of bird that could eat the seeds?

8. Dye corn seeds and follow Step B, p. 20.

9. Enclose the seeds in a container, such as a bird house, that has an opening large enough to permit only small birds to enter.

You should now be able to

Recognize the basic parts of a controlled experiment.
Recognize a variable factor in an experiment.
Recognize control factors in an experiment.
Design a controlled experiment to solve a problem.

---

1. Sight.
2. Fan a small amount of the vapor toward your nose. Never inhale the vapors directly.
3. Use your senses. Notes may be used to check experimental results, for comparison with other students' results, to refer back to for data, and to study from.
4. Metric.
5. All units in the metric system are based on multiples of ten. There is no such easy conversion factor in the English system.
6. Meter, centimeter, and millimeter.
7. Notebooks, charts, information systems.
8. Photographs, microfilms, Knit-Pick cards, etc.
9. The "yes" answers had holes opened; these cards fell off the knitting needle.
10. The control group.
11. The experimental group.

Science terms

centimeter
control factors
control group
experimental group
interpretation
meter
metric system
millimeter
observation
variable factor

Review questions

1. Which one of your many senses do you use the most to receive stimuli?
2. How should you smell an unknown material?
3. What must you use in order to make good observations? In what way(s) could you use the notes taken on each experiment?
4. What system of measurement is used for most scientific work in the world?
5. Why is it easier to change from one measurement unit to another in the metric system than it is in the system usually used in the United States?
6. What are three metric units of length mentioned in this chapter?
7. How should you store the information you get from your experiments?
8. Name two methods of storing information.
9. How were the "yes" answers found when you used the Knit-Pick cards?
10. What is the part of an experiment that is kept the same throughout the experiment?
11. What is the part of an experiment that has been changed from what it usually is?

Check your understanding

See Teacher's Guide section for answers to Questions 12-18.

12. What sense(s) might you use to determine which room you were in if you were blindfolded in your own home?

13. Why was it helpful to restrict the number of flavors when you gathered information about ice cream?
14. How would you organize a Knit-Pick card system to find out which school clubs are preferred by the students in your class?
15. Why was it essential that all of the punched cards used in Problem 1-3 be prepared exactly alike?
16. What was done to make sure the punched cards would all be stacked facing the same direction?
17. Explain the difference between an observation and an interpretation.
18. Explain why an experiment may have several control factors but only one variable factor.

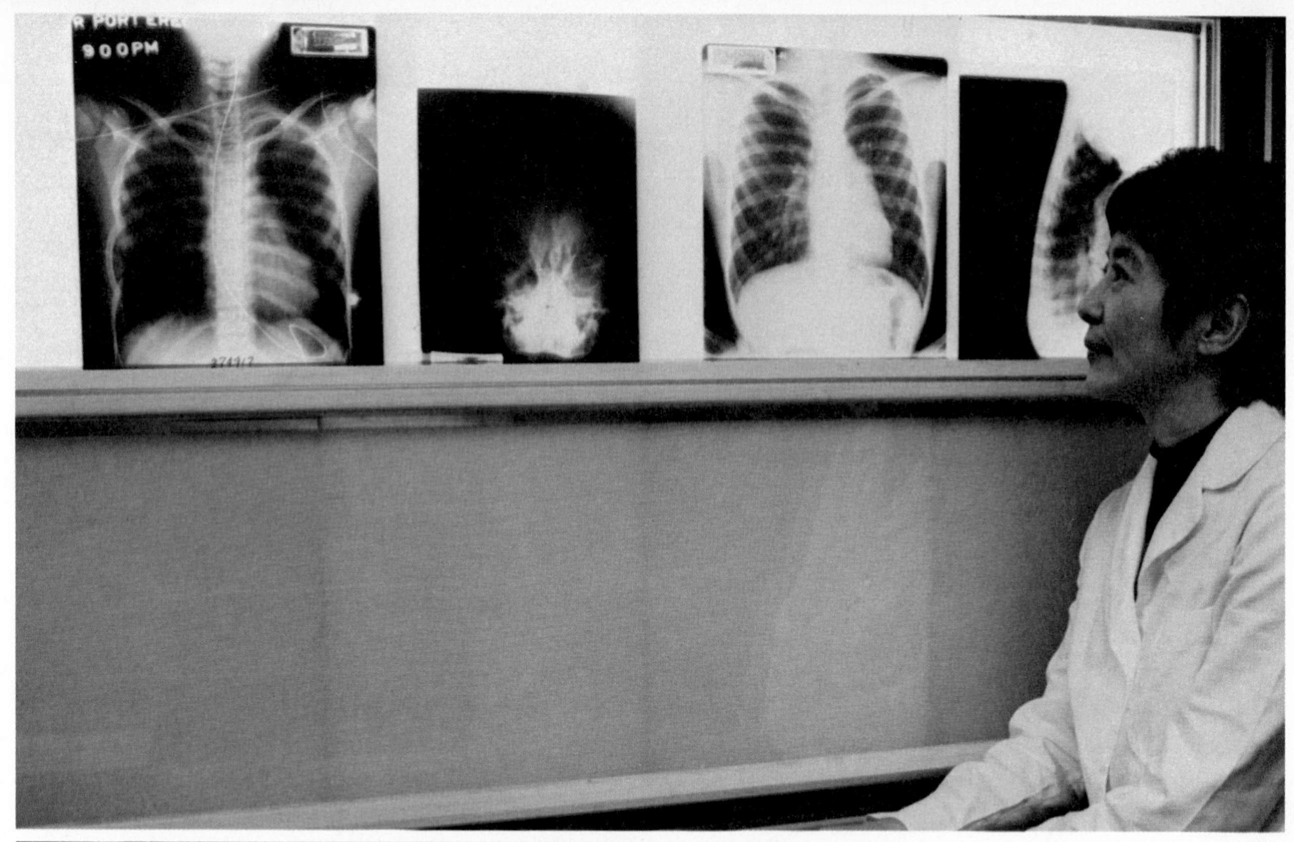

Chapter 2 Organizing and interpreting information

Chapter-opening photo illustrates one of the many forms information can take. Unlike most graphs that students will interpret during this course, interpreting the information on X rays is not always a cut-and-dry procedure.

A woman wanted to keep a record of her son's growth. She started on the boy's sixth birthday. Then and each year afterwards, the mother cut a length of board equal to the boy's height. She nailed the boards to a wall of her garage.

After 12 years, the woman stopped making measurements. She studied the pattern shown by the 12 boards. At a glance she could see the child's growth pattern for the 12-year span. By measuring the difference in the length of each board, she could tell how much the boy had grown in any one year. The total growth during the 12 years was equal to the distance between the top of the shortest board and the top of the longest board.

Suppose a number scale had been marked along the side of the boards to show the length of the boards. And suppose another scale

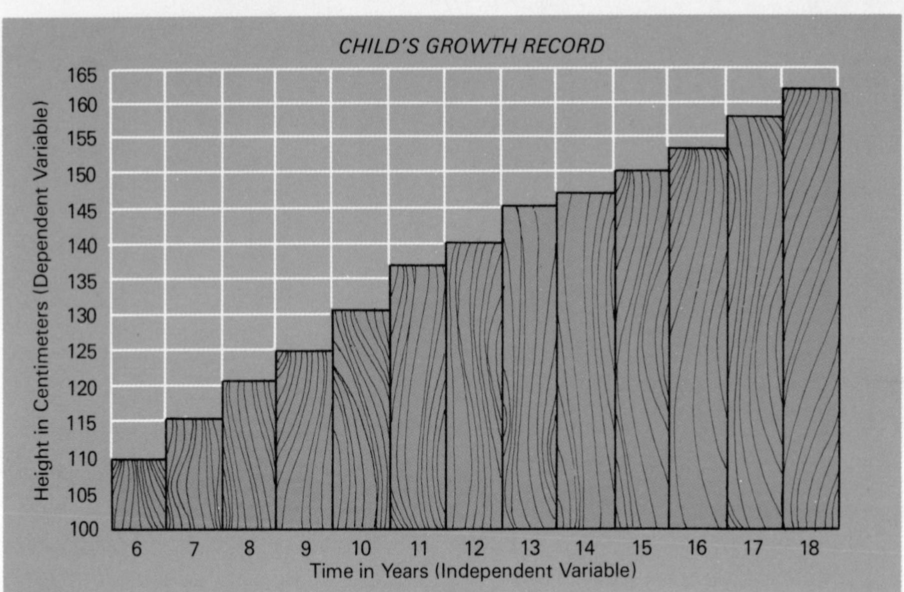

2-1. If a child's growth is marked every year with boards on a wall, the arrangement of boards forms a graph.

had been marked across the bottom of the boards to show the time in years. The boards would have formed a picturelike presentation, which we could call a **graph.** This is shown in Figure 2-1.

Graphs are used to show numerical data about how objects or events change. The "board graph" just described showed the change in the height of the child over a long span of time. These two related sets of information, height and years, are called the **variables** in the record. The one that is determined in advance is called the **independent variable.** In the example, that was the time in years. The independent variable is most often placed on the **horizontal axis,** or the bottom of the graph.

Discuss the difference between dependent and independent variables, using several examples.

The other variable, in this case the child's height, is called the **dependent variable.** It is "dependent" because it is affected by, or changes with, the independent variable. The child's height depended on the time the height was measured. The dependent variable is most often shown on the **vertical axis.** Its number scale is marked along the left side of the graph.

By showing each year's height with a different board, the mother organized data about her son's height. The pattern of boards against the wall showed a type of graph called a **bar graph.** Bar graphs are simple and are commonly used to show experimental results.

Another type of graph, a **line graph,** could have been used to show the relationship between the boy's height and age. Such a graph is shown in Figure 2-2. The line graph shows the growth record in much the same way as the bar graph did. At a glance you can see the trend of height increasing with age. You should note several features of the line graph because you will be preparing one in Problem 2-1.

Observe the horizontal axis. It is labeled "Age in Years" to show the variable that is recorded along it. Notice the number scale below the horizontal axis. The numbers are evenly spaced below the grid lines on the graph. The scale is sufficient to record all the years for which height data are given (ages 6 through 18).

The same details are seen in the preparation of the vertical axis. This axis represents the child's height each year it was measured. The number scale in centimeters is evenly spaced along this axis.

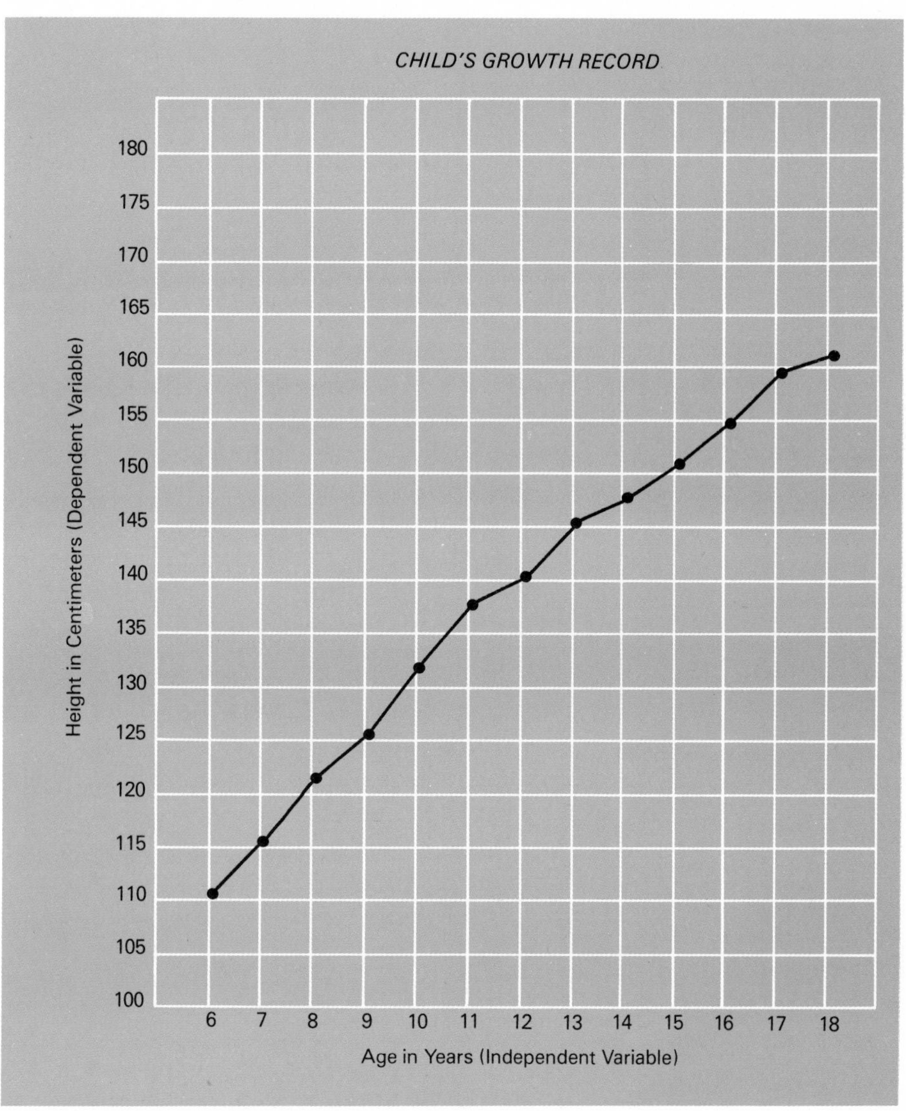

2-2. A line graph showing a child's growth.

The graph is prepared by first marking the **plot points.** These are shown as small circles and represent each height/age relationship. The plot points are connected by a smooth line called the **slope line.** It shows the relationship that exists between age and height for the child over the 12-year period measurements were made. Graphs provide a visual representation of data.

In the next problem you will be given numerical information (**data**) and asked to organize it in a table. From the data in the table, you will be able to construct a bar graph and a line graph to show the results of an experiment.

Problem 2-1 How may information be presented in tables and graphs?

Purpose To learn to prepare tables and graphs from collected experimental data.

Materials graph paper colored pencils or pens (3)

Procedure A student had three pets — a hamster, a mouse, and a rat — each in its own cage. While caring for the pets, the student became interested in the amount of daily activity shown by each animal. The student decided to measure how many times each animal rotated (turned) its exercise wheel. Connecting a meter to each of the three wheels, the student read the meters every day for five days. The results showed the following information.

On Day 1: the hamster turned the wheel 98 times; the mouse, 104 times; the rat, 33 times.

On Day 2: the hamster turned the wheel 84 times; the mouse, 114 times; the rat, 24 times.

On Day 3: the hamster turned the wheel 92 times; the mouse, 110 times; the rat, 30 times.

On Day 4: the hamster turned the wheel 64 times; the mouse, 94 times; the rat, 26 times.

On Day 5: the hamster turned the wheel 72 times; the mouse, 88 times; the rat, 22 times.

You will use the data from this experiment to learn how information may be presented in tables and graphs.

2-3. The machine (*above*) records the number of times that the hamster turns the wheel.

Part One: Preparing a data table

A. The results of the experiment just described have been recorded. But the data have not been organized in tabular form. Make a table in your notebook similar to Table 2-1. Use the data given for each pet to complete the table.

1. What is the independent variable in this experiment?
2. What is the dependent variable?

1. The number of days the experiment was conducted.
2. The number of times each animal turned the wheel.

B. Calculate the *average* daily number of turns for each pet. (For each pet, add the results for each of the five days and divide the

You may need to review the procedure for finding an average.

TABLE 2-1 TURNS ON EXERCISE WHEEL BY THREE DIFFERENT ANIMALS

	Rotations of Exercise Wheel		
Day	*Hamster*	*Mouse*	*Rat*
1	98	104	33
2	84	114	24
3	92	110	30
4	64	94	26
5	72	88	22
Total	410	510	135
Average	82	102	27

See annotated Table 2-1 for how students' completed tables should look.

total by five.) The average number of turns an animal completed per day is an important bit of information. It represents the amount of activity that could be expected.

3. Data are organized and grouped, making it easier to see relationships and to make comparisons.

C. In the row marked "Average" in your notebook table, enter your findings from Step B.

3. How does a data table make information easier to examine?

Part Two: Preparing a bar graph

A bar graph is used chiefly to show comparisons between different objects or events. You will make a bar graph to compare the average activity of the three animals. The table you made in Part One will provide the data you need.

A bar graph is prepared by first drawing the axes. Axis lines are arranged vertically and horizontally as in Figure 2-4. The vertical axis is sometimes called the **y-axis**. The horizontal axis is the **x-axis.**

The objects being compared are written just below the x-axis line. There should be an even spacing between notations. For this graph, the names of the animals tested will be used.

The vertical axis, or y-axis, will be used for the average number of times each animal turned its exercise wheel each day. You will need to put a number scale along the y-axis. And the scale must have enough range to record the data for all three animals. Since the highest average number of turns was 102, the vertical scale must include numbers that large. The numbers should be evenly spaced and lie next to the horizontal lines on the graph paper.

D. On a sheet of graph paper draw the x-axis and the y-axis. Copy the number scale and axis labels shown in Figure 2-4.

E. First plot the hamster's average activity. Your table from Part One should list this as 82 turns per day. Draw a line to mark the top of a bar across from where 82 would be on the vertical axis. This line should be directly above the name "Hamster." Draw vertical lines to mark the sides of the bar. Shade in the area inside the bar.

Students' completed graphs should be similar to the bar graph shown in Figure 2-4.

F. In a similar fashion, plot the average number of turns listed in your table for the mouse and the rat.

From the heights of the bars it is easy to see which animal was most active, which was least active, and how the three animals compare in average activity.

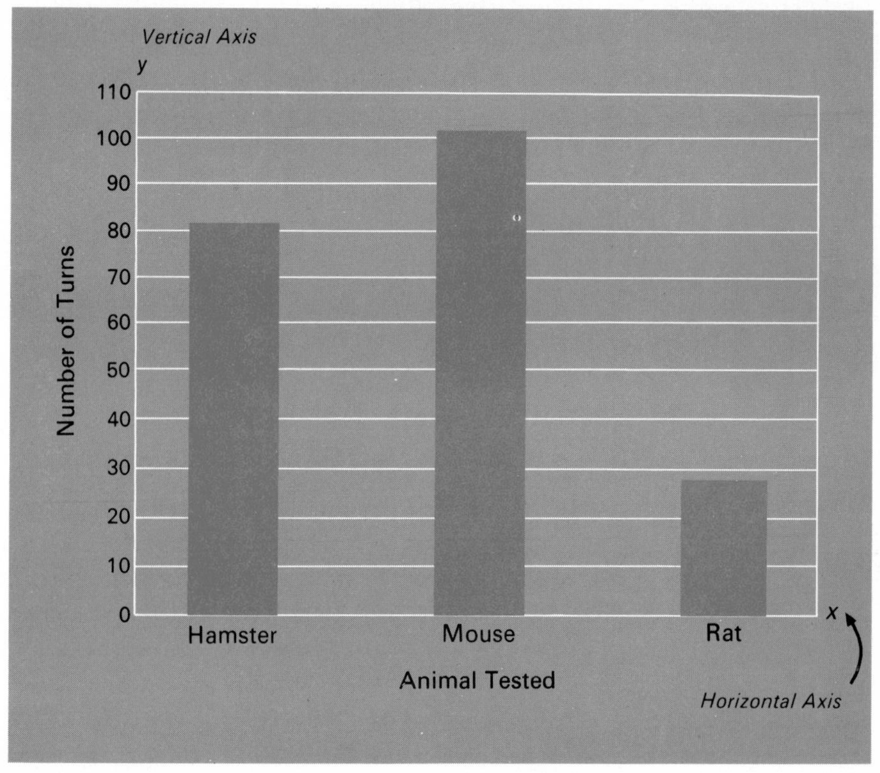

2-4. Axes for a bar graph. It is important to use unit spacings of equal amounts. On this y- axis, for example, the units go up by tens (0, 10, 20, . . .). And the grid lines must be evenly spaced to show how the plot points compare on the same scale.

Part Three: Preparing a line graph

See annotated Figure 2-5, p. 33, for how students' completed graphs should appear.

Now you will prepare a line graph to show the daily activity of the three animals tested. This time you won't use an average. You will plot the actual number of turns each day for each animal.

G. On a sheet of graph paper, draw the two axes as before. This time label the x-axis "Day" and the y-axis "Number of Turns." (See Figure 2-5.) Number the two axis scales so that all the data you have to plot may be represented.

H. Use a symbol such as a small triangle for hamster plot points. Mark a plot point for the activity of the hamster on Day 1. This point should be marked directly above the *1* on the x-axis and across from *98* on the y-axis.

I. Continue to mark the plot points until the data for the hamster for all five days are plotted. Use a colored pencil to draw the slope line for the hamster. It should connect all five plot points.

J. Now plot the data for the mouse for the five-day period. Use a different symbol for your plot points than you used for the hamster. And use a different colored pencil to connect the five plot points.

K. Repeat the plotting process for the five-day activity of the rat. Use a third symbol for your plot points. Connect the points using a different colored pencil than the two used before.

L. The completed graph should have three different colored lines. Each slope line represents the number of wheel rotations from one day to the next for each animal.

4. Which animal recorded the highest activity on a single day?
5. Which animal showed the greatest change in activity over the five-day period?
6. What two observations can you make about the rat's activities over the five-day period?
7. What would happen to the average of the mouse's activity if it showed no movement one day?
8. How could the graph be used to tell the average activity of the mouse on the days it was well?

Compare your completed line graph with the data that was originally provided to you on page 28. Compare it with the data table you made and with the bar graph you made. Data tables, bar graphs, and line graphs are all methods of organizing information. Such organization lets you see relationships and patterns that are not so easily seen otherwise. And this is the first step in making sound interpretations.

4. The mouse.
5. The hamster. On the first day, it turned the wheel 98 times. On the fourth day, it turned the wheel only 64 times. The difference between its maximum and minimum activity was 34 turns.
6. It showed less activity and less variation in amount of activity than the other two.
7. The graph would show a mark at the zero point, and the average of the mouse's five days' activity would be much lower.
8. Choose a straight line parallel to the x-axis whose value seems to best represent the average of the four points showing the activity of the mouse on the days it was well. This should be done by examining the graph rather than computing the average.

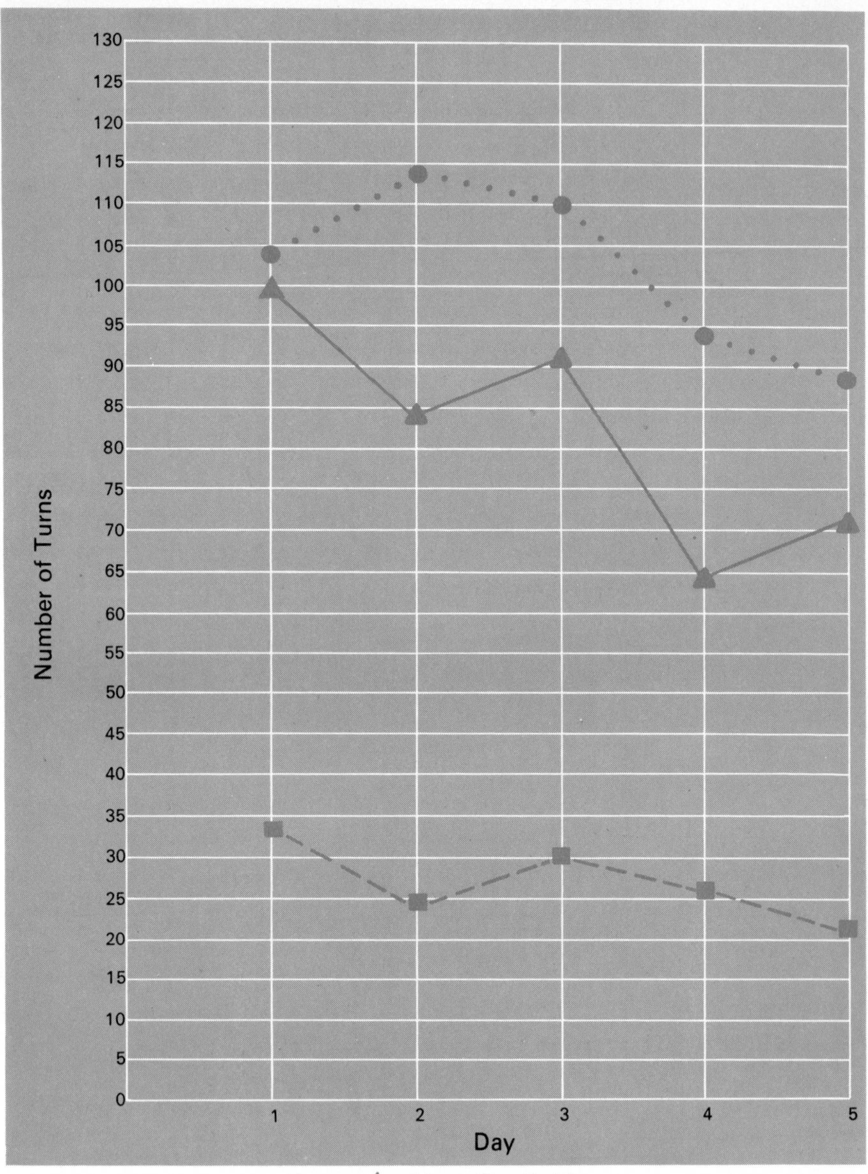

2-5. Axes for a line graph of each animal's daily activity.

You should now be able to

Present data in the form of tables.

Present data in the form of a bar graph or a line graph.

Determine the independent variable and the dependent variable in an experiment.

Using line graphs and bar graphs

Remind students that in the last problem they used a bar graph to compare the average activity of three animals, but used a line graph to compare how the activity of each animal changed from day to day. The line graph in this case was used to compare three individual sets of data.

Tables and graphs are very useful tools in science. Tables organize information from experiments. Graphs summarize the information and present it like a picture. By the use of graphs, trends in behavior can be readily identified. A bar graph may be used to compare two or more individual items. But a line graph is usually the one to use when you want to see how two or more sets of data *change* over a period of time. The line connecting the dots shows the trend in performance of an item, person, or object.

Some students wanted to find out how the temperature of water in a small beaker would change after an ice cube was added. They measured the temperature in the beaker before the ice was added. Then they added the ice cube and measured the temperature of the water each minute for the next ten minutes. Their data are shown in Table 2-2.

In Figure 2-6, a line graph has been prepared to show the information in the table. Notice that the bottom of the graph is labeled for the time in minutes. The time intervals were defined by the students. Therefore, time is the independent variable. The dependent variable is temperature. It is shown along the vertical axis of the graph.

Before the ice was added, the water temperature was 22°C. This, then, is the temperature plotted at zero minutes. The readings each

TABLE 2-2 TEMPERATURE CHANGE AFTER ADDITION OF ICE CUBE TO A SMALL BEAKER OF WATER

Time in Minutes	*Water Temperature °C*
0	22
1	16
2	11
3	9
4	6
5	4
6	5
7	4
8	5
9	6
10	6

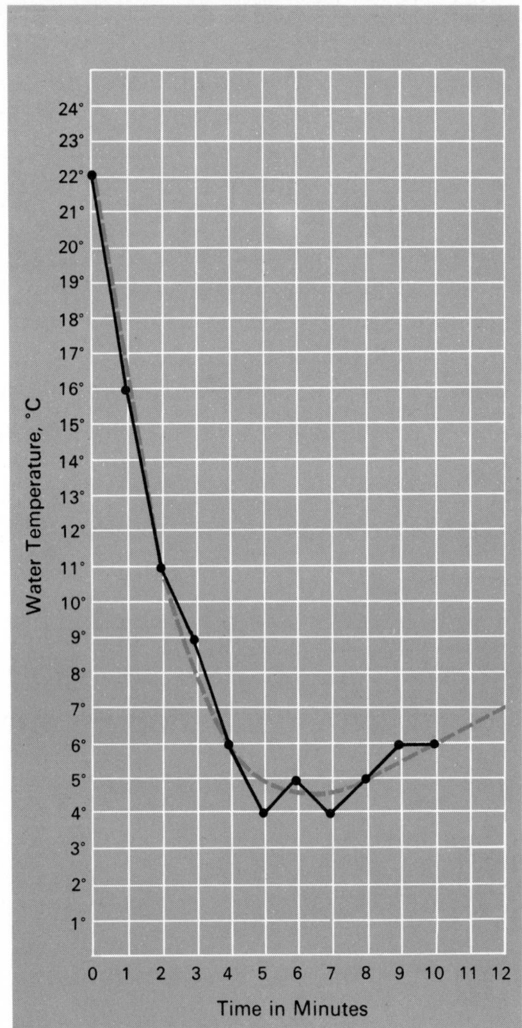

2-6. The broken line of the graph represents an average of the individual data points. This "best fit" line is drawn when the change is continuous.

minute after that are shown by the remaining plot points. The line that connects the plot points shows the temperature change. It shows a rapid decrease in temperature just after the ice was added. This cooling was followed by a gradual warming trend during the last four minutes.

Demonstrate how to find a line of best fit by using several hypothetical examples.

Often, as here, a series of plot points does not fall along a straight line. Then, a smooth curved line is used to represent the points. This line, called a **line of best fit**, shows the general pattern of the data but does not necessarily pass through all the points plotted. The broken line shown in Figure 2-6 is a line of best fit for the plot points.

In the experiment with the ice cube, the temperature was recorded for the first ten minutes only. It is sometimes desirable to predict a

To clarify when bar graphs and line graphs are used, show several examples of each to the class and discuss the important features. Point out that there is often no hard-and-fast rule about where each kind of graph should be used.

value beyond the last one shown on a graph. Suppose you wanted to predict the temperature twelve minutes after the start of the experiment. You would observe the change in temperature shown on the graph during minutes eight, nine, and ten. The temperature changes during this period show a slight warming trend. If this trend continues, you could expect the temperature after twelve minutes to be between 7°C and 8°C. This range was predicted by extending the broken line in Figure 2-6 to the twelve-minute line on the graph.

The type of graph you use depends on the type of relationship you wish to illustrate. Use a line graph when you wish to show numerical relationships that are proportional. Each line on a line graph represents one item, person, or object only. When you wish to compare quantities, sizes, or other relationships that are not proportional, use a bar graph.

In Problem 2-2 you will prepare another bar graph. You will learn how to interpret information shown on line and bar graphs.

Problem 2-2 How may graphical information be interpreted and used?

Purpose To learn to interpret and predict information from graphs.

Materials graph paper

Procedure

Part One: Interpreting information from graphs

Students who do not remember how to prepare a bar graph should refer back to Problem 2-1, Part Two (pages 30-31).

A. Look at Table 2-3. It shows the average speeds of winning cars in the Indianapolis 500-Mile Auto Race. Data for every fifth year from 1920 to 1970 are included. The speed of the winning car of one race does not influence the results of another race. The relationship is not proportional. So a bar graph, rather than a line graph, should be used to show the results.

B. Plot the data in Table 2-3 in a bar graph. Choose a range on the numbered scale sufficient to show all of the winning speeds. After you have prepared the graph, answer the following questions about the racing speeds.

1. 67.1 mph.

1. What is the difference between the highest and the lowest average speeds in miles per hour?

2. The speeds are increasing as time passes.

2. What general trend in speeds is shown by the graph?

TABLE 2-3 AVERAGE SPEED OF WINNERS OF INDIANAPOLIS 500

Year	*Winning Car's Average Speed in Miles Per Hour*
1920	88.6
1925	101.1
1930	100.4
1935	106.2
1940	114.3
1945	(no race held)
1950	124.0
1955	128.2
1960	138.8
1965	150.7
1970	155.7

3. In the range of 156-170 mph. Any reasonable value greater than the 1970 speed should be accepted.

4. New types of engines, better engineering, and better fuels may increase the speed in an unpredictable fashion. Weather conditions might reduce speed. Accept anything reasonable.

5. Most likely 155-170 mph. Accept any reasonable range that includes the student's answer to Question 3. (The actual winning speed in 1975 was 149.2 mph. This fact can be used to point out the potential problems with predicting from graphed data.)

3. On the basis of the information presented in the graph, predict what the average winning speed was for the 1975 Indianapolis 500.
4. Why do you think your prediction is probably not exactly right?

C. Sometimes a value predicted from a graph is expressed as a range of numbers. A range of numbers takes into consideration the lowest and highest numbers that could be expected.

5. Within what range of speeds would you expect the winning car to have averaged in 1975?

Part Two: Interpreting information from a line graph

D. The graph in Figure 2-7 shows the population growth of the United States between the years 1900 and 1975. The estimated population projected to the year 2000 is shown by a dotted line on the graph.

6. On the graph, what trend is shown in the United States' population between 1900 and 1975?
7. How may a graph be used to predict the population of a country for some future year?
8. What was the approximate population of the United States in the year 1920?

6. It is increasing.

7. By examining the graph of the past population record and noting the slope of the line, one can extend the line and predict what the future population will be.

8. About 110 million.

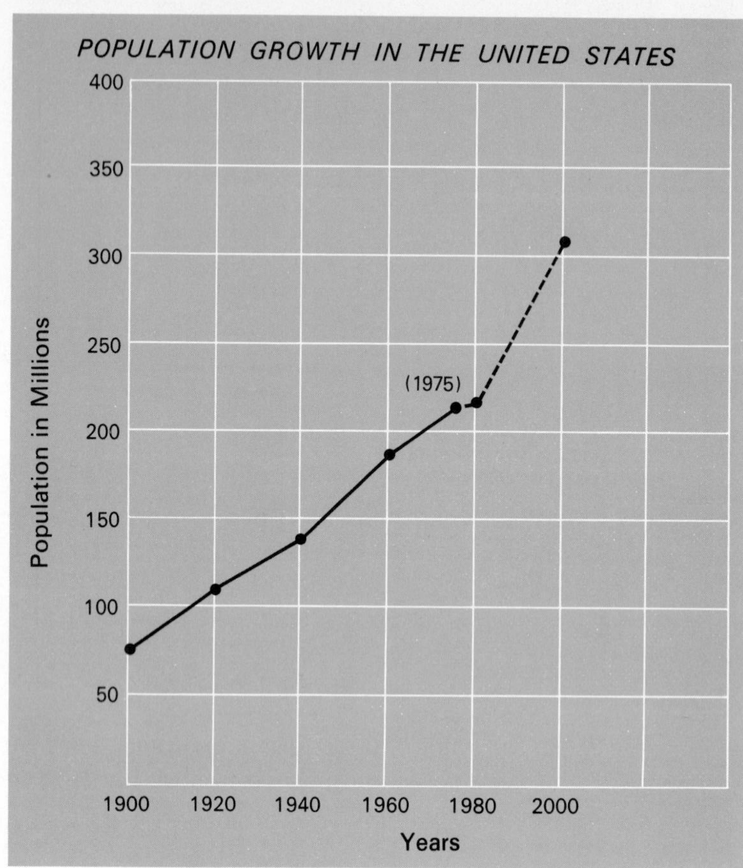

2-7. The population growth of the United States projected to the year 2000.

To determine the answer to question 8, find the year 1920 on the horizontal axis. Move up the vertical line for that year until you come to the slope line. Read the value on the number scale at the left opposite that point on the slope line. You must estimate the actual population figure since the value lies between 100 million and 150 million people.

9. About 160 million.

9. Estimate the population in the year 1950. (This time you must estimate the position of the point for the year 1950, since that point is not directly plotted on the graph.)

You should now be able to

Read numerical information from bar graphs and line graphs.
Describe trends shown on graphs.
Predict future trends based on information shown on a graph.

Science terms

bar graph	horizontal axis (x-axis)	plot point
data	independent variable	slope line
dependent variable	line graph	variable
graph	line of best fit	vertical axis (y-axis)

Review questions

1. What is a graph?
2. List two ways in which data may be presented.
3. How does the use of a table help to organize information?
4. What is meant by a variable factor in an experiment?
5. In graphing a child's weight change over a period of years, which variable — weight or years — would be independent?
6. Which variable is usually placed on the vertical axis of a graph? Which variable is placed on the horizontal axis?
7. What is the purpose of the line connecting the plot points on a graph?
8. What term is commonly used to describe numerical information collected in an experiment?
9. What is the line on a graph called that represents the general pattern shown by the plot points?
10. Which type of graph does *not* use plot points connected by lines to show relationships between variables?

1. A way of presenting quantitative relationships by means of a diagram.
2. Tables and graphs.
3. A table organizes data systematically, so that relationships can be more easily seen.
4. Any part of an experiment that is allowed to change.
5. Years. Weight is dependent on the time (year) at which the child is weighed.
6. *Vertical axis:* dependent variable. *Horizontal:* independent variable.
7. The line helps a person to visualize the manner in which the numerical data change. It relates changes in the dependent variable to changes in the independent variable.
8. Data.
9. Line of best fit.
10. Bar graph.

See Teacher's Guide section for answers to Questions 11-19.

Check your understanding

11. What kind of information should be presented in the form of a line graph rather than a bar graph?
12. Which of the graphs in Figure 2-8 shows:
    a. numbers increasing as time passes?
    b. numbers decreasing as time passes?
    c. numbers remaining steady as time passes?

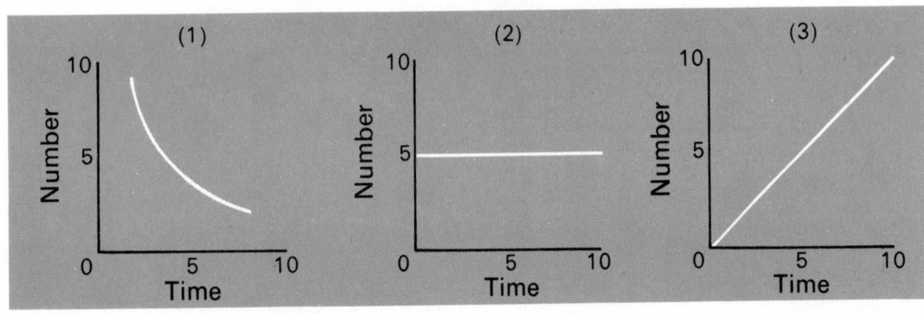

2-8. Use for question 12.

13. When preparing a graph, why is it usually better to use the average of several measurements rather than just one measurement?
14. When conducting an experiment, why is it necessary to keep constant all the factors that are not being tested?
15. What do the plot points on a line graph represent?
16. Why is paper with evenly spaced lines useful for preparing graphs?
17. How can graphs be used to make predictions of data dealing with future events?
18. Figure 2-9 shows a line graph of data accumulated by measuring a growing plant. Use the graph to answer questions a-g.
    a. For how long was the period of growth measured?
    b. What was the independent variable being tested?

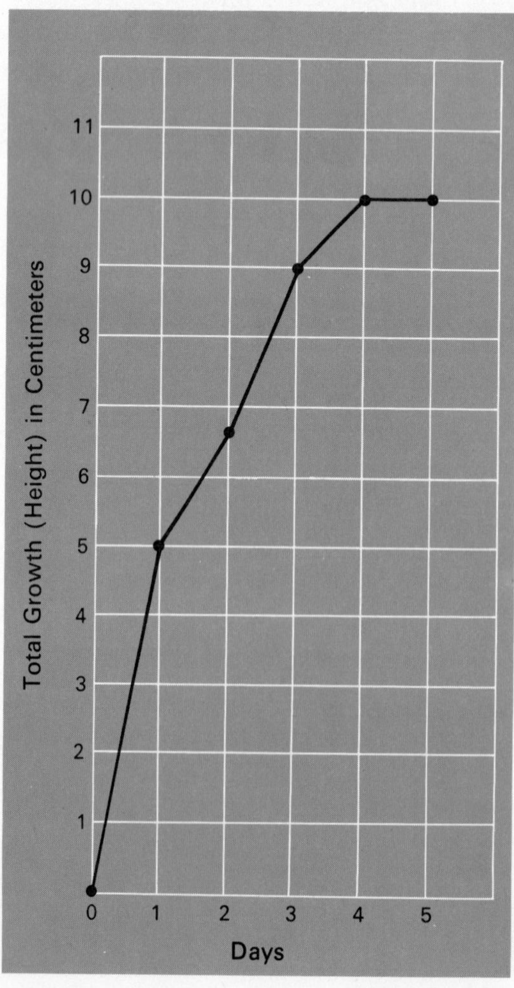

2-9. Use for question 18.

c. What was the dependent variable?
d. How much growth in centimeters took place the first day?
e. How did the first day's growth compare to the total growth, or height, of the plant on Days 2, 3, and 4?
f. What growth pattern does the graph indicate between Days 4 and 5?
g. What information does the graph present?

19. Refer to the bar graph shown in Figure 2-10. This graph contains information about the growth of six plants, all the same kind, measured for ten days.
    a. What range of numbers (centimeters) is required to show the growth of all six plants?
    b. How many centimeters of growth does each line along the side of the graph represent?
    c. Which of the plants tested grew the same amount during the ten-day period?
    d. How did the total growth of Plant B compare to the total growth of Plant D during the ten-day period?
    e. Why was this information presented in a bar graph instead of a line graph?

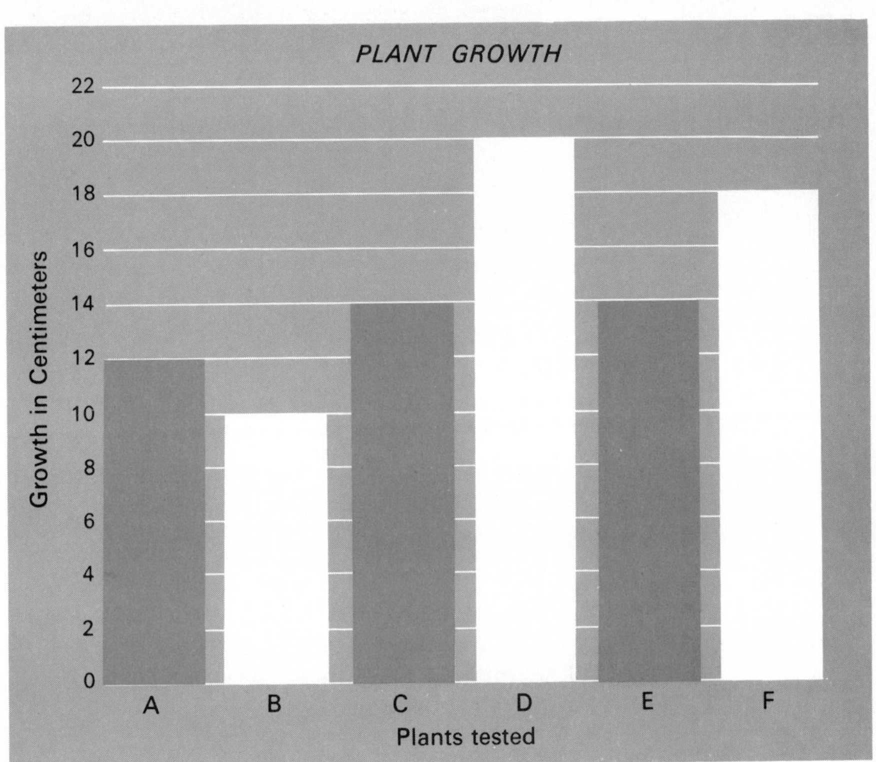

2-10. Use for question 19.

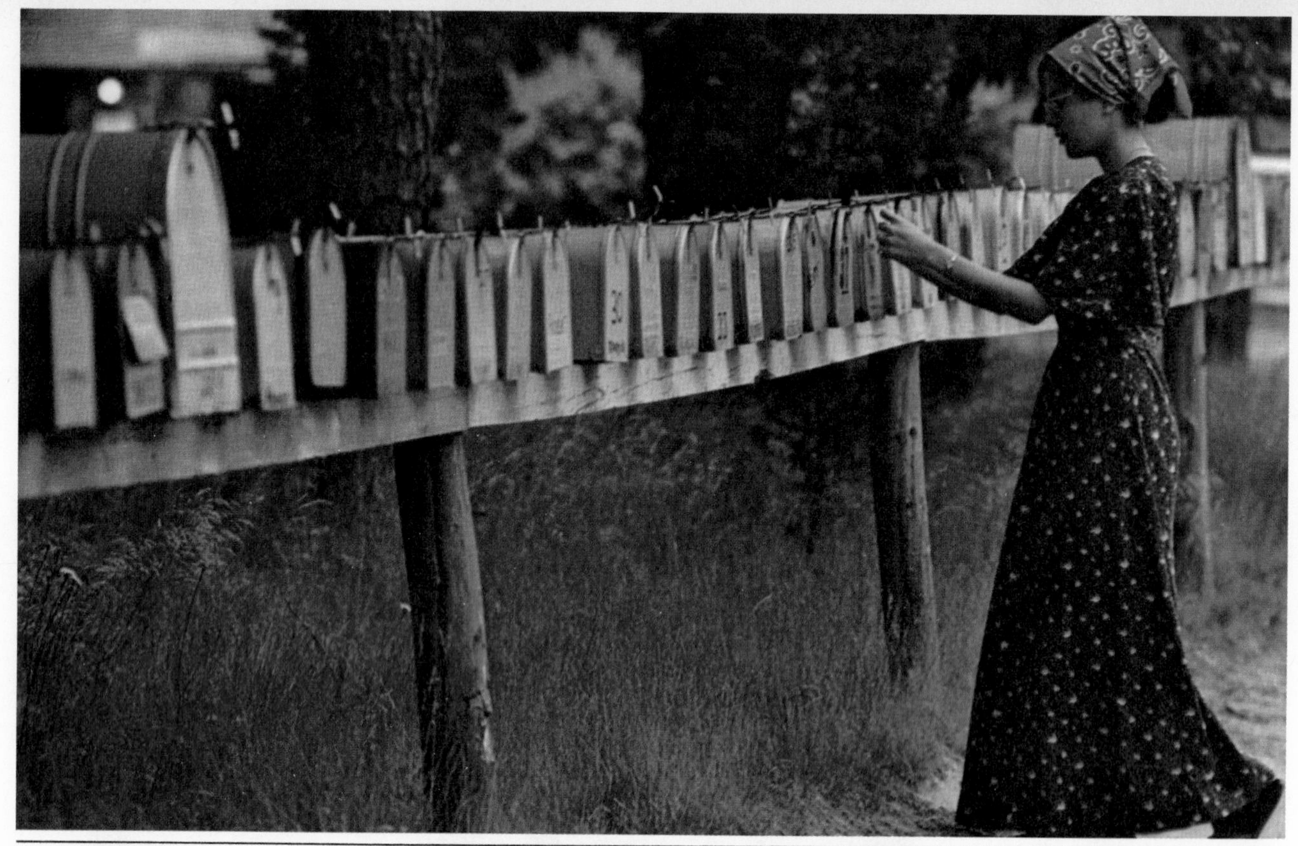

Chapter 3 **Classifying objects**

Chapter-opening photo illustrates one of the major classification systems we depend on daily. Mail is classified by weight, bulk, and type and speed of delivery as well as by the receiver's address. The latter aspect of the classification is evidenced in the photo.

Have you ever helped someone with the dishes in an unfamiliar kitchen? Before you could put the dishes away you probably had to ask where the plates belonged, or where the silverware went. And when you put the plates away, you may have noticed that the saucers, cups, and bowls were stored nearby. In the silverware drawer, you probably found separate sections for knives, forks, and spoons. And you may have found another drawer for the cooking utensils. These are examples of how objects are often grouped together for convenience. Whenever objects are grouped together for some purpose, the objects are said to be **classified.**

People classify just about everything around them. They might have started out by simply calling some things "good" and some things "bad", depending on how the things affected them. As the world became more complex, better systems of identifying and classifying objects became necessary.

Classification systems are seen in nearly every activity you might name. Supermarkets have meat departments, dairy sections, spice racks, and all the other areas you see when you shop. You can find things much more quickly when you know where to start looking for them.

Most public libraries in this country use the Dewey Decimal System to classify books. In this system the subject of the book is the basis for classification. Each subject is given its own decimal number. So no matter what library you go to, you will find natural science and physical science books in the 500 section. History books are found in the 900 section.

In class discussion, emphasize that the purpose behind all classification systems is to give organization to diverse objects.

All classification systems have certain things in common. All are designed to organize objects. The **organization** may take the form of grouping things with similar shapes, like the dishes. It might be an organization based on usage or content, as in the yellow pages or the telephone book. Or it might be based on letters of the alphabet, as in a glossary. Whatever the method, if the system is well organized, the objects in it will be easier to find and to store.

Once a classification system has been set up, anyone can use it. The key is to know how the system is organized. The Dewey Decimal System is useful because most libraries follow the same rules for numbering the books. The instructions for classifying the books have

3-1. Classification systems are used in our daily lives.

been very clearly written. Any given book will be classified and placed on the shelves in the same way by anyone using the Dewey Decimal System.

In Figure 3-2 you see an example of grouping as it might be applied to methods of transportation. All the methods to be grouped are placed in the first large category. The next step is to choose two major categories into which all the vehicles will fit. Two such categories might be wheeled and nonwheeled vehicles. These two categories are used in Figure 3-2.

Another way to group vehicles could be into those used on land and those not used on land, or those that have motors and those that don't. There are still many other ways of classifying vehicles. Whatever system is chosen, it must be followed when grouping the different methods.

If "wheeled vehicles" were one of the major groups, as in Figure 3-2, it would include bicycles, trucks, cars, skateboards, and all other objects that have wheels. The division made here of wheeled and nonwheeled vehicles might cause some problems. Airplanes, for instance, have both wheels and wings. It was decided to classify on the basis of the structure responsible for most of the motion of the vehicle. The airplane would then be included in the nonwheeled group since it depends on wings more than on wheels for flight.

Once the first major categories are chosen, they must then be divided into more specialized areas. Vehicles with only one wheel might be one group while those with more than one wheel would be another group. The category of more than one wheel could then be divided into vehicles with two wheels or more than two wheels.

You might try to separate the nonwheeled methods into two groups. You could find several characteristics that will work. Be sure that all of the nonwheeled methods fit into either one group or the other. By the time the classification system is completed, anyone who knows the system should be able to categorize any vehicle. You can see from this brief example that a lot of thought must be given to the design of a classification system.

Organization in science is important. There is a huge variety of living things. Scientists needed to simplify the task of describing any single one. So they classified all living things into groups or subgroups. In this chapter you will learn some guidelines for setting up a classification system. And you will build some simple ones yourself. Doing this will help you appreciate the more complex systems that classify all living things.

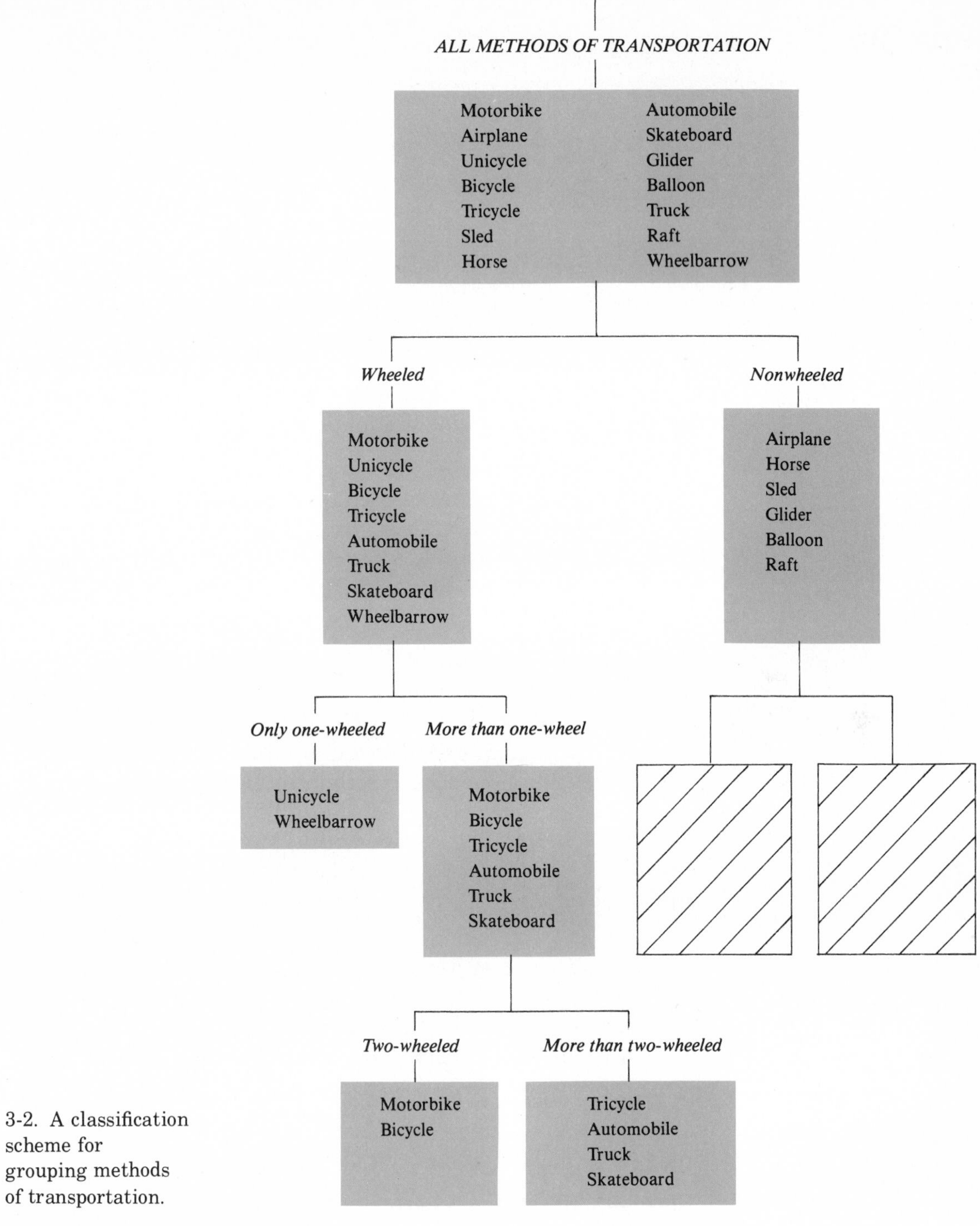

3-2. A classification scheme for grouping methods of transportation.

Problem 3-1 In what ways may different objects be grouped?

Purpose To look for differences between similar types of objects so that they can be divided into separate groups.

Materials assorted bottles (20)

Procedure

Part One: Characteristics of groups

A. In your study of living things you will see many types of organisms. And you will discover relationships between the different organisms. One way to do that is to have some kind of system for grouping objects. As you try to develop a useful system of classification, you should consider the following questions.

1. What is the purpose of the system?
2. Are the descriptions of different groups clearly defined? (Will anyone who uses the system group objects in the same way?)
3. Is the system consistent throughout so that others can follow it?

If more than one person is to use the system, each of the three questions must be considered.

A good example is the filing system that office workers might use for their correspondence. (1) The purpose of the system is to keep records in case questions come up about what was said or agreed to. (2) The descriptions of the groups, or the people with whom correspondence occurred, have to be clearly defined. Anyone should be able to file a letter with the other letters for a certain person. (3) The system has to be consistent so that anyone can find a letter when the person who filed it is out of the office.

B. To develop and use a system that groups objects, you must have some knowledge about the objects themselves. Objects can be separated according to their physical **characteristics.** These include such properties as color, size, shape, weight, and so on.

1. Blue: 1,6,8,10,16. Striped: 2,4,9,11,15. White: 3,5,7,12,13, 14,17.

1. Separate the objects in Figure 3-3 into three groups using their colors as a basis for sorting them. List the numbers of the objects that should be included in each color group.

In Figure 3-3 all the objects are blue, white, or striped. If a fourth characteristic were present, such as a red object, you would need four different groups.

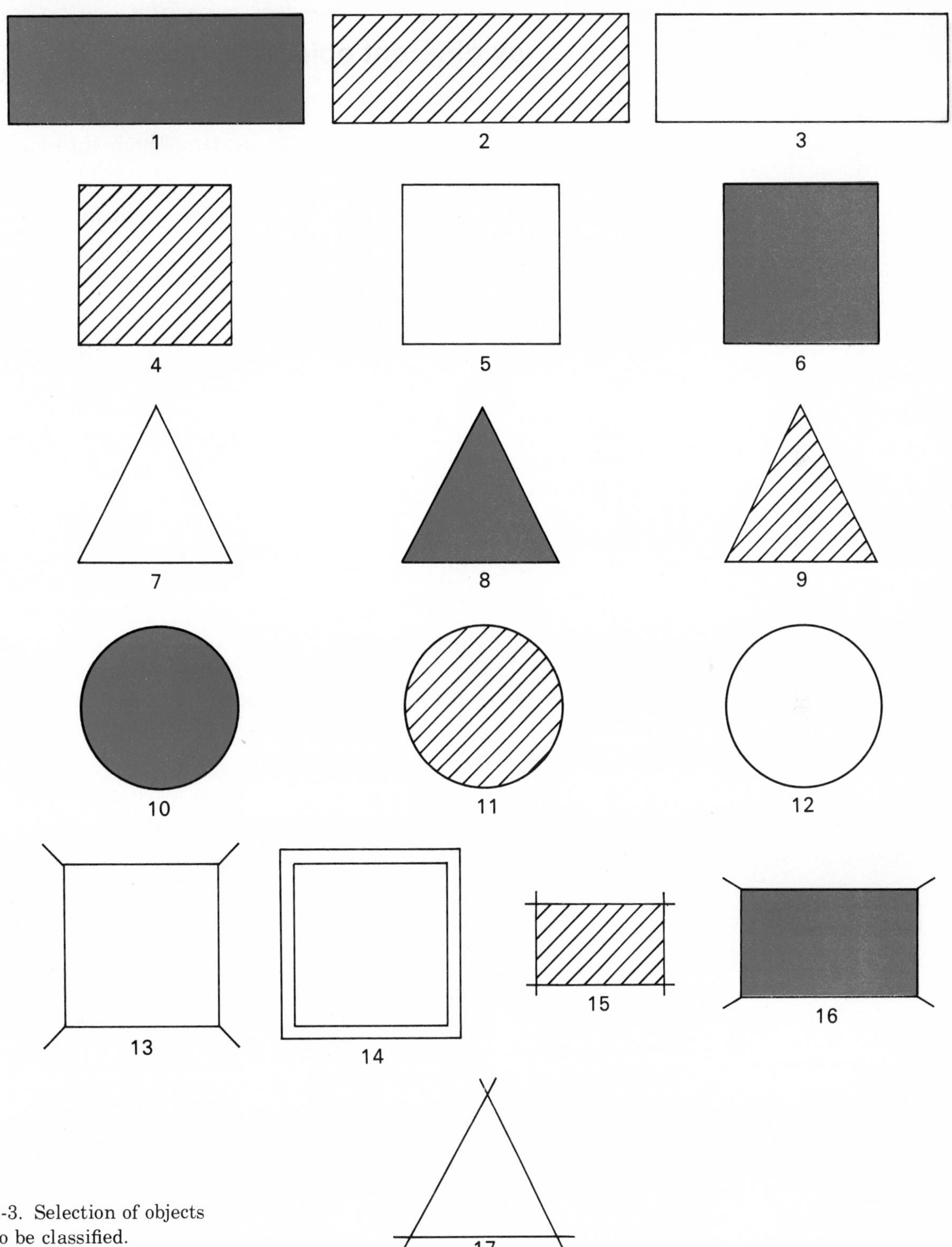

3-3. Selection of objects to be classified.

2. Now go on the basis of general shape. How many different groups of shapes are present in the objects found in Figure 3-3? Name each general shape and list the numbers of the objects that belong in each group.

C. You will now classify the objects by separating them into subgroups.

3. Using the numbers of the square objects, separate them into as many groups as you can.
4. Do the same with the circular objects and separate them into as many groups as you can.

The most important consideration of grouping is to determine the purpose of the groups. How will they be used? Suppose the circular objects represented materials that were harmful to your body. And suppose that squares represented things that were good to eat. The purpose would be to separate the food items from the harmful items.

Part Two: Practice in grouping

D. Obtain the 20 numbered bottles that are assigned to your team. Divide the bottles into not more than six groups. To separate the bottles, you will need to gather information about them. Consider their color, size, shape, and other characteristics. Choose the requirements for each group so that each bottle will fit into only one particular group. You may further subdivide any group in order to make your system more meaningful.

5. Give each group a short descriptive name. Make a list of the group names with the large group first and its subdivisions next.
6. List the characteristics that are common to each bottle in a particular group.
7. State the reason you grouped the bottles as you did.

E. Trade bottles with another team. Arrange their bottles into a grouping system. Compare your bottle classification system with that of the other team to see if you used the same system. Discuss the differences between your system and theirs. Adjust both lists so that they agree.

8. What bottles were found in different groups from those in which the original team grouped them?
9. What requirements of a classification system may not have been considered when grouping some of the bottles in different ways?

2. Four different groups. Rectangles: 1,2,3,15,16. Squares: 4,5,6,13,14. Triangles: 7,8,9,17. Circles: 10,11,12. (Since Objects 13-17 have somewhat unusual shapes, students may suggest additional categories. Accept any reasonable answers.)
3. Answers will vary; accept reasonable groupings.
4. Accept any reasonable groupings.
5. Criteria that may be used include shape, color, material, type of cap, etc. Any one of these may be used to separate the bottles into large groups; the others would then determine the subdivisions.
6. Answers will vary, but may include size, color, function, etc.
7. Groupings should be obvious and easily recognized. Differences between groups should be clear. Any grouping that satisfies these requirements is acceptable.
8. Answers will depend on grouping criteria chosen by different teams. A discussion may be necessary to determine which grouping is most satisfactory.
9. Possibly the purpose of the system; categories not clearly defined; inconsistency within the system.

10. How would you change the requirements of these groups to eliminate the problem?
11. How does the grouping system use the rules described in Step A of this problem?

10. Be more specific about the characteristics used to group the bottles. The class as a whole might discuss which criteria are best to use.
11. Accept any evidence that the rules in Step A, p. 46, have been followed.

You should now be able to

Gather data necessary to classify objects.
Recognize differences in similar objects.
Recognize similarities in different objects.
Determine characteristics that can be used to classify objects into useful groups.

Classifying different objects

In Problem 3-1 you were asked to develop a classification system for some bottles. You also arranged objects of different colors and shapes into separate groups. In each of those activities you were given a collection of similar objects and asked to separate it into smaller groups.

Suppose you had been asked to classify objects that were not at all alike. That may sound like a hard job, but it really isn't. You would approach it in the same manner as the problem with the bottles. You would start by choosing two major categories into which all the objects would fit. You would then divide each of these groups into subgroups. Each subgroup would have characteristics of its own. This process of making smaller and smaller divisions is continued as long as a useful purpose is served.

This basic classification method can be applied to all the things on earth. The two major groups could be living things and nonliving things. The group of living things could be separated into plant and animal groups. And these could be subdivided into smaller groups until one particular living thing is identified.

In Problem 3-2 you are asked to separate a list of different objects. Refer to the questions asked in Problem 3-1 in order to make a consistent grouping system. Try to choose categories that are useful. And remember to define them clearly so they will mean the same thing to anyone who might use your system.

Problem 3-2 How are classification systems developed?

Purpose To learn how to develop classification systems that may be used to divide many kinds of objects into separate groups.

Procedure

A. Classification systems often start by separating living things from nonliving things.

1. Divide the objects pictured in Figure 3-4 into two separate groups, living things and nonliving things. List them in your notebook.

B. Most large groups can be further separated. To do this, more detailed characteristics are used. Living things, for instance, are usually divided into groups based on their physical structures.

2. Divide the living things into two groups and include this in your notebook.
3. What characteristics of the living things did you use to separate them into two groups?
4. Divide one of the two groups of living things into smaller groups. State the characteristics you used to separate the living things further.

C. The purpose for the grouping system often dictates what items should be grouped together. You have separated the living things from the nonliving things. What if the purpose were to separate food items from nonfood items? The system used to group the items would probably change.

5. Divide the objects into groups of human food items and nonfood items.
6. What factors must be considered in placing objects in each group?

D. Look again at the living things in Figure 3-4. Develop a system of grouping them that will be useful to you.

7. List the factors you considered for each group.
8. What characteristics did you use as a basis for separating the groups of living things from each other?
9. How many groups do you think should be developed in order to have a meaningful grouping system for all of the objects illustrated?

To the untrained eye, Figure 3-4 appears to show 16 totally different objects. But, as you have seen, similarities can be found and useful groupings can be made.

1. *Living:* salamander, seaweed, celery, vine, toad, rose, snail, mold, carrot, human, earthworm, frog. *Nonliving:* bottle, diamond, rock, block.

2. (Probable answer.) *Animals:* salamander, toad, snail, human, earthworm, frog. *Plants:* seaweed, celery, rose, vine, mold, carrot.

3. Probably whether they were plants or animals.

4. Answers will vary.

5. *Edible items:* snail, frog, seaweed, celery, vine, carrot. Others are inedible.

6. Dietary differences; e.g., some people won't eat snails.

7. Answers will depend on rationale behind the classification system. One student may group organisms according to habitat, another according to structure, etc.

8. Possibilities include plant-animal, habitat, usefulness to humans, etc.

9. Answers will vary, but students should be able to think of six or more groups (living and nonliving, plant and animal, edible and nonedible, etc.).

3-4. Classify the above objects into two different groups.

You should now be able to

Classify objects into meaningful groups.

State some characteristics useful in classifying objects.

Determine the factors that will make a classification system useful in a particular situation.

State the purpose of classifying objects into special groups.

---

1. (a) The systematic arrangement of objects into meaningful groups. (b) A grouping based on common characteristics. (c) A trait that enables an object to be distinguished from other objects.
2. It provides a method of sorting objects into groups so that similarities and differences can be easily seen.
3. Answers will vary; e.g., color, structure, etc.
4. Answers will vary. Supermarket departments include meat, canned goods, bakery, produce, etc.
5. They give organization to a number of objects.
6. Because science depends on seeing relationships. Organization makes this possible.
7. A group of objects within a large group. The members of the subgroup have the characteristics of the large group, and another characteristic that differentiates them from the others in the large group.

Science terms

characteristic
classification system
classify
organization

Review questions

1. Define each of the following terms: (a) classification; (b) category; (c) characteristic.
2. What is the purpose of a classification system?
3. What was one way that was used in this chapter to classify a group of objects?
4. What are three large categories used to group foods in a supermarket?
5. What do all classification systems have in common?
6. Why is organization important to science?
7. What is a subgroup or a subcategory?

Check your understanding

See Teacher's Guide section for answers to Questions 8-12.

8. How are the names in a telephone book classified?
9. Explain how the address on a letter may be called a classification system.
10. Study Figure 3-5 and answer the following questions:
    a. What one characteristic do all the objects have in common?
    b. Into how many categories or groupings could these objects be placed?
    c. What special characteristic does each individual group show?
    d. In what way are the grouped objects better organized than when they are not grouped?
    e. Suppose that after you had grouped all the objects in Figure 3-5 you were given another object that was larger and had a pattern different from all the others. Would the new object require a separate group? Explain.

11. What characteristics could be used to group different cars? How do you determine if one characteristic is more useful than another?
12. List three rules for preparing a good classification system.

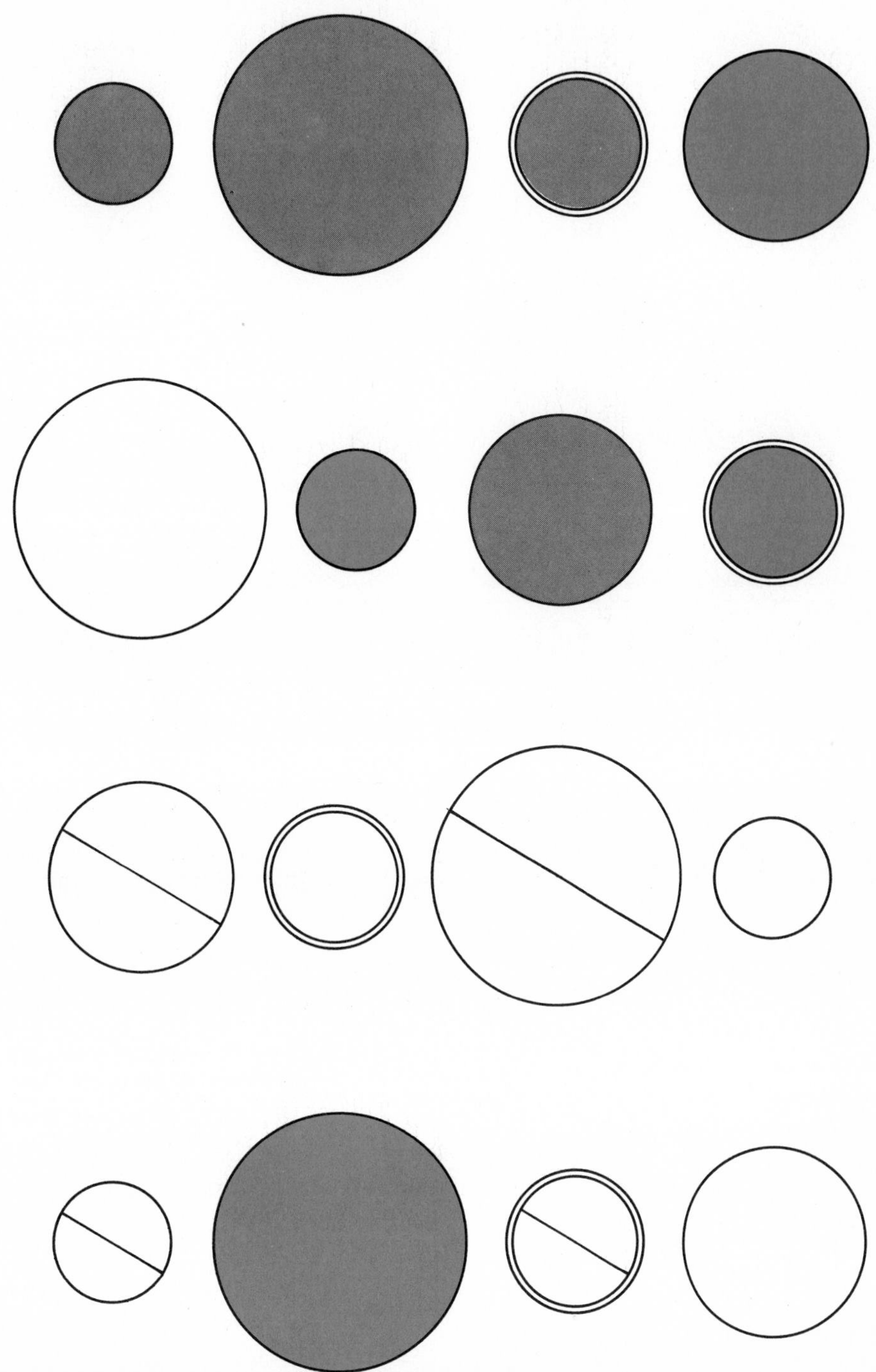

3-5. Use for question 10.

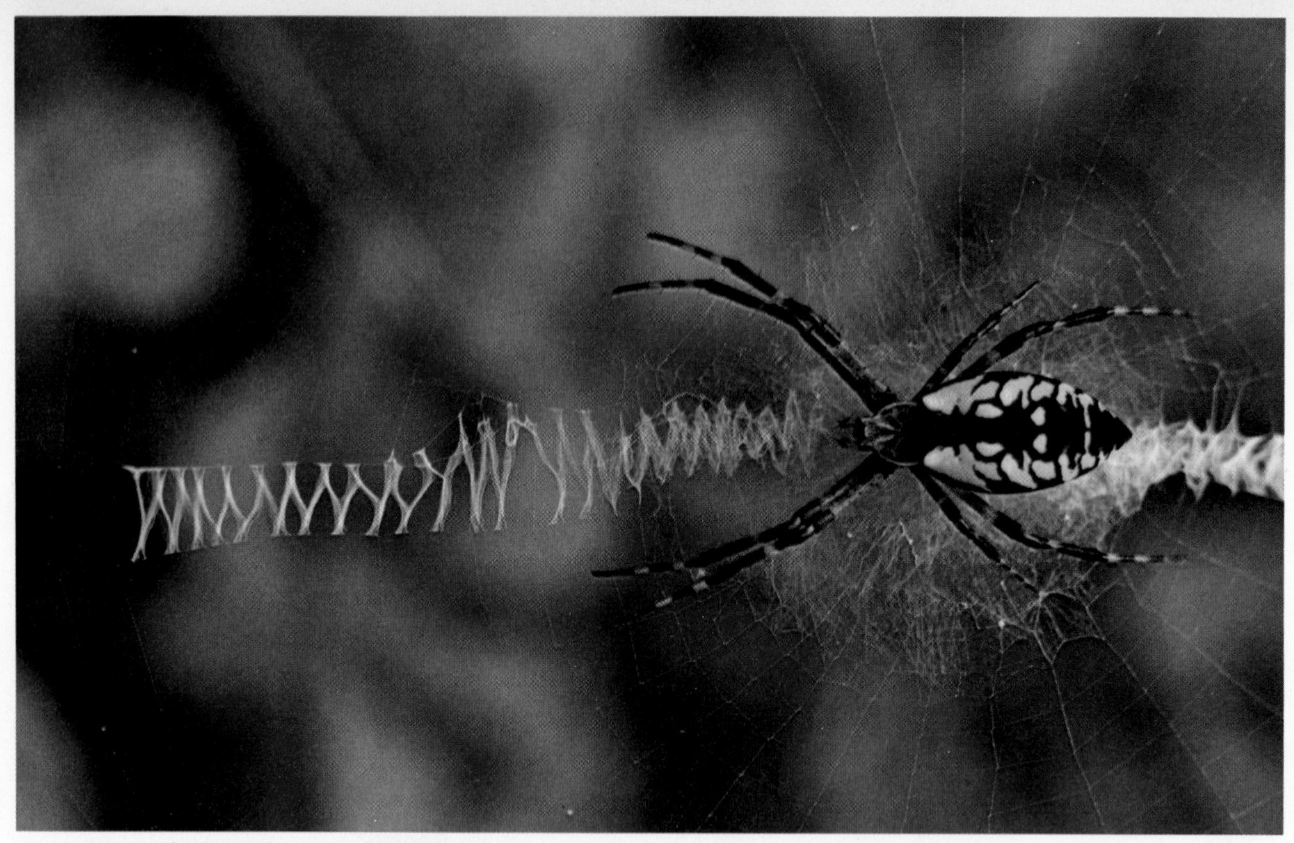

Chapter 4 Characteristics of living things

Chapter-opening photo of a spider and its web implies that characteristics of living things go beyond body structure to include behaviors exhibited by the organisms.

In Chapter 3 you classified objects as living or nonliving. You probably had little trouble finding the living things. The names of the objects were given and all were quite common.

How could you tell if something were living or nonliving if no name was given and you had never seen the thing before? You would need to know about the traits, or characteristics, of living things. You would need to know what it is that makes something "alive."

Living things differ from nonliving things by showing what are called **life processes.** Living things, for example, react to changes in their surroundings. They are sensitive. All living things also show movement of some kind. Other life processes are taking in food, using food for growth and energy, and transporting materials within the body. Reproducing is another life process. By closely observing the behavior of an object, you can usually tell if it is alive or not.

Identification of living things

A living thing will often give you clues that will help you to identify what kind it is. Such clues, or characteristics, include size, shape, and structure. Direct observation often helps you to distinguish among objects within a group. A group of pond animals, for example, might include a fish, a frog, a beaver, and a water snake. Each animal has its own unique characteristics.

These pond animals, however, also have a lot in common. They are all living things. They are all animals. They all may be found in or near water. They also all have backbones.

Biologists group together living things that have similar body structures. Therefore, the pond animals mentioned are grouped into the same large category in the animal kingdom. Animals in this category are called **vertebrates.** All animals in the vertebrate category have backbones, or *vertebrae.*

Classification keys

There are many kinds of animals. To divide them into subgroups, a device called a classification key is often used. A **classification key** looks for the presence or absence of many traits that an animal might have. The characteristics are organized into subdivisions. And these help to determine the subgroups to which the animal belongs. In this way, each animal can be identified.

Shown below is an example of a classification key. This one can be used to put vertebrates into five subgroups called **classes.** There are two statements about each characteristic. The first statement carries

KEY TO CLASSES OF VERTEBRATES

A.	Body fish-like and covered with mucus and scales.	(Fish)
AA.	Body not fish-like. (Go to B)	
B.	Body covered with moist skin and has four legs.	(Amphibians)
BB.	Body not covered with moist skin. (Go to C)	
C.	Body covered with dry scales.	(Reptiles)
CC.	Body not covered with dry scales. (Go to D)	
D.	Body covered with feathers.	(Birds)
DD.	Body not covered with feathers. (Go to E)	
E.	Body covered with hair.	(Mammals)

a single capital letter. The second statement carries double capital letters. (Notice the A and AA, for example.) In each case, the single letter means that the characteristic is present. The double letters mean that the characteristic is not present.

The key is constructed in such a way that all vertebrates can be put into either group "A" or group "AA." When an animal has the traits listed in the first statement, the animal belongs to that class (fish). When the characteristics do not agree with the first statement, the process continues on to the next statement. The characteristics must agree with the second statement in order to go on to the next pair of statements in the key.

Use the key to determine the class of vertebrates to which a human being belongs. Remember to start with the "A" statement. Repeat the process for a frog, a beaver, and a snake.

Problem 4-1 is based on a demonstration you give. See Teacher's Guide section for details.

As you might suspect, there are many kinds of classifications. Keys are constructed for very specific purposes. In Problem 4-3, later in this chapter, you will construct a classification key to sort a collection of leaves.

Problem 4-1 What do living things do?

Purpose To observe and compare some of the activities normally carried on by living things.

See annotated Table 4-1 for probable responses to Step B.

Materials Containers "A" and "B"

Procedure

1. *Container A:* rapid movements; "eating." *Container B:* movement, response to stimuli, respiration.

3. Mercury (nonliving).

4. Fish (living).

5. It uses oxygen, can reproduce, is able to move, etc. Accept any valid description.

6. Living things perform all of the activities in Table 4-1. Responses to this question may vary, depending on student's concept of what constitutes a living thing.

A. Observe the objects in the two containers provided by your teacher. One container is labeled "A" and the other "B."

1. List the life processes taking place in both containers.

B. Prepare a table in your notebook like Table 4-1. Record your observations of the life processes in each container. Do this by marking "yes", "no", or "not certain" in the proper column of the table.

2. All of them, but not necessarily all at the same time.

2. Which of the life activities listed should a living thing show?
3. What is the object in Container A?
4. What is the object in Container B?
5. Explain what is meant when we call something alive.
6. Try to write a definition of life that applies to all living things and does not apply to any nonliving thing.

Student responses in their copies of this chart will vary. Although students cannot directly observe the goldfish reproducing or growing, most students will realize that a goldfish does do these things.

TABLE 4-1 LIFE ACTIVITIES RECORD

Life Activity	*Object in Container "A"*	*Object in Container "B"*
Takes in food	not certain	yes
Moves	yes	yes
Grows	no	yes
Responds to stimuli	not certain	yes
Produces new organisms	no	yes
Takes in oxygen	no	yes

You should now be able to

Identify some processes that are characteristic of life.

Determine some processes that are carried on by both living and nonliving things.

Discuss life in terms of the processes performed by living things.

Classifying living things

You have seen that living things carry on some processes that nonliving things do not. Most living things grow and take in food and oxygen. They reproduce their own kind and respond to changes in their environment. Sometimes, however, it's not easy to distinguish a living thing from a nonliving thing. For example, scientists still are not sure whether a virus should be called living or nonliving. A virus in a living cell will reproduce itself in great numbers. But out of the cell the virus exists in the form of a "nonliving" crystal.

There are many ways to classify living things. Biologists, who study living things, start with a category called a **kingdom.** (See Figure 4-1.) They divide kingdoms into **phyla** (singular *phylum*). Each phylum is broken into **classes.** Classes are further divided into **orders.** Orders are divided into **families,** and families into **genera** (singular *genus*). And, finally, genera are divided into **species.** The species level is the most selective group. Only one type of organism belongs to each species.

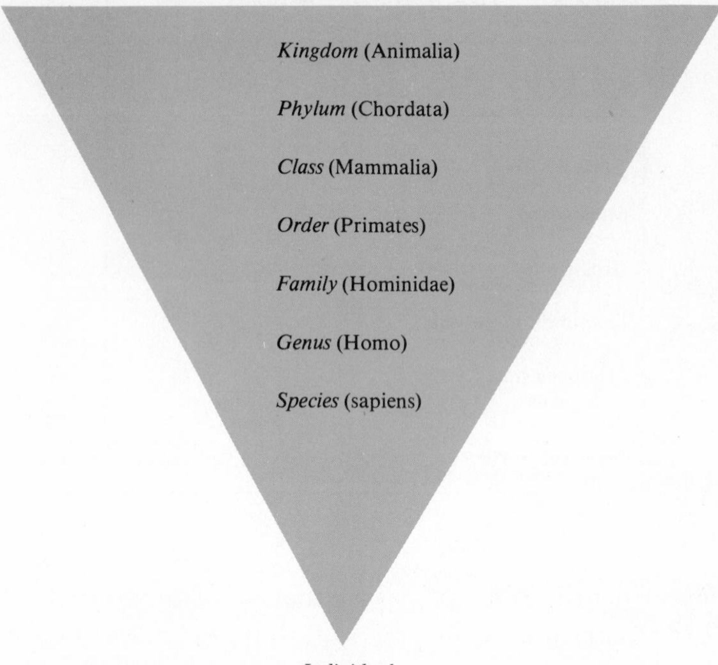

4-1. The groups in which all human beings are classified.

Earlier in this chapter you saw how animals with backbones could be sorted into classes. Each class contained only those animals that had similar group characteristics. The class called Mammalia includes only animals with fur or hair on their body. Other traits shared by all mammals include being warm-blooded, nourishing their young with milk, and having four-chambered hearts. In the next problem, you will use additional group characteristics to classify mammals into **orders.** These are more limited categories than classes are.

Problem 4-2 How are characteristics used to group living things?

Purpose To classify mammals into orders based on the characteristics of each order.

Procedure

Point out the fact that some animals might fit into two different orders if only one body feature were considered. Also note the fact that the more selective the subdivision, the more similar are all the members of that group.

A. Figure 4-2 shows a group of mammals. Scientists divide mammals into subgroups called orders. Ten orders of mammals are found in the United States. Each order has specific characteristics found in only a few animals. By examining the pictures in Figure 4-2, you can sort the animals into the ten different orders.

4-2. A group of mammals.

See annotated Table 4-2 for correct grouping of the animals.

1. What it looks like, how it moves, the general structure and activities, and anything else that distinguishes it from other organisms.
2. How it reproduces, its normal body temperature, what it eats, etc.
3. Animals in the same category would have certain similar characteristics.

B. Prepare a table in your notebook similar to Table 4-2. Include the columns for "Order" and "Example Shown." The "Characteristics" column is there for your information. You do not need to include it in your table.

1. What is meant by the characteristics of an animal?
2. What characteristics of mammals cannot be told simply by looking at an animal's picture?
3. How does classifying the different kinds of mammals help you to study them?
4. Why are body structures often used to help classify animals?
5. What other characteristics besides body structure could be used to classify animals?

You should now be able to

4. They can easily be seen and identified.
5. Habitat, coloration, food preference, etc.

Name the major divisions of the classification system for living things.

Classify a mammal into a special group known as an order.

Use given characteristics to separate groups of mammals into special groups.

Classification keys

Classification keys are scientific tools. They help people to sort and organize objects. The world of living things is made up of over two million species. With that great number and variety of living things, the need for a system of classification is clear.

You have used a simple key to sort vertebrates into classes. You have sorted mammals into orders. You have seen the order and pattern that classification systems provide. When objects are grouped into categories, similarities and differences in the objects are easier to see.

Classification keys, like other learning tools, must be used properly if they are to serve a purpose. Only those characteristics that may be clearly observed should be used. The key must be constructed so that an object either belongs in a given group or does not. This means that only one characteristic may be described in each step of the key.

In the next problem, you will devise your own key for classifying plant leaves. This activity will test your understanding of the construction and use of a classification key.

TABLE 4-2 ORDERS OF MAMMALS

Order	*Characteristic*	*Example Shown*
Carnivora	teeth especially fitted for tearing flesh; claws usually sharp; strong jaws; keen eyesight	bear, wolf
Cetacea	marine organisms; hind legs absent; notched, fishlike tail; breathe by lungs	dolphin, whale
Chiroptera	small; fly at night; web of skin between fingers and limbs for flight; eat insects	bat
Edentata	no front teeth; protected with an armor; burrow into the ground	armadillo
Insectivora	soft hair; live underground; eat insects; teeth primitive	mole
Marsupialia	animals in which the female has a pouch on the ventral side of the body where the very young are placed after they are born and where they are fed on milk	opossum
Primates	nails present on fingers and toes; most walk somewhat erect; fingers used for grasping	human
Rodentia	chisellike incisor teeth; small in size; forelimbs adapted for running, climbing, and food-getting	beaver, squirrel, mouse
Sirenia	front legs formed into flippers; aquatic animals with a rounded tail; large; plant-eating; have no external ears; no hindlimbs.	manatee
Ungulata	toes developed into hooves; teeth used for grinding grasses, leaves, etc.	horse, reindeer

Problem 4-3 How can you make and use a dichotomous key to classify living things?

Purpose To develop a dichotomous key based on characteristics that will separate living things into groups.

Materials leaf assortment

Procedure In this problem you will prepare a dichotomous key to classify leaves. A **dichotomous key** has two divisions or choices at each step. For example, in classifying people, a dichotomous division would be female or male.

The key starts with all the organisms to be considered. This group is then divided in two. The division is based on two statements about a given characteristic. The traits of the object agree with one statement or the other.

A person would be either a male or a female. If the person being classified were a male, he would next be sorted to see how he com-

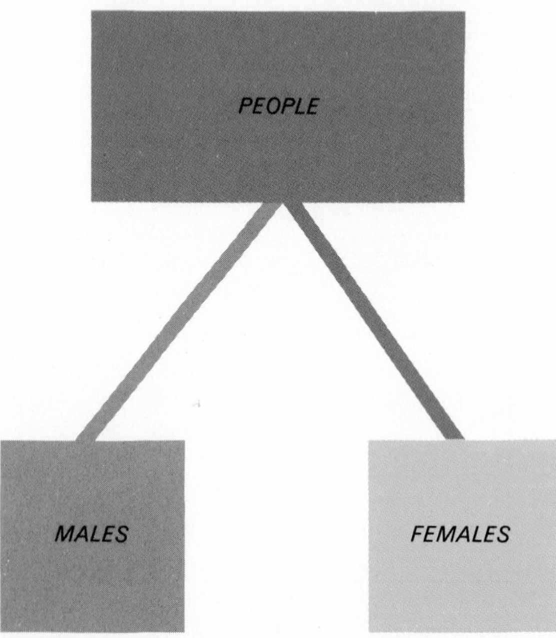

4-3. A dichotomous key divides the characteristics of a group into two categories.

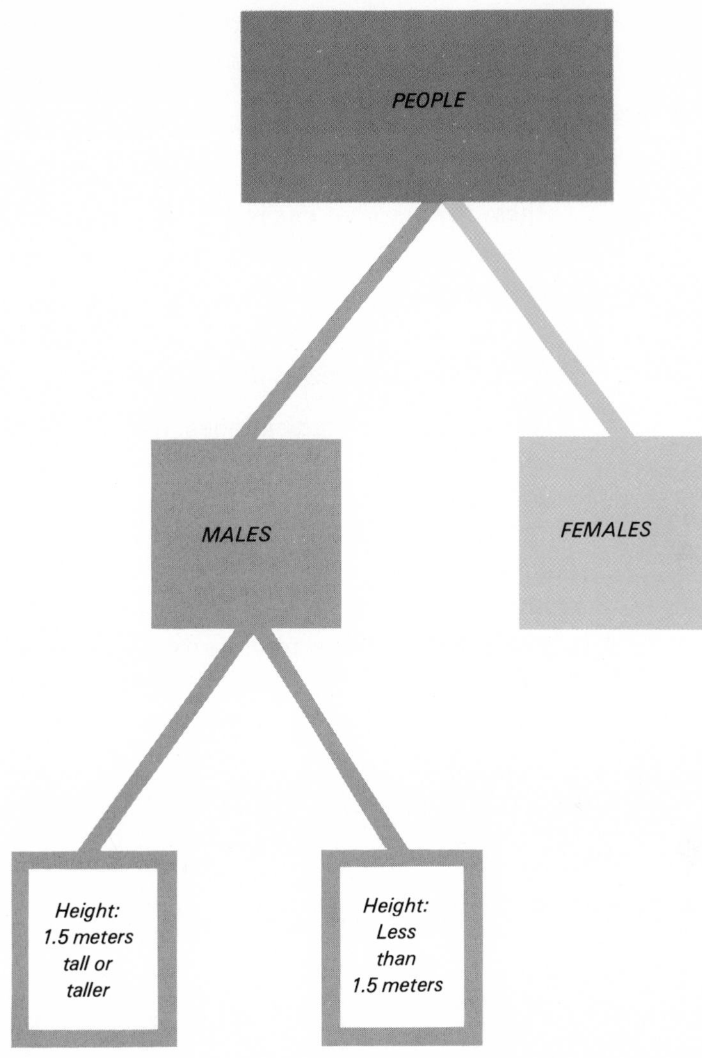

4-4. The further division of groups should be distinct to avoid confusion.

pared to other males. Heights might be compared, for instance. Males 1.5 meters tall or taller, or less than 1.5 meters, provide two groups of classification. (See Figure 4-4.) The statements that make two groups out of one must be carefully worded. There must be complete division and no confusion.

A. Obtain an assortment of leaves. Separate the leaves according to the characteristics found in each type. You may use such traits as shape, edge type, vein pattern, and so on.

See Teacher's Guide section for a sample dichotomous key that students might develop.

1. Shape of leaf, type of venation, type of edge, size, color, arrangement, etc.
2. Answers will vary, but should indicate a consistent use of dichotomous divisions.
3. Leaves with similar characteristics are grouped together as a result of an "either-or" separation process. Classification is easy because it is done by a series of clear-cut choices.

B. Develop a dichotomous key for the groups of leaves you sorted. Remember to separate each group by one characteristic only. Each new division must be more specific than the former division.

1. What similarities and differences do your leaves have that allow them to be sorted easily?
2. Describe the dichotomous key you developed for your assortment of leaves.

C. Test the usefulness of your key. Ask someone not in your team to sort out your leaves using your key.

3. What are some advantages of a dichotomous key in grouping leaves?

You should now be able to

Design categories that will separate living things into two groups.

Develop categories that will isolate one special type from a similar group.

Use a dichotomous key to classify an assortment of leaves.

Science terms

class	genus	phylum
classification key	kingdom	species
dichotomous key	life processes	vertebrate
family	order	

1. Taking in food, motion, growth, response to stimuli, breathing, reproduction. (Accept any 5 of these.)
2. Reproduction.
3. Primates.
4. Mammals.
5. Orders.
6. It has 2 divisions or choices at each step. An organism is classified according to the characteristics it possesses.
7. Phylum, class, order, family, genus, species.

Review questions

1. List five life processes characteristic of living things.
2. What life process is responsible for the continuation of a living species?
3. What order of mammals has nails on fingers and toes, and walks erect?
4. Name the class of vertebrates to which humans belong.
5. What classification group is subdivided into families?
6. Give a definition of a dichotomous classification key.
7. Into what six subgroups of living things may kingdoms be divided?

See Teacher's Guide section for answers to Questions 8-13.

Check your understanding

8. What important differences exist between the activities of living things and nonliving things?
9. How is a classification key used to identify a living thing?
10. What body characteristics do bats have that require their classification as mammals rather than as birds?
11. Why is a dichotomous key sometimes referred to as an either-or system of classification?
12. Study Figure 4-5 and answer the following questions:
    a. What two characteristics do all the insects pictured have in common?
    b. Describe some of the differences seen in the insects shown.
    c. Into what groups might the insects pictured be arranged to classify them?
13. A sugar crystal grows from a saturated sugar solution, yet we call it nonliving. Why is a growing sugar crystal called nonliving?

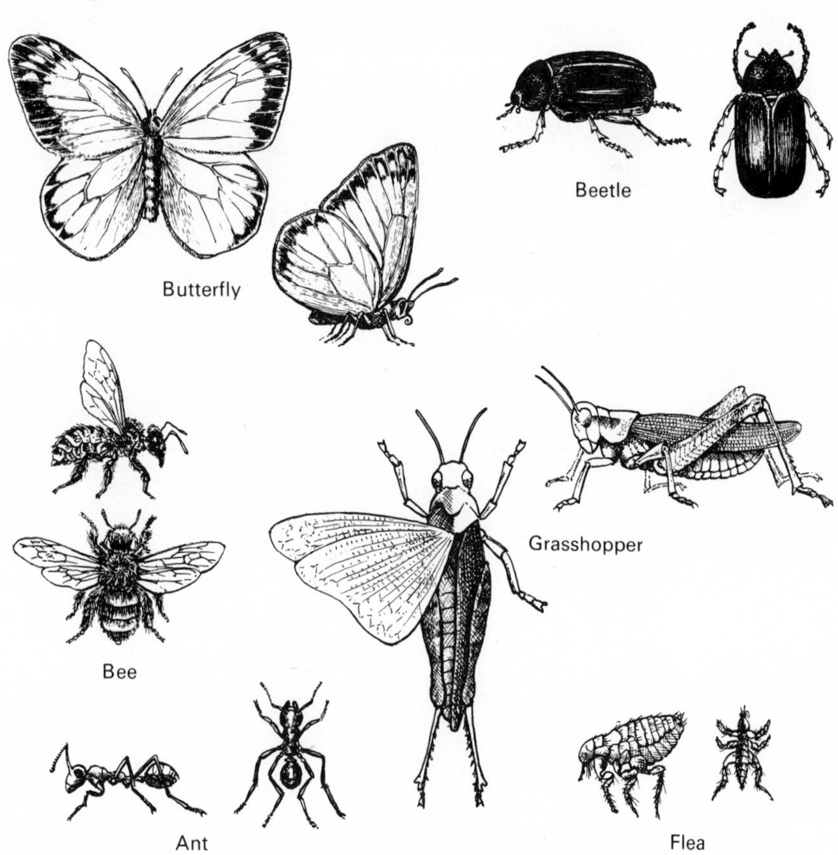

4-5. Use for question 12.

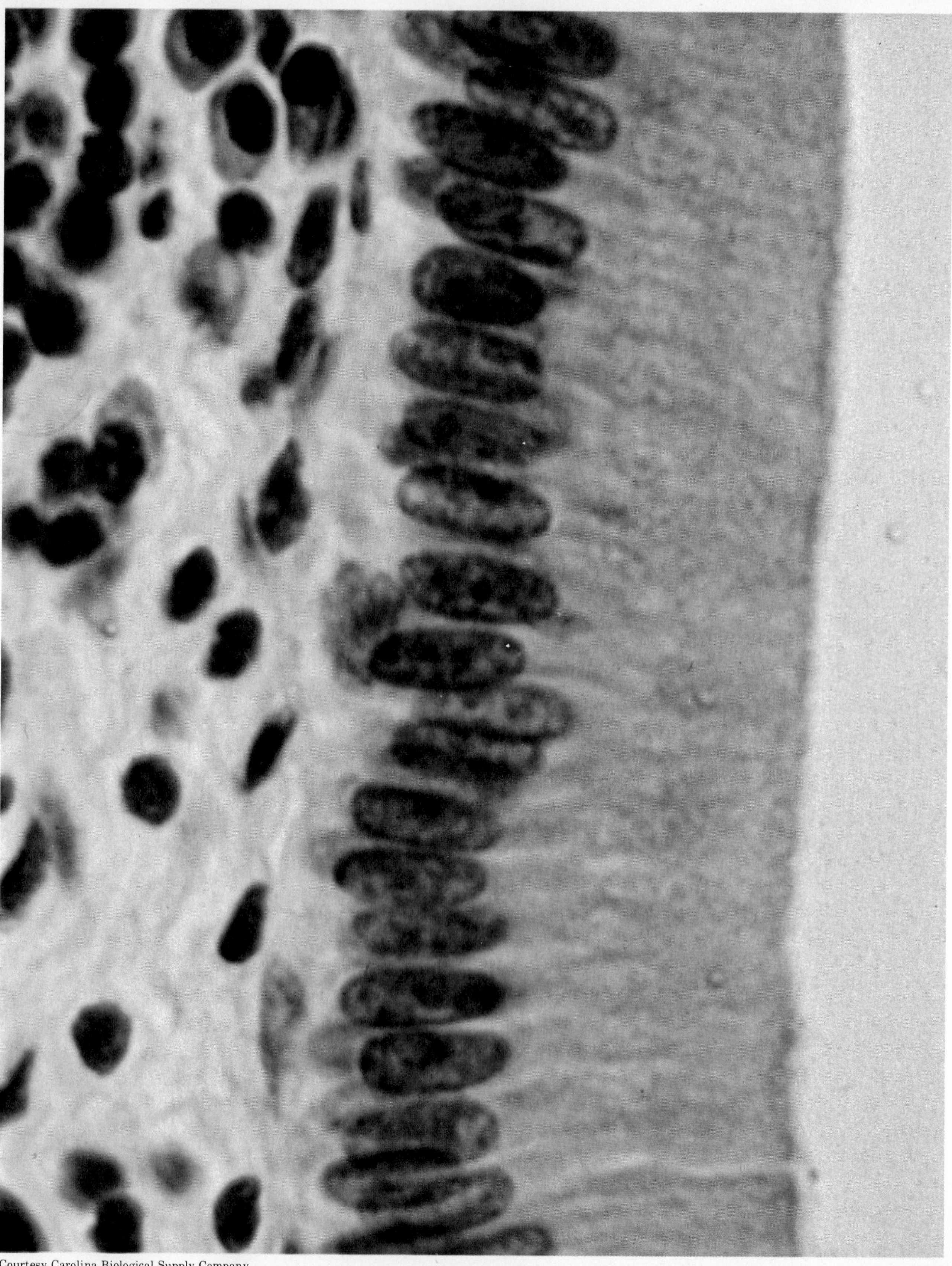

Courtesy Carolina Biological Supply Company

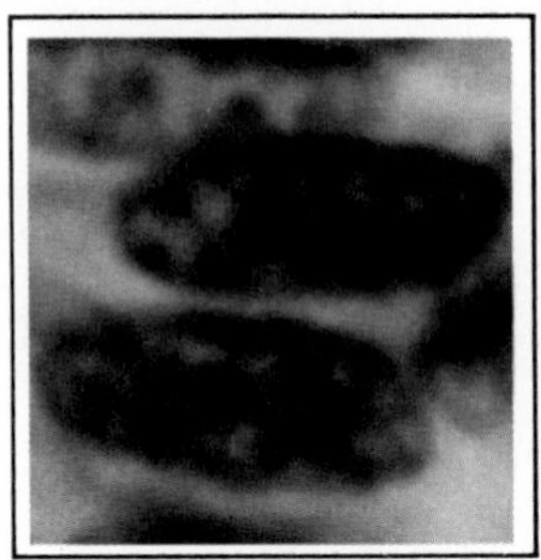

Unit 2

The Cell — Building block of living things

Unit-opening photo shows the tissue called simple columnar epithelium. It is "simple" because it consists of a single layer of cells. The cells are "columnar" because they are tall and rodlike.

There are many kinds of living things on earth today. And people have built classification systems to organize them all into groups. You saw in Unit One how useful such systems can be.

Chapter 4 gave you a brief look at some of the many activities carried on by living things. These included all of the activities that you can observe. They also included activities that you cannot observe directly because they take place inside the body.

In Unit Two you will study living things in more depth. You will study the structures and activities of some of their smallest parts. The most important of these structures are **cells**. They are tiny living parts that are found in nearly every organism. You will see why cells are called "the building blocks of living things."

(Opposite page) Simple columnar epithelium.

Besides studying cells and their makeup, you will also look at some of the ways cells are organized to do certain jobs. Special cells are

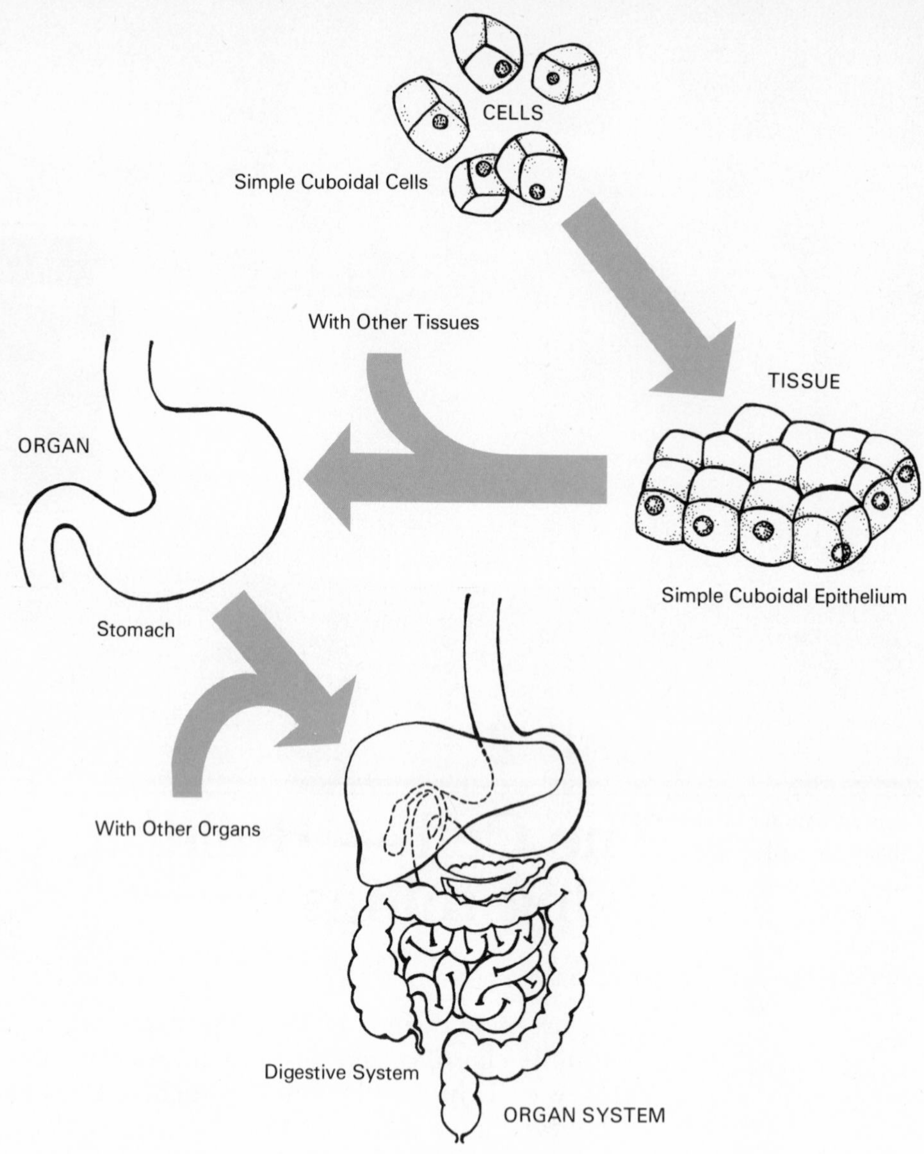

grouped together into **tissues**. Tissues are combined to form **organs**. Two or more organs working together are called **organ systems**.

The most useful tool for studying small objects is the **microscope**. Your first activity in this unit will be to learn how to use this instrument. The microscope is the key to observing the world of little things. Organisms that can be observed only with the aid of a microscope are called **microorganisms**.

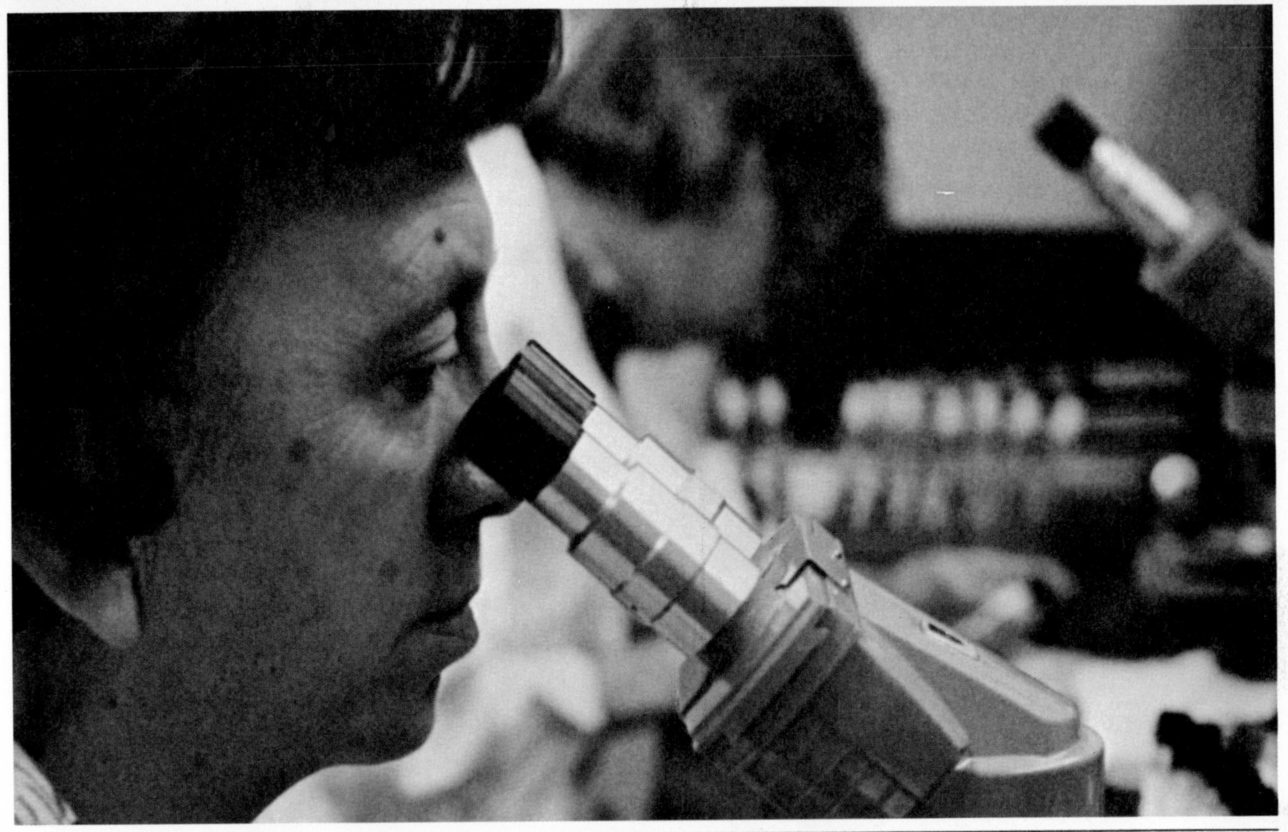

Chapter 5 The microscope

Chapter-opening photo shows a pathologist at work in a center for disease control.

The microscope is the basic tool of the biologist for studying tiny objects. You may already have used a microscope or at least looked through one. If so, you know how much more may be seen through a microscope than with the eye alone. You may also know that it can be difficult to focus and observe with a microscope if you have not been taught how to do it.

Learning how to use and care for a microscope is the main purpose of this chapter. Before you begin using the microscope, you should know something about its history.

Looking for little things

Who do you think first viewed and described objects too small to be seen with the naked eye? You might think of the early Greek and Roman civilizations. They were seekers of meaning and order in the world more than two thousand years ago. But the "natural philos-

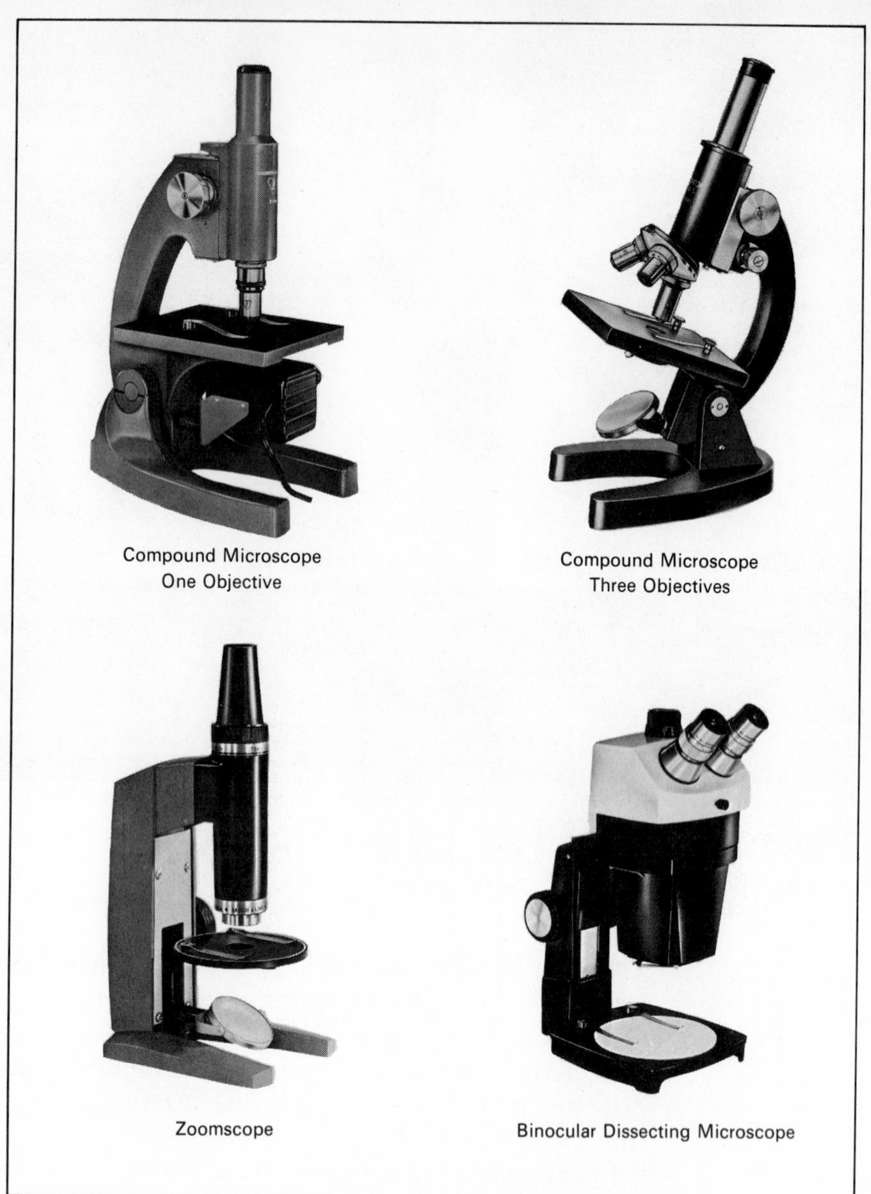

5-1. Different types of microscopes.

ophers" of ancient Greece were not able to see objects invisible to the eye. The microscope had not yet been invented. This important tool was not invented until the early 1600s.

Have you ever used a magnifying glass? That tool is a type of **simple microscope**. It is good for viewing objects such as stamps. But it can magnify only about ten times. So extremely small things cannot be observed with a magnifying glass.

5-2. A magnifying glass is a simple microscope.

5-3. Anton van Leeuwenhoek and one of his microscopes.

One of the first people to see and keep records about microorganisms was Anton van Leeuwenhoek [LAY-ven-hook]. He was a Dutch naturalist who lived from 1632 to 1723. Leeuwenhoek built many microscopes. All were of the simple (single-lens) type. But he ground his lenses so skillfully that some of them could magnify as much as 270 times.

Leeuwenhoek was not trained as a scientist. But he had a talent for careful observation. He paid attention to the smallest details. So carefully did he work that he saw and described one-celled animals that no one else did again until nearly 200 years later.

Follow Leeuwenhoek's example as you begin to use the microscope. Observe as carefully as you can. Raise questions about what you see and what it may mean. Many fascinating discoveries have been made because somebody took time to wonder, "Why?"

Microscopes today have more magnifying power than those used by Leeuwenhoek. When great magnification is desired, a compound microscope is used. The Englishman Robert Hooke (1635-1703) is credited with inventing it. A **compound microscope** is one that has at least two lenses or two sets of lenses. One lens magnifies the object being viewed. The second lens magnifies the image even more. To figure the total magnification, you multiply the power of the first lens by the power of the second. You will learn where these lenses are located and how they are used when you do Problem 5-1.

Problem 5-1 How is the compound microscope used?

Purpose To learn the parts of the compound microscope, to learn how each part functions, and to learn how to prepare wet mount slides in order to view objects under the microscope.

Materials

- compound microscope
- disposable tissues
- scissors
- tweezers
- glass slide
- cover glass
- small newsprint
- medicine dropper

Procedure

Part One: Parts of the compound microscope

Remind students that the microscope is a delicate instrument, and that they should always use both hands when carrying it.

If you carry the microscope to your work area, there is a certain procedure to follow. You are moving a delicate and expensive instrument. Place one hand on the arm and support the base with your other hand. (See Figure 5-4.) *Do not* carry any other equipment at the same time.

Steps A-H that follow describe the parts of a microscope. No two brands of microscopes are exactly alike. But the following applies to most microscopes that are used in classroom laboratories. If yours is different in some way, your teacher will tell you.

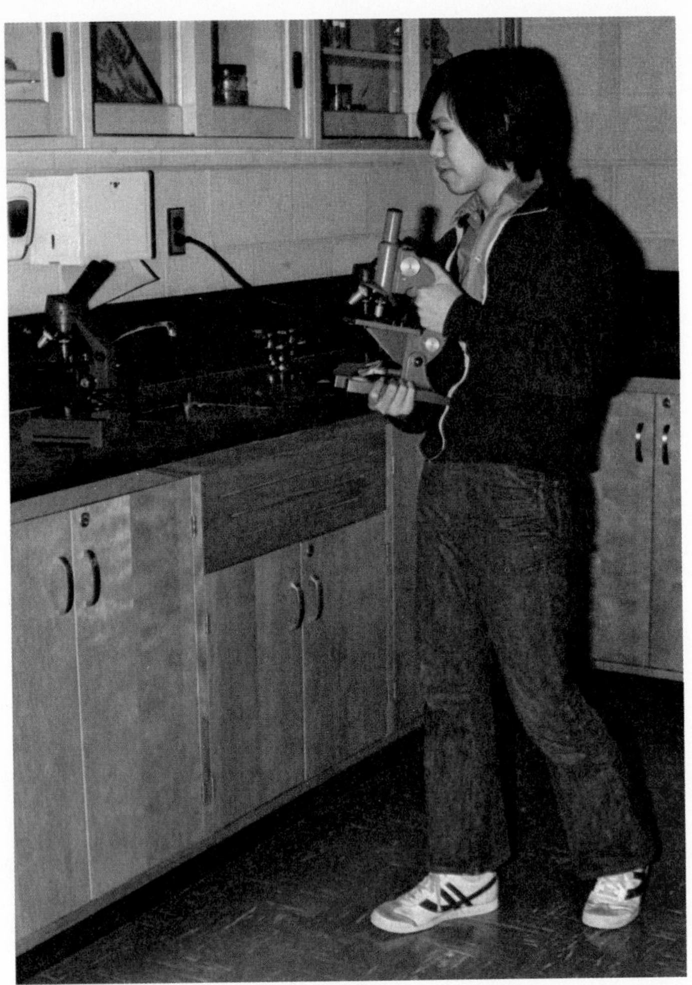

5-4. Carry a microscope with both hands.

Locate and examine each part of your microscope described in Steps A-H. Refer to Figure 5-5 as you work.

A. The **ocular lens** or **eyepiece** is at the top of the microscope. It contains a set of lenses that help magnify the object being viewed.

B. The eyepiece is located at the upper end of the tube. The *tube* is the long, hollow, upright cylinder. It forms the body of the microscope.

C. At the bottom of the tube are one or more **objective lenses**. Most microscopes used in school labs have two objective lenses. These are called the *low-power objective* and the *high-power objective*. Each has a different magnifying power. It is marked on the outside of the tube that holds the lens.

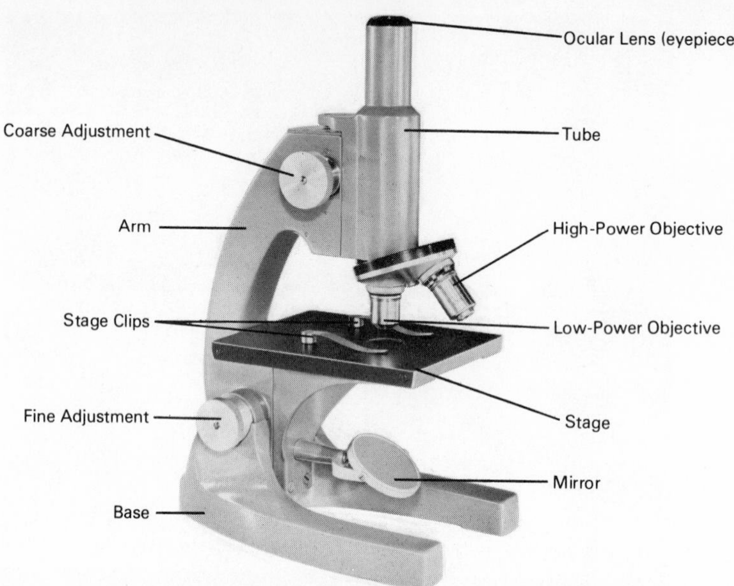

5-5. Parts of a compound microscope.

Explain that the total magnification is found by multiplying the objective magnification by the eyepiece magnification.
1. Probably 2 or 3.
2. Answer depends on microscope being used.
3. Answer depends on microscope being used.

Suppose an objective is marked "10×." That means the lens forms an **image** that is ten times greater than the real size of the object being observed. The image formed by the objective lens is further magnified by the ocular lens.

1. How many objective lenses does your microscope have?
2. What is the lowest magnification of your microscope?
3. What is the highest magnification of your microscope?

D. The tube is attached to the *arm*. On the arm are the two knobs that are used to focus the microscope. The *coarse-adjustment knob* is usually the larger of the two knobs. It is located near the top of the arm. The *fine-adjustment knob* is usually at the bottom of the arm, near the base.

When you turn the adjustment knobs, the tube will go up or down. In some models it is the stage that moves. This movement of the tube or stage **focuses**, or sharpens, the image of the object being viewed.

E. The *stage* is the platform upon which the object is placed for observation. There is an opening in the center of the stage. The opening permits light to pass from below upward through the object being studied.

F. Two *spring clips*, or *stage clips*, are mounted on the stage. These hold the slide firmly in place.

G. The *mirror* is attached to the base on a movable arm. It is used to direct light upward through the lenses. Some microscopes are equipped with a direct light source rather than a mirror.

H. The *base* is the heavy, U-shaped anchor that supports the microscope on the table.

Part Two: How to prepare wet mount slides

Demonstrate the procedure for preparing a wet mount, particularly how to lower the cover glass.

I. Obtain a microscope slide and a cover glass. *Handle the slide and cover glass carefully. They are easily broken.* Carefully clean the slide and cover glass with a tissue. *Handle the slide and cover glass by the edges only. Avoid getting fingerprints on the glass.*

J. Use a medicine dropper to put a small drop of water in the center of the slide. In the **wet mount slide** you are making, water is the *mounting medium*. A mounting medium is necessary for a clear image of the specimen.

K. From the small newsprint, cut a single word containing the letter "e." Pick up the word with tweezers. Place the word right side up in the drop of water on the slide. Let the newsprint absorb the water. Then add a small drop of water to the top of the word.

L. With your thumb and forefinger, place the edge of the cover glass on the slide at the edge of the water drop. As shown in Figure 5-6, hold the cover glass at about a 30° angle to the slide. Then gently lower the cover glass over the drop.

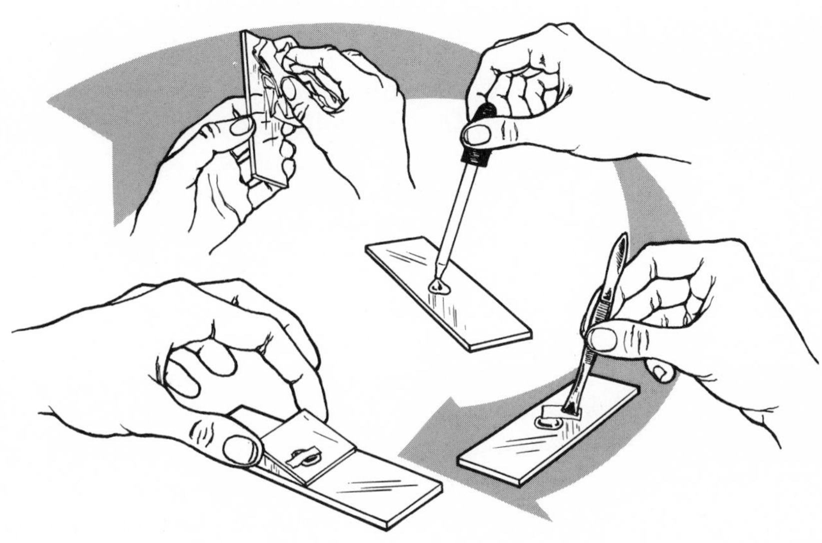

5-6. Preparing a wet mount slide.

4. If air bubbles are present, they were caused by air trapped under the cover glass while it was being lowered onto the slide.

4. Can you see any air bubbles? How would they get there?
5. Why should you try to avoid trapping air bubbles?

5. They can interfere with observation.

Part Three: How to focus a microscope

M. Put the microscope on the table or counter top with the arm toward you and the base a safe distance from the edge. Adjust your position so that you can look into the eyepiece easily.

You may want to demonstrate how to clean lenses with lens tissue, and have students do this themselves.

N. If the lens appears dirty, ask your teacher to clear the glass surfaces with lens paper. Clean the eyepiece, the objectives, and the mirror. *Only lens paper should be used.* Lenses should be wiped in one direction only — *not* with a circular motion.

O. Place your wet mount slide on the stage of the microscope. Clip the slide in place, then move it with your thumbs and forefingers until the "e" is centered over the opening in the stage.

CAUTION: Raise the tube so that the lenses will not hit the slide as you do Step P.

P. The objective lenses are attached to a movable plate. Rotate that plate until the low-power objective clicks into place. This puts the objective in line with the tube of the microscope.

If students' microscopes have iris diaphragms or other light-regulating devices, demonstrate how these are used.

Q. While looking through the eyepiece, turn the mirror toward a light source. *Never aim the mirror directly toward the sun.* Adjust the mirror until a uniform circle of light, without any shadow, appears. This circle of light is the **field of view** of the microscope. Your microscope probably has a device to further regulate the amount of light. Your teacher will show you how to use it. This *iris diaphragm* is a common device used to adjust the amount of light.

R. Look throuqh the eyepiece with one eye only, but *keep both eyes open*. Do not squint the eye you are not using. You may cover it loosely with your hand or a blank piece of paper, but keep it open. This is important to avoid straining your eyes.

S. Now look at the microscope from the side. Turn the coarse-adjustment knob to lower the low-power objective toward the slide. Lower it as far as it will go. The bottom of the objective should then be about one centimeter from the slide.

T. Now look through the eyepiece again. With the coarse adjustment, raise the tube slowly until the letter appears. Move the coarse-adjustment knob back and forth to find the clearest image of the letter. After this coarse adjustment, carefully turn the fine-adjustment knob to improve the focus.

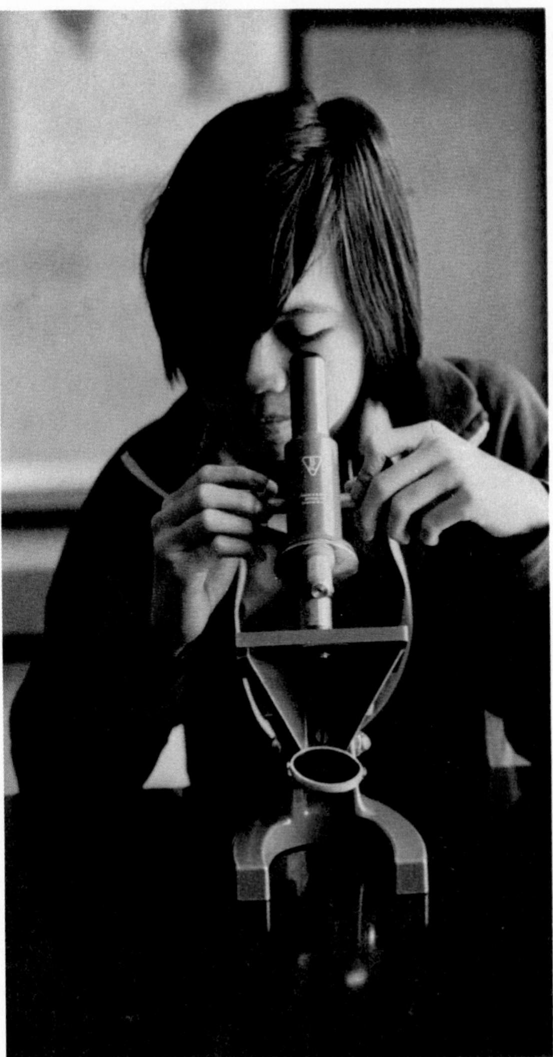

5-7. The student on the left adjusts the mirror, and the student on the right focuses the microscope.

When using low power, always focus first with the coarse adjustment. Then sharpen the focus with the fine adjustment.

U. Now look from the side again. Carefully switch to the high-power lens. Be sure that the tube is high enough that the lens will not hit the slide. Look at the letter through the eyepiece. If the letter is not in focus, slowly turn the *fine*-adjustment knob until the letter is in sharp focus.

CAUTION: Never use the coarse adjustment with the high-power objective lens.

6. Student's answer should summarize techniques described in Part Three, Steps M-U (pages 76-78).

7. Answer should summarize technique described in Part Two, Steps I-L (pages 75-76).

An object is always focused first under the low-power objective. Use the coarse adjustment first, then the fine adjustment. If greater magnification is desired, switch the lens to high power. When using high power, use only the fine-adjustment knob to focus.

V. Preparing wet mount slides and focusing are important aspects of biological lab work. If you have time, repeat Steps I-U with other letters and words to improve your techniques.

6. Briefly outline the major steps you should follow when focusing a microscope.
7. Describe how to prepare a wet mount slide.

You should now be able to

Identify the main parts of the microscope.
Demonstrate or describe how each part of the microscope functions.
Focus the microscope at different magnifications.
Prepare wet mount slides for use with the microscope.

Movement under the microscope

You have just finished your first lab problem using the compound microscope. You are beginning to learn how useful a tool the microscope is. You probably noticed that the microscope "changed" the letters you looked at. The image you saw through the eyepiece looked different than the letters you put on the slide.

Consider what happens when you view a slide with a projector. If you put the slide in right side up, the image on the screen is upside down. If you push the slide into the projector from the right, the image comes onto the screen from the left.

Magnifying lenses in certain optical instruments turn the image upside down and backwards. This effect is known as *inversion*. In Problem 5-2 you will study how the image seems to move when the object on the stage is moved.

You learned in Problem 5-1 the correct way to handle and use a microscope. You are to follow these directions in all further use of the microscope. If you did not do Problem 5-1, see your teacher for special instructions.

Problem 5-2 How does the position of an object appear to change when viewed through a microscope?

Purpose To learn how the position of the image seen through the eyepiece differs from the position of the object on the stage of the microscope.

Materials

compound microscope	cover glass	tweezers
scissors	newsprint	slide

Procedure Before starting this investigation, be sure you know the parts of the microscope and know how to focus it. (Refer to Problem 5-1.)

Caution students to be very careful when moving microscopes. They should use two hands to carry the instrument, and never set the microscope down near the edge of the table.

A. Position the microscope for low-power magnification. While looking through the eyepiece, turn on your light source and adjust the mirror. You should have a uniform, bright field of view.

B. Prepare a wet mount slide of the letter "e" from small newsprint. (See Problem 5-1, Part Two.) Use the tweezers to place the word on the slide *right side up*.

C. Place your wet mount slide on the stage of the microscope. Center the letter "e" over the opening in the stage. Check to be sure the letter "e" is right side up on the stage. Focus the microscope, still at low power.

D. Compare the position of the letter as it is mounted with its appearance in the eyepiece.

1. How has the microscope changed the position of the letter?

1. Letter is upside down and reversed.

E. While looking through the eyepiece, slowly push the slide away from you with your thumbs.

2. In which direction does the letter move in the field of view?

2. Toward the student.

F. Reposition the slide so that the "e" is again centered over the opening. Look through the eyepiece and move the slide to the left.

3. How does the position of the letter seem to change?

3. The letter appears to move to the right when the object is moved to the left.

In Steps E and F, you moved the object on the stage and watched what happened to the image as seen through the eyepiece. This showed you how an object *appears* to move when the slide is moved. But you were really watching the image move. In Step G, you will leave the object in one place on the stage. This time you will watch what happens to the image as you move the objective lenses.

6. Letter should be drawn upside down and reversed.

7. Only a small portion of the letter is seen. The letter does not appear to be perfectly solid and students should indicate this in their drawings.

G. Move the letter "e" to the exact center of the field of view. Check for sharp focus. Now, switch to the high-power objective. Remember, focus *only* with the fine adjustment when using high power.

4. Is the same amount of the letter "e" visible under high power as under low power? 4. No. Less of the letter is seen.
5. Is the light in the field of view brighter under high power or under low power? 5. Under low power.
6. Make a drawing of the letter "e" as it appears in the low-power field.
7. Then draw the portion of the "e" that remains in the high-power field.

You should now be able to

Describe how the position of the image seen through the eyepiece differs from the position of the object on the stage.

Predict which way the image will move when the slide is moved on the stage.

Describe how the image will change as the magnification is increased or decreased.

Metric measurement

You have seen how the image appears to move when the actual object is moved under the microscope. You have seen how the image of an object appears reversed when compared to the object. In the next problem, you will measure the diameter of your microscope's circular field of view. (A circle's *diameter* is the length of an imaginary line drawn from one edge of the circle through the center to the other edge.)

To measure the diameter of the field of view, you will look at a clear plastic ruler under the microscope. Suppose you looked at a ruler with a magnifying glass. The ruler would look bigger, right? You will see the same effect with your microscope. A small section of the ruler will fill the entire field of view. (See Figure 5-8.)

Put a diagram of a small section of a metric ruler on the board. Label the divisions (centimeter and millimeter) and indicate that one millimeter equals 1,000 microns.

As you learned in Chapter 1, the **metric system** of measurement uses units related in multiples of ten. Its basic unit of length is the meter. A meter is about 39 inches, or slightly more than a yard. The units you will use in the next problem are centimeters, millimeters, and microns, all smaller divisions of the meter.

A **centimeter (cm)** is 1/100 of a meter. A **millimeter (mm)** is 1/1,000 of a meter. A **micron** (μ) is 1/1,000 of a millimeter, or 1/1,000,000 of a meter. You will be making measurements with a metric ruler. When you measure length in metric units, keep the following in mind —

$$1 \text{ cm} = 10 \text{ mm}$$
$$1 \text{ mm} = 1{,}000\ \mu$$

A centimeter is approximately as wide as the end of your little finger. A millimeter is approximately the thickness of a dime.

Problem 5-3 How is the field of view of the microscope measured?

Purpose To measure the diameter of a microscope's field of view.

Materials compound microscope; clear plastic metric ruler

Procedure

A. Place the clear plastic ruler on the stage of the microscope. Bring the lines on the ruler into sharp focus under low power. Move the ruler so that one of the lines is just visible at the edge of the field.

B. Now count how many lines you can see within the field of view from one side to the other. The space between each line is one millimeter (mm).

5-8. You can measure the field of view for both a hand lens and a microscope by counting the millimeter marks seen in each.

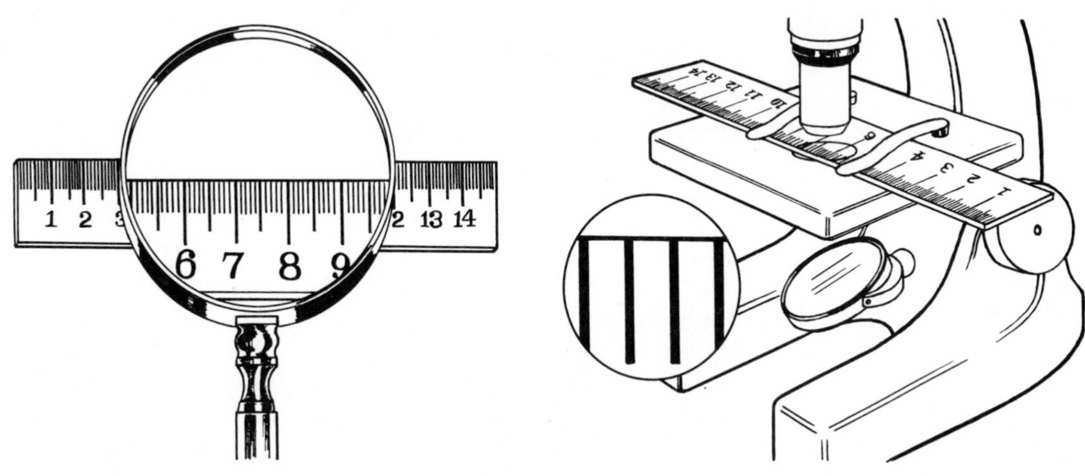

1. Answers depend on microscope being used.

1. What is the diameter in millimeters of the low-power magnification field of your microscope?

C. Now use the ruler to measure the diameter of the field at high-power magnification.

2. Answers depend on microscopes being used.

3. Smaller.

2. What is the diameter of the field at high power?

3. Did the size of the field get larger or smaller as the magnification increased from low to high power?

D. There are 1,000 microns in one millimeter. To change millimeters to microns, multiply the millimeters by 1,000.

4. See student answers to Questions 1 and 2. To find diameter in microns, multiply these values by 1,000.

4. What is the diameter of the field in microns at low power? At high power?

E. The total magnification of the microscope and the size of the field are said to be *inversely proportional*. As the magnification *increases*, the size of the field *decreases* by the same factor. For example, suppose a field of view measured 20 mm at 50× magnification. It would measure 5 mm at 200× magnification. As the magnification increased by a factor of four, the field size became one-fourth of the original size.

You should now be able to

Measure the diameter of the field of view of a microscope at different magnifications.

Convert the field diameter measurement from millimeters to microns.

Calculate the decrease in size of the field by knowing the increase in magnification.

Measuring with a microscope

You have learned how to measure the field diameter of a microscope at two magnifications. You will now use that knowledge to estimate the size of some small objects viewed through the microscope. Consider an example, on a larger scale, of how you could estimate the size of objects in a field of known size.

A football playing field is one hundred yards long. It is divided into ten-yard sections by lines called yard markers. Look at Figure 5-9. Read the caption to see how you can estimate the lengths of cars parked on an unused playing field.

5-9. Notice that none of the cars reaches from one yard marker to the next. This tells you that no car is 10 yards long. Look at the bumper-to-bumper cars between the 40- and 50-yard lines. From this, you can estimate each car to be about 5 yards long.

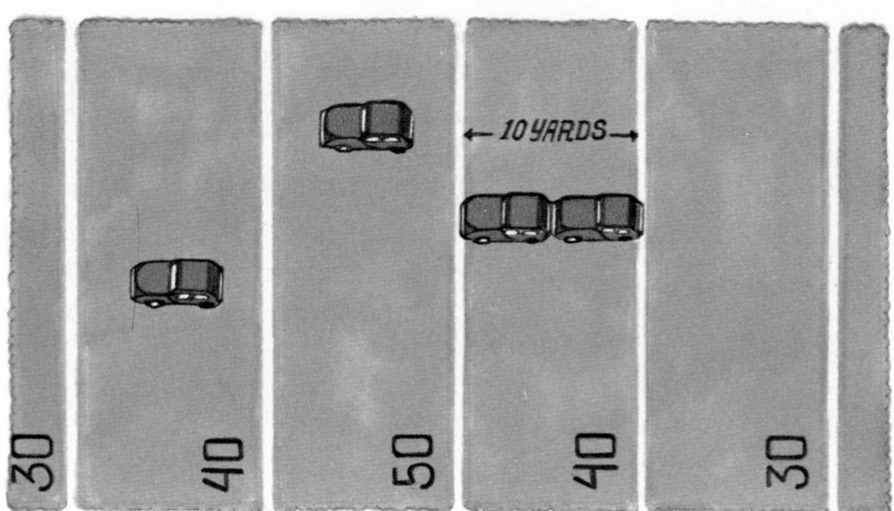

In the next problem you will estimate the size of objects under the microscope. The millimeter marks on the ruler will be your "yard markers." You will have to estimate size when an object does not extend exactly from one marker to the next. And remember that the field diameter gets smaller as the magnification gets higher. Don't try to do Problem 5-4 unless you have done Problem 5-3.

Problem 5-4 How is the microscope used to measure small objects?

Purpose To estimate tbe size of objects by comparing the size of their images with the field diameter. To compare an object's high-power and low-power diameters.

Materials

compound microscope	cover glass	cotton thread
glass slide	scissors	piano wire (very fine)
medicine dropper	tweezers	string

Procedure

A. Prepare a wet mount slide of a single piece of cotton thread.

B. Place the wet mount slide on the stage. Observe under *low* power. Estimate the diameter of the cotton thread. (Recall the low-power field diameter of your microscope. See Problem 5-3, question 4.)

1. Value should be that recorded for Question 4 in Problem 5-3.

1. What is the diameter in microns (μ) of your microscope field under low power?

2. One-half of value recorded for low-power field diameter in Question 1.

3. Average diameter for size 50 thread is 250-300 microns. (You should measure the thread before class.)

4. See Problem 5-3, Question 4.

5. Should approximate student's answer to Question 3.

6. Should be approximately equal. Students may be able to estimate more accurately with high power, since thread may occupy nearly 1/3 of field.

2. If the width of an object took up half the field of view under low power, how many microns wide would the object be?

3. What is your estimate of the diameter of the cotton thread in microns?

C. Change to high power. Focus with fine adjustment if necessary.

4. What is the diameter in microns (μ) of your microscope field under high power? (See Problem 5-3, question 4.)

5. What is your estimate of the diameter of the thread under high power in microns?

6. How does your estimate of the diameter of the thread under high power compare to the estimated diameter under low power?

D. Figure 5-10 shows a microorganism viewed under both low power and high power. Notice that the cell looks larger in the high-power field. But notice also that the high-power field diameter is much smaller than the low-power field diameter.

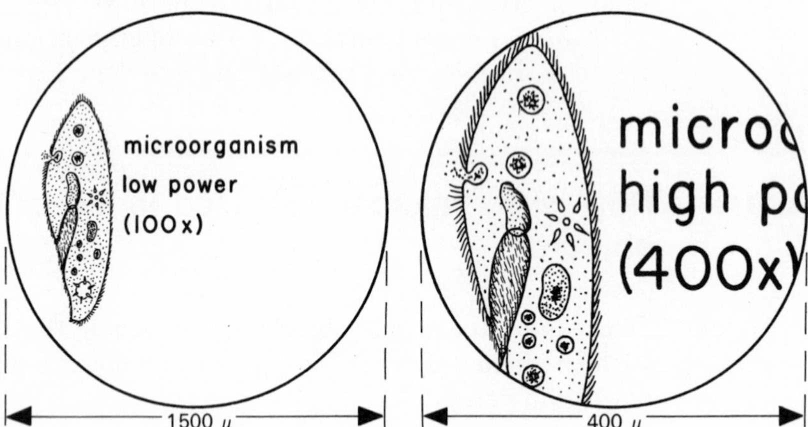

5-10. Microorganism viewed under low power (*left*) and under high power (*right*).

7. No. (But estimate may become more accurate.)

8. Yes. (Since object occupies more of field of view.)

9. The values found for each of the objects may vary. You should measure the objects beforehand and accept a reasonable range of answers from the class.

7. Does increasing the magnification change the estimated size of an object?

8. Does higher magnification help you measure more accurately?

E. Prepare slides of wire, string, and human hair.

9. What is the diameter in microns of each of these strands at both low-power and high-power magnifications? (Record the measurements in a chart like Table 5-1.)

A small piece of nylon stocking is interesting when viewed under high and low power.

TABLE 5-1 MEASURING WITH THE MICROSCOPE

Material	*Diameter in Microns*	
	50x	200×
Cotton Thread		
Piano Wire		
String		
Human Hair		

You should now be able to

Estimate the size of an object in microns from the known diameter of the field.

Use the microscope to measure the size of tiny objects in microns.

1. It has a clearly defined image.
2. Object magnified 50 times actual size.
3. Light source and adjustment knobs.
4. (a) *Arm:* holds lens assembly and is used for carrying microscope. (b) *Mirror:* reflects light into lenses. (c) *Stage clip:* holds slide on stage. (d) *Coarse-adjustment knob:* moves objective (or stage), thus focusing microscope.
5. Student should describe the technique outlined in Part Two of Problem 5-1 (pages 75-76).
6. Image would appear upside down and backwards.

Science terms

centimeter (cm)
compound microscope
field of view
focus
image
metric system
micron (μ)
microorganism
millimeter (mm)
objective lens
ocular lens (eyepiece)
simple microscope
wet mount slide

Review questions

1. What do you mean when you say that an object is "in focus"?
2. What does 50× mean?
3. What parts of a microscope are used to get an object in focus?
4. Give the function of the following parts of the microscope:
   a. arm
   b. mirror
   c. stage clip
   d. coarse-adjustment knob
5. Describe the preparation of a wet mount slide.
6. How would the image of the letter "b" appear when viewed through the microscope?

7. Image becomes darker.
8. To the left.
9. 10 mm.
10. 1,000 microns.
11. 1,000 microns.
12. A simple microscope has only one lens. A compound microscope has 2 lenses or 2 sets of lenses that together form the image.
13. It becomes smaller.
14. (a) eyepiece lens, (b) tube, (c) arm, (d) coarse adjustment, (e) stage clips, (f) objective lens, (g) stage, (h) mirror, (i) base. Answers should also include the functions, as described in Problem 5-1.

7. How does the brightness of an image change when the magnification is moved from low to high power?
8. If a microscope slide on the stage is moved to the right, in which direction does the image move?
9. How many millimeters are there in one centimeter?
10. How many microns are there in one millimeter?
11. Estimate the diameter in microns of the object in Figure 5-11.
12. What is the difference between a simple and a compound microscope?
13. How does the field of view change when you move from low to high magnification?
14. Refer to Figure 5-12. Identify the parts of the microscope indicated by the letters. Write the letters in your notebook and write the name of each part next to each letter. Briefly describe the function of each part. (Do not write in this text.)

See Teacher's Guide section for answers to Questions 15-21.

Check your understanding

15. Why should only lens paper be used to clean a microscope lens?
16. Suppose an ocular lens is 10×. What power must the objective lens be to give a total magnification of 250×?
17. Why must only thin objects be viewed through a compound microscope?
18. Why is water added in making a wet mount slide?

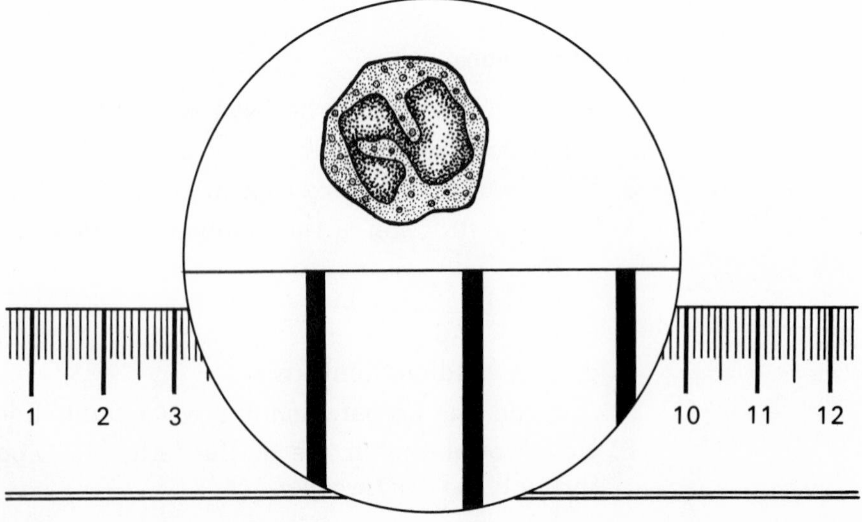

5-11. Use for question 11. Remember that the smallest divisions on the ruler are each equal to one millimeter.

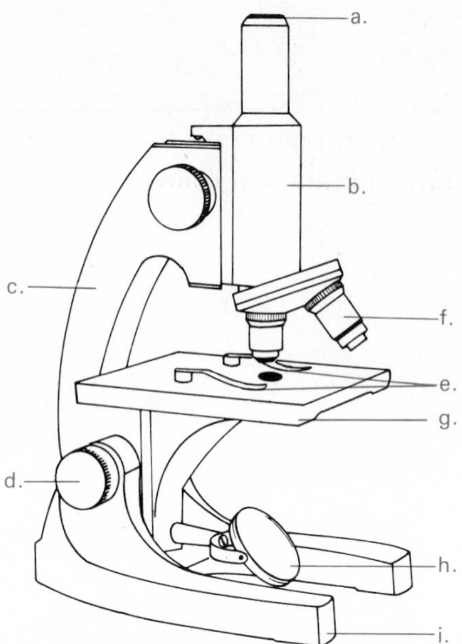

5-12. Use for question 14.

19. Why should air bubbles be removed from wet mount slides?
20. The micron is a unit of measurement you may never have used before. How is this unit now useful to you?
21. Why is it difficult to find an object on a slide when you try to locate it under high power?

Chapter 6 Cell structures

Chapter-opening photo of elodea leaf cells could be compared with the cork cells seen by Robert Hooke (Figure 6-1).

Robert Hooke was an English scientist who lived from 1635 to 1703. He was the first person to observe cells. He discovered them in a very thin piece of cork under a crude microscope. This was soon after the invention of the microscope in the early 1600s.

Figure 6-1 shows what Hooke saw — some very tiny spaces in the cork. Even though he called the spaces "cells", Hooke did not know anything about them. It was not until the early 1800s that the first clear ideas about cells were presented.

Two German biologists, Matthias Schleiden [SHLY-den] and Theodor Schwann [SHVON], are credited with the "cell theory." They made the first complete statements about the structure and function of cells in 1839. The observations of other scientists also contributed to the cell theory.

Briefly, the **cell theory** states:

(*Above*) Elodea leaf cells.

1. Living things are composed of cells and cell products.

6-1. In 1665, with this microscope, English scientist Robert Hooke saw cork cells that looked like these.

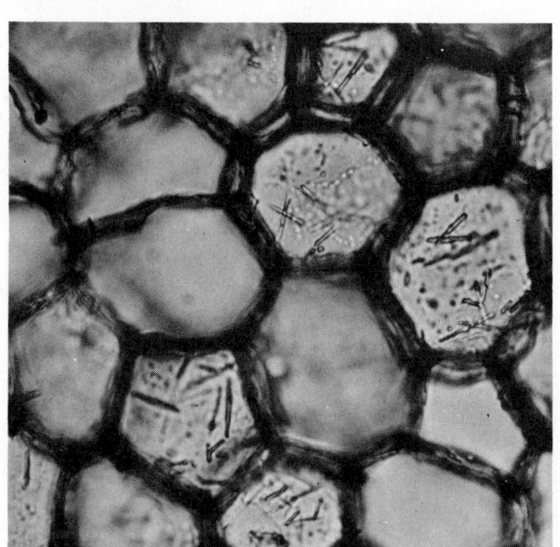

6-2. Cork cells as seen through a modern microscope.

2. All life functions are performed by individual cells or groups of cells.
3. Cells are produced from other cells.

The cell theory has been one of the key ideas that have helped to explain the activities of living things. You will better understand the theory after you use your microscope to examine different kinds of living things.

6-3. Matthias Schleiden (*left*) and Theodor Schwann (*right*).

What are cells like?

Have you heard the story about the six blindfolded people who tried to describe an elephant? One of them felt the side of the elephant and said, "This animal is very like a wall." Another person felt the tail and said, "This animal is like a rope." Still another person touched the elephant's trunk and said it was like a snake. The other three blindfolded people came up with three other descriptions based on their "observations."

Trying to describe a cell in one simple statement is like trying to describe that elephant without seeing it. You will need to observe a few different cells. Then you should be able to form your own answer to the question "What are cells like?"

6-4. Each blindfolded person described the part of the elephant he or she happened to touch.

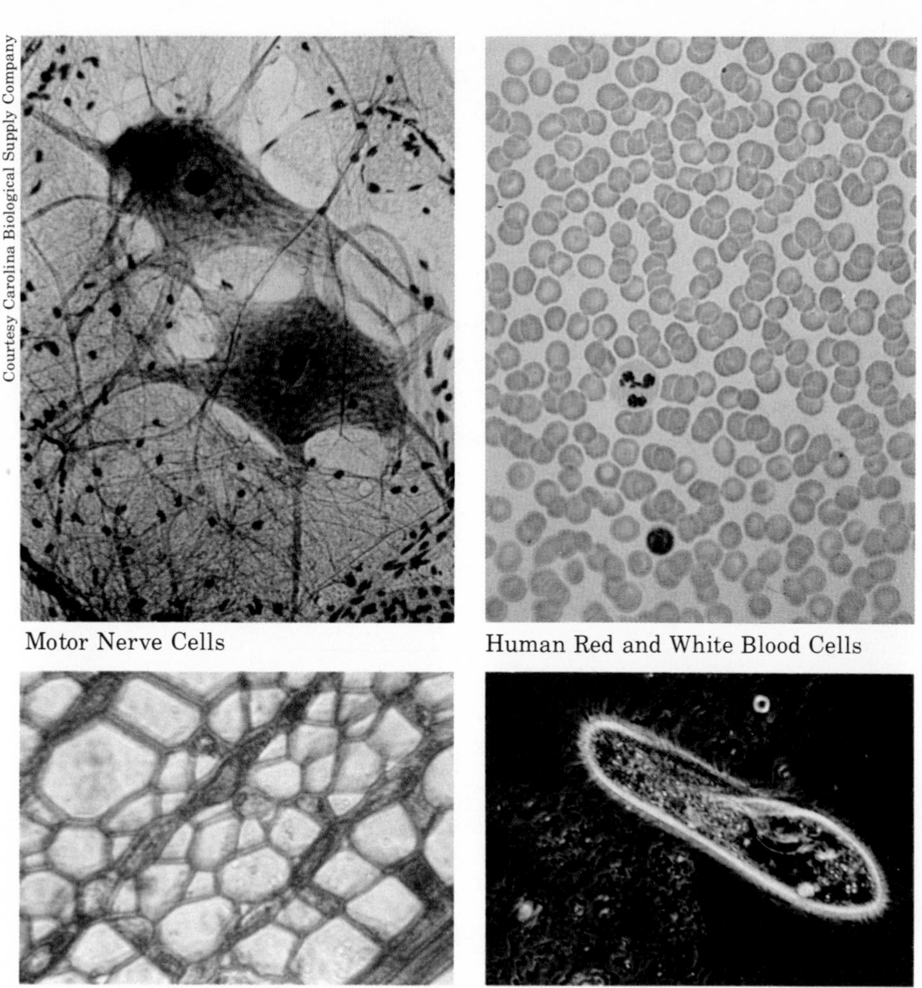

Motor Nerve Cells
Human Red and White Blood Cells
Plant Conducting Cells
Paramecium, a Single Cell

6-5. Several types of cells as seen through the microscope.

A few types of cells as seen under a microscope are shown in Figure 6-5. One important thing to keep in mind is that cells are living material. They are responsible for all the life processes carried on by living things. Life processes were discussed in Chapter 4.

Cells come in many sizes and shapes. You can see some of the shapes in Figure 6-5. As for sizes, a nerve cell that connects the spinal cord with a finger or toe may be as long as a meter. But you would have trouble seeing a nerve cell because it is very narrow. Most cells are invisible to the unaided eye and can be seen only through a microscope. One cell that you can see with the unaided eye is an egg cell. Would you believe that the egg of a chicken is a single cell?

To get an idea how small the average cell is, see Figure 6-6 on the next page. The head of a pin is about one millimeter in diameter. Suppose it were covered with cells of the average size found in your

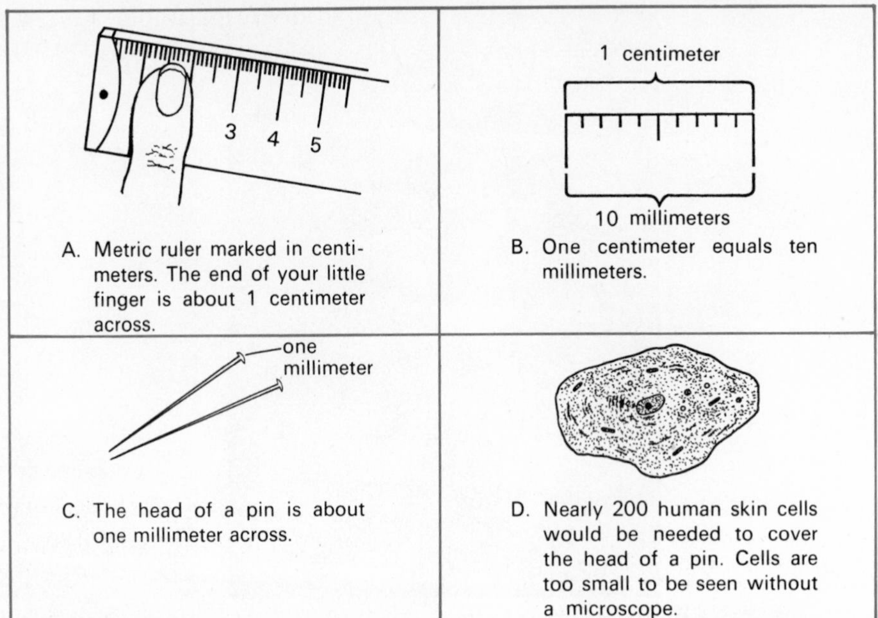

A. Metric ruler marked in centimeters. The end of your little finger is about 1 centimeter across.

B. One centimeter equals ten millimeters.

C. The head of a pin is about one millimeter across.

D. Nearly 200 human skin cells would be needed to cover the head of a pin. Cells are too small to be seen without a microscope.

6-6. Comparing the sizes of objects in metric units.

body. The head of the pin would have from 175 to 200 cells on it. A cell in your skin is about one-hundredth of a millimeter, or ten microns, in diameter. (One micron equals one-thousandth of a millimeter.) You can see why a microscope is needed to look at cells.

Parts of the cell

You will examine several kinds of living cells with a microscope. Figure 6-7 shows some of the structures that you are likely to see. No one description of the parts of a cell will fit every kind of cell. Figure 6-7 shows some "typical" cell features.

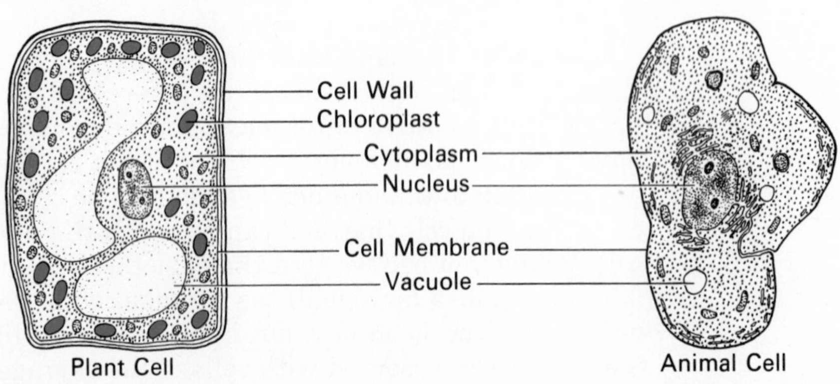

6-7. Typical plant and animal cells.

When a cell is stained and viewed under a microscope, some special structures stand out. One structure is the **nucleus**, a rounded, darker body often near the center of the cell. Another kind of living material that is easily seen is the cytoplasm. The **cytoplasm** is a granular liquid between the nucleus and the boundary of the cell.

The boundary of the cell is the **cell membrane**. Plant cells have an additional covering outside the membrane called the **cell wall**. The cell wall is composed of a nonliving substance called **cellulose**.

Some plant cells also contain green structures within the cytoplasm. These are **chloroplasts**. They contain a substance called **chlorophyll**. Chlorophyll converts light energy into chemical energy, which the plant uses to make food.

Found in the cytoplasm of both plant and animal cells are **vacuoles**. A vacuole appears as a clear area within the cytoplasm. It is surrounded by a thin membrane. Vacuoles seem to be used by the cell for storage of food, water, or waste materials. They also release waste materials from the cell.

Table 6-1 lists the cell parts mentioned above, along with the function of each part. Cells contain many other structures that we have

TABLE 6-1 CELL STRUCTURES AND WHAT THEY DO

Part of a Cell	*What It Does*
Nucleus	Controls total life activity of cell
Cytoplasm	Part of cell outside nucleus; contains other important cell structures
Cell membrane	Outer covering of a cell; holds in the cytoplasm but allows dissolved material to enter and leave the cell
Vacuole	Clear area within the cytoplasm surrounded by a membrane; contains food or cell wastes for storage or removal
Cell wall	Structure found outside the membrane of plant cells; composed of nonliving cellulose; strengthens plant tissues
Chloroplast	Green-colored body in the cytoplasm of most plant cells; contains chlorophyll

not mentioned. These structures, however, are too small to be seen through your microscope. You may not even be able to find all the structures listed in Table 6-1 in each cell that you observe. The important thing is to recognize the structures that all cells have in common and to get some understanding of what these structures do.

Back to the laboratory

In Problem 6-1, you will use what you have learned about making measurements with the microscope and preparing wet mount slides. You will prepare slides of living cells and make your own observations of them. As you do this, keep in mind that no other person has seen the same cells you are seeing. Don't be afraid to ask about something you don't understand. You may see something that has not been described. Many discoveries have been made because someone was curious enough to look for things not described in a book.

Problem 6-1 What are the parts of an onion skin cell?

Purpose To observe onion skin cells and to locate the various parts of a plant cell.

Materials

microscope	methylene blue stain	kitchen knife
slides (2)	medicine dropper	metric ruler
cover glasses (2)	onion	tweezers

Procedure

If some teams have difficulty with the procedure, you may want to demonstrate the removal of a scale and peeling the membrane from it. Float the tissue in a dish of water for the use of any teams that need it.

A. Prepare a wet mount slide of onion skin cells as follows. Cut the onion into four sections. (See Figure 6-8.) Separate the layers of one section. Each layer is a *scale*. Take one scale. Use tweezers to remove the thin, transparent membrane from the inner surface as shown in Figure 6-8.

Place a small, flat piece of this onion membrane on a glass slide. Cover the membrane with a drop of water and a cover glass. Be careful to keep the membrane from folding and wrinkling.

B. Observe the slide under both low-power and high-power magnifications.

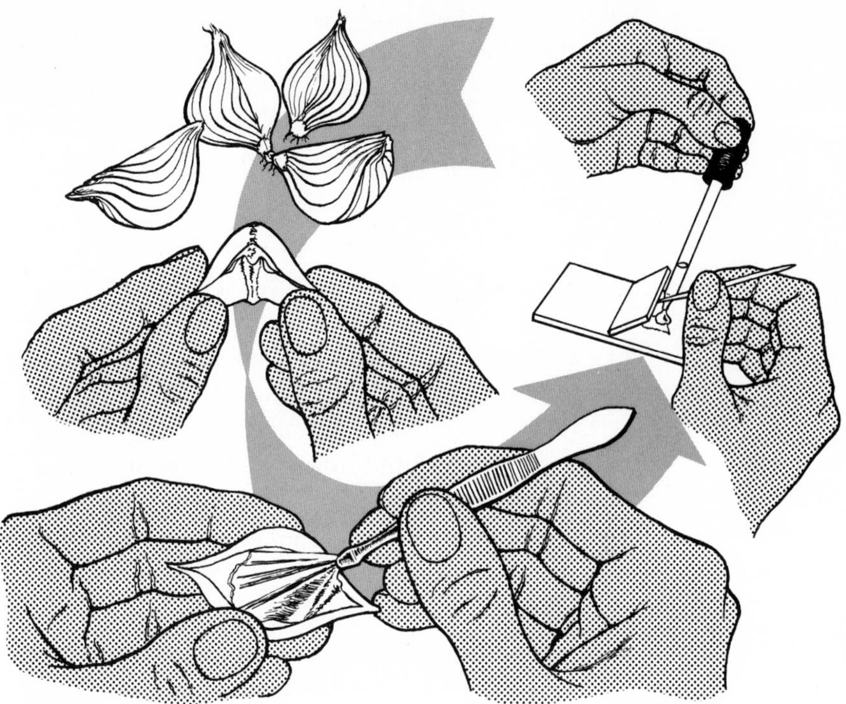

6-8. To prepare an onion skin slide, cut an onion into quarters. Next, remove the inner membrane from one scale, as shown. Place the membrane on a slide, add a drop of water, and carefully place a cover glass on top.

1. Many cells.
2. Rectangular.
3. Objects most likely to be seen in sketches are nucleus, cytoplasm, and cell wall.
4. Length will vary from 100 to 400 microns.
5. Yes.
6. Most students will see nucleus and cytoplasm.

1. Is the membrane composed of one cell or many cells?
2. What is the general shape of these cells?
3. Make a sketch of a few cells as seen under high power.
4. Estimate the length in microns of the cells as seen under high power. (Count the number of cells, laid end-to-end, necessary to cross the diameter of the field. Divide the number of cells into the known field diameter. Refer back to Problem 5-3, if necessary, to find the field diameter under low or high power.)
5. Do the cells have a cell wall?
6. Can you see any other structures inside of the cell? If so, label them in your drawing.

C. Carefully lift the cover glass and add a drop of methylene blue stain to the onion skin.

D. Observe the slide under both low-power and high-power magnifications.

8. To color the cytoplasm and nucleus so that they can be seen more easily. The stain increases the contrast between nucleus and cytoplasm.

7. Can you still see the double outer layer, the cell wall? 7. Yes.
8. Why was the stain added? (Compare the detail of this slide with the unstained slide that you prepared in Step A).
9. Can you see the dark, round nucleus inside the cell? Do all the cells have a nucleus? The nucleus (plural *nuclei*) is the control center of the cell. 9. Most cells will have visible nuclei.
10. Can you see more than one nucleus inside the cell?

10. No. If students reply "yes," they may be seeing a double or folded layer of cells.

11. Can you see the lightly stained, granular cytoplasm within the cells? 11. Yes.
12. Draw a few cells of the stained onion skin as seen under both low and high power. Label the structures you can see.

You should now be able to

Prepare a wet mount slide of a piece of onion skin so that the cells can be observed as a single layer.

Identify the cell wall, cytoplasm, and nucleus of an onion skin cell under the microscope.

Use methylene blue to stain the contents of a cell.

Locate the dark, central nucleus and granular cytoplasm of a cell by the use of methylene blue stain.

Estimate the length of a single onion skin cell.

12. Structures most likely to be drawn and identified are nucleus, cytoplasm, and cell wall. Several cells should be seen under low power, but only 1 or 2 under high power.

Observing animal cells

You have now prepared and observed onion skin cells. They represent one kind of plant cell. You will now look at some animal cells that are very near to you — the cells that line your own cheek. While you are studying these cells, keep in mind the differences between animal cells and plant cells. Look for features that are similar as well as features that are different.

Another reminder: Keep your notebook neat and complete. Remember that good record-keeping forms the foundation for scientific knowledge. It provides the basis on which further work can depend. Therefore, the most important function of your lab notebook is that it act as a complete record of your experiments. Other people should be able to pick it up and get an accurate picture of what you observed and how you interpreted results.

So be sure to make all drawings neat and label them. Answer questions with complete statements. If you are absent, ask your teacher for instructions concerning makeup work.

Problem 6-2 What are the parts of a human cheek cell?

Purpose To observe cheek cell structures and describe their functions. To compare plant cells with animal cells.

Materials

microscope
slide
cover glass
medicine dropper
methylene blue stain
toothpick, flat-edged

Procedure

Part One: Preparing a wet mount slide of cheek cells

In Step D, too much light will make the colorless cheek cells almost invisible. Direct students to look for single cells in order to observe their characteristic structure and shape.

A. Put a drop of water in the center of the slide.

B. *Gently* scrape the inside of your cheek with the side of a flat-edged toothpick to obtain the cells. *Be careful not to injure your cheek.*

C. Stir the drop of water with the toothpick. This will transfer the grayish cheek material to the slide.

D. Add a cover slip. Observe the slide under both low power and high power. Use the lowest light intensity.

1. What color are the cheek cells?
2. Look at the dark outline around the cells. How does this outer boundary compare with that of a plant cell? (Is it a single or double layer?) The outer edge of an animal cell is the **cell membrane**.
3. What is another difference between a cell membrane (animal cell) and a cell wall (plant cell)?

1. Almost colorless.

2. Membrane is thinner than outer boundary of onion cells. It is a single layer, and is not as distinct as the cell wall of an onion skin cell.

3. The cell walls of plant cells are rigid, giving them a definite rectangular shape.

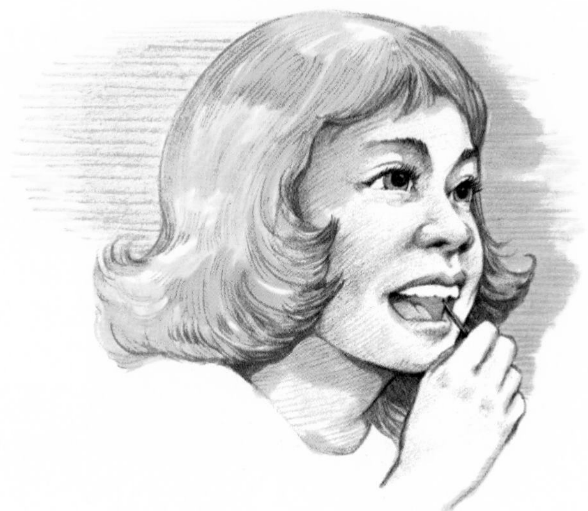

6-9. *Gently* scrape the inside of your cheek with the flat edge of a toothpick.

Part Two: Examining stained cheek cells

7. To stain the internal structures so that they could be seen.

8. Nucleus and cytoplasm. (The cell membrane cannot be seen in an onion skin cell.)

9. Drawings should show nucleus, cytoplasm, and cell membrane. *Nucleus:* controls cell's activities; *cytoplasm:* contains materials that carry on cell's activities; *cell membrane:* regulates materials that enter or leave cell.

E. Lift the edge of the cover glass with a toothpick and add a drop of methylene blue. Lower the cover glass back gently.

F. Observe the stained cells under low and high power.

4. Estimate the diameter of a cheek cell in microns.
5. Can you see the dark, round nucleus inside the cell? Do all the cells seem to have a nucleus? This spherical structure is the control center of the cell.
6. Can you see the lightly stained, granular cytoplasm inside the cell? This is where most of the cell's chemical reactions occur.
7. Why was the methylene blue added to the slide?
8. What cell parts did you find in both the onion skin cells and the human cheek cells?
9. Draw and label a few cheek cells as seen under high power. Describe the function of each structure.

4. 40-80 microns.

5. Yes. Most of the cells should have a nucleus.

6. Yes.

You should now be able to

Prepare a wet mount slide of human cheek cells.

Use methylene blue to stain the contents of cheek cells.

Identify the nucleus, cytoplasm, and cell membrane of an animal cell under the microscope.

Tell the difference between cell walls (plants) and cell membranes (animals) as seen under the microscope or in a drawing.

Estimate the diameter of a single cheek cell.

Special structures in green plant cells

You have compared plant cell parts with animal cell parts. You have observed cell walls, cell membranes, nuclei, and cytoplasm. In Problem 6-3 you will discover what part of a green plant cell contains the green coloring, chlorophyll. You will also see the effect of adding salt solution to a green plant cell.

The green plant that you will study is called elodea. Elodea is often used in aquaria. (If elodea is not available, another plant will be suggested by your teacher.) You will be asked to measure parts of the cells. If you need help, don't hesitate to ask for it.

Problem 6-3 What part of a green plant cell has the green coloring material in it?

Purpose To find and observe the green parts of a plant cell. To observe the effect of salt solution on a plant cell.

Materials

microscope	scissors	medicine dropper
slide	elodea *(Anacharis)*	salt solution (saturated)
cover glass	tweezers	paper towel

Procedure

Part One: Observing green plant structures

A. Prepare a wet mount slide of elodea as follows. Cut a single leaf from the growing tip of elodea. Cut the single leaf in half. Place the pointed end in a drop of water on a slide and add a cover glass.

B. Observe the leaf under both low power and high power. Use the mirror to vary the light intensity as you work.

1. Can you see the small, individual cells?
2. What color is the inside of the cell?
3. Is the color located in certain bodies or spread throughout the cell?
4. What is the shape of these green bodies?
5. These green bodies are called **chloroplasts**. How many chloroplasts can you count in one cell?
6. What substance gives these chloroplasts their color?
7. What is the function of chloroplasts in a cell?

1. Yes.
2. Green.
3. Located in certain bodies.
4. Spherical.
5. Answers will vary; there are about 20-40 chloroplasts in most cells.
6. Chlorophyll.
7. Chloroplasts contain chlorophyll, which plays an important role in photosynthesis.

6-10. Chloroplasts in elodea cells. The cut-away section *(right)* shows the internal structure of a chloroplast.

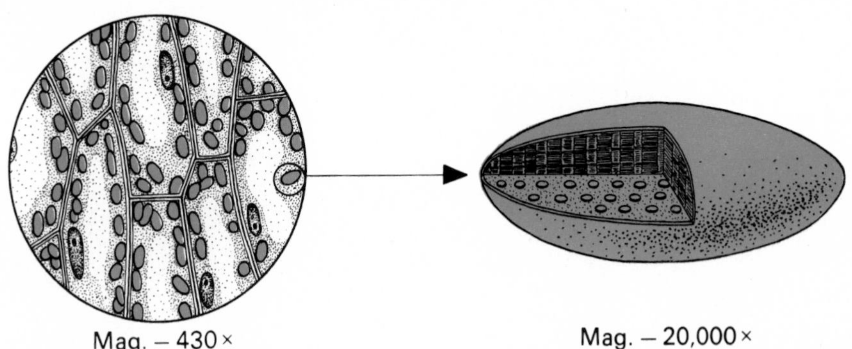

10. Structures usually illustrated are cell wall, nucleus, cytoplasm, and chloroplasts.

11. Heat from the light speeds up the leaf activities, and chloroplasts move more rapidly. (This effect is not easily seen.)

12. Answer should be in range of 50-150 microns.

14. Answer should be in range of 5-15 microns.

8. Do the chloroplasts move around inside the cell? 8. Yes.

9. If you see the chloroplasts moving, what must the fluid inside the cell be doing? 9. Moving.

10. Draw an elodea cell. Label all the structures you can see. Use arrows to show the movement of the chloroplasts in the cell fluid.

11. How does the amount of light on the slide affect the movement of the chloroplasts?

12. Observe the elodea cells under high power. Estimate the length of an elodea cell in microns.

13. How many chloroplasts, placed end-to-end, would it take to reach across the length of the cell? 13. About 20-40.

14. What is the length of a chloroplast in microns? (Divide the length of the cell from question 12 by the number of chloroplasts from question 13.)

Part Two: Observing the effect of salt solution on a green plant cell

C. Lift the cover glass. Remove the water by blotting gently with a paper towel. (See Figure 6-11.) Then add two or three drops of salt solution. Replace the cover glass over the elodea leaf.

D. Observe the slide under low power and high power for about five minutes.

15. Yes. the chloroplasts and other internal materials seem to be clumped near the center of the cell.

15. Did you observe any changes in the appearance of the cells after the salt solution was added?

16. Near the center.

16. Where is the cytoplasm in these cells?

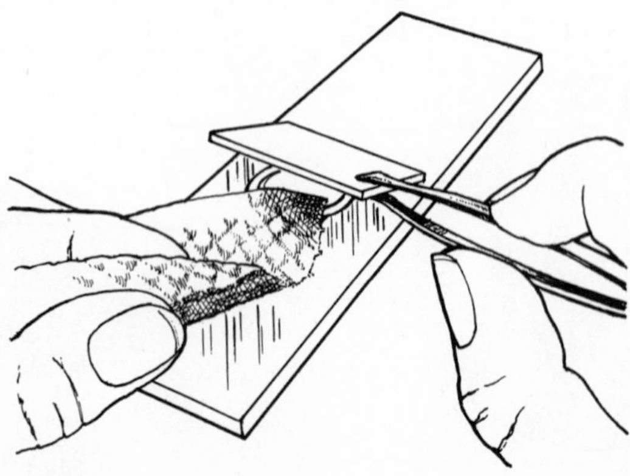

6-11. Blot the edge with a paper towel.

17. Yes; it can now be seen around the cytoplasm.

18. Drawings should show cell wall, cell membrane, chloroplasts, nucleus, and cytoplasm.

19. Water.

20. Remove the salt solution with a paper towel and add fresh water. This will work if done within 10 minutes after the addition of the salt solution.

21. Cell membrane.

17. Do plant cells have a cell membrane around the cytoplasm?
18. Draw one or two salt-treated cells. Label the structures you can see.
19. What material do you think the salt solution removed from these cells?
20. How could these cells be returned to their normal shape? Try your idea. What happened?
21. What cell structure(s) did the salt solution help you observe?

You should now be able to

Prepare a wet mount slide of a leaf so that the individual cells can be seen.

Identify under the microscope the green chloroplasts inside a plant cell.

Classify a cell as plant or animal on the basis of whether it has a cell wall.

Estimate the length of an elodea cell.

Estimate the length of a chloroplast.

Observe the cell membrane of a plant cell after treating the cell with a salt solution.

Examining cork cells

So far, you have looked at living cells. In Problem 6-4, you will examine the nonliving cells of cork. Cork comes from the outer layer of trees and has many uses. Your job will be to prepare and observe a thin section of cork. You will compare the structure of cork cells with the cells you observed in the last three problems.

As you study cork cells, remember that Robert Hooke was viewing the same kind of material when he suggested the name "cell." Think how excited Hooke must have been when he found different kinds of "spaces" or "cells" in other plants too.

The microscope had been invented about 50 years before Hooke sketched and named cells. Do you think that anyone else saw these tiny building blocks before Hooke did? Probably so. But they failed — as he did — to see the important relationship between cells and all living things.

Problem 6-4 What structure or structures remain in a nonliving plant cell?

Purpose To determine the cell structure(s) present in cells of cork.

Materials

microscope	medicine dropper	new, single-edged razor blade
slide	large bottle cork	cardboard, thick piece
cover glass		

Procedure

Caution students against careless use of razor blades.

A. Cut or scrape a small piece of cork so thin that it is almost white in color. The thinner the section of cork, the lighter the color will be. It takes a little practice. Hold a large bottle cork firmly against a piece of thick cardboard. (See Figure 6-12.) Hold a razor blade in the other hand and slice downward with a back-and-forth motion over the surface of the cork. *Never draw the blade toward your fingers.*

After several trials, you will be able to cut off tiny flakes of cork. Do not try to make long (large) cuts from the surface, as the resulting pieces will be too thick. If you cannot get a very thin piece of cork by slicing, try scraping the surface of the cork with your razor blade.

B. Prepare a wet mount slide of one of the thin flakes (or several scrapings).

C. Observe the slide under both low power and high power. Move the slide until you find the *thinnest* edge of the flake. This will be a single layer of cells.

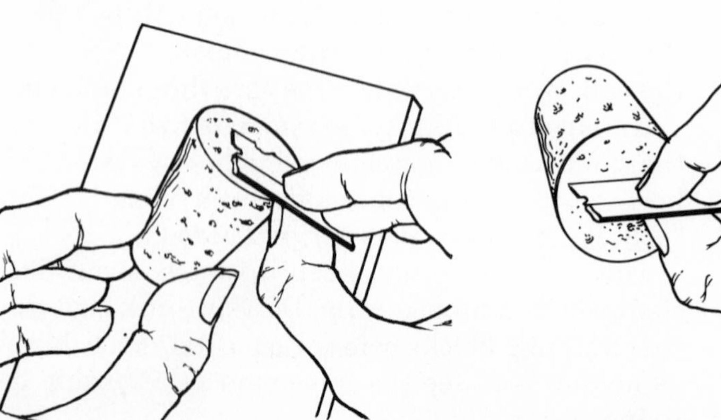

6-12. Two methods of slicing and scraping a piece of cork.

1. By a cell wall.

2. Filled with dark-walled bubbles.

3. Air. Yes; the air spaces make the cork light.

5. No. There is nothing inside the cell for methylene blue to stain.

6. They are dead. They contain no nucleus or cytoplasm, and perform no life activities.

8. Answer should be in the range of 15-25 cells.

1. Are the cork cells surrounded by a cell membrane or by a cell wall?
2. Are the cells empty or filled with dark-walled bubbles?
3. What do you think the substance is within the dark walls? Would this substance help the cork to float in water?
4. What cell structure(s) do you see inside each cell? 4. None.
5. Do you think methylene blue would help you to observe the cell structures? Explain.
6. What evidence do you have to support either statement: "These cells are alive" or "These cells are dead"?
7. What material makes up the cell wall of these cells? 7. Cellulose.
8. How many cork cells, placed end-to-end, does it take to cross the field under high-power magnification?
9. What is the length of a cork cell in microns? (Divide the distance in microns across the high-power field by the number of cells from question 8.)
10. Draw a cork cell exactly as you see it.

You should now be able to

9. Answer should be in the range of 25-70 microns.

10. Drawing should be similar to the cork cells shown in Figure 6-2, p. 89.

Prepare a wet mount slide from bottle cork so that a single layer of cells can be seen.

Locate and identify the cell wall, the one remaining structure in cork cells.

Identify cork cells as either plant cells or animal cells.

Supply evidence that cork cells are nonliving.

Estimate the length of a single cork cell.

A closer look at cells

Biologists have very carefully studied the cell structures you have seen in the past few problems. You have used methylene blue stain to bring out certain structures in the cells you have looked at. Biologists have used special stains to bring out many kinds of details.

Biologists have used high-powered light microscopes. The highest magnification you have been able to use on your microscope is probably 200× or less. But light microscpoes that permit magnification of about 2,000× have been built. Biologists for many years thought they would never be able to see things beyond the range of 1,500× to 2,000×.

The electron microscope

The compound microscope you are using is also called a light microscope. Light waves are directed through the object on the stage. The light waves are focused by the objective lens and an image is formed. The image formed by the objective lens is further magnified by the eyepiece lens.

The **electron microscope** is an instrument that uses a beam of electrons instead of light to form an image. A high voltage is used to drive the beam of electrons through the object. The object is pretreated with special metallic solutions. Like the stain you used, the metallic solutions bring out structural features of the object. Magnetic coils, rather than glass lenses, focus the beam of electrons. The coils focus the electrons in much the same way as the glass lens focuses light waves in your microscope.

The focused electron beam passes through the object to produce a magnified image on a special screen. Electrons have properties that enable the electron microscope to magnify far better than a light microscope can. Objects may be enlarged more than five hundred thousand times.

A photograph of a leaf cell taken through an electron microscope is shown in Figure 6-14. See how much more detail it is possible to ob-

6-13. An electron microscope.

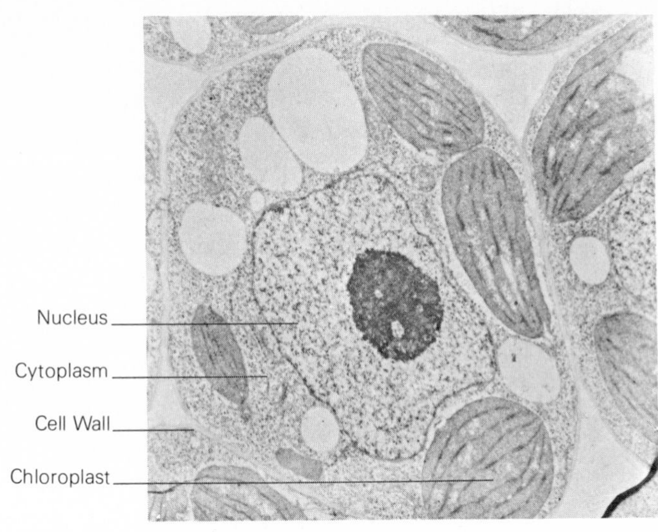

6-14. Photograph of a plant leaf cell taken with an electron microscope.

serve with such high magnification. New instruments and techniques are used every year to learn more about the structure and function of cells.

Science terms

cell
cell membrane
cell theory
cell wall
cellulose
chlorophyll
chloroplast
cytoplasm
electron microscope
nucleus
vacuole

Review questions

1. What is the cell theory?
2. How many microns are there in one millimeter?
3. What is the function of a chloroplast?
4. Name two cell structures found in plant cells but not in animal cells.
5. What structure of a cell is darkly stained when methylene blue is added?
6. What parts of an onion skin cell did you see with your microscope?
7. What structures did you observe in a human cheek cell?

1. Answer should summarize cell theory on pages 88-89.
2. 1,000 microns.
3. It is involved in photosynthesis.
4. Cell wall and chloroplasts.
5. The nucleus.
6. Cell wall, nucleus, and cytoplasm.
7. Nucleus and cytoplasm.

8. (a) nucleus, cytoplasm, cell membrane; (b) cell wall and chloroplasts; (c) none that students should be familiar with.

9. Answer should be in the range of 100-400 microns.

10. Answer should be in the range of 5-15 microns.

11. Cell wall.

12. Mainly cellulose.

13. Electron microscope.

14. Determine the field of view in microns, then estimate the number of cells that will fit across the field diameter. Divide this number into the field diameter.

15. It causes the fluid to decrease.

16. Cell membrane.

8. Make three lists using the following headings:
   a. cell structures usually found in all cells
   b. cell structures found only in plant cells
   c. cell structures found only in animal cells
9. What is the length, in microns, of an onion skin cell you observed in the lab?
10. What is the approximate length, in microns, of a chloroplast you observed in the lab?
11. What cell structure(s) were found in the bottle cork cells?
12. What material makes up the cell walls of plants you observed?
13. What instrument is used by scientists to magnify small objects many thousands of times?
14. Outline the procedure for finding the length of a cork cell when it is viewed under high power.
15. How does the presence of salt solution outside a cell affect the amount of fluid found inside the cell?
16. What cell structure not usually observed in plants is more easily seen after the addition of salt solution?

Check your understanding

See Teacher's Guide section for answers to Questions 17-21.

17. How do you think the flat shape of cheek cells helps the cells protect the cheek?
18. The cells of the onion skin and of your cheek lining have similar shapes. Why might these cells from very different living things be of similar shape? (Consider the function of each cell.)
19. When a plant cell is surrounded by salt solution, the contents of the cell seem to shrink. What clear, colorless liquid found in all living cells is probably leaving the cell? How does this colorless substance get out of the cell?
20. The movement of what material in a green plant cell could cause the chloroplasts to move around?
21. Thin slices of material are always used when preparing wet mount slides. Why?

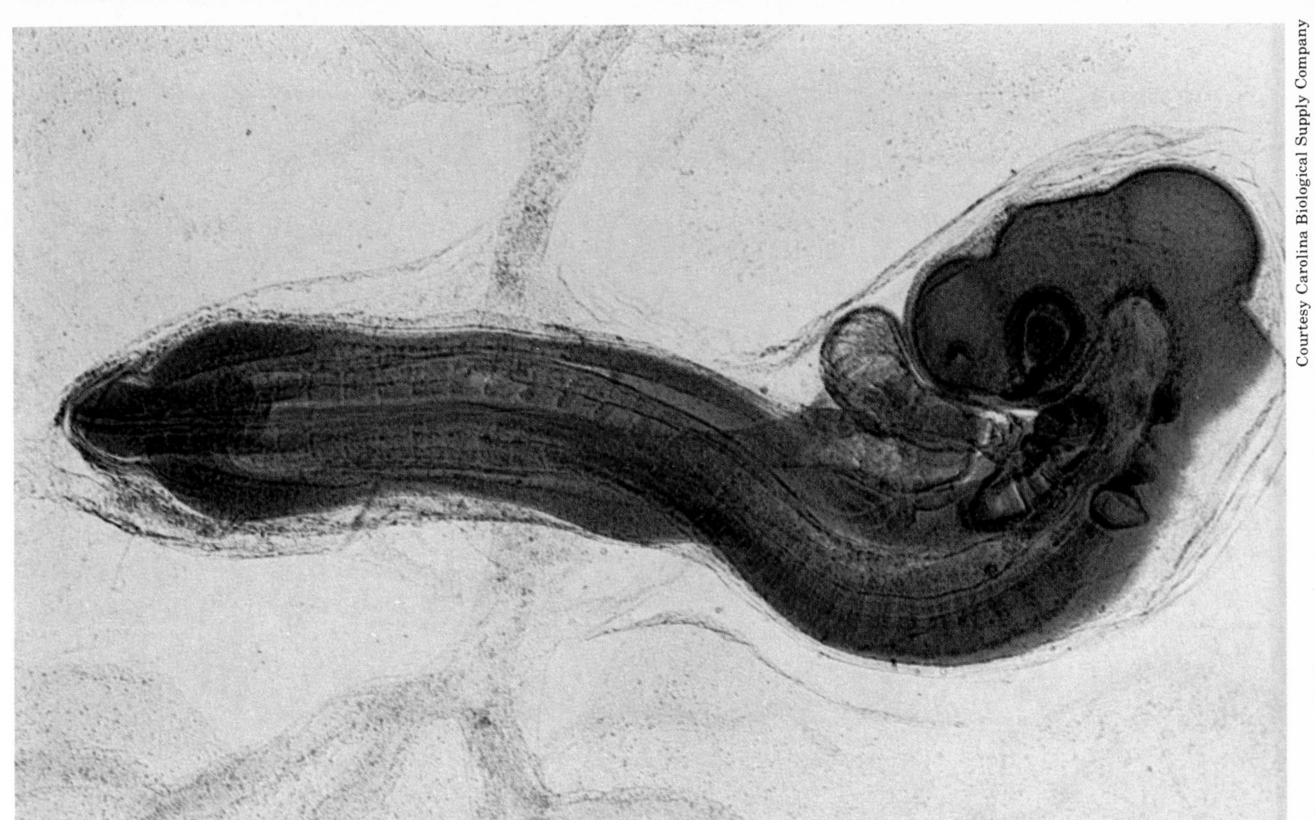

Courtesy Carolina Biological Supply Company

Chapter 7 **Cells work together**

Chapter-opening photo shows some of the organs formed in a chick embryo before it is even 3 days old. Point out the system of blood vessels and the beginnings of the brain, heart, and eye.

Cells are the building blocks of living matter. The cells of an organism are of different shapes and sizes. But all cells have at least two things in common: (1) a membrane, which defines the boundaries of the cell, and (2) cytoplasm, which is chemically similar from cell to cell.

Remember, however, that these "building blocks" contain many small structures. You have seen nuclei and cell membranes. You have seen cell walls and chloroplasts in green plant cells. There are other cell structures too small to be seen with your microscope. All the cell structures are made up of various kinds of chemicals. These chemicals are responsible for the life processes carried on within the cell.

Cells divide

(*Above*) A 60-70 hour chick embryo.

Cells multiply by dividing. Almost every living organism begins life as a single cell. As a single cell grows, it divides into two cells.

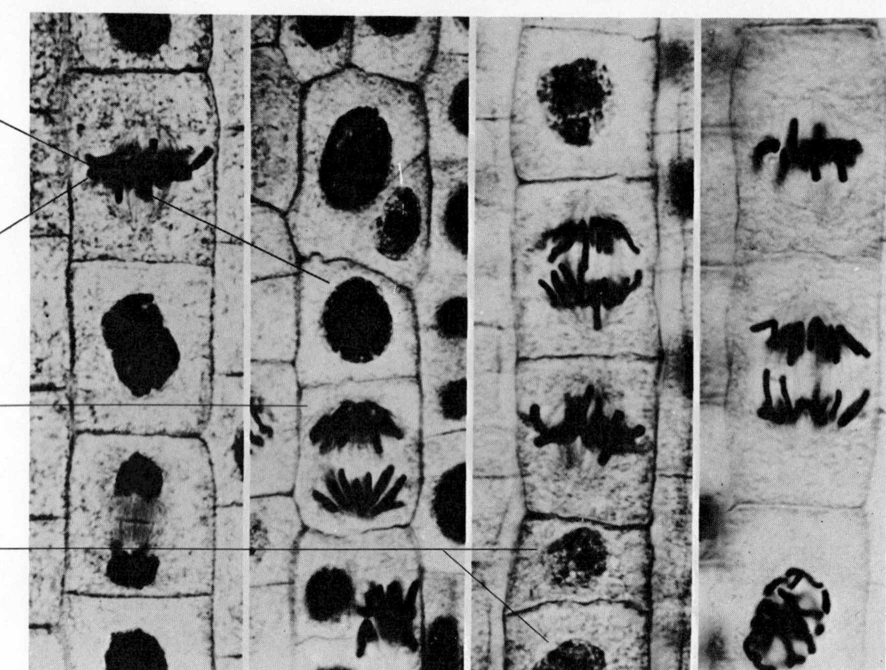
Interphase: Cell in "resting" stage (not shown).
Prophase: Chromosomes in nucleus become shorter and thicker and duplicate themselves.
Metaphase: Chromosome pairs arranged at center and attached to *spindle fibers* at opposite ends of cell.
Anaphase: Pairs of chromosomes separate and are drawn along the fibers to opposite ends of cell.
Telophase: Cell has divided into two new cells, each with own set of chromosomes.
Courtesy Carolina Biological Supply Company

7-1. Plant cells dividing by the process of *mitosis*. The photographs show various changes that the nucleus undergoes during cell division.

Two cells divide into four cells, and on the process goes. Through many cell divisions, a single cell may develop into an organism having billions or trillions of cells.

As cells grow, they develop into special cells with special functions. Human *nerve cells*, for example, are long and narrow. This shape allows them to relay information from one part of the body to another. Your cheek cells are *epithelial cells*, flat and fairly regular in shape. Epithelial cells combine to form a protective layer over all exposed surfaces.

With your microscope, you have seen some of the structures that make up cells. Do you think the cells you looked at could live if they were isolated from the rest of the cells? The human cheek cells and the onion skin cells that you looked at could not live long as isolated cells.

Think how different the parts of your body are. Think of your eyes, stomach, bones, and skin. Each different structure contains several different kinds of cells. It is the "cooperation" of the different cells and structures working together that makes you a successful organism.

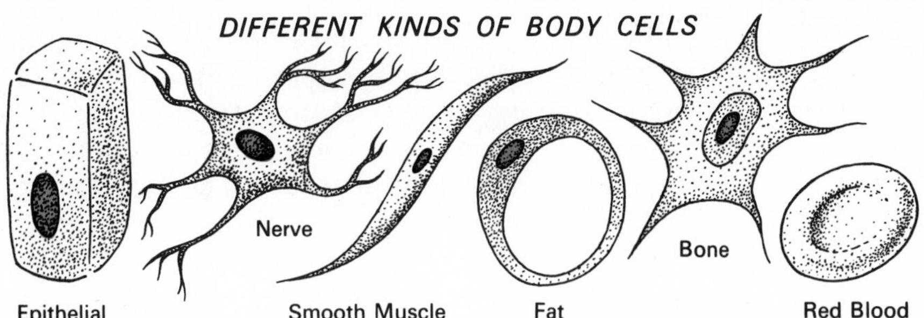

7-2. Specialized cells of the human body.

Tissues, organs, and organ systems

Cells scraped from the lining of your cheek all look much alike. This is not surprising since they all have the same function. They cover and protect other cells below them. Groups of cells that have the same structure and function are called **tissues**. Examples of tissues are blood and muscle in humans, and bark in trees.

Later in this chapter, you will examine a thin section of leaf. You will find different shapes of cells and different structures inside. Finding different cells in the leaf suggests that there are different tissues working together. Such cooperating tissues are called **organs**. The leaf is an organ.

Your blood vessels are organs. An artery, for instance, is made of three layers of cells. (See Figure 7-3.) Each layer has a special function. Each layer is a different kind of tissue. Together the three tissues function as an organ that transports blood.

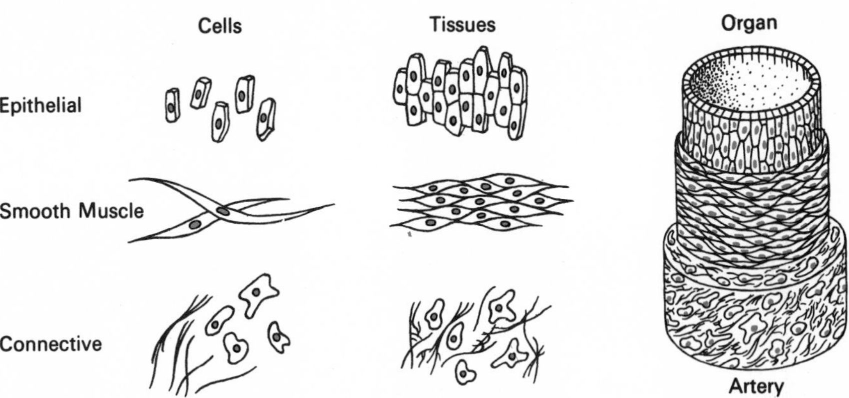

7-3. Cells combine to form tissues, and tissues combine to form organs.

In all of the more complex animals and in some plants, groups of organs work together as **organ systems**. Several organs cooperate to carry on processes such as circulation, respiration, or digestion. Your circulatory system moves blood to each cell in your body. The system is made of three kinds of organs. The heart pumps the blood, arteries take it to the cells, and veins return the blood to the heart.

Different cells must work together in many life activities. Only when this working relationship between similar cells is present do you have a tissue. Only when tissues cooperate do you have an organ. Without this close organization from the cellular level on up, an organism could not live.

Cell types in a leaf

In Problem 7-1 you will examine the upper and lower surfaces of some leaves. The layer that forms the upper surface of a leaf is called the *upper epidermis* [ep-ih-DER-miss]. It serves to enclose and protect the tissues below. The **lower epidermis** covers the lower surface of the leaf. It also serves to support and protect the internal tissues. There are some differences in the two leaf surfaces, as you will see in Problem 7-1.

Certain leaf surfaces contain many tiny openings called **stomata** (singular *stoma*). These openings are formed and enclosed by special cells called **guard cells**. Gases that are used or given off by the plant enter and leave through the stomata. (See Figure 7-4.) Your work in Problem 7-1 should reveal a difference in the number of stomata in the upper and lower epidermis.

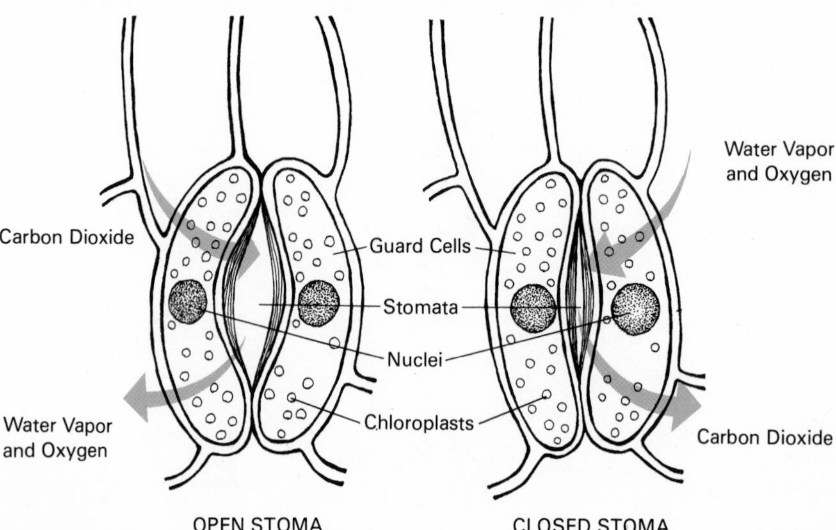

7-4. Stomata help regulate the gaseous content of leaves.

Problem 7-1 What different kinds of cells are found in the epidermis of leaves?

Purpose To observe the types and numbers of cells found in the epidermis of different leaves. To learn how these cells work together to perform their function.

Materials

microscope	razor blade, new single-edged	tweezers
slides	cover glasses	medicine dropper
leaves		

Procedure

Students should peel off only very thin sections of the leaf epidermis. If razor blades are being used, caution students to be very careful.

A. Prepare wet mount slides of both the upper and the lower epidermis of each kind of leaf. You can peel the epidermis off some leaves by breaking the leaf blade and pulling the two pieces apart. (See the leaf on the left in Figure 7-5.) Having broken the leaf blade, hold the upper epidermis away from you and tear slowly. A transparent layer of epidermis will separate. Reverse the leaf to remove the lower epidermis.

You can also obtain a section of epidermis by sliding a single-edged razor blade across the surface for a short distance. (See the leaf on the right in Figure 7-5.)

7-5. Tear leaf so that the epidermis may be peeled off, or carefully slice off a thin section of epidermis.

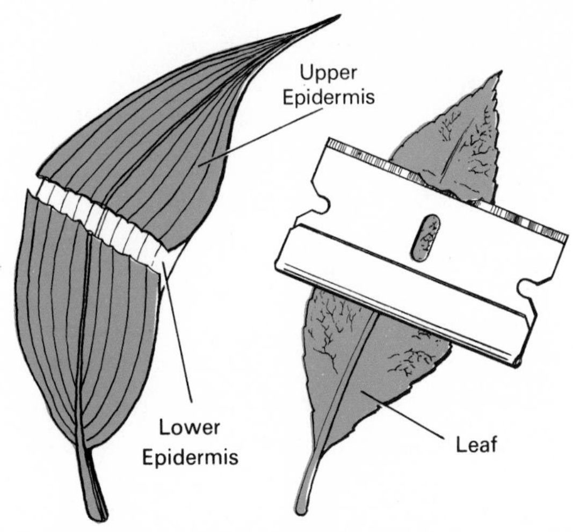

Remind students to scan surface cells to find best area for viewing.

1. No, the cells do not have the same shape. (See Figure 7-6, page 114, for cells of epidermis.)
2. Drawing should show guard cells similar to Figure 7-4, page 110.
3. Yes.

Remind laboratory teams that the structure and shape of a cell are generally related to its function.

6. Counts will differ, depending on the leaf examined.

You may want to have students skip Step D if time is short.

7. Lower.
8. Carbon dioxide, oxygen, and water vapor.
9. The leaf could die since there would be a great deal of water loss.
10. Tropical. The more water, the more stomata.
11. Since leaves lose water through stomata, the fewer stomata, the less water loss. Small leaves reduce the surface area exposed to the sun, thus slowing evaporation.

B. Observe each slide under both low power and high power. The cells of the epidermis are irregularly shaped. They look like pieces of a jigsaw puzzle.

1. Do all the cells of the epidermis have the same general shape? Draw a few epidermal cells.
2. Make a drawing of those cells that appear to be *different* from the epidermal cells.
3. Do these different cells have dark black areas in the center of them?

C. This dark place is a **pore**, or opening, in the leaf epidermis. It is a stoma. The cells on each side that control the opening and closing of the stoma are the guard cells.

4. Do the guard cells contain chloroplasts? 4. Yes.
5. Do the other epidermal cells contain chloroplasts? 5. No.
6. How many pairs of guard cells can you count in the low-power field?

D. Make a table in your notebook to record the following informaton. Record each type of leaf, upper epidermis, lower epidermis, and the number of stomata you count in the low-power field for each epidermal layer.

7. Does the upper epidermis or the lower epidermis of a leaf have more stomata?
8. What gases pass through these stomata? (Refer to Figure 7-4 if you need to.)

E. Food-making (**photosynthesis**) occurs in sunlight. In photosynthesis, carbon dioxide enters the plant through the stomata and oxygen is released. Respiration, which occurs day and night, is another chemical process that involves an exchange of gases through the stomata.

You would expect more stomata to be open during the day than at night because both photosynthesis and respiration take place during the day. At night, only respiration occurs.

9. What do you think might happen to a leaf if its epidermis were damaged?
10. Which type of leaf do you think would have more stomata, tropical or desert? How is the number of stomata in a particular kind of leaf related to the amount of water present in the environment?
11. Explain why plants in desert climates have fewer stomata and smaller leaves than tropical plants have.

You should now be able to

Identify guard cells, stomata, and epidermal cells of different leaves.

Describe how the guard cells and the stomata function together in the processes of photosynthesis and respiration.

Relate the structure of epidermal cells to their function in the leaf.

Relate the number of stomata per unit of surface area to the amount of water present in the environment.

Leaf tissues

You have located the upper and lower epidermis, the stomata, and the guard cells of leaves. You may have seen various other kinds of cells as well. In the next problem, you will continue your examination of leaf tissues. This time you will study some cross sections.

Sections cut at right angles to the length of an object are called **cross sections**. The slice of onion put on a hamburger is a cross section of the onion. This slice would be much too thick to use under the microscope. You will learn a technique for making a thin cross section of a leaf. Don't be discouraged if it requires several trials before you are able to cut a cross section thin enough.

What cells might you expect to see in a leaf cross section? All the cells between the upper and lower epidermis form a tissue called the **mesophyll** [MEZ-uh-fill]. The cells of the mesophyll are similar in structure, but tbey are arranged into two layers. The mesophyll cells just below the upper epidermis are called **palisade cells**. They are regular, oblong cells. They are stacked compactly at right angles to the surface. (See Figure 7-6 on the next page.) The **palisade layer** may contain one or more rows of palisade cells.

Between the palisade layer and the lower epidermis is the second layer of mesophyll cells. These are called **spongy cells**. They are loosely packed and more irregular in shape. Between these loosely packed cells are large air spaces. The spaces permit the gases that enter through the stomata to circulate through the leaf.

The mesophyll cells are the main food-making cells in the leaf. In order to produce food, they must contain chloroplasts. The food-making process in green plants is called **photosynthesis**. The green plant combines carbon dioxide and water to produce a simple sugar called *glucose*. The carbon dioxide is taken into the plant through the

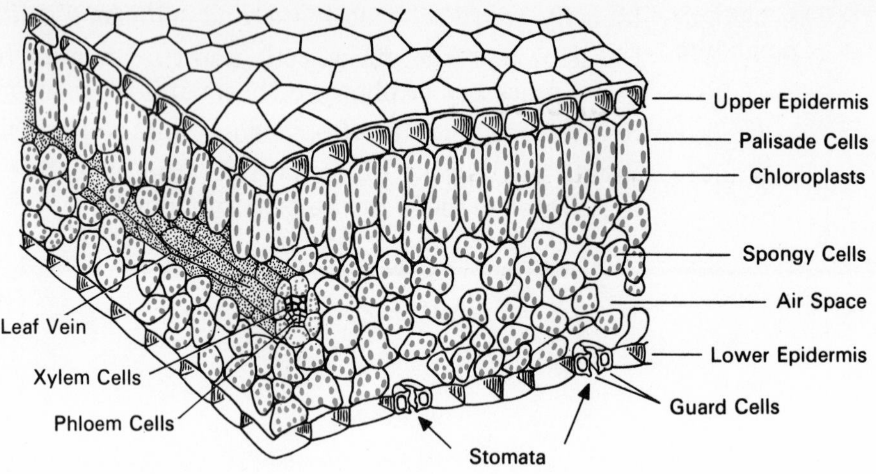

7-6. Cross section of a leaf.

stomata. And the energy needed for the chemical activity comes from light, usually sunlight. This light energy is trapped by the chlorophyll in the chloroplasts. Most of these chloroplasts are located in the mesophyll cells.

In addition to glucose, oxygen gas and some water are also produced during photosynthesis. The oxygen is released through the stomata. (See the open stoma diagram in Figure 7-4, page 110.) The water used or discarded during photosynthesis may also pass in and out of the stomata as gaseous water vapor.

The mesophyll layer is thus essential as the food-making part of the leaf. Another tissue you are likely to see in a leaf cross section is the **vascular tissue**. It is the conducting and supporting tissue in the leaf. The vascular tissue is organized in bundles (the veins that you can often see without a microscope). A vein is composed of a ring of supporting cells that surrounds two types of elongated cells.

Look at the vein in Figure 7-6. The thick-walled, larger-diameter tube cells are called **xylem** [ZY-lum] cells. Xylem cells conduct water to the leaf from the roots. Xylem cells also provide support to the plant. The smaller cells in the vascular bundle are the **phloem** [FLO-um] cells. Phloem cells carry food made by photosynthesis to other parts of the plant for storage or use.

As you do Problem 7-2, try to relate the structure and arrangement of the cells and tissues to their functions in the leaf. Also think about the environment from which each leaf came. You would expect leaves from a water lily to be different from those of a cactus.

Problem 7-2 What special cells and tissues may be found in a leaf cross section?

Purpose To observe the cells and tissues found inside a leaf. To learn how these cells work together to carry on photosynthesis.

Materials

microscope	razor blade, new, single-edged
slides	leaves, freshly picked (or prepared slide)
cover glasses	medicine dropper
tweezers	

Procedure

It may be necessary to demonstrate the technique used to obtain a thin cross section of a leaf.

A. Prepare a thin cross section of a leaf as follows. Place the leaf between two glass slides in a sandwich form. Use the edges of the glass slides to guide the razor blade as shown in Figure 7-7. Cut off the thinnest slice possible from the edge of the leaf.

Obtain one thin cross section after you have made several sample cuts. Place the cut edge of the section on the surface of the slide. *Be careful not to fold the thin section.* Add a drop of water and a cover glass.

B. Observe the slide under both low power and high power. Be sure to move the slide to find the thinnest sections. If the section is dark and the cells are hard to see, prepare another slide.

1. See Figure 7-6 for model drawing of leaf cross section.
2. Long, narrow, and flattened. They protect inner cells and regulate water.

1. Draw and label the locations and general shapes of the various cells found inside the leaf.
2. Describe the shapes of the upper and lower epidermal cells. What is the function of these layers?

7-7. Cutting a thin cross section of a leaf.

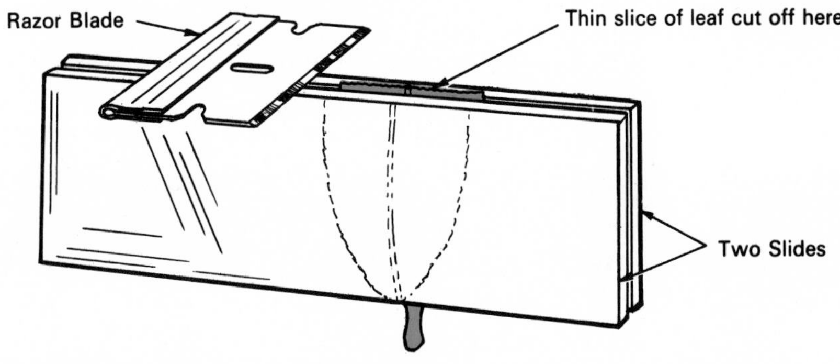

3. Yes; yes.

4. The elongated structure of the cell is effective in trapping sunlight. These cells also contain many chloroplasts.

5. Yes.

6. No. They are loosely packed.

7. Yes.

8. The vascular bundles may be difficult to locate. The student may have to make another leaf section. The slide should be moved around until the cells are located.

3. Can you locate the layer of cells that is perpendicular (at right angles) to the upper epidermis? Do these cells contain chloroplasts?
4. The palisade cells are specialized to trap light for photosynthesis. Describe how the structure of a palisade cell is related to its function.
5. Can you locate the irregularly shaped cells below the palisade cells?
6. Do these spongy cells form a solid layer as you found in the palisade layer?

C. The carbon dioxide used in photosynthesis, along with water vapor and oxygen, is found in the spaces between the spongy cells. The spongy cells plus the palisade cells make up the mesophyll tissue.

7. Can you find the stomata in the lower epidermis?
8. Can you locate a group of thick-walled cells arranged in a circular pattern?

D. These large, thick-walled cells conduct water from the roots to the leaf. These xylem cells, along with some thin-walled phloem cells, may be enclosed by a ring of supporting cells. Together these cells make up a vascular bundle. The vascular bundles, or veins, are the conducting and supporting tissue of the plant.

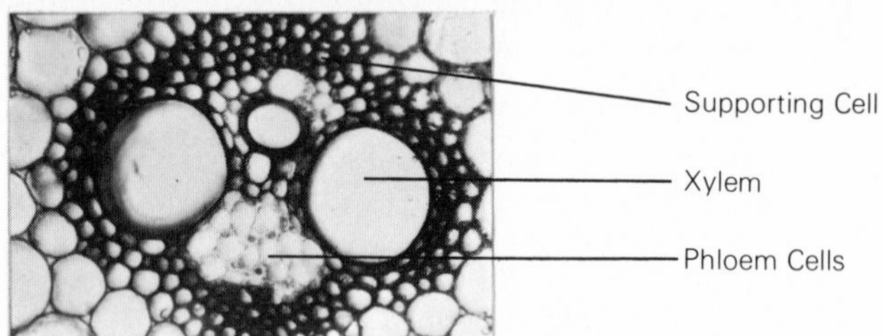

You should now be able to

Prepare a wet mount slide of a cross section of a leaf.

Identify three types of tissue in a plant leaf — epidermal, mesophyllic, and vascular.

Identify the palisade cells and the spongy cells of the mesophyll, and describe the function of each.

Locate the xylem and the phloem cells of the vascular tissue and describe the function of each.

Animal organ systems

Through different investigations you have seen how cells work together as tissues. You have studied how tissues cooperate in structures called organs. When several organs work together in a living thing, the combination of organs is called an organ system. In Problem 7-3 you will study some tissues, organs, and organ systems of a living animal.

You will be working with an earthworm. You could spend days examining all the organ systems in worms. Your objective in this problem is to observe the muscular and circulatory systems in the living earthworm.

The earthworm circulatory system

The circulatory system of the earthworm consists of: (1) a simple heart, (2) blood vessels that run lengthwise in the body, and (3) smaller, branching blood vessels. The simple heart actually consists of five pairs of muscular tubes. (See Figure 7-8.) The tubes are near the anterior (front) of the worm's body. They expand and contract, forcing the blood to circulate through the blood vessels.

The blood vessel that runs the length of the bottom side of the earthworm is called the **ventral** blood vessel. The ventral blood vessel brings fresh blood to the organs of the worm. The used blood returns to the heart through the **dorsal** (top) blood vessel.

The blood, the blood vessels, and the simple heart of the earthworm transport food and oxygen to the cells. And they remove carbon dioxide and other waste products from the cells. The many cells that are working together to perform these functions are organized into tissues. The tissues combine into organs, and the organs work together as an organ system. Blood is a tissue. The blood vessels are organs made of three tissue layers. And the organs — the blood vessels and the heart — form the circulatory system.

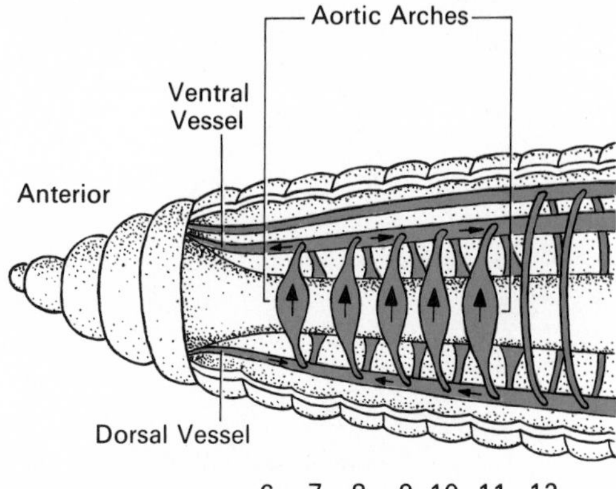

7-8. Circulatory system of the earthworm, showing aortic arches around esophagus.

Problem 7-3 What special structures are visible in the organ systems of an earthworm?

Purpose To observe how several tissues or organs work together to carry out special functions.

Materials microscope paper towel petri dish earthworm, live

Procedure

Part One: The muscular system

1. The earthworm becomes alternately longer and shorter. (It moves by alternate contractions of the longitudinal and circular muscles.)

2. It becomes alternately smaller and larger in diameter.

3. A muscle tissue. Some students may also suggest "fiber."

4. Circular muscles.

5. Longitudinal muscles.

A. Place the earthworm on a wet paper towel. Observe the way the earthworm crawls over the surface.

1. How does the earthworm change in length as it crawls?
2. How does the earthworm change in diameter?

B. The muscle cell is a special type of cell used by the earthworm to change shape. Muscle cells cause movement by contracting or relaxing. The earthworm has two layers of muscle tissue. One layer circles the worm as the *circular muscle*. The other layer runs the length of the worm as the *longitudinal muscle*.

3. What is a name for a group of muscle cells?
4. Which layer of muscle cells contracts and causes the earthworm to increase in length?
5. Which layer of muscle cells contracts to cause the worm to increase in diameter and become shorter?

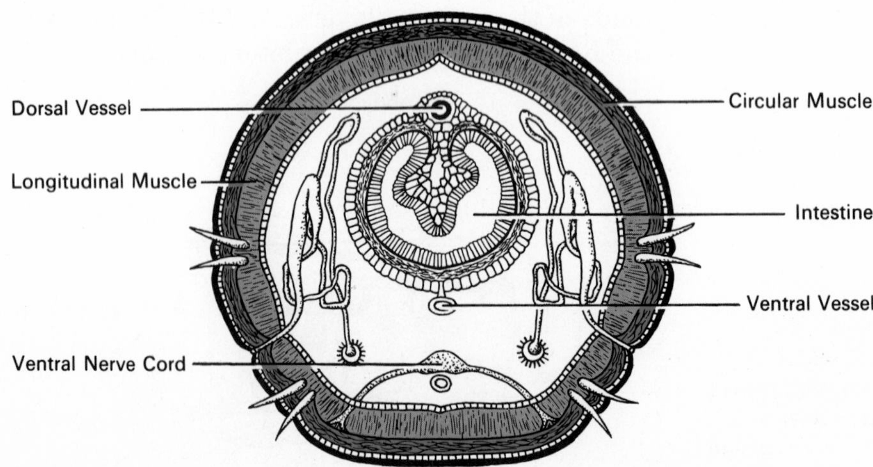

7-9. In this cross section of an earthworm, two layers of muscle are seen just beneath the outer surface.

Students should be able to see the movement of the blood. Use as much light as possible to study circulation.

C. Muscle tissue, along with blood tissue and nerve tissue, makes up an organ. The combination of both sets of muscle layer organs makes up the muscle organ system.

Part Two: The circulatory system

6. Toward the front (anterior) of the worm.

7. Toward the rear (posterior) of the worm.

8. Toward the rear of the worm.

9. Students may answer "heart" or "muscles." Either is acceptable, although the earthworm has no true heart.

10. In spurts.

11. Answers will vary, but about 3-10 beats per minute. (Clocks or watches with sweep second hands can be used to time the activity. Stopwatches are unnecessary.)

D. Place the earthworm in a petri dish. Locate the red line that runs down the center of the upper surface of the worm. This red line is the *dorsal blood vessel*. Place the petri dish on the stage of your microscope. Examine the dorsal blood vessel under low power.

6. In what direction is the blood moving in the dorsal blood vessel?

E. Hold the petri dish up to observe the ventral (lower) surface of the worm. Locate the *ventral blood vessel*, which runs the length of the body. The earthworm has only the two major blood vessels.

7. In what direction must the blood flow in the lower vessel if the blood is to circulate through the worm?
8. In what direction is the blood flowing in the ventral blood vessel?
9. What organ is used by the earthworm to circulate the blood through these vessels?
10. Does the blood move in spurts or in a steady flow?
11. Count the number of times the blood pulsates in the blood vessels in the earthworm per 15 seconds. How many beats is this per minute?

You should now be able to

Describe the two types of muscle tissue used for locomotion by the earthworm.

Describe the circulation of blood in the earthworm.

Name some of the cells, tissues, and organs found in the circulatory system of the earthworm.

Observing a preserved earthworm

You have observed structures in the circulatory and muscular systems of a living earthworm. Next, you will study the digestive system of a preserved earthworm.

Preserved organisms are useful for several reasons. They are not moving and may be observed for as long as necessary. Scissors or other instruments may be used to reveal body organs that cannot be seen otherwise. Work carefully so that the small, delicate organs are not destroyed before you locate them.

Problem 7-4 What organs may be found in the digestive system of an earthworm?

Purpose To locate the different organs in the digestive system of the earthworm. To relate the structure of the digestive organs to their function in the organ system.

Materials

earthworm, preserved
dissecting pan
dissecting kit
medicine dropper
dissecting pins

Procedure

Caution the students to be careful when working with specimens preserved in formalin. Emphasize the danger of getting formalin in eyes and mouth.

A. Rinse the preserving fluid off of the earthworm.

B. Locate the bottom (ventral) surface of the earthworm. You should be able to see bristles and pores on the flattened ventral surface. Place the worm on the dissecting tray with the flattened ventral surface down.

C. Use the scissors to cut through the outer skin and muscle layers of the worm. Cut from one end to the other. (See Figure 7-10.) *Be sure to keep the points of the scissors from going too deep.* You don't want to cut the organs inside the worm.

D. Use the dissecting pins to tear the thin walls that are located inside the body wall. After the thin walls are broken, pin the skin and muscle layers out as shown in Figure 7-10. This procedure will enable you to see the internal organs of the earthworm.

E. Locate the large tube that runs the length of the worm. This large tube with various parts is the digestive system.

1. No. It will probably look larger at the front end.

1. Does the tube appear to be the same size and shape at both ends?

There are four main functions of the digestive system. The first is to take in food material. The second is to grind and break down the food chemically. The third is to absorb the digested food. And the fourth is to get rid of the left-over materials. These functions are performed as the food passes down the tube from the mouth to the anus.

F. Locate the front, or **anterior**, end of the tube. This is the *mouth*, or head end, of the worm. The first section of the tube after the mouth is the **pharynx** [FAIR-inks]. The pharynx contains some glands, which secrete chemicals. These chemicals help to break the food into smaller pieces.

2. Thick-walled.

2. Is the pharynx thin-walled or thick-walled?

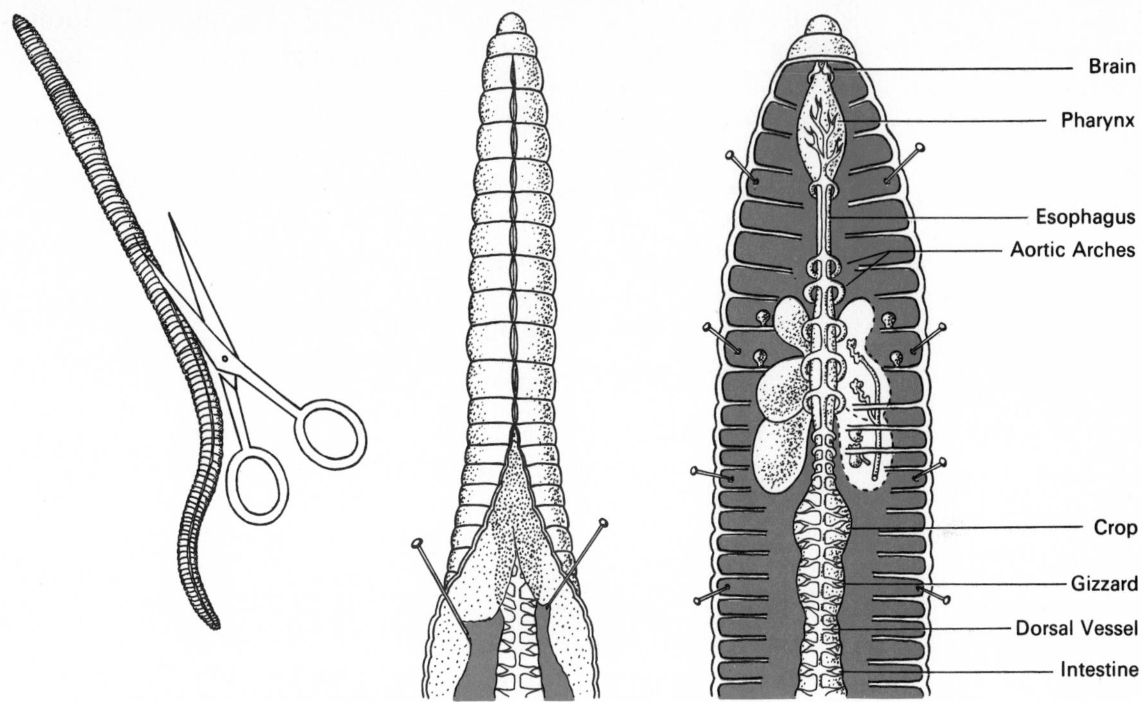

7-10. To dissect the earthworm, carefully cut through the skin and muscle layers. Use dissecting pins to tear the thin inner walls. Finally, pin back the outer walls to expose the internal organs of the earthworm.

G. The thickness of the walls of the digestive tube changes because of the layers of muscle present in some of the organs. From the pharynx, the food passes through a long, thin-walled section called the **esophagus** [ee-SAHF-uh-gus]. The food passes from the esophagus into the **crop** and then into the **gizzard**. Locate these organs.

3. Gizzard.

4. Gizzard.

3. Which structure is thick and muscular, the crop or the gizzard?
4. Which of these two structures would be better structured for grinding food?

The crop acts only as a temporary storage place for the food. The food then passes into the gizzard. Grains of sand are present in the gizzard. The thick, muscular walls of the gizzard work the food and the sand back and forth until the food is ground up.

5. Teeth.

5. Mammals do not have gizzards. What structures do mammals have that perform the same function?

Provide a receptacle such as a large plastic bag for disposing of worms. Instruct students to wash their hands after this activity is concluded. You might also provide hand lotion.

The ground-up food is then forced into the **intestine**. The intestine is the longest section of the digestive system. It contains glands that secrete digestive chemicals. These chemicals complete the process of digestion by breaking down the finely ground food into small chemicals.

The small chemicals, the digested foods, pass through the walls of the intestine into the bloodstream. The bloodstream circulates the digested foods to other parts of the organism.

H. Cut through the upper layer of the wall of the intestine. Wash away the material inside with water.

6. No. It appears to have many folds.

6. Does the inside of the intestine look round like the outside?

The shape of the inside of the intestine provides added surface area to help absorb the food material. The food that is not digested and absorbed passes out the tail end, or **posterior**, of the worm. The opening at this end of the intestine is called the **anus**.

You should now be able to

Dissect a preserved earthworm.

Identify the various organs of the digestive system of the earthworm.

Relate the location of the organ to the function performed.

Relate the structure of the organ to the function performed.

Trace the path of food through the digestive system of the earthworm.

Science terms

anterior	guard cell	photosynthesis
anus	intestine	posterior
crop	mesophyll	spongy cells
cross section	organ	stoma
dorsal	organ system	tissue
epidermis	palisade layer	vascular tissue
esophagus	pharynx	ventral
gizzard	phloem	xylem

Review questions

1. Possible examples include: (a) red blood cells, leaf epidermal cells; (b) blood, leaf epidermis; (c) heart, leaf; (d) circulatory system, plant vascular system.

2. Carbon dioxide.

1. Give an example of each of the following: (a) cell, (b) tissue, (c) organ, (d) organ system.
2. What gas used in photosynthesis enters the leaf through the stomata?

3. Chloroplasts.

4. Stomata.

5. Palisade, spongy, guard, xylem, and phloem cells.

6. Circular muscles.

7. Dorsal and ventral blood vessels.

8. Takes in food, breaks it down mechanically and chemically, absorbs digested particles, and collects and eliminates wastes.

9. Two: mouth and anus.

10. Gizzard.

11. Crop.

3. What structure is used by green plant cells to carry on photosynthesis?
4. What are the openings in the surfaces of leaves called?
5. Name five different kinds of cells found in a leaf.
6. Which set of muscles is used by the earthworm to increase body length?
7. Name two organs found in the circulatory system of the earthworm.
8. List the four main processes carried out by the digestive system.
9. How many openings are there in the digestive tube of an earthworm?
10. What organ of the earthworm is used to grind food?
11. What organ of the earthworm is used to store food?

Check your understanding See Teacher's Guide section for answers to Questions 12-16.

12. As a cell becomes more specialized, it also becomes more dependent on other cells. Why do you think this is true?
13. Bone is a tissue. What special features would bone cells have?
14. A leaf is a plant organ. What structures must a leaf contain in order to be called an organ? Name three such structures.
15. In what ways does the circulatory system of a worm depend on the muscular system?
16. What structures might you expect to see in a cross section of an earthworm near the tail end?

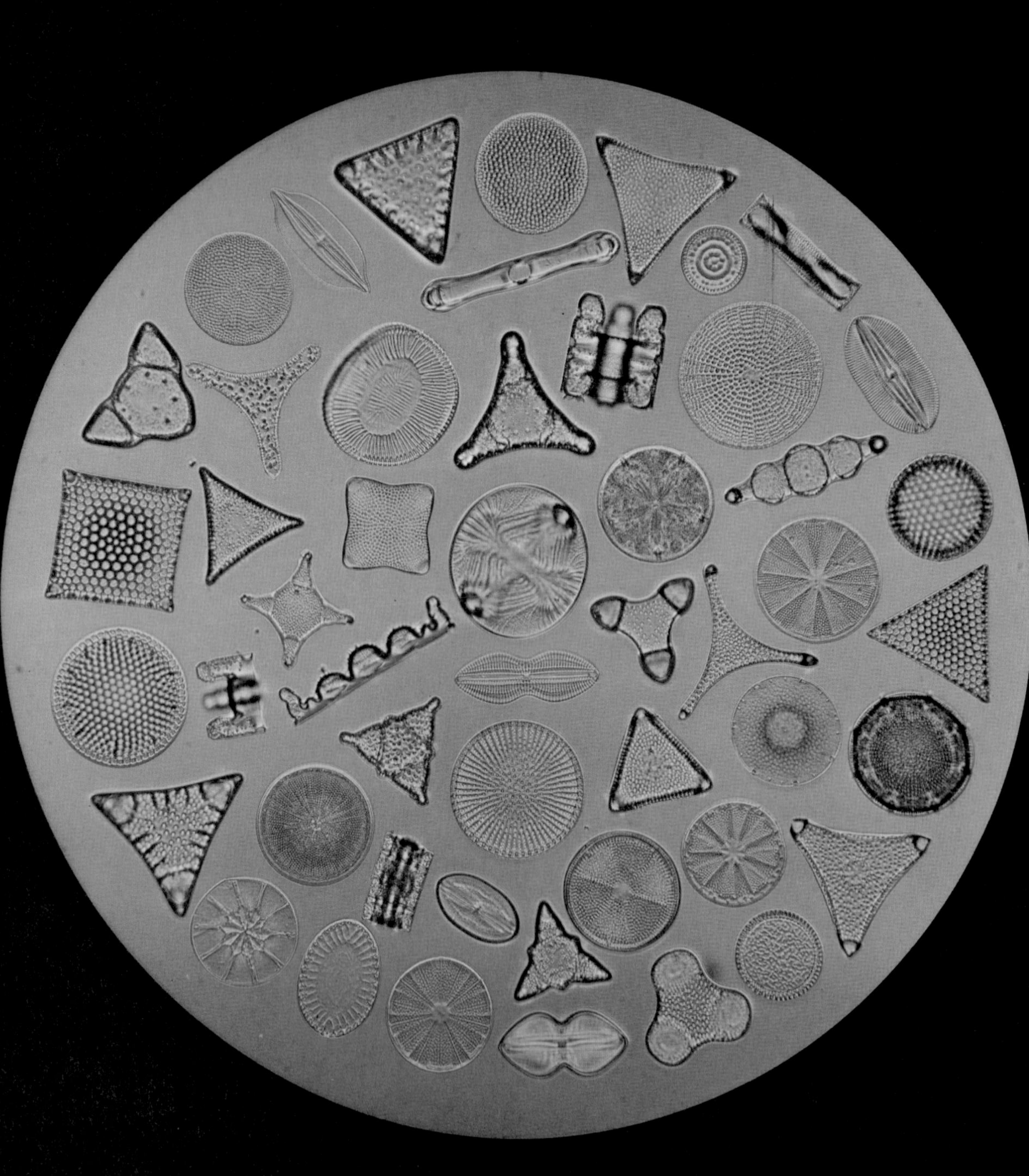

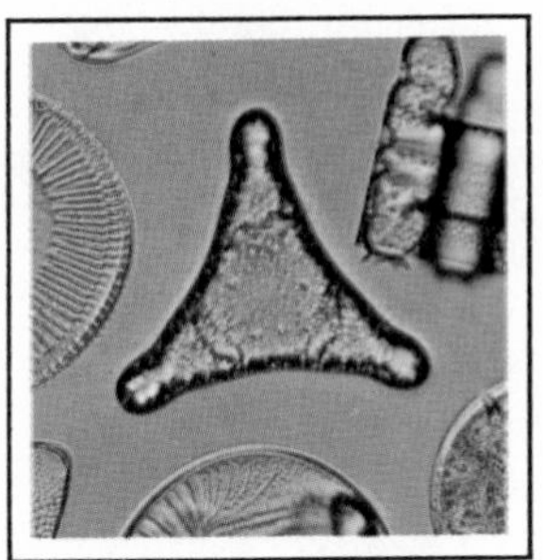

Unit 3

The protists

Unit-opening photo indicates the huge variety that may be found in a single group of organisms. Diatoms are unicellular or colonial planktonic algae. Their silicified skeletons form diatomite, useful to humans as a filter material.

Most of the living things you see are classified as plants or animals. Some organisms have characteristics of both, but are different from either group. To help solve this problem, these organisms are included in a third group of living things. They are called **protists.** Scientists, however, still cannot agree just which organisms should be placed in the protist group.

Protists are found all over the world. They are found in fresh water and salt water, in salty pools and hot springs. They are even found in snow and ice. What determines whether a microorganism is a protist, a plant, or an animal? One-celled or very simple organisms are classified as protists.

Protists include molds, bacteria, and one-celled living things called **protozoa** (singular *protozoan*). Because protozoa are capable of locomotion, they are often classified as animals. Another type of protists are the **algae** [AL-jee]. Algae (singular *alga*) are usually single-celled organisms. Algae are able to manufacture their own food. For

(*Opposite page*) Diatoms, single-celled protists.

Volvox (*upper left*), a colony of single-celled, flagellated protists. Spirogyra (*upper right*), a freshwater green alga with spiralling bands of chlorophyll. Several single-celled algae (*lower left*). Stentor (*lower right*), an organism that is free-swimming except when feeding.

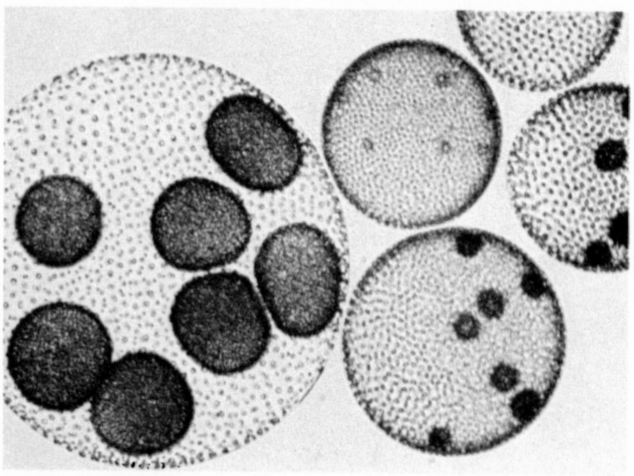

Courtesy Carolina Biological Supply Company

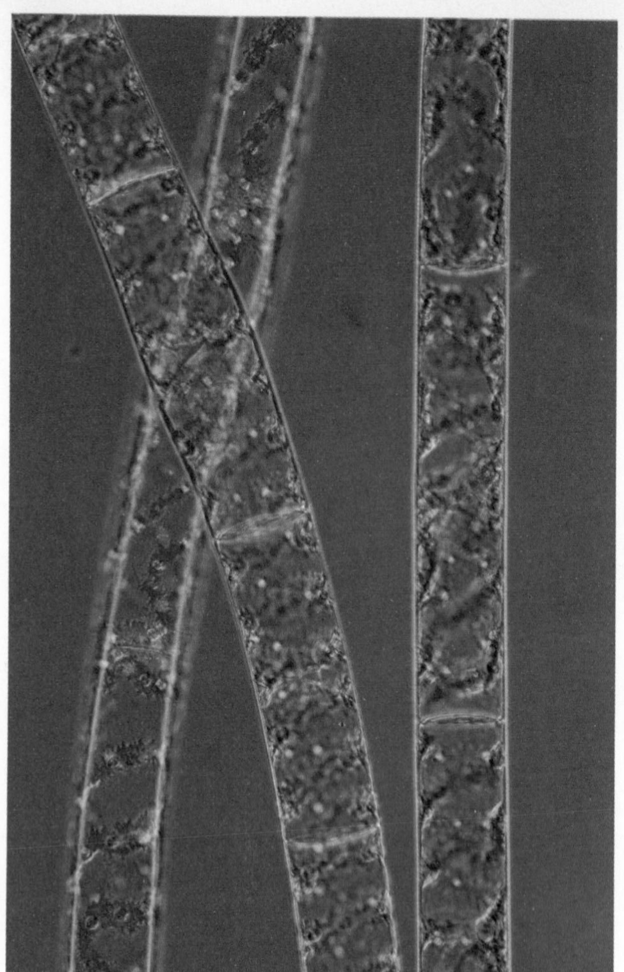

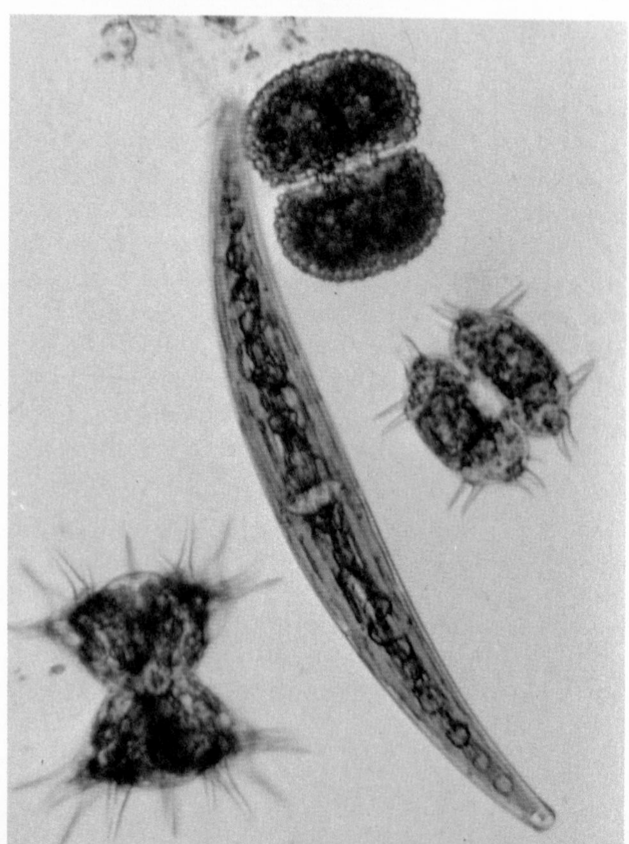

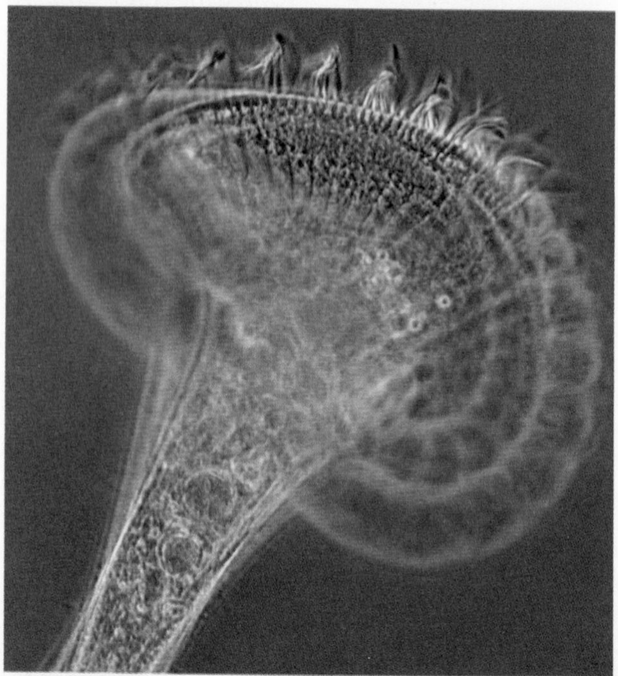

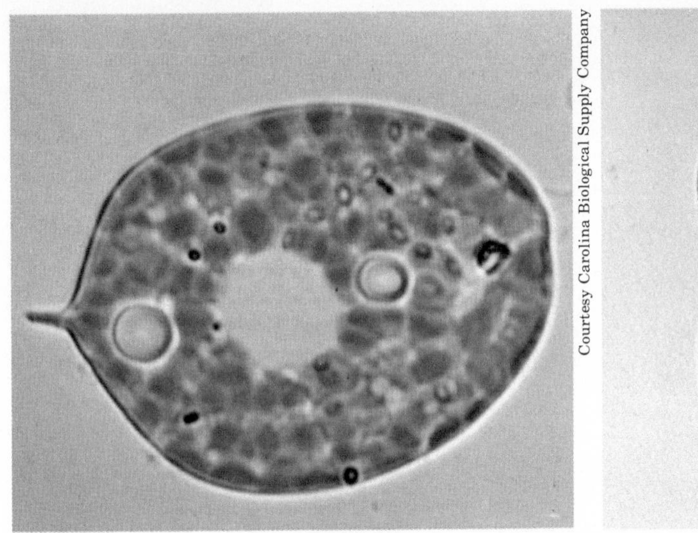

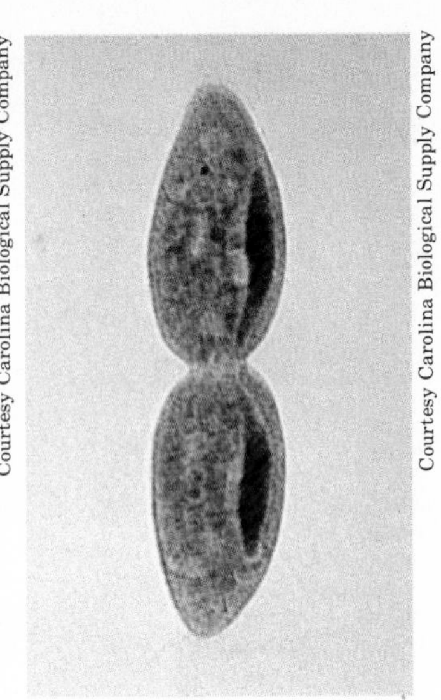

A euglenoid (*left*), a single-celled, flagellated protist, green due to the presence of chlorophyll. The red area is an eye spot. Paramecium (*right*), undergoing fission into two paramecia.

that reason they are sometimes classified as plants. Algae are found floating in lakes and ponds and on the walls of fish tanks and swimming pools. When seen in the ocean they are referred to as seaweed.

By using the protist category, scientists avoid the problem of where to place a one-celled organism that contains chlorophyll but also has a mouth and swims. This type of organism could be called a plant because it contains chlorophyll. Or it could be classified as an animal since it has a mouth and is able to move.

However, scientists are still not sure how to classify viruses. A virus has characteristics of a living cell, but it also exists as nonliving material. That is why a virus is so difficult to classify. When a virus is not inside a living cell, it does not carry out any life processes. But once inside a cell, a virus will reproduce rapidly.

All living things are capable of some method of producing more of their own kind. In Chapter 7 you saw how certain cells divide by **mitosis** to form two new cells. Mitosis takes place among cells in higher forms of life. Protists divide by a process called fission. **Fission** [FISH-un] is the division of a single-celled organism into two separate single-celled organisms.

Since a protist consists of a single cell, fission can occur very rapidly. If conditions of temperature, food, water, and space are ideal, many thousands of organisms can be produced from a single protist in a 24-hour period.

In this unit you will examine many protists. You will make your own culture of pond water organisms. You will collect molds from the air around you and from the dust in your own classroom. Finally, you will grow and study bacteria.

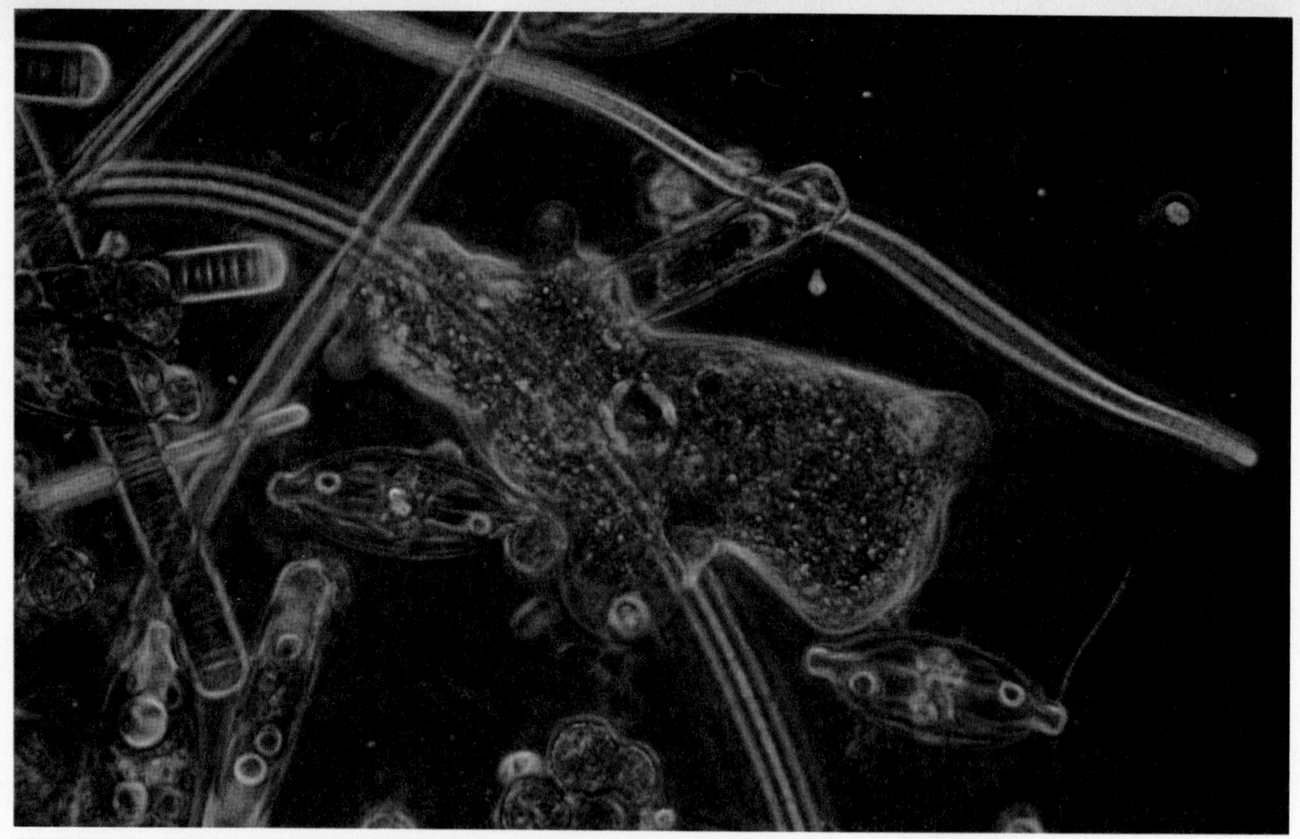

Chapter 8 Living things in a drop of water

Chapter-opening photo shows an ameba making its way through a sea of single-celled protists and algal filaments.

The world around us is full of living things. Birds, insects, trees, and grass are seen everywhere. But there is another world of living things — the world of plants and animals that exists in a drop of pond water. In that world are millions of tiny living things. They are called **microorganisms**. They include single-celled protists and many-celled organisms that are so small they can be seen only with a microscope.

Unlike the living things you studied in Chapter 7, protists do not have tissues, organs, or organ systems. Each protist is a complete living thing, usually made up of only a single cell. But each protist carries out the same life processes as the more complex plants and animals.

(*Above*) Organisms in a drop of pond water.

Where a higher form of life may have eyes that see images, some protists have "eye spots" that can detect only light and dark. (See

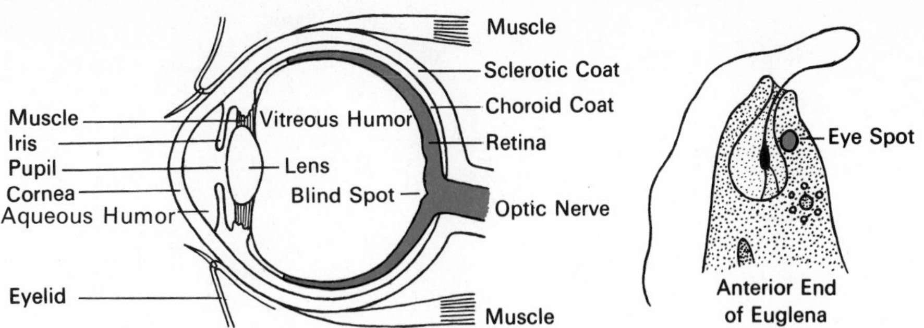

8-1. The human eye compared to the simple eye spot of a euglena.

Figure 8-1.) While many animals have complete digestive systems, some protists have only tiny cavities in their cytoplasm where food is digested. (See Figure 8-2.)

You read in Chapter 5 about Anton van Leeuwenhoek. Leeuwenhoek was the first person to see protists. He called them "animalcules", or little animals. The protists he saw were in a drop of rainwater. How they got there or what happened to them when the rainwater dried, Leeuwenhoek did not know. That information was not known for many years later.

Protists are important for a great variety of life to exist in water. The smaller organisms are eaten by the larger ones, which in turn are eaten by tiny worms and insects. Larger water animals, such as fish, depend on insects for food. Birds and land animals that eat the fish may in turn be used as food by other animals. When the fish in the pond die, parts of their bodies are used as food by the protists. This type of **food chain** is shown in Figure 8-3 (next page). There is a continuous food cycle in which larger organisms depend on smaller ones for food.

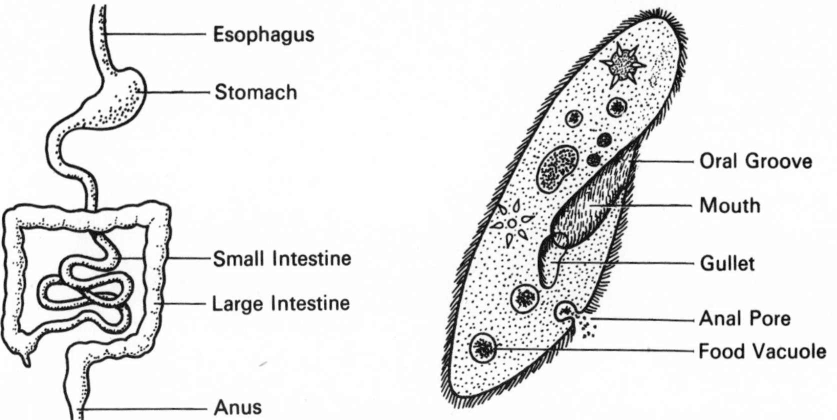

8-2. Comparison of a complex digestive system to a simple food cavity.

8-3. A food chain in the water environment.

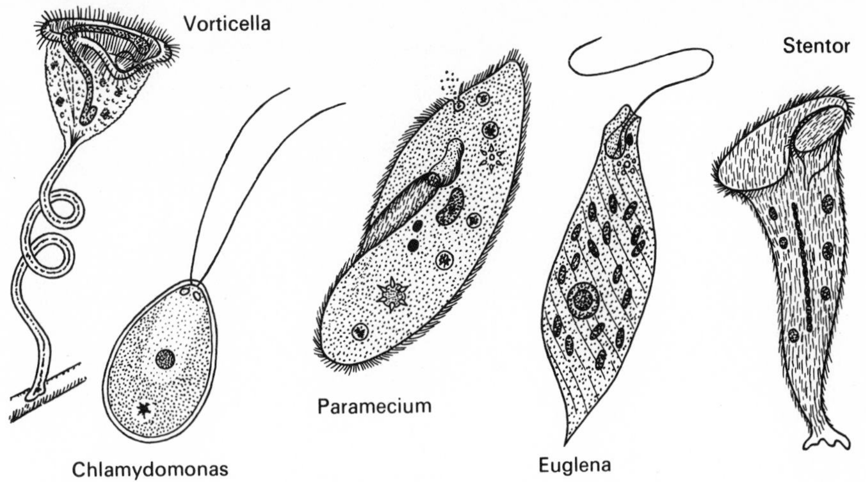

8-4. Vorticella, paramecium, and stentor move by means of cilia. Chlamydomonas and euglena use flagella.

How protists move

Most protists are capable of moving in the water. Some of them have tiny hairlike projections called **cilia** [SILL-ee-uh]. In order for the organism to move forward, the cilia beat backward, like oars moving a boat.

Other kinds of protists, such as euglena, have a flagellum [flah-JEL-um]. A **flagellum** (plural *flagella*) is a long, whiplike extension on one end of the cell. The flagellum is extended and its tip is curled and snapped. This causes the organism to move. This whiplike motion is usually too fast to be seen under your microscope.

The movement of another protist, the ameba, is also interesting. The cytoplasm inside the cell is a watery liquid. It constantly flows into many slender, fingerlike extensions called **pseudopods** [SUED-uh-pods], or "false feet." This type of movement, due to the flowing of

8-5. The ameba uses its pseudopods for food-getting and for locomotion.

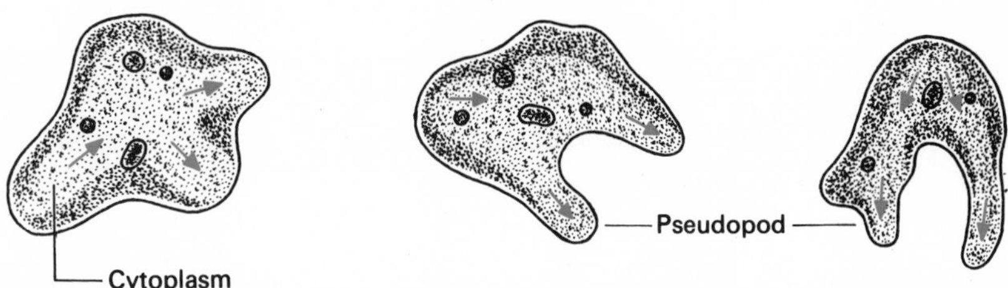

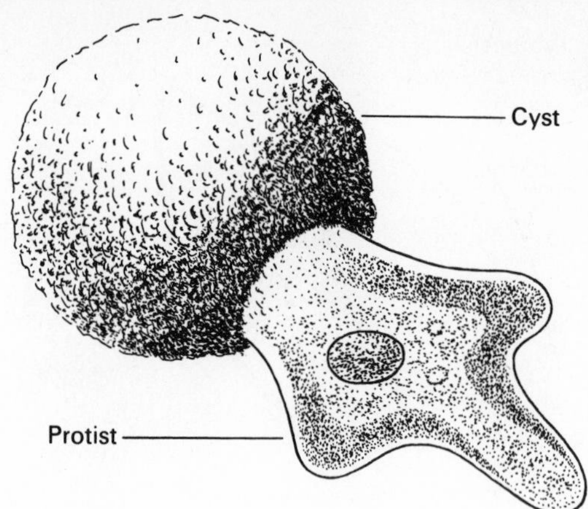

8-6. Under favorable conditions the protist emerges from the cyst to resume normal activities.

living material inside the cell, is very slow. The ameba moves in the direction in which its cytoplasm is flowing.

As stated earlier, protists are found in almost any moist environment. But where do they come from? This was a question that the scientists of Leeuwenhoek's time were unable to answer. We now know that many of these protists enclose themselves in cysts.

A **cyst** is a very hard covering around the living material. It is resistant to extreme heat, cold, and strong chemicals. Cysts are produced by the microorganisms when conditions become unfavorable. Winds can blow these cysts from place to place. As a result, cysts are found almost everywhere. When one falls into a place where conditions are right for its growth, the cyst will open and the protist inside becomes active again.

Besides the cysts of protists, the eggs of worms and insects are often found on hay and grass. When you examine a pond water culture in the laboratory, you will probably see tiny worms, insects, and other many-celled organisms. You may also notice some green algae. Algae are protists that contain chlorophyll. Algae are thus able to make their own food.

In the following problems you will explore the amazing world of microorganisms found in a drop of pond water. You will grow your own cultures of protists. You may also observe the kinds of structures found in these organisms when you view the culture through the microscope. You will even be able to see how protists react to stimuli. You will conduct experiments that will enable you to observe their responses.

For many of you this is your first chance to examine the world of microorganisms. It is a world that was unknown just 300 years ago.

Scientists know there is still a great deal to be learned. Perhaps something you will see in your pond water culture will add to the body of scientific knowledge.

Problem 8-1 What kind of life may be found in pond water?

Purpose To observe organisms found in pond water.

Materials

- medicine dropper
- slide
- pond water culture
- cover glass
- microscope
- cotton ball

Procedure

A. Prepare a wet mount slide using the water from the pond water culture.

CAUTION: Do not stir the contents of the culture dish.

B. Use a medicine dropper to obtain the sample as follows. Squeeze the bulb *before* putting the dropper in the water. Put the end of the dropper near the solid material either at the surface or on the bottom of the jar. Then release the rubber bulb. Allow the water to stand in the dropper for about one minute.

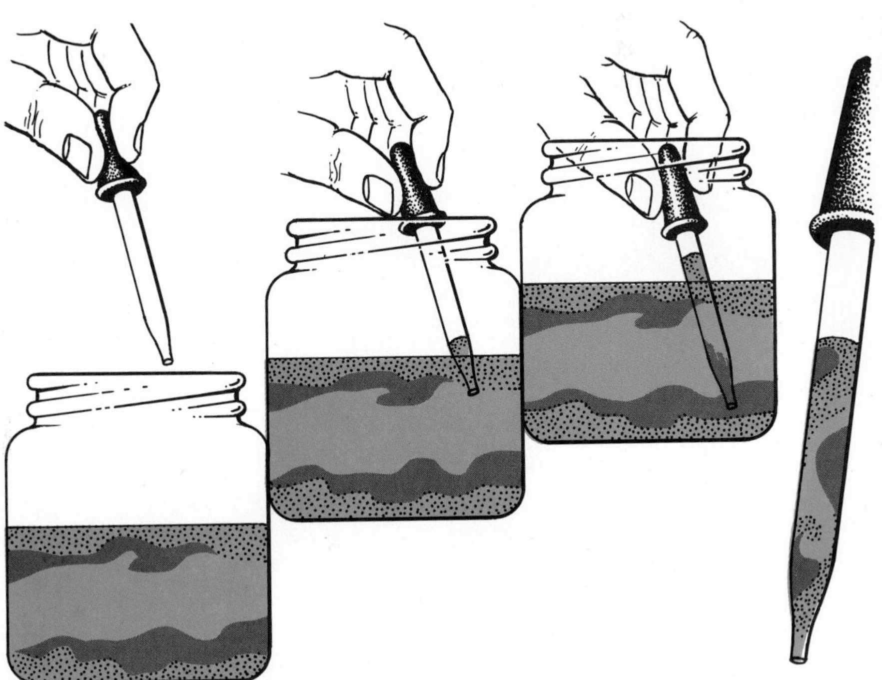

8-7. Obtaining a sample of pond water culture.

C. Add a few cotton fibers to the center of the slide before you add the water sample. Discard the first drop from the dropper. Use two drops of the remaining water to prepare the wet mount slide.

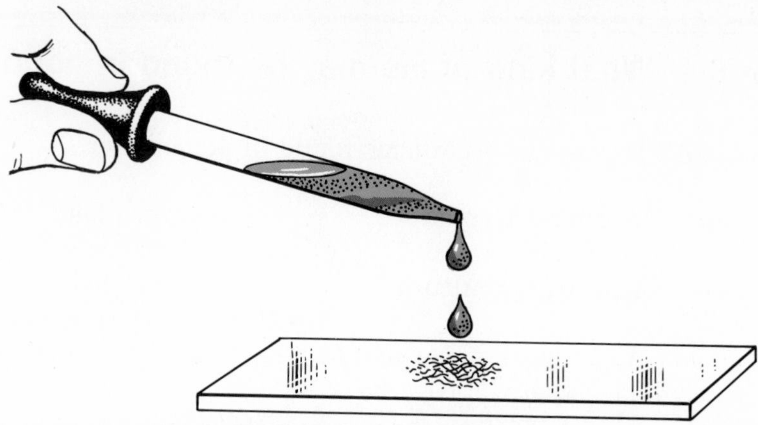

D. Observe the slide under both low power and high power. You should be able to find at least six different organisms.

Drawings of protists that are likely to be observed appear throughout this chapter. Students may also observe algae and small crustaceans and coelenterates.

TABLE 8-1 ORGANISMS FOUND IN WATER

	Organisms Observed in Jar Number ______ .					
Identification or name, if possible	ameba					
Plant, animal, or protist	protist					
Estimated size in microns	300 µ					
Single or many-celled	single					
Produce own food or consume food	consume					
Sketch of organism						

E. Copy Table 8-1 into your notebook. Record the information listed for each organism you find in the pond water. An example is shown in the first column.

F. You will continue to sample the organisms found in the container for the remainder of this unit. Save all pond water cultures since they will be used again in Problem 8-2.

1. Why do you think the cotton fibers were used in preparing the wet mount slide?
2. What substance must be present within the cells of some of these protists for them to be able to make their own food?
3. Which protist was the largest?
4. Which protist was the smallest?
5. Of the organisms you observed, which group was most common: plant, animal, or protist?

1. To restrict or confine the movement of the organisms.

2. Chlorophyll.

3. Answers will vary. Probably stentor or paramecium.

4. Answers will vary. Probably diatom.

5. Answers will vary. Probably protist.

You should now be able to

Use a dropper to obtain samples of organisms from culture dishes.

Determine if the organisms are single-celled or many-celled.

Estimate the size of protists in microns.

Determine if the organisms are able to produce food or must obtain food elsewhere.

Classify organisms as protists, plants, or animals.

Variety in water microorganisms

You have examined some of the organisms that grow in pond water. There are probably quite a few types of microorganisms that you did not see in your particular culture. The many kinds of life in pond water are constantly being studied. Scientists and students alike find this study an interesting and meaningful experience.

One reason scientists study the organisms in water is that certain protists that cause diseases in people spend part of their lives in pond water. Among these disease-causing protists is the bacterium that causes typhoid fever. You will learn more about bacteria in Chapter 10.

In your own pond culture you may have seen tiny protists darting quickly from place to place. You may have observed wormlike organisms whose body length was longer than the field of view of your microscope. If you saw green-colored cells, or long strings of green cells, they were probably algae. These are plantlike protists that are able to manufacture their own food.

You should now be ready for a more detailed study of the protists. Observe carefully and patiently in Problem 8-2. You should see these organisms perform many activities you may not have noticed before. You will examine the methods by which these organisms move and take in food.

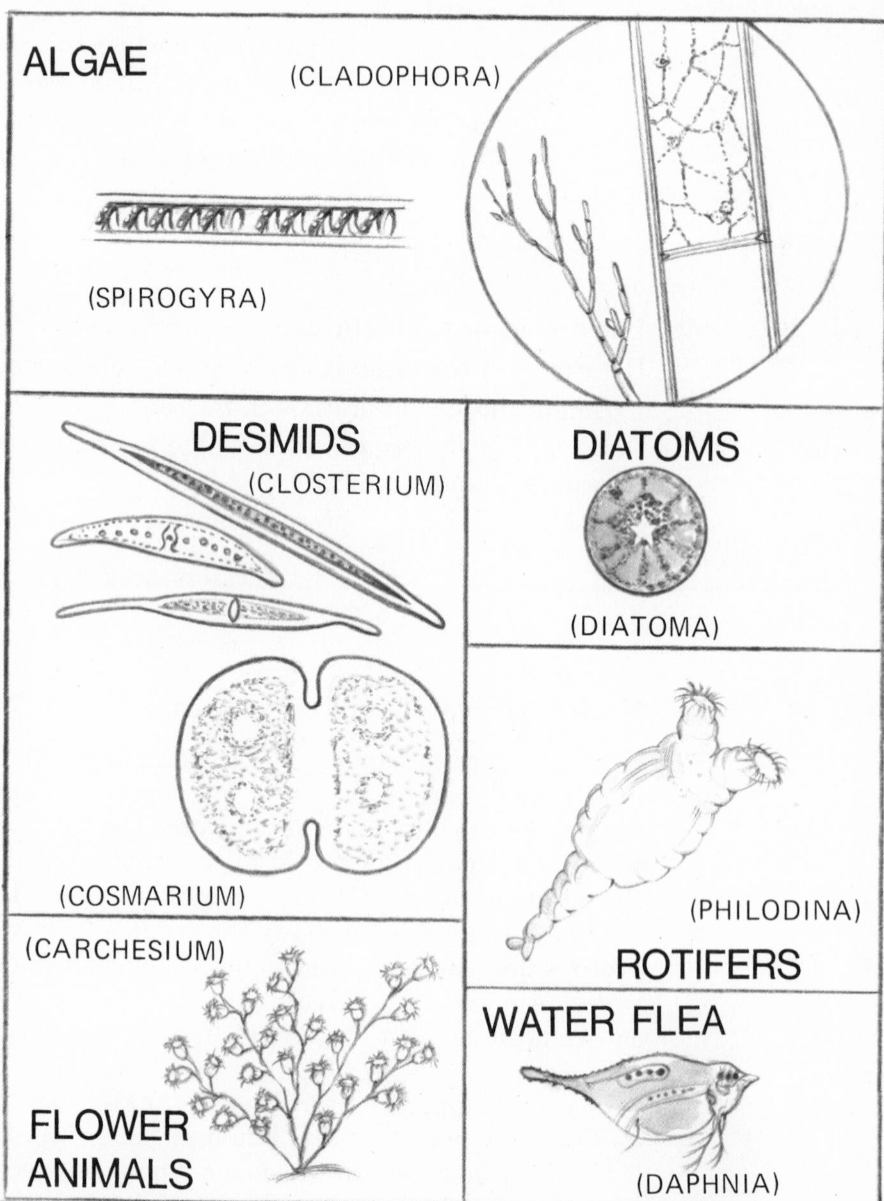

8-8. Some common organisms found in pond water.

Problem 8-2 What activities of pond water organisms can you observe?

Purpose To observe how organisms obtain food, move, and react to obstacles in their path.

Materials

pond water culture	microscope slide	microscope
dropper	cover glass	cotton ball

Procedure

A. Use the dropper technique described in Step B of Problem 8-1 to obtain a sample from the solid material in the container.

B. Place several strands of cotton fibers in the center of a glass slide.

C. Discard the first drop of water, then add two drops of the culture water to the cotton. Put a cover glass over the cotton fibers.

D. Observe under both low power and high power.

E. Locate and observe one type of organism in the cotton fibers. Observe its pattern of locomotion.

1. Why are the cotton fibers used? 1. To restrict movement of organisms.
2. Does the organism have any visible structure that is causing the movement?
3. What is the reaction of the organism to an obstacle in its path? Use a diagram to show how the organism moves around the obstacle.

F. Most of the organisms you will observe move by the use of *flagella, cilia,* or *pseudopods*. (See Figures 8-4 and 8-5, page 131.) Some other organisms may have jointed legs or similar structures for movement. The organisms that seem to wiggle are using a flagellum. Those that move in a straight line are using many cilia. If you look closely and adjust the light properly, you will probably be able to see these structures.

4. What type of structure is used for locomotion by the organism you are observing?
5. How many of these locomotion structures are present on this organism?
6. Observe the swimming pattern of the organism. Does it wiggle or move along a straight line?

G. Study the information asked for in Table 8-2. Prepare a table like it in your notebook.

2. Structures are difficult to see in living, unstained organisms. Cilia and flagella may be seen if light is subdued. A darkened field is recommended.

3. Organisms will generally hit an obstacle, back off, and go forward again at another angle. They will repeat the procedure until the obstacle is passed.

4. Various appendages may be seen, including cilia, flagella, pseudopods, and jointed legs.

5. These may be difficult to count. Cilia are quite numerous, flagella usually 1 or 2 per organism. Legs may vary.

6. Answer depends on the type of organism and the activity in which it is engaged. Generally, the ciliated organisms move along a relatively straight line, and flagellated cells move in a zig-zag pattern. The others usually move randomly.

TABLE 8-2 MOVEMENT OF MICROORGANISMS

Drawing of Organism	*Single-Celled or Many-Celled*	*Structure Used for Locomotion*	*Pattern of Movement*

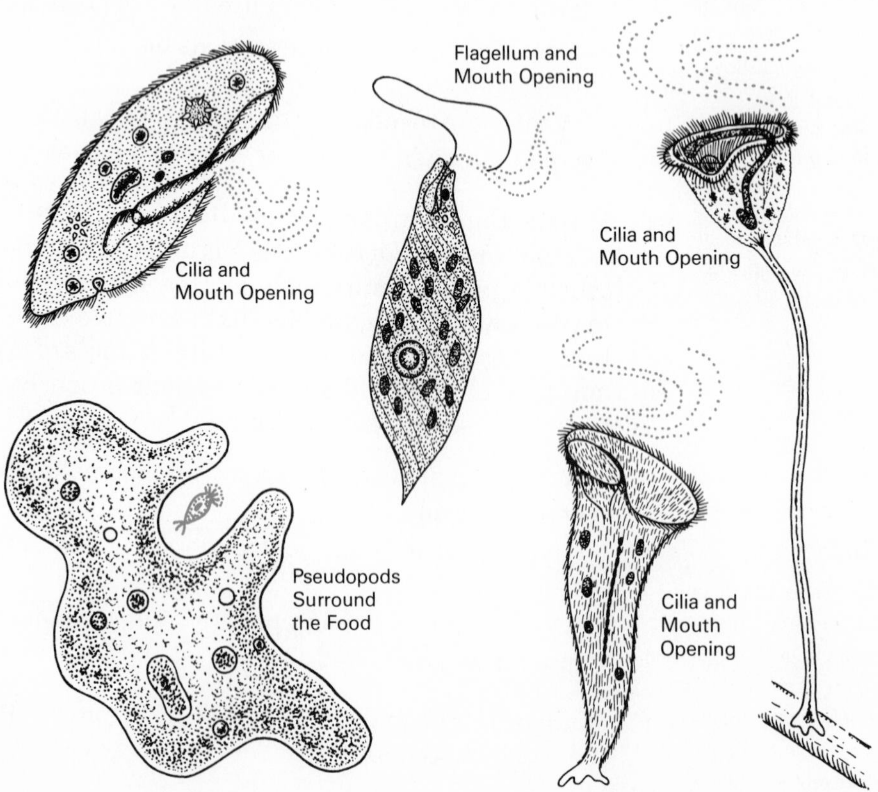

8-9. Structures used by microorganisms for taking in food.

H. Observe other organisms. In your notebook table, describe the pattern followed when the organism moves. List the structures used for locomotion.

I. Observe each organism to determine how food is taken into its body. Most organisms will have a mouth to allow food to enter the body. Other organisms just surround their food.

7. No. These organisms can manufacture their own food.
8. Drawings should show mouth or pseudopods.

7. Would organisms with chlorophyll need to have a mouth or some other method of surrounding their food? Explain.
8. Make drawings in your notebook to show how food enters each kind of organism you have observed.

You should now be able to

Determine the type of structure used for locomotion by each organism.

Indicate patterns of movement of the organism by the use of diagrams.

Locate on a drawing the structure or structures used by the organism to take in food.

Animal responses to the environment

In the last problem you saw how single-celled protists reacted when they touched a cotton fiber. You may have watched one of the microscopic organisms feeding. You may even have followed the path of the food into its body. You should also have observed how the different organisms moved. Some rotated, some wiggled, and some moved with a side-to-side motion.

In order to get food, to avoid harmful conditions, and to maintain other life processes, organisms must react to changes in their surroundings. Such changes in the environment are called stimuli (singular *stimulus*). A **stimulus** is anything that will cause a change in the activities of a living organism.

Taxis responses

Most organisms respond to stimuli through a movement known as a taxis [TAX-sis]. A **taxis** is a response involving locomotion or movement of the entire organism. Special terms are used to describe a response to a particular change in the environment. **Phototaxis** is a response to light. **Thermotaxis** is a response to temperature. **Thigmotaxis** is a response to touch. **Chemotaxis** is a response to chemicals. If the movement of the organism is toward the stimulus, it is called a **positive** taxis. If the movement of the organism is away from the stimulus, it is a **negative** taxis.

Tropisms

A protist, plant, or animal that lacks locomotion may also react to stimuli. These reactions are usually very slow. Those slow reactions are called **tropisms.** If the organism moves toward the stimulus, it is a positive tropism. If the movement is away from the stimulus, it is a negative tropism. For example, the roots of a plant display a positive tropism toward gravity. But the stem of the plant shows a negative tropism to gravity.

You are now going to observe a many-celled animal called a brine shrimp. A brine shrimp is large enough to be seen with the naked eye. But you will use your microscope in order to observe more details of its responses to stimuli.

Problem 8-3 How do water animals react to stimuli?

Purpose To observe how environmental changes affect the activity of brine shrimp.

Materials

microscope
cover glass
glass rod
medicine droppers (2)
brine shrimp eggs
petri dish
salt solution or salt
graduated cylinder
plastic bag
ice cube
aluminum foil
balance

Procedure

Part One: Hatching brine shrimp eggs

The brine shrimp *(Artemia salina)* is a tiny animal found in salt waters. This animal can be used to study many questions about living things. Brine shrimp eggs can be stored for long periods of time and hatched easily in the laboratory.

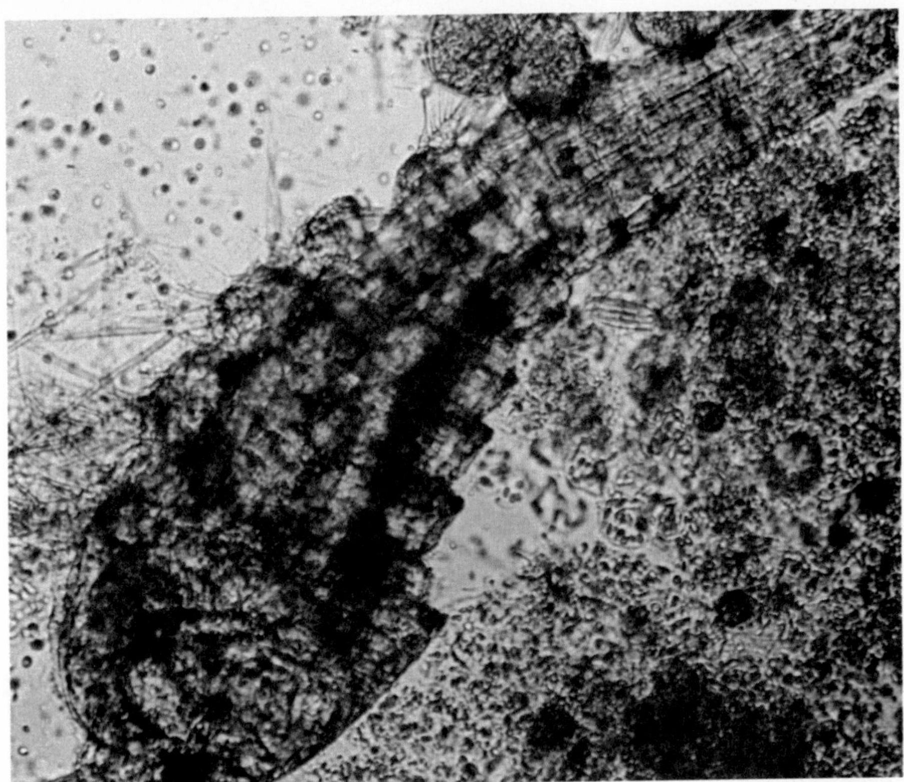

8-10. Brine shrimp (*Artemia salina*), a tiny salt-water organism.

If possible, prepare this salt solution ahead of time. Be sure to use distilled water.

A. Prepare or obtain a 0.35 percent salt solution for hatching the eggs. Your teacher has probably already prepared it. If not, an easy way to make a hatching solution is as follows. Add 3.5 grams of sodium chloride to 1 liter of distilled water. (Be sure the salt is *not iodized*.)

B. Use a graduated cylinder to add 20 ml of salt solution to the bottom of a petri dish.

C. Dip the end of a glass rod into the salt solution in the petri dish. *Gently* touch the wet end of the glass rod to the dried brine shrimp eggs. The eggs are so small that just covering the tip of the rod will supply hundreds of brine shrimp for the experiment. Transfer the eggs to the petri dish by carefully passing the rod through the solution.

D. Observe the brine shrimp eggs in the petri dish under low power and high power. Be careful that your objective lens does not touch the salt solution.

In Step E, students should describe the eggs at 0 hours as small brown spheres.

E. Make a copy of Table 8-3 (next page) in your notebook. Describe and draw the appearance of the eggs for 0 hours.

F. Cover the petri dish and store it for about 24 hours.

TABLE 8-3 OBSERVATION OF BRINE SHRIMP EGGS

0-Hours	*24-Hours*	*48-Hours*
Description:	Description:	Description:
Appearance:	Appearance:	Appearance:

Drawing for 24 hours may show some structures such as legs, digestive tract, eye spot, etc. After 48 hours, the eggs should be hatched or ready to hatch.

G. Observe the eggs after 24 hours. In your copy of Table 8-3, describe and draw any changes in the appearance of the eggs.

H. Store the solution for another 24 hours and then observe the eggs. In your copy of Table 8-3, describe and draw any changes in the appearance of the eggs.

Part Two: Responses to light

A *taxis* is a direct movement in response to some stimulus in the environment. If the organism goes toward the stimulus, the reaction is a *positive taxis*. If the organism goes away from the stimulus, the reaction is a *negative taxis*. If the organism fails to respond either positively or negatively, the stimulus is said to have no effect.

Photo- means "light." In the next step, you will see if brine shrimp display a response to light, or *phototaxis*.

I. With a medicine dropper, pick up as many moving brine shrimp as possible. Take them from places where they are crowded in the petri dish. Then repeat this procedure *with another dropper*.

1. The shrimp should have moved from the section covered by the foil into an area near the light source. (This observation may vary from group to group.)

1. Examine the brine shrimp in the droppers. Where are they located?

8-11. Phototaxis.

If time permits, have students repeat this procedure (Steps I and J) a second time. Lab teams should compare results.

2. As a control.

3. The brine shrimp will generally move toward the light, showing a positive phototaxis.

J. Wrap aluminum foil around one of the droppers as shown in Figure 8-11. Leave only 10 mm of the solution-filled tip exposed. Place both droppers under a light source. Observe the droppers for at least 10 minutes *without* touching the droppers or foil.

2. Why is it necessary to include a dropper without the aluminum foil wrapping in the experiment?
3. In what general direction do the brine shrimp seem to be moving? Should the motion be described as a positive or a negative phototaxis?

K. If time permits, repeat Part Two to check your results.

Part Three: Responses to temperature

Thermo- means "heat." A procedure to see if brine shrimp have a positive or negative *thermotaxis* follows.

L. Repeat Step I or, if possible, use the samples from the phototaxis experiment.

M. Place an ice cube in a small plastic bag. Balance the medicine dropper on the plastic-wrapped ice cube as shown in Figure 8-12. One portion of the solution should be resting on the ice cube and the rest not touching it. Place the other dropper on a flat surface.

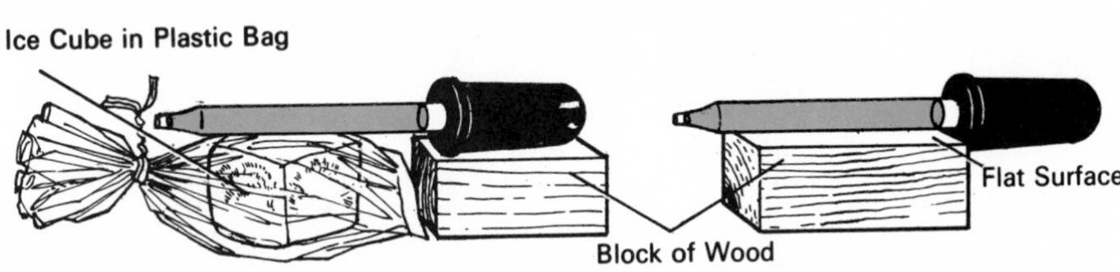

8-12. Thermotaxis.

4. Negative. (The shrimp moved away from the ice.)

5. One was the control and the other was the experimental. A comparison between the two can thus be made.

N. Observe the droppers for at least five minutes.

4. Should the change in movement be described as a positive or negative thermotaxis?
5. Why did you use two droppers?
6. What response did the brine shrimp show in the dropper at room temperature?

Part Four: Responses to gravity

6. Usually no pattern of movement. Organisms should be found scattered throughout the dropper.

7. Negative (usually).

8. Yes. Light, temperature, availability of oxygen, and other variables.

Geo- means "earth." A response to gravity is a **geotaxis.** A procedure to see if brine shrimp have a positive or negative geotaxis follows.

O. If possible, use droppers from your thermotaxis experiments, or repeat Step I. Lay one dropper on a flat surface. Hold the other tube in an upright position. (See Figure 8-13.)

7. Is the change in movement within the upright dropper a positive or negative geotaxis?
8. Is there anything else which may account for your observation in question 7?
9. If your answer to question 8 is "yes", can you design an experiment to eliminate all stimuli except gravity? Describe the experiment you would do.

Part Five: Designing an experiment

9. Answers will vary. Accept anything that will fulfill the requirements mentioned. One possibility: Set up a series of test tubes containing brine shrimp in places that have uniform light, constant temperature, and the same amount of oxygen throughout the solution. Observe shrimp for geotactic response.

There are other stimuli that living organisms can respond to. Such stimuli include touch, electricity, and chemicals.

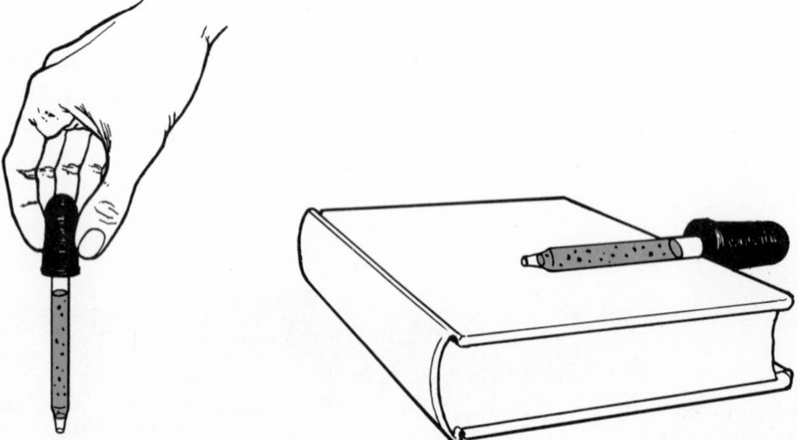

8-13. Geotaxis.

10. See Teacher's Guide section for possible answers to this question.

11. Accept any reasonable answer that indicates that the behavior of the shrimp is much less complex than that of a dog, cat, etc.

P. Design an experiment similar to the ones you have been doing. Design it to test the response of brine shrimp to one of these stimuli — touch, electricity, or chemicals.

10. Describe your experiment in your notebook.
11. Compare the behavior of brine shrimp with that of a dog, cat, or some other familiar animal.
12. Why should two droppers be used to determine the results of these experiments?

You should now be able to

12. One is experimental, and the other is the control.

Describe the reaction of brine shrimp to various environmental stimuli as positive, negative, or no reaction.

Interpret the results of an experimental group by the results of a control group.

Design an experiment to determine the response or taxis of brine shrimp to a stimulus.

Science terms

algae
chemotaxis
cilia
cyst
fission
flagellum
food chain
geotaxis
microorganism
mitosis
negative taxis
phototaxis
positive taxis
protist
protozoan
pseudopod
stimulus
taxis
thermotaxis
thigmotaxis

Review questions

1. Any living organism too small to be seen with the unaided eye.

2. Answers will vary. Common pond water organisms: paramecia, algae, rotifers, daphnias, etc.

3. Common protists include paramecia, spirogyra, stentor, ameba, vorticella, algae, etc.

4. When it sustains itself as an independent living thing.

5. Cilia.

6. Cyst.

7. Flagella, cilia, and pseudopods.

8. Mitosis.

1. What is a microorganism?
2. List three microorganisms that may be found in pond water.
3. Name three different protists found in pond water.
4. When could a single cell be called an organism?
5. What special structures does a paramecium use for locomotion?
6. What is the hard covering that protects some protists during long periods of dryness?
7. List three types of locomotion used by protists.
8. Reproduction by fission involves the division of a single-celled organism into two new single-celled organisms. What is the name of the cell division process in higher forms of life which also produces two new, identical cells?

Check your understanding

See Teacher's Guide section for answers to Questions 9-14.

9. Describe what is meant by a positive phototaxis.
10. How would you distinguish between a many-celled organism and a single-celled organism?
11. When conditions are favorable, a paramecium divides and forms two paramecia every hour. How many hours would it take to produce eight paramecia from one which has just been formed?
12. Describe how a paramecium moves and obtains food.
13. When placed on a slide and examined with a microscope, paramecia have been seen to move to the edge of the cover glass. What condition may have caused this negative response?
14. Fifty microorganisms were found in a drop of pond water. If microorganisms were distributed equally throughout, explain how you would estimate the total number in a jar.

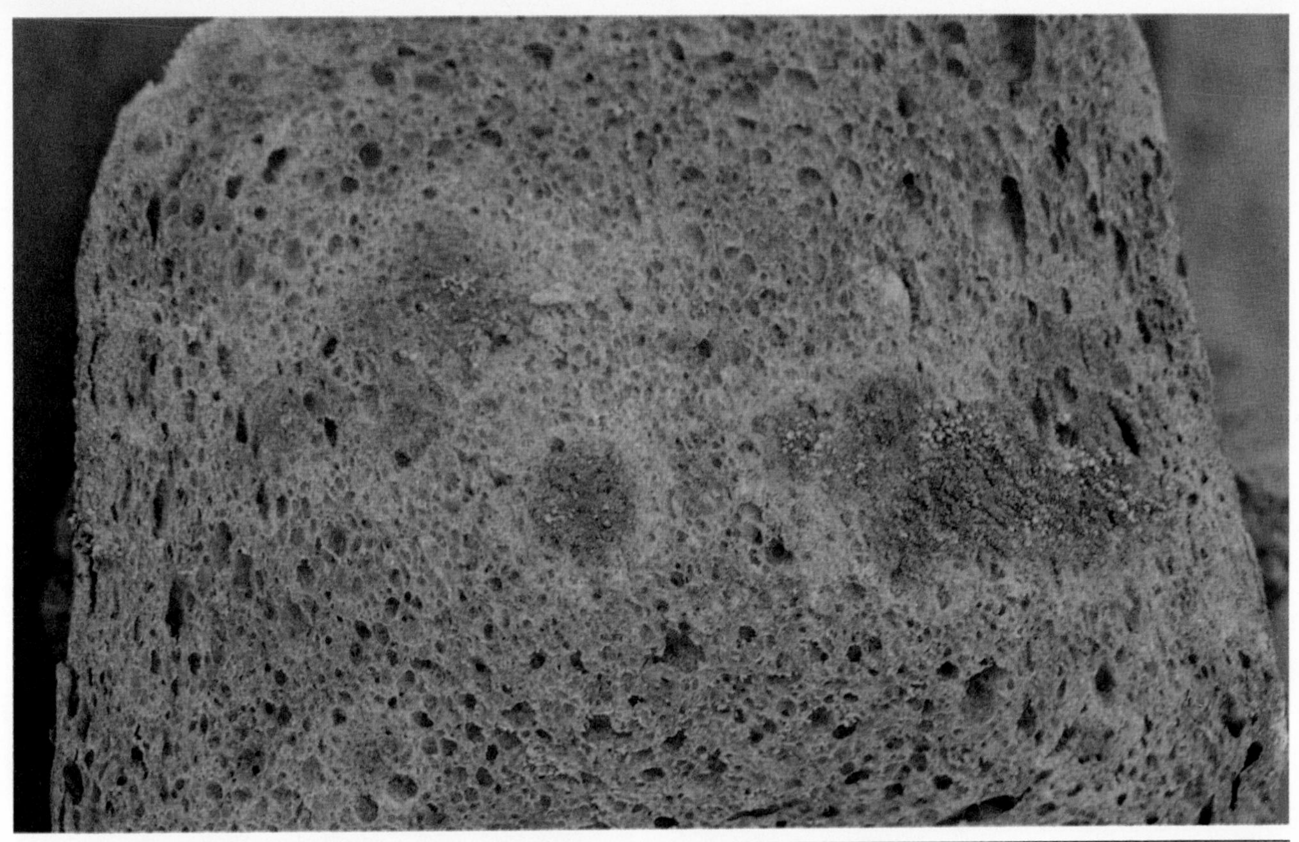

Chapter 9 **Yeasts and molds**

Chapter-opening photo combines the idea of "yeasts and molds" titling the chapter. *Penicillium* mold is growing on bread, which has yeast as one of its ingredients.

There are many kinds of nongreen protists. Some of these are the single-celled **yeasts** and the many-celled **molds.** They do not contain chlorophyll and thus cannot make their own food. So they have to live on organic matter. **Organic matter** is any living substance, such as a tree or a human. It can also be anything that is not alive now but once was alive, such as bread and wood.

If a mold takes its nourishment from a living plant or animal, the mold is called a **parasite.** If a mold lives on dead organic matter, it is called a **saprophyte** [SAP-ruh-fite]. All yeasts and molds are either parasites or saprophytes.

Yeasts and molds produce spores. The **spores** are tiny reproductive cells. Each spore is able to produce a complete new colony. A **colony** is a group of the same organisms growing in one place. Mold spores are found everywhere. Spores are produced by the thousands and are so light that the slightest breeze will take them with it. Mold spores settle to the floor, on your food, and even on your body. If con-

The term *fungus* can be applied to any saprophytic or parasitic, nongreen protist. Fungi include yeasts and molds as well as mushrooms, rusts, smuts, and mildews.

Yellow coral mushroom (*top*) and oyster mushrooms (*lower right*), named because of their color and shape. Bracket fungi (*lower left*) are parasitic, growing on the wood and bark of trees.

The *Amanita muscaria*, an extremely poisonous mushroom.

ditions are right for their growth, the spores will open and begin to grow into a new colony.

There are certain conditions necessary for mold growth. Food and water must be present. There are many kinds of molds, and each type needs a particular food. Bread mold usually grows on bread. Cheese mold usually grows on cheese. And the mold that causes athlete's foot generally grows only in the moist, dark areas between the toes.

Besides food and water, molds require a warm, dark environment. Some mold spores will not reproduce when exposed to the ultraviolet rays of sunlight. For that reason many butchers keep ultraviolet lamps in their meat coolers. Barbers may use this light on their stored combs and brushes to slow the growth of molds and other microorganisms. Of course many molds can grow in light. Molds that attack wheat, oats, roses, and other plants can live and reproduce in sunlight.

(*Above*) The mold *Penicillium* growing on an orange. (*Below*) Corn smut on sweet corn.

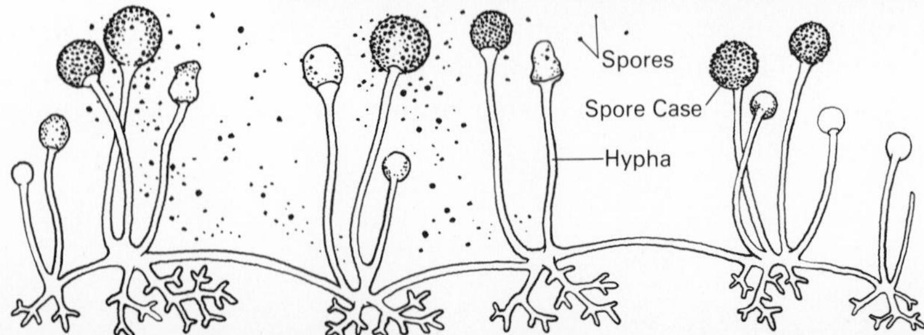

Mold spores can be carried by the wind to various locations.

Another way people control mold growth is with chemicals called **fungicides.** These chemicals are in the form of powder or liquids and can be sprayed on crops. Unfortunately, nothing is very effective against the athlete's foot mold. Keeping the feet clean and dry is the best way to get rid of this itchy growth.

Not all yeasts and molds are harmful. Indeed, many of them are very beneficial to people. Some yeasts are used in the baking industry. When those yeasts have the proper conditions, they reproduce rapidly and produce carbon dioxide gas. That gas causes bread and rolls to rise. In the making of beer and wine, yeasts are used to ferment the beverages.

Molds are of vital importance in medicine. **Penicillin** comes from the mold *Penicillium.* Many of our modern "wonder drugs" are made from molds. Whenever the name of a medicine ends in *-mycin* [MY-sin], that means it was made from a mold.

In the laboratory you are going to grow some mold in a petri dish. Petri dishes are used by scientists to grow organisms under controlled conditions. To grow molds you will have to supply them with food, moisture, warmth, and air. The most commonly used food, or **nutrient,** that many molds can use is beef broth. Since broth is a liquid, it is mixed with a gelatinlike material called **agar** to make it easier to work with. Agar comes from algae that grow in the ocean.

Mixed together in proper proportions, beef broth, agar, and water form the culture medium. The **medium** will provide the proper environment for the organisms to be grown on it. But first, the mixture must be sterilized to kill any microorganisms that may already be present.

Sterilizing is accomplished by heating the petri dishes and contents under steam pressure at a high temperature. It can also be done by heating the dishes and contents in an oven. When you are handling molds in the laboratory be sure to use proper techniques. Otherwise you will grow unwanted microorganisms.

As mentioned earlier, mold spores are everywhere. When handling molds and spores in the lab, keep your fingers and pencils away from your mouth. Don't eat in the lab or drink from any beaker or flask. In case of accidental spillage of a container with mold in it, tell your teacher. When you complete a problem, be sure to throw all solid materials into the special container provided.

Since the discovery of penicillin, molds have been studied with great interest. In this chapter you will make carbon dioxide gas using yeasts. You will grow bread mold, and collect mold spores from your surroundings.

Problem 9-1 How do temperature extremes affect the production of carbon dioxide gas by yeast?

Purpose To determine the effects of low and high temperatures on yeast cells by measuring the amount of carbon dioxide produced at each temperature.

Materials

test tubes, 22 × 175 mm (3)
test-tube rack
 (to fit large test tubes)
dry yeast
beakers, 250-ml (3)
beaker, 600-ml
stirring rod
medicine dropper
ring stand and clamp
salt
sugar
aluminum foil
graduated cylinder
methylene blue solution
 (dilute)
thermometer, Celsius
marking pen
metric ruler
ice cubes (4)
wire gauze
Bunsen burner
test-tube clamps

Medicine droppers used in Part One should be absolutely dry. Droppers may be dried by heating them over a burner flame, then allowing them to cool.

Procedure

Part One: Yeast cells in the oven and refrigerator

A. Take a dry dropper and remove the rubber bulb (Figure 9-1). Use a marking pen and ruler to draw a line 1.5 cm (15 mm) from the

9-1. Mark the dropper, fill it, and add the yeast to labeled test tubes.

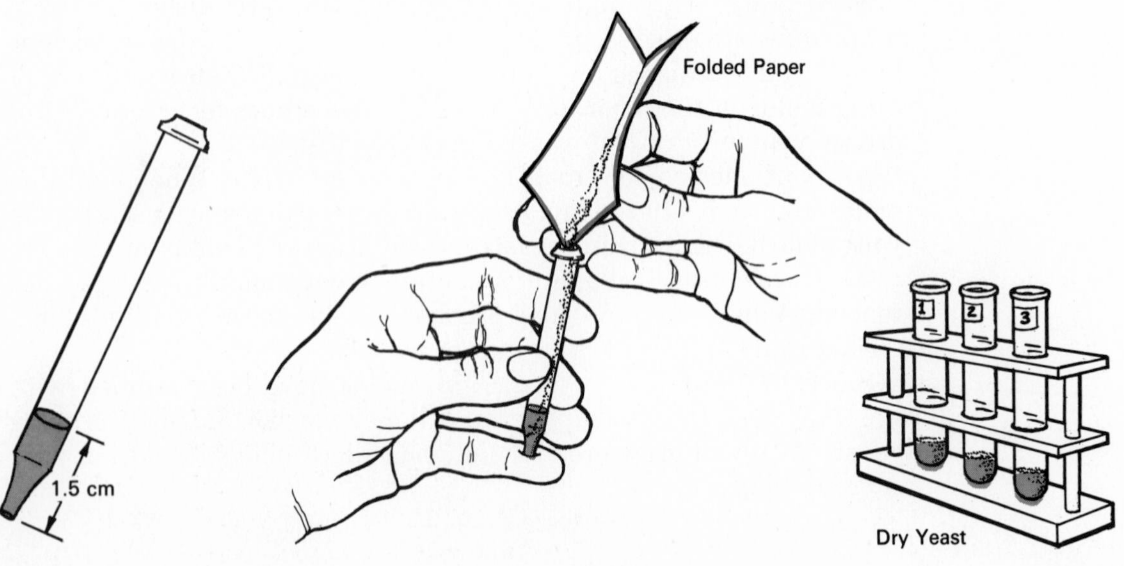

TABLE 9-1 EFFECT OF TEMPERATURE ON YEAST SOLUTIONS

Test Tube Number	*Yeast Solution*	*Temperature Extreme*	*Amount of Gas Collected*
1	Cold		
2	Hot		
3	Normal		

The amount of yeast added to each tube and the concentration of sugar solution are critical. If too much yeast is added or the sugar concentration is too high, the amount of gas produced will be greater than the volume of the test tubes.

narrow tip of the dropper. Hold the dropper as shown in Figure 9-1, with your little finger blocking the tip of the dropper. Fill the dropper with dry yeast to the 1.5-cm mark. Then transfer this amount of yeast to a dry test tube. Label this test tube as number "1."

Repeat this procedure twice more to put dry yeast in test tubes labeled "2" and "3." Replace the rubber bulb on the dropper.

B. Obtain a 600-ml beaker. Prepare a sugar solution by dissolving 5 grams of sugar in 500 ml of water. Use a graduated cylinder to measure the water. Stir the sugar and water with a glass rod until the sugar is completely dissolved. Add 10 ml of the sugar solution to each of the test tubes numbered 1, 2, and 3.

1. Why do you think the sugar solution must be added to the yeast?

1. The yeast cells need it for food.

C. Study the information asked for in Table 9-1. Then copy Table 9-1 into your notebook. Record the temperature extremes (highest and lowest temperatures) reached by the yeast solutions as you do Steps D, E, and F.

D. Place Test Tube 1 containing yeast and 10 ml sugar solution into a 250-ml beaker. Gently place the thermometer in the test tube. Add four ice cubes to the beaker. Cover the ice with approximately 3 grams of salt. (See Figure 9-2, next page.) The salt is added to lower the temperature of the ice water.

E. Record the lowest temperature reached after ten minutes. While one member is recording the data, the rest of the team may proceed with Step F.

The temperature recorded in Step E should be about 5-10°C.

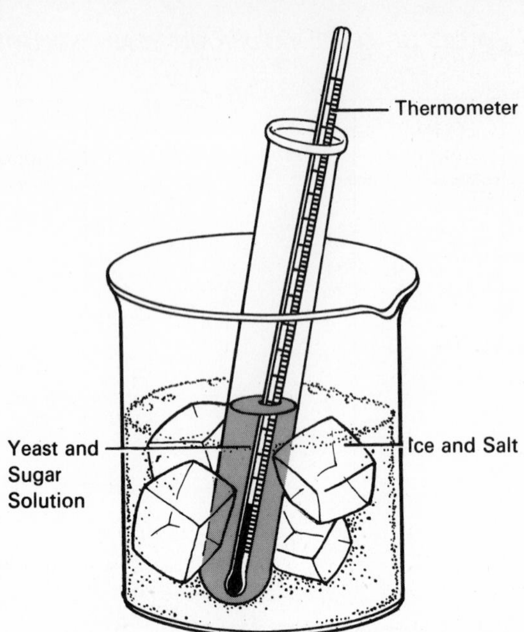

9-2. Record the lowest temperature reached after ten minutes.

CAUTION: In Step F, be sure the solution does not completely evaporate or splatter out of the test tube. Be sure the test tube is always pointed away from you and other people.

The temperature recorded in Step F should be 100°C.

F. Heat Test Tube 2 containing yeast and 10 ml sugar solution over a Bunsen burner. Boil the solution for *five* minutes. When the solution starts to boil, it will rise in the test tube. Remove the test tube from the flame until the solution settles down. Keep returning the test tube to the flame to keep the solution boiling. Record the temperature of this boiling solution in the table in your notebook.

G. Return the test tube to the rack after heating.

H. Remove Test Tube 1 from the beaker and dry the outside with a paper towel. Put the dried test tube back in the rack with Test Tubes 2 and 3. Empty the beaker with the ice-salt mixture into the sink.

I. Now prepare Test Tubes 1, 2, and 3 as follows. Completely fill each test tube with sugar solution so that some of the solution spills over the sides of the test tube. Cap each test tube with a 5-cm square piece of aluminum foil. (See Figure 9-3.) Try not to leave any air in the test tubes. The rest of the sugar solution will be used in Step J.

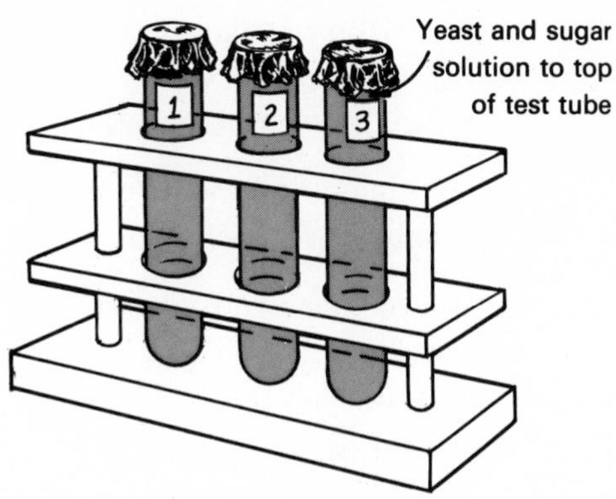

9-3. Fill each test tube completely and cap with foil.

J. Divide the remaining sugar solution evenly into three 250-ml beakers. If each beaker is not half full, add equal amounts of water to half fill each beaker. Label the beakers with the same numbers as the test tubes (1, 2, and 3).

K. Carefully invert one of the foil-capped test tubes into the beaker with the same number. (See Figure 9-4.) Do the same with the other two test tubes and beakers. Be sure to match the numbered beaker with the same number test tube.

L. Store beakers and test tubes in a place where they will not be disturbed until the next day.

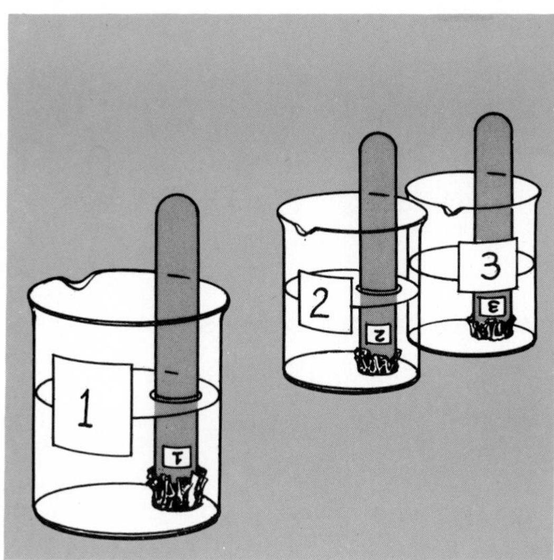

9-4. Invert each test tube in a beaker of the same number.

2. Measure the amount of liquid remaining. Measure the amount of liquid a test tube will hold. Subtract the amount left from the total volume to get the amount of gas in the test tube. (Any variation of this method is satisfactory.)

The amounts of gas measured and recorded in Step N will vary somewhat with the technique used.

M. After 24 hours draw a line on each test tube to show where the gas and sugar water reached in the tube. Save the yeast and sugar solution from Beaker 3 for Part Two.

2. Design a method for measuring the volume of gas collected in each tube. Describe the method you will use.

N. Measure the amount of gas produced in each of the three test tubes. In your notebook copy of Table 9-1, record the volume of gas collected in each tube.

It is necessary to make an assumption before examining your data further. Your experiment has not measured yeast activity directly. Yeast cells produce carbon dioxide gas (CO_2) in carrying out cell activities. The assumption is: *A small amount of gas shows little activity, and a larger amount of gas shows a greater activity of yeast cells.* In other words, more gas means the yeast cells are more active.

(If you did not know how the experiment had been set up, you might make a different assumption. You might assume that more carbon dioxide means that more yeast cells are present. But you know that in Step A you prepared the three test tubes to contain approximately the same amount of yeast.)

3. Probably Tube 3 (room temperature), although Tube 1 (cold) will have almost the same amount.

4. Tube 2.

5. As a control.

3. Which tube had the most carbon dioxide produced in it?
4. Which tube had the least carbon dioxide?
5. Why was a third test tube set up that was not exposed to a hot or cold temperature extreme?

If carbon dioxide gas is passed through limewater solution, the limewater will turn cloudy.

6. Bubble the gas through limewater.

6. How could you set up this experiment in order to test to see if the gas produced is really carbon dioxide?

You will use the limewater solution as a test for the presence of carbon dioxide later, in a problem on seed germination.

Part Two: Microscopic observations of yeast cells

O. Obtain a glass slide and cover glass.

P. Place a drop of sugar-yeast solution from Beaker 3 on the glass slide.

7. The yeast cells have not been affected by the temperature variable.

7. Why was the sugar solution from Beaker 3 suggested rather than Beaker 1 or 2?

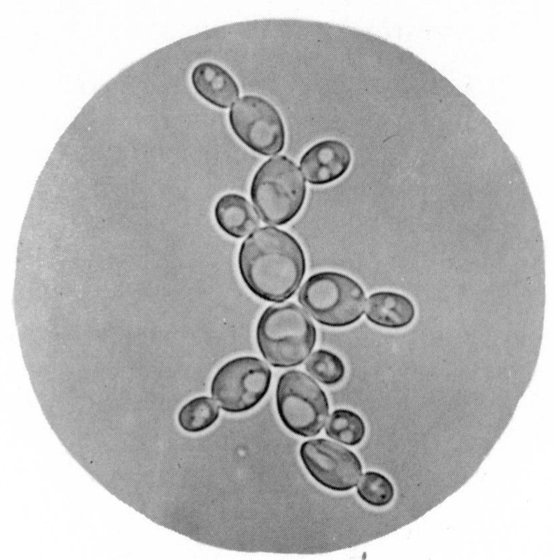

9-5. Photomicrograph of yeast cells greatly magnified.

Q. Add a drop of *dilute* methylene blue solution to the sugar solution on the slide. Place a cover glass over the solution. Observe this stained wet mount of yeast cells under high power (200×).

R. Under low power, all you can see are tiny dots. Each of these is a yeast cell. When you observe the solution under high power, you can see the structure of a yeast cell in greater detail. Look at the photomicrograph of yeast cells (1000×) in Figure 9-5.

8. Protist.

8. On the basis of your observations and reference materials, are yeast cells plant, animal, or protist?

S. Attached to many of the yeast cells, you may see tiny projections.

9. Yes. (Careful observation should reveal buds.)

9. Can you observe these tiny projections under high power?

As a yeast cell grows, it begins to divide and pinch off a little part of itself to form a new cell. This method of reproduction is called **budding**.

You should now be able to

Predict the effect of high and low temperatures on yeast cells by the amount of CO_2 gas produced.

Determine the volume of CO_2 gas produced by the yeast in a test tube.

Identify yeast cells as seen under the microscope.

Preparing nutrient agar

Now that you have grown some yeast, you are ready to grow molds. To do this you must have a medium from which the mold can get its food. In Part One of the next problem you will use ordinary bread. For Part Two you will use an agar medium. When grown on agar, the molds stay in one area, forming a colony. Mold colonies are thus kept separated and can be identified by their color and texture.

The nutrient agar solution you will use must be carefully prepared. Twenty-three grams of nutrient agar are dissolved in 1,000 milliliters of water. The solution is then boiled. And this boiled mixture is sterilized. It is then poured immediately into sterilized petri dishes. The mixture cools and hardens into a gelatinlike solid.

To grow organisms in the lab, all equipment used must be sterilized. Sterilization is accomplished by heating under 15 pounds of steam pressure for 15 minutes at 121°C. It can also be done by heating in an oven for one or two hours at 160°C (320°F).

After the agar is in the sterilized petri dish, do not remove the cover until directed to do so. With mold spores in the air, unwanted spores could fall into the dish and contaminate your colony. A different, unknown mold would start to grow in your pure culture.

When you grow your mold, keep the petri dish in a warm area. This is called **incubating** the mold. Temperature is one of the conditions that must be controlled if mold is to grow rapidly.

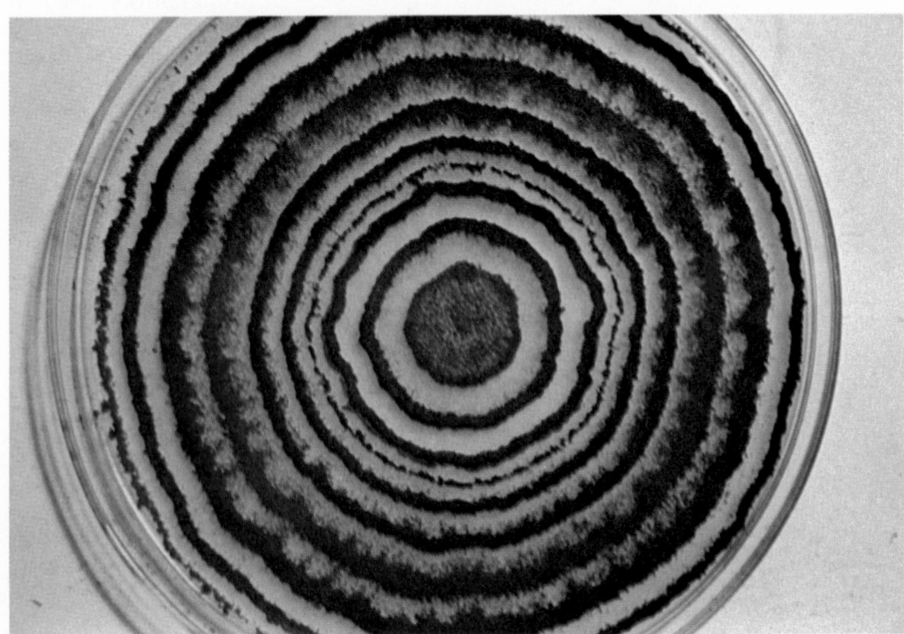

9-6. The mold *Trichoderma viride*, source of the antibiotic Gliotoxin used in agriculture.

9-7. An autoclave is a special sterilizer, used in hospitals as shown here and in large laboratories to sterilize equipment.

Problem 9-2 How does bread mold reproduce?

Purpose To grow a culture of bread mold and to study the structures and growth of this microorganism.

Materials

sterilized agar medium
stale piece of bread
microscope or hand lens
food jar with twist-off cap (jam or peanut butter)
tweezers
slide and cover glass
paper towel
marking pen
incubator or dark storage area
Bunsen burner

Procedure

Part One: Growing mold

Remind students to keep the paper towel moist but not soaked during the growth period.

A. Crumple a small handful of paper toweling. Sprinkle the paper towel with water until it is damp, but not limp. *Do not soak.* Too much water will give poor results. Place the ball of damp paper toweling in the bottom of a clean food jar.

B. Get a 3-cm square piece of stale bread. Rub one side of it on some dusty surface in the room.

C. With the dusty side up, carefully set the square of bread on the damp towel in the jar. Be sure the dusty side is up.

Students should go ahead with other problems while the mold is growing.

1. To prevent contamination by dust and other foreign matter, and to prevent evaporation.

D. Replace the cover on the jar. Store the culture in a warm, dark part of the room. Your teacher may ask you to test the effect of different environments on the growth of mold.

1. Why is it important to replace the cover?

E. Observe the bread every 24 hours for the next few days.

2. Did drops of moisture form on the inside of the jar?
3. Does the surface of the bread appear "fuzzy"?

Part Two: Mold structures

2. Yes.

3. Yes. (That is the mold growth.)

Begin this part after the bread is covered with the "fuzzy" growth of mold.

F. With tweezers, remove a tiny sample of the mold. Prepare a wet mount slide of these strands of bread mold.

G. Observe the wet mount slide under low power (50×). Compare Figure 9-8 with the mold under your microscope.

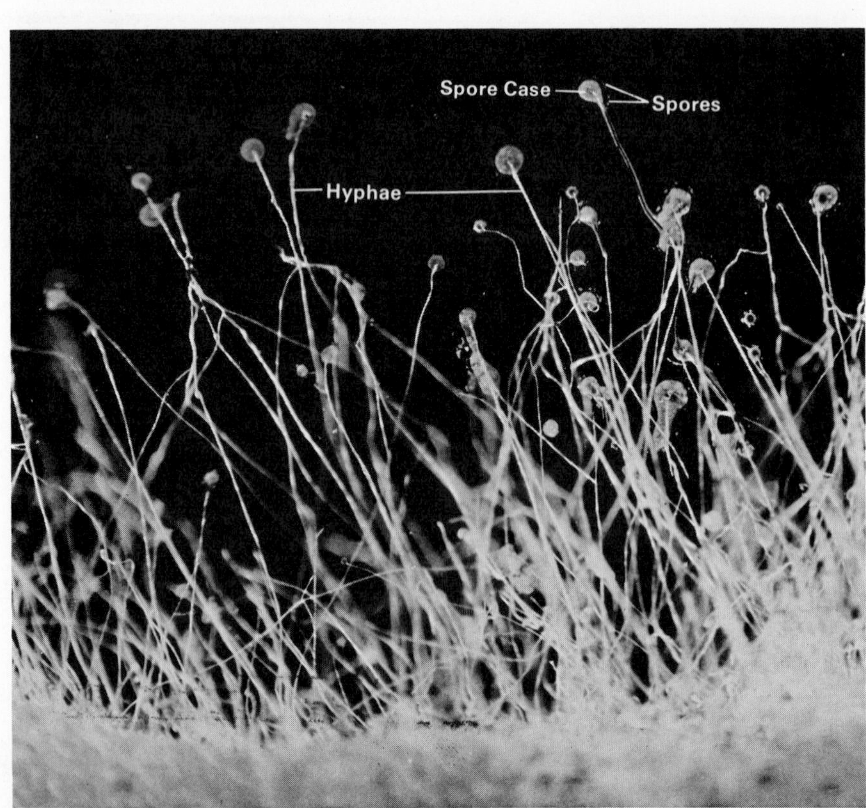

9-8. Photomicrograph of bread mold.

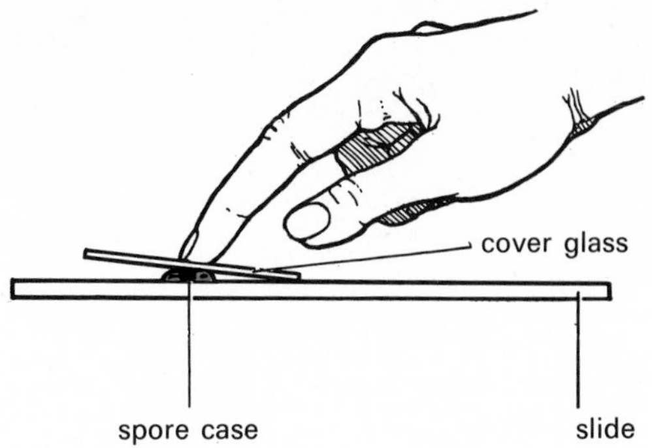

9-9. Break open the spore case.

4. Spore cases, hyphae.
5. Individual hyphae, spores.

4. What structures of the bread mold shown in Figure 9-8 can you find with your microscope?
5. What structures of the bread mold are you unable to see with the unaided eye?

Caution students to crush spore case *gently* in Step H.

H. Prepare a wet mount slide of a black spore case as follows. Gently remove a black spore case with your tweezers and place it on a glass slide. Place a drop of water on the spore case and add a cover glass. *Gently* press the cover glass down with your finger. (See Figure 9-9.)

6. Spores.

6. What was inside the spore case?

I. Examine the slide under both low power and high power.

7. Less than 10 microns.
8. Thick.

7. What is the estimated size of a single spore in microns?
8. The spore case protects the living material inside from harmful environmental conditions. Is the wall of the spore case thick or thin compared to the overall size of the spore case?

Part Three: Mold reproduction RECOMMENDED FOR DEMONSTRATION

If you want students to perform Part Three, it would still be a good idea to demonstrate sterile techniques and the transferring of microorganisms from one dish to another.

The mold that grew on the bread was probably not all the same kind. You or someone else in your class may have seen green, orange, or other colors of mold on the same piece of bread. This means that the culture contains several kinds of molds. Now you will grow a pure culture. A **pure culture** contains just one kind of mold. To prevent other organisms from entering the dish, you will follow a *sterile technique*.

Before you begin Step J, obtain a petri dish containing sterile nutrient agar. You will need it handy for Step L.

J. Carefully put the open end of a pair of tweezers in a flame for two or three seconds. Allow the tweezers to cool briefly.

9-10. With tweezers, place the spore case onto the agar in the petri dish.

K. With the tweezers, gently remove one or two black spore cases from the bread mold.

L. Lift the lid of the petri dish just a little. Against the side of the dish, gently tap the spore case over the surface of the agar. Then place the spore case in another part of the dish with your tweezers. Lower the lid back quickly to prevent the entrance of other microorganisms.

M. Store the petri dish in a warm, dark area for 48 hours. After 48 hours examine the growth in the petri dish.

9. Yes.

9. Does the new growth appear to be the same color and type as the mold from which you removed the spores?

10. Spores.

10. If the new mold is the same, what structure of the mold started the growth in the petri dish?

Reinforce the idea that a tremendous number of mold spores are produced. Fortunately for us, very few find favorable growing areas.

N. Mold must be able to be moved to find new food supplies. The thick-walled spores of molds can be carried through the environment without being destroyed by unfavorable conditions. When the spores find favorable conditions, they start to grow and produce new colonies.

11. What are two main functions of a spore?

11. Reproduction and protection of living material.

You should now be able to

Identify a mold by observing the appearance of the growth.

List factors necessary for the growth of bread mold.

Transfer bread mold to a petri dish by the use of a spore case.

Identify the structures found in a bread mold colony.

Identify the structure of a mold that enables it to be dispersed, giving rise to new colonies in different places.

Collecting mold spores

Now that you have studied bread mold, you should be able to recognize other mold colonies. In Problem 9-3 you will obtain and culture spores from different places in your school. Some of the spores that you grow may produce colonies very different from bread mold.

You may also find bacterial colonies growing. Bacterial colonies will be studied in Chapter 10. There is an easy way to tell the difference between a mold colony and a bacterial colony. The mold colony has a "fuzzy" surface. The surface of a bacterial colony is usually smooth.

The spores you are going to culture may have been inactive for many months. They haven't opened and grown into colonies yet because the conditions have not been suitable.

As you learned in the last problem, the thick outer covering of the spore, the **spore case,** protects it from most unfavorable conditions. The spore case prevents water from leaving the spore. And it is hard enough to withstand extreme heat and cold. Although a mold colony produces thousands of spores, only a few may finally find a suitable environment. The hard, thick spore cases protect the mold's reproductive spores until the right conditions for growth are present.

Problem 9-3 Where can microorganisms be found?

Purpose To discover where microorganisms are found in the environment. To observe the different types of colonies of microorganisms that grow in the petri dish.

Materials

roll of cellophane tape
sterilized agar medium
incubator or dark storage area
marking pen

Procedure

Make sure that students mark the bottoms of the petri dishes, not the tops. Show them how to do this.

Allow students to sample a great variety of areas in the school.

A. Obtain a sterile petri dish containing sterilized nutrient agar. With a marking pen, divide the outside bottom of your petri dish into quarters. Number the quarters 1 through 4. (See Figure 9-11.)

B. Pull a 10-cm strip of cellophane tape from a roll. Fold over one end of the tape for about 2 cm in order to have a nonstick end for holding the tape.

C. Hold the tape at the folded end. Put the sticky side on *one* solid surface. You might choose a surface in the classroom or cafeteria, on the water fountain or shower-room floor. Select only one sur-

9-11. Mark the bottom of the petri dish into four quarters.

Caution students to use a new piece of cellophane tape for each surface.

face for each tape. (You'll use more tapes in Step E.) Use cleaned surfaces as well as dirty surfaces. Take your petri dish with you.

D. Pull the tape from the surface. Remove the cover from the petri dish and immediately place the sticky side of the tape on the agar surface of Quarter 1. Gently press the tape onto the agar to transfer the microorganisms. (See Figure 9-12.) Replace the cover on the petri dish and throw away the tape.

1. To prevent contamination by other organisms.

1. Why should the cover be kept on the petri dish?

E. With a fresh strip of cellophane tape, repeat Steps C and D on another surface. Transfer the microorganisms to Quarter 2. Use a third strip of tape and another surface for Quarter 3. For Quarter 4 use a fourth strip of tape that has not been placed on any surface. Touch this clean tape to Quarter 4.

2. It acts as a control.

2. What is the purpose of the fourth strip of tape?

F. Copy Table 9-2 in your notebook. Record in your table the source (surface used) of the microorganisms for each of the four quarters.

9-12. Transfer the microorganisms from the tape to the agar.

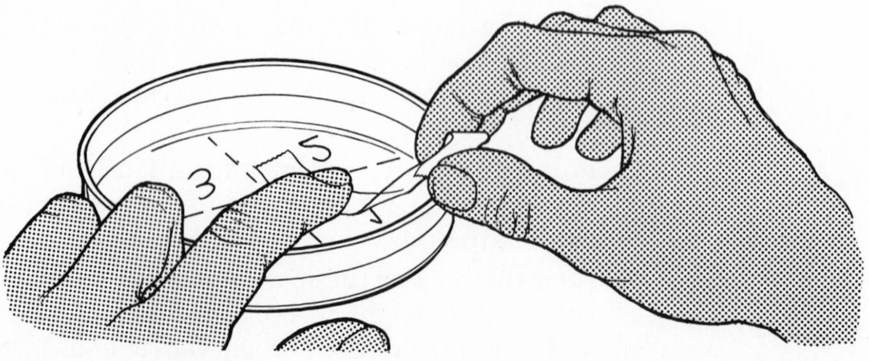

TABLE 9-2 SOURCES OF MICROORGANISMS IN THE ENVIRONMENT

Microorganisms will usually appear after 2-3 days.

Section Number	*Source*	Description of Daily Observations			
		1st Day	2nd Day	3rd Day	4th Day
1					
2					
3					
4					

G. Incubate the petri dish in a dark storage area at room temperature for four days. Observe the petri dish daily and record the results in your table. Save your petri dish with microorganisms for use in Chapter 10. Store the dish as directed by your teacher.

3. Were any surfaces free of microorganisms?
4. Did the clean or the dusty surfaces usually have the most microorganisms?
5. How is it possible for disease microorganisms to be spread from one surface to another?
6. What must be present in the petri dish for the microorganisms to grow?
7. What type of microorganism will produce spore cases at the end of stalks?
8. Are most of the organisms growing in your dish molds or bacteria?
9. Why is the cellophane tape used in this experiment?
10. Did the cellophane tape alone have microorganisms on it? (See Quarter 4.)

3. Probably not.

4. The dusty surfaces.

5. Air currents, direct contact, etc. Sneezing and coughing may be included.

6. Nutrient material, water, and air.

7. Mold.

8. Molds.

9. It is sticky and is thus able to pick up microorganisms.

10. Probably not.

You should now be able to

State where microorganisms may be found in your environment.

State the factors necessary for the growth of microorganisms in a petri dish.

Distinguish a mold growth from a bacterial colony.

Science terms

agar
budding
carbon dioxide
colony
fungicide
incubate
medium
mold
nutrient
organic matter
parasite
penicillin
pure culture
saprophyte
spore
spore case
sterilize
yeast

Review questions

1. Nutrient agar.

2. The growth of only one kind of organism.

3. Food, moisture, acceptable temperature, and oxygen. (Accept any 3 of these.)

4. Chlorophyll.

5. Spore case.

6. Yeast.

7. Carbon dioxide.

8. Organic.

9. Fungicide.

10. Ultraviolet light, steam, boiling water.

1. What is the name of the gelatinlike material used in the laboratory to grow molds?
2. What is meant by a pure culture?
3. What are three things that all molds need in order to grow?
4. What green material found in plant cells is not present in molds?
5. Name the structure in the mold that holds the spores.
6. Which microorganism that you studied reproduces by forming buds?
7. What gas produced by yeast cells causes bread dough to rise?
8. What term describes any substance that is, or was, alive?
9. What chemical is used to stop mold growth on plants?
10. Name another method you can use to sterilize laboratory apparatus besides heating it in an oven.

Check your understanding

See Teacher's Guide section for answers to Questions 11-16.

11. Why must tweezers be allowed to cool after they are sterilized in a burner flame?
12. Bread coming from an oven is usually sterile. How does it become infected with bread mold?
13. Name a mold that can affect your body. How would you prevent this infection from spreading?
14. In what ways do molds depend on their environment?
15. What advantage can you see in the production of spores as a form of reproduction?
16. Yeast cells seem to live everywhere. How are they spread?

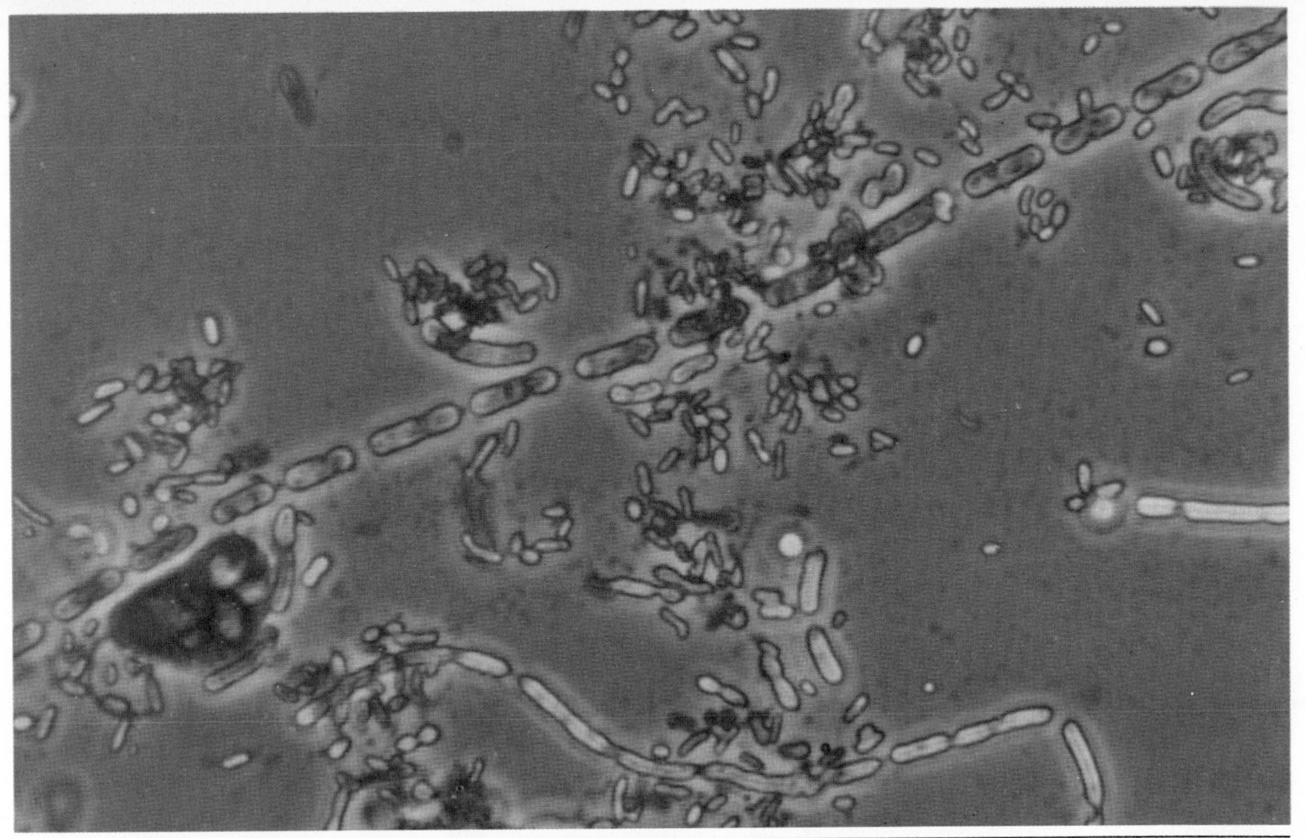

Chapter 10 Bacteria

Chapter-opening photo shows some of the bacterial forms found in a drop of sewage.

In Chapter 8 you studied protists found in pond water. In Chapter 9 you examined yeasts and molds, which are also protists. Another group of protists are the bacteria. Bacteria are single-celled organisms, usually less than two microns long. Anton van Leeuwenhoek was probably the first person to observe bacteria.

Bacteria are known to have a cell membrane, a cell wall, and a slime layer. The cell wall of a bacterial cell is not the same as the cell wall found in multicellular plants. A layer of slime surrounds the cell wall. It may completely surround the cell to form a capsule. Bacteria lack chlorophyll and are, therefore, dependent on other sources for their food. These sources may be plants or animals. Sometimes the sources are human beings.

Bacteria are everywhere

(*Above*) Sewage bacteria.

Bacteria are found in the air, the soil, water, milk, in your bodies, and on your hands. When a bacterium lands in a place that has the

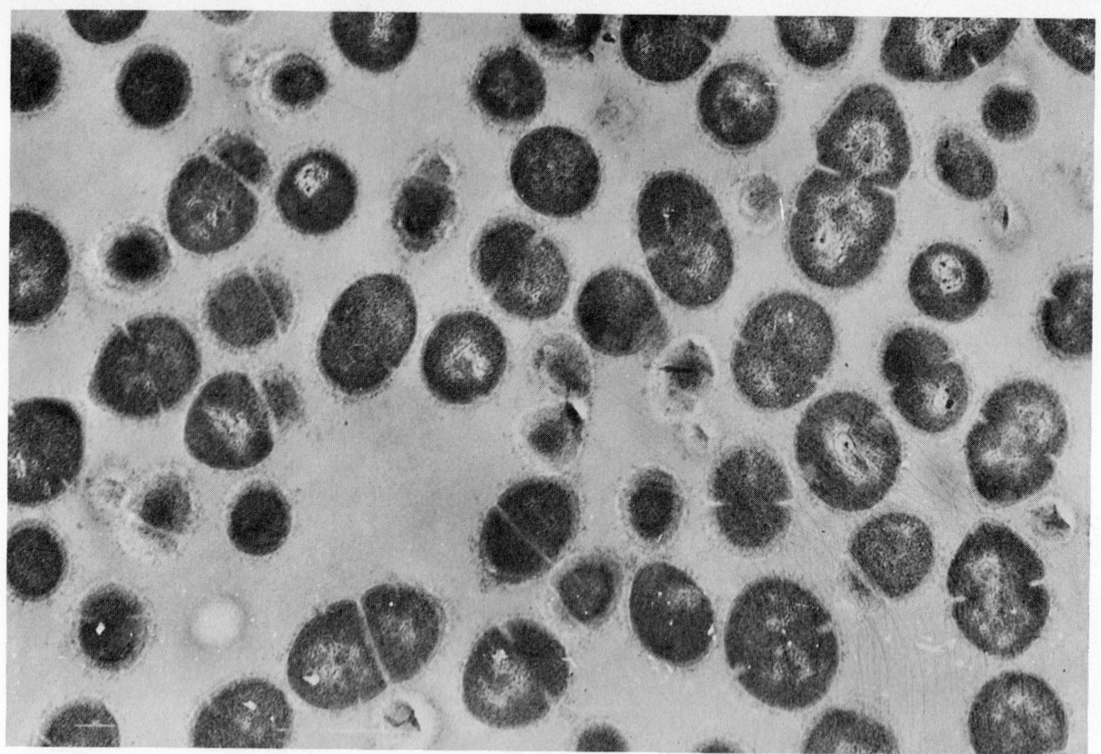

Electron micrograph (*above*) of coccus-type, or round-shaped, bacteria. The enlargement at right of one diplococcus (two bacteria) shows its characteristic shape.

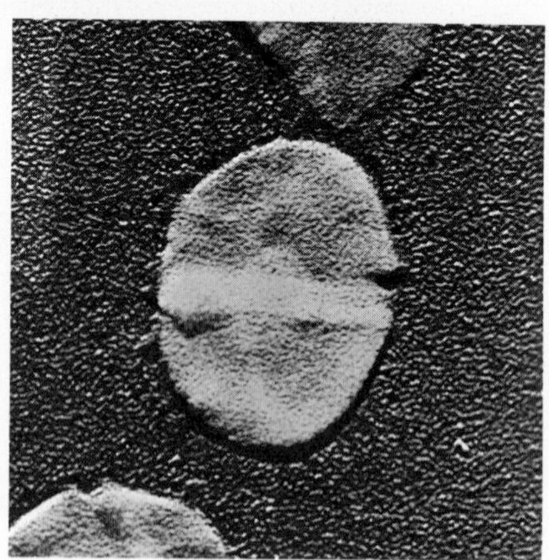

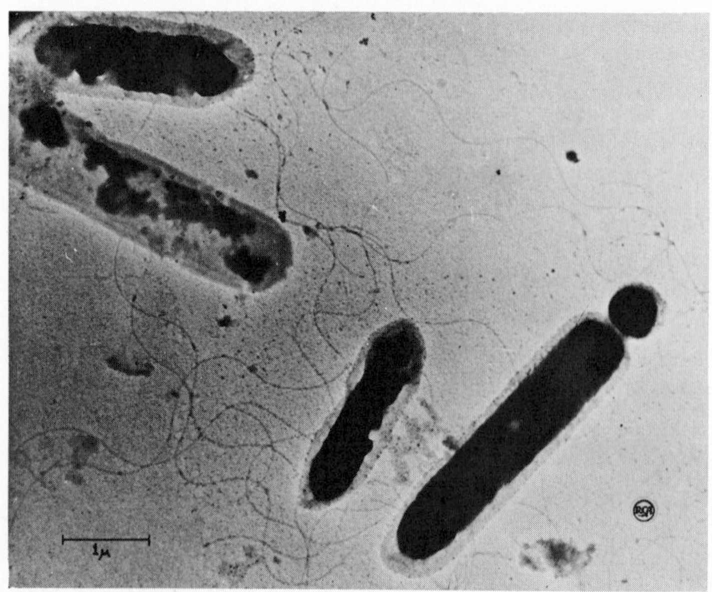

Electron micrograph (*left*) of some tetanus bacteria.

conditions needed for life, it divides again and again, forming a **colony.** Bacterial colonies look much like mold colonies, except that molds have a mass of threadlike hyphae.

Bacteria multiply at a tremendous rate when conditions are right. Fortunately, the "right" conditions do not exist for long periods of time. Lack of food, a buildup of waste products, and competition with other organisms usually keep bacteria in check.

Bacteria may be sorted into three general groups: harmless, beneficial, and disease-producing. The harmless bacteria comprise the largest group. Beneficial bacteria include those responsible for the decay of dead plants and animals. Soil contains a great number of bacteria that indirectly affect the welfare of people.

Disease-producing bacteria

Of the great many kinds of bacteria, only a few are disease-producing. Most people use the word "germs" for microorganisms that cause disease. One group of disease-producing bacteria is found growing in milk. Great care is taken in milk processing to keep those bacteria at a minimum.

First, the milk is cooled immediately after milking. This slows the growth of bacteria already present. Then, any harmful bacteria that may be present are killed by a process called **pasteurization.** Milk is

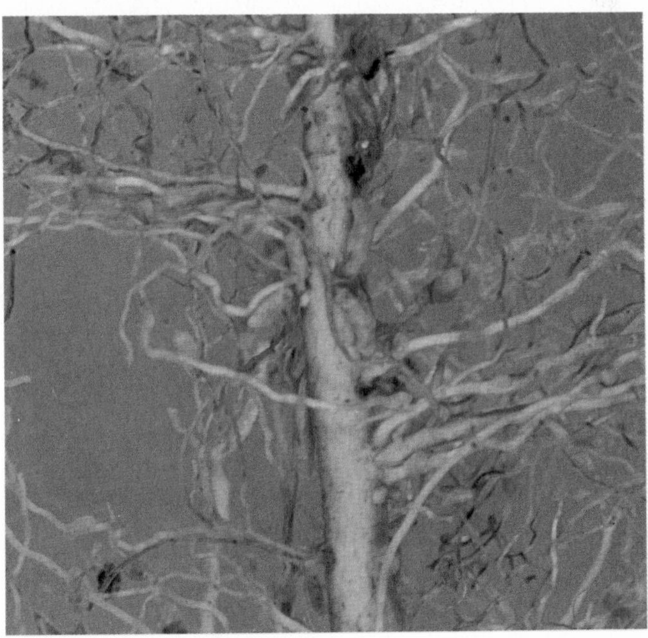

10-1. These roots of a clover plant have nodule formations due to *nitrogen-fixing bacteria*. These bacteria provide the plant with a form of nitrogen that the plant needs.

10-2. Milk pasteurization machine in a dairy.

pasteurized by heating it to a temperature of 71°C (160°F) for 15 seconds, then cooling it. Pasteurization does not kill all the bacteria present in milk. But it does kill most of those known to be harmful to people.

Besides pasteurization, many other ways are known to kill bacteria. These methods include extreme heat, disinfectants, sunlight, and antibiotics. You will study the effectiveness of some disinfectants in Problem 10-2.

When used in limited amounts, some types of radiation such as ultraviolet light have an unusual effect. The radiation may not kill the bacteria, but it may produce changes in the chemical makeup of the cells. Such changes are called **mutations.** The changed forms of bacteria are known as mutants. Mutations are of great interest to scientists because they represent changes in the nuclei of cells. Molds and bacteria are often used as test subjects because they reproduce so rapidly. The mutations appear in the colonies in a very short time.

Growing and studying bacteria

Bacteria must be studied in a sterile environment. All instruments, dishes, and even the nutrient agar on which bacteria grow must be free of other forms of life. You must use the same care in working with bacteria that you used with molds in Chapter 9.

Transferring bacteria from one culture to another requires great care. You will use a thin wire called an **inoculating loop** to transfer bacteria. The end of the inoculating loop will need to be sterilized before each use. A technique known as flaming is used. (See Figure 10-3.) **Flaming** involves placing the loop end into a flame, heating until it is red hot, and then not letting the loop touch any surface while it cools. The sterile loop may then be used to transfer bacteria from one culture medium to another.

You will have a chance to study bacteria under many different conditions in the laboratory. It is especially important that you follow instructions carefully when working with bacteria. Otherwise you might contaminate the cultures.

The rules for handling bacteria are stressed for your safety. Keep your fingers and pencils out of your mouth. Do not eat in the laboratory or drink from any beaker or flask. In case of accidental spillage of any container with bacteria in it, tell your teacher. When you complete a problem, be sure to throw all solid materials into the special container provided by your teacher.

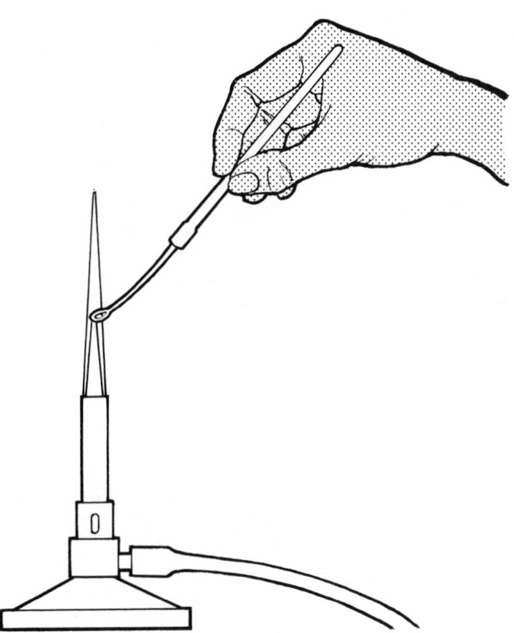

10-3. Sterilizing an inoculating loop by the flaming technique.

It is important to distinguish between individual bacteria and colonies of bacteria. You can see colonies of bacteria growing on nutrient agar. You can't see individual bacteria without a microscope.

Individual bacteria have three main shapes — rod, round, and spiral. The bacteria shown here (*right*), as viewed under a microscope, are rod-shaped.

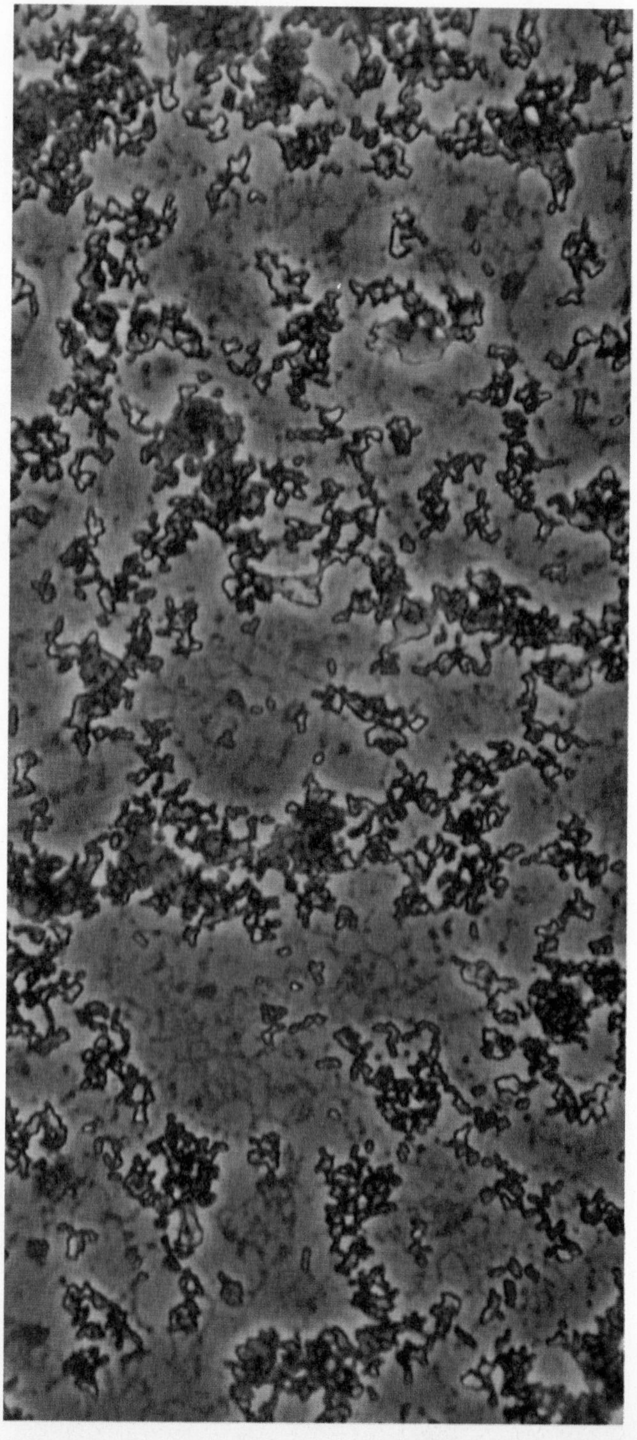

Different kinds of bacterial colonies differ in color, edge-shape, texture, and thickness. Several colonies of one kind of bacteria are shown here (*below*).

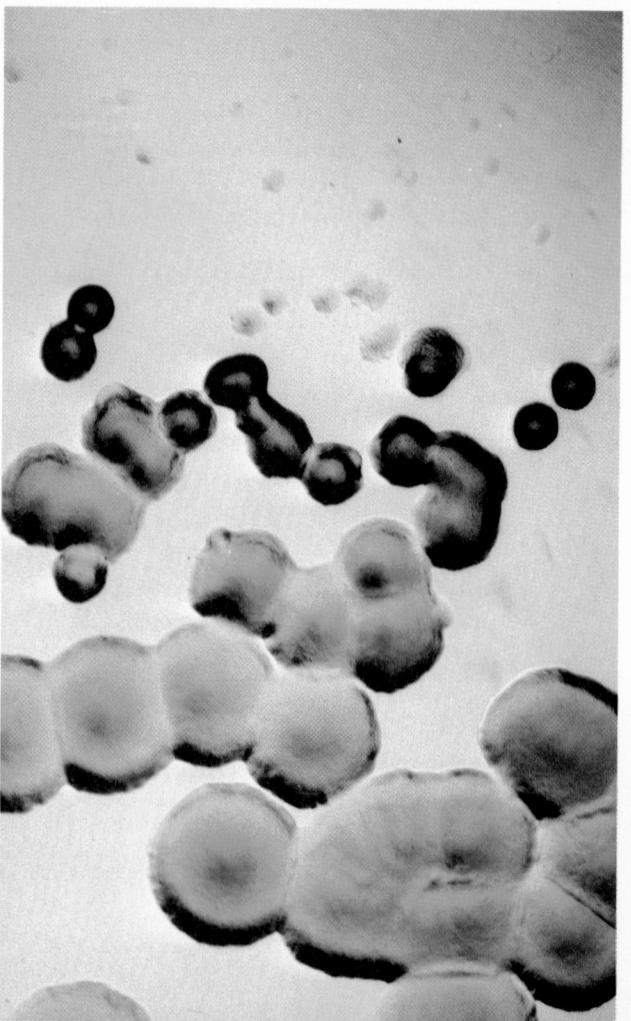

Problem 10-1 What are some types of bacterial colonies?

Purpose To observe the different types of colonies formed when bacteria grow on nutrient agar.

Materials petri dish from Problem 9-3

Procedure Before and after working with bacterial cultures, always wash your hands thoroughly.

Caution students not to remove tape holding the petri dish sections together.

A. Observe the surface of the agar to locate growths of bacteria. The growth of single bacterial colonies will appear as raised spots in the agar. The growth is held in a small area because of the solid nature of the nutrient agar.

Each different kind of bacterium has a growth form, or colony, that will be somewhat different from all other types. By examining the kinds of colonies you can predict how many kinds of bacteria entered the petri dish.

B. Study the information asked for in Table 10-1. Copy the table into your notebook. (As you record your observations during Step C, don't worry if you can't find five different colonies as allowed for in the table.)

It is possible that the agar plates will not contain five different kinds of colonies. Students should be evaluated on the accuracy and completeness of their observations, not on the number of different kinds of colonies that they find.

TABLE 10-1 BACTERIAL COLONY CHART

Colony Number	*Colony Form*	*Edge Shape*	*Thickness*	*Surface*
1				
2				
3				
4				
5				

1. Probably off-white, although various other colors may be present.

2. Round. Many, however, may have irregular edges.

3. Perhaps. Yes, it could be a mold.

5. Answers will vary, but should agree with student's record (Table 10-1).

6. No. One kind of bacterium can form only one kind of colony.

7. See answer to Question 5. As many different kinds of bacteria as there are different colonies.

C. Some things to look for in each dish are colonies that differ in color, shape, texture, and thickness. Use Figure 10-4 to locate and describe as many kinds of colonies as you can.

1. What color were most bacterial colonies?
2. What shape were most of the colonies?
3. Did you find any growth that did not appear to be bacterial? Could this growth be a mold?
4. Could bacteria form colonies if grown in a liquid? 4. No.
5. How many kinds of colonies of bacteria did you find?
6. Would one kind of bacterium be able to form all of these different colonies?
7. If your answer to question 6 is no, how many bacteria would be required to form all the colonies?

D. Dispose of the contents of your petri dish as directed by your teacher. Your teacher may want you to save the contents for Problem 10-2.

You should now be able to

Recognize different types of bacteria from the types of colonies formed.

Classify colonies on the basis of color, shape, texture, and thickness.

Classifying bacteria

It takes a great deal of careful observation to classify bacteria. The appearance of a colony gives you many clues that help to identify it. Colonies differ in color, size, shape, and texture. Certain stains are also helpful when bacteria are viewed under the microscope. The transparent forms of bacteria are given color by the stain.

Microscopic observations are most helpful for identifying a bacterium. It is only with the microscope that you can see the shape of the bacterial cell. There are three basic shapes. (See Figure 10-5.) There are *round-shaped* bacteria, called **cocci** [KAHK-eye]. There are *rod-shaped* bacteria, called **bacilli** [buh-SILL-eye]. And there are *spiral* forms, called **spirilla** [spy-RILL-ah]. Bacteria may exist as single cells, in pairs, or in groups or clusters. Some bacteria have also been found to have flagella.

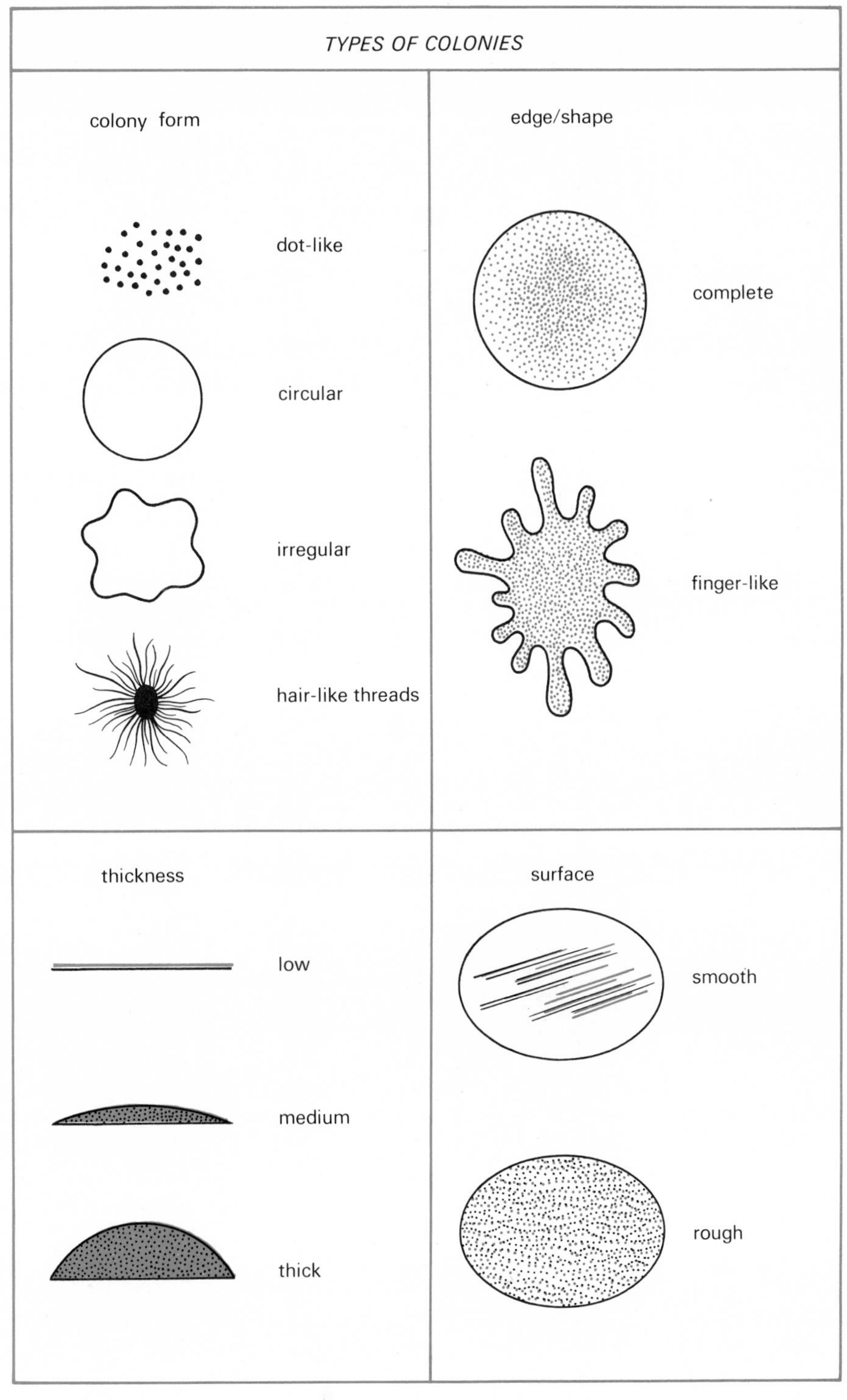

10-4. Bacterial colonies differ in color, shape, texture, and thickness.

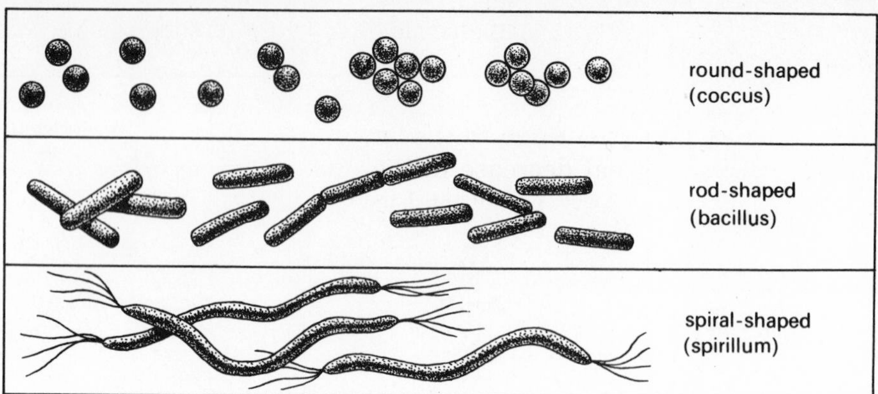

10-5. The three basic shapes used in classifying bacteria.

A **bacteriologist** is a scientist who studies bacteria. Knowing the characteristics of a bacterium, a bacteriologist can sometimes relate the organism to a certain condition or illness. Bacteria that cause pneumonia have been identified and studied in this way. Grown in a pure culture, an organism may be tested to see how fast it grows, what materials it needs, and how it reacts to materials such as antibiotics.

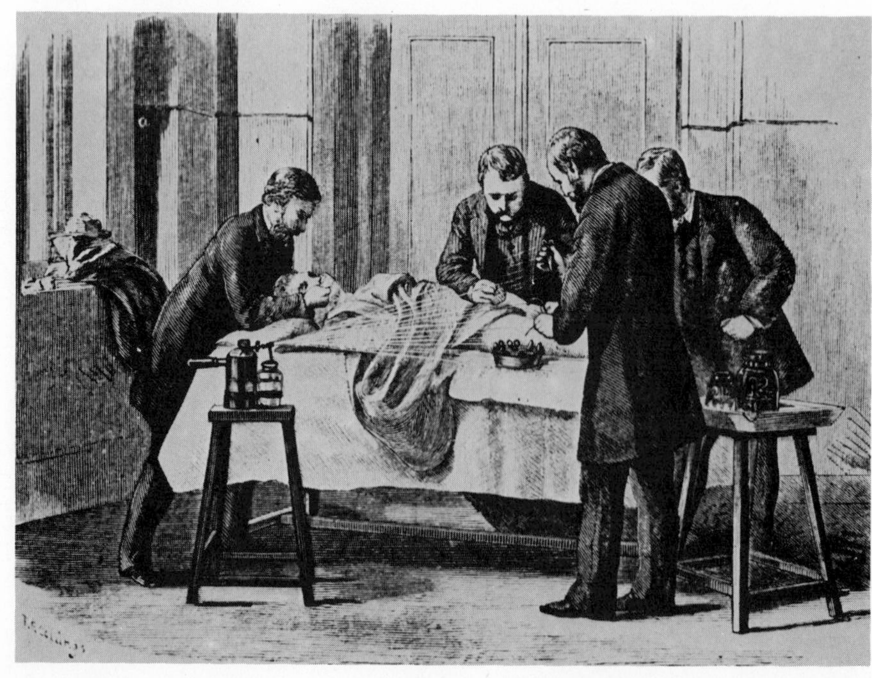

10-6. Lord Joseph Lister was the first surgeon to see the importance of aseptic surgery. Here a patient's skin is being sprayed to prevent infection.

The use of chemicals to kill microorganisms is a fairly new science. A noted British surgeon, Lord Joseph Lister, used a chemical spray during an operation in 1852. He sprayed carbolic acid on the skin of a patient and in the air of the operating room. Over time, he noticed a great decrease in the number of bacterial infections in his patients.

As a result of Lister's technique, called **asepsis,** more patients lived. Aseptic technique is commonly used in hospitals and bacteriology labs. To prepare a room aseptically, surfaces are washed with disinfectant solutions. Sterile clothing is worn and sterile instruments are used. Asepsis is a condition in which *most* bacteria are killed. (Sterilization, on the other hand, is the destruction of *all* forms of living things, including the bacteria.)

In the next problem you will test three common antiseptics and observe their effects on bacterial growth.

Problem 10-2 What effects do antiseptics have on bacterial growth?

Purpose To observe the effects of some common antiseptics on the growth of bacteria. To learn to prepare pure cultures of a common bacterium.

Materials

- sterile agar medium
- pure culture of microorganism (Problem 9-3)
- inoculating loop
- tweezers
- Bunsen burner
- paper towels
- types of antiseptics (3)
- scissors
- incubator or dark storage area

Procedure

Demonstrate the entire procedure for inoculating an agar plate. Caution students to slide the loop gently across the surface of the agar, and not to dig into the agar.

A. Select three types of antiseptics or "germ killers" for this experiment. Examples include iodine, alcohol, bacitracin, commercial mouthwash, and hydrogen peroxide.

B. Obtain a petri dish that contains sterile agar. Select a colony from one of the dishes in Problem 9-3. Or, your teacher may have a commercially prepared pure culture for your use.

C. Flame the inoculating loop as described on page 171. Be sure it "glows red." Then allow it to cool.

D. Carefully scrape some of the pure culture onto the loop. Be sure to close the culture container.

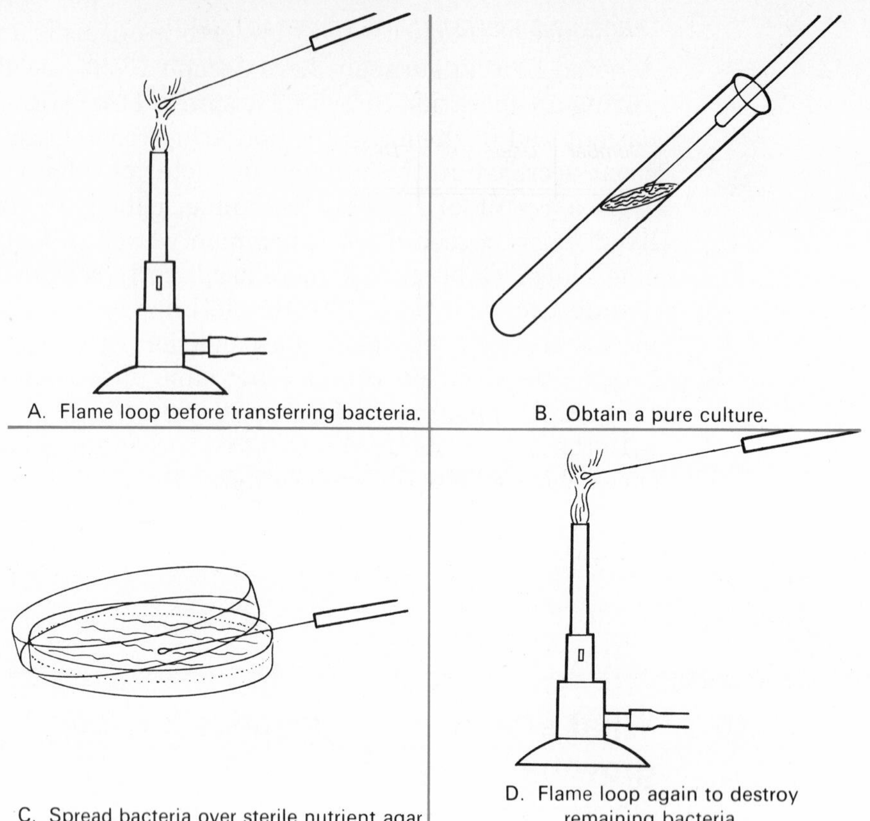

A. Flame loop before transferring bacteria.
B. Obtain a pure culture.
C. Spread bacteria over sterile nutrient agar.
D. Flame loop again to destroy remaining bacteria.

10-7. Steps in transferring bacteria.

E. Open the cover of the sterile petri dish just enough to fit the wire loop inside. (See Figure 10-7.) Extend the loop into the dish until it reaches the agar. *Be careful not to touch the glass with the loop.* Move the loop back and forth across the entire surface of the agar so that the streaks overlap. *Do not dig the wire into the agar.* Lower the cover back onto the dish. Flame the loop again when you are finished with it.

F. Copy Table 10-2 into your notebook.

G. Cut four 1-cm squares of paper towel. With a pencil, mark each square with an identifying number. Thoroughly wet three of the squares with a different kind of antiseptic. Leave the fourth square dry. Record in your table which antiseptics were used on which squares.

In Step H, have students be sure that the soaked squares are placed over streaks made by the inoculating loop.

H. With tweezers, place one of the squares in one quadrant of the agar. (See Figure 10-8.) Do not lift the cover of the petri dish any higher than you have to. Rinse the tweezers. Place the other

TABLE 10-2 EFFECTIVENESS OF ANTISEPTICS

Towel Square Number	*Type of Antiseptic Used*	*Colony Description*	*Daily Results*			*Effectiveness Rating (most, least)*
			1st Day	2nd Day	3rd Day	
1						
2						
3						
4						

three squares in the other three quadrants, rinsing the tweezers between each use. Be sure the squares do not touch each other.

1. As a control, to see if there is any inhibition of growth by the paper itself.

1. What is the reason for placing a dry square in the dish?

I. Place the petri dish in your incubator or storage area. Record daily observations in your table until you can answer the following questions.

2. The antiseptic inhibited bacterial growth around the squares.
3. This will depend on the antiseptics used. Check the students' results on their tables.

2. What conclusion can you make about the growth of microorganisms under the antiseptic squares as compared to the growth in areas away from the squares?
3. How effective are your antiseptics against the growth of microorganisms? Indicate on your chart which antiseptic was most effective and which was least effective.

10-8. Placing four squares of paper toweling in a petri dish.

4. Definition a.

4. Which of the following definitions best describes an antiseptic?
   a. "Something that checks the spread of and slows the growth of certain microorganisms."
   b. "Something that kills all microorganisms."

J. A substance that will kill microorganisms is said to be a germicide.

5. There may be one. Mouthwashes are not strong enough, but one of the other antiseptics, such as alcohol, may do so.

5. Did you find any substance that was able to kill all microorganisms?

K. Dispose of the contents of your petri dishes as directed by your teacher.

You should now be able to

Determine the effect of an antiseptic on bacterial growth by comparing the area under the antiseptic-soaked cloth with the surrounding area.

Prepare a pure culture of a given bacterium.

Distinguish between an antiseptic and a germicide.

Conditions for bacterial growth

The conditions needed for bacterial growth are varied. Some bacteria grow only in very specific environments. Others can adapt to changing environments. Some require air for their supply of oxygen, and others will not grow in the presence of air. Water, temperature, and sunlight also affect bacterial growth.

All bacteria require water to grow. When foods are dried, bacteria will not grow. Large amounts of salt or sugar in foods also inhibit bacterial growth. This is why salted meat keeps well. And jelly, which contains a lot of sugar, also keeps well.

Bacteria survive and reproduce within certain temperature ranges. Below or above their range, bacteria and their spores are killed. Disease-producing bacteria are killed at 60°C (140°F) after ten minutes. These same bacteria grow well at body temperature (37°C, 98.6°F).

Bacteria may be killed when exposed to direct sunlight. The effect of ultraviolet rays, which are contained in sunlight, is the subject of the next problem.

Problem 10-3 What effect does ultraviolet light have on the bacterium *Serratia marcescens*?

Purpose To learn the effects of ultraviolet light on the growth and reproduction of the bacterium *Serratia marcescens*.

Materials None. You will be provided with the results of an experiment that has been previously completed.

Procedure

A. A scientist prepared six large test tubes. Each test tube contained 10 ml of nutrient broth and a cotton plug. These tubes were sterilized in an autoclave.

B. Ten petri dishes were then prepared by pouring 2-3 ml of nutrient agar in each. These petri dishes were also sterilized in an autoclave.

C. Using an inoculating loop, the scientist inoculated the nutrient broth in Test Tube 1 with *Serratia marcescens* bacteria. A sterile loop was then used to inoculate Test Tube 2 from material in Tube 1. These tubes were incubated at 25°C for 24 hours.

1. How did the dilution of Test Tube 2 compare with the dilution of Test Tube 1?

1. Test Tube 2 was more dilute than Test Tube 1.

D. A *serial dilution* of Tube 2 was made using tubes labeled A, B, C, and D. This procedure is shown in Figure 10-9.

10-9. Making a serial dilution. Each tube contains less of the bacteria than the tube before it.

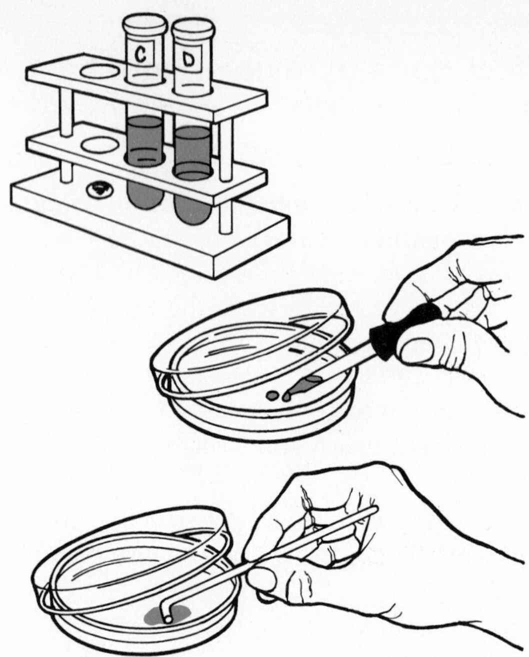

10-10. Adding the broth from Tubes C and D to the petri dishes. The tops of the petri dishes should not be lifted any higher than necessary.

2. Two drops of solution in each test tube. (But each time the solution was more dilute.)

3. Tube A.

4. Tube D.

2. How many drops of solution were placed in Tubes A, B, C, and D?
3. Which tube (A, B, C, or D) probably contained the most bacteria?
4. Which tube probably contained the fewest bacteria?

E. Two drops of solution from Test Tube C were used to inoculate each of five petri dishes. This solution was spread over the surface of the nutrient agar using a sterile glass rod. (See Figure 10-10.)

F. Two drops of solution from Test Tube D were used to inoculate each of the five remaining petri dishes. The solution was again spread over the surfaces using a sterile glass rod.

G. One petri dish from Tube C and one petri dish from Tube D were taped shut and set aside for use as controls.

5. Controls provide a basis for comparison against the experimental groups.

5. What is the purpose of controls in an experiment?

H. The other eight petri dishes were exposed to differing amounts of ultraviolet light. (See Figure 10-11.)

I. After 48 hours the dishes were examined. The data were recorded as shown in Table 10-3.

6. 80 seconds (for each experimental dish).

7. 0 seconds for the control dishes. (10 seconds for the experimental dishes.)

6. What exposure times had the fewest bacteria?
7. What exposure times had the most bacteria?

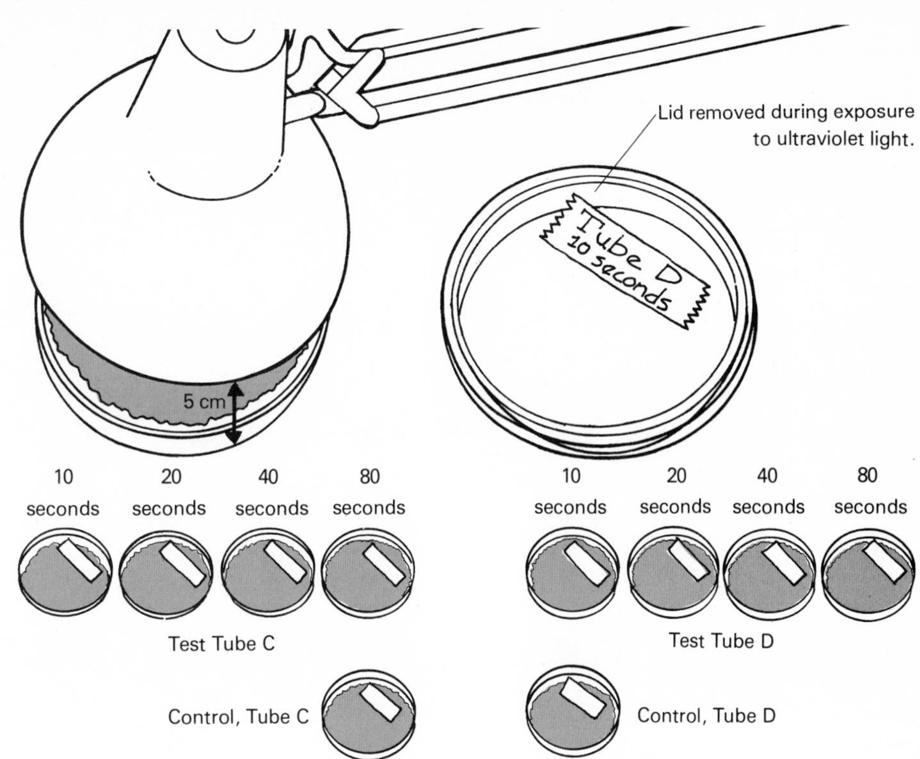

10-11. Times of exposure to ultraviolet light.

TABLE 10-3 COMPARING PETRI DISHES TO SEE THE EFFECTS OF EXPOSURE TO ULTRAVIOLET RADIATION

	Control Dishes		*Experimental Dishes*							
			Test Tube C				*Test Tube D*			
	0 seconds		10 seconds	20 seconds	40 seconds	80 seconds	10 seconds	20 seconds	40 seconds	80 seconds
Number of Colonies	125	75	100	75	50	25	50	35	25	10
Color of Colonies	pink	pink	pink	pink	pink	pink	pink	pink	pink	pink
Division of Colonies	yes	yes	yes	yes	yes	yes	yes	yes	yes	yes
Other Observations	← Bacteria spread to form colonies. →									Some white bacteria present.

Students' graphs prepared for Step J should include two graph lines, one for Tube C and one for Tube D.

J. Prepare a line graph to show the number of colonies in each exposure time for both Tubes C and D. As shown in Figure 10-12, use "Exposure Time in Seconds" for the horizontal axis and "Number of Colonies" for the vertical axis. Use different colors of pencil for the Tube C and Tube D graph lines.

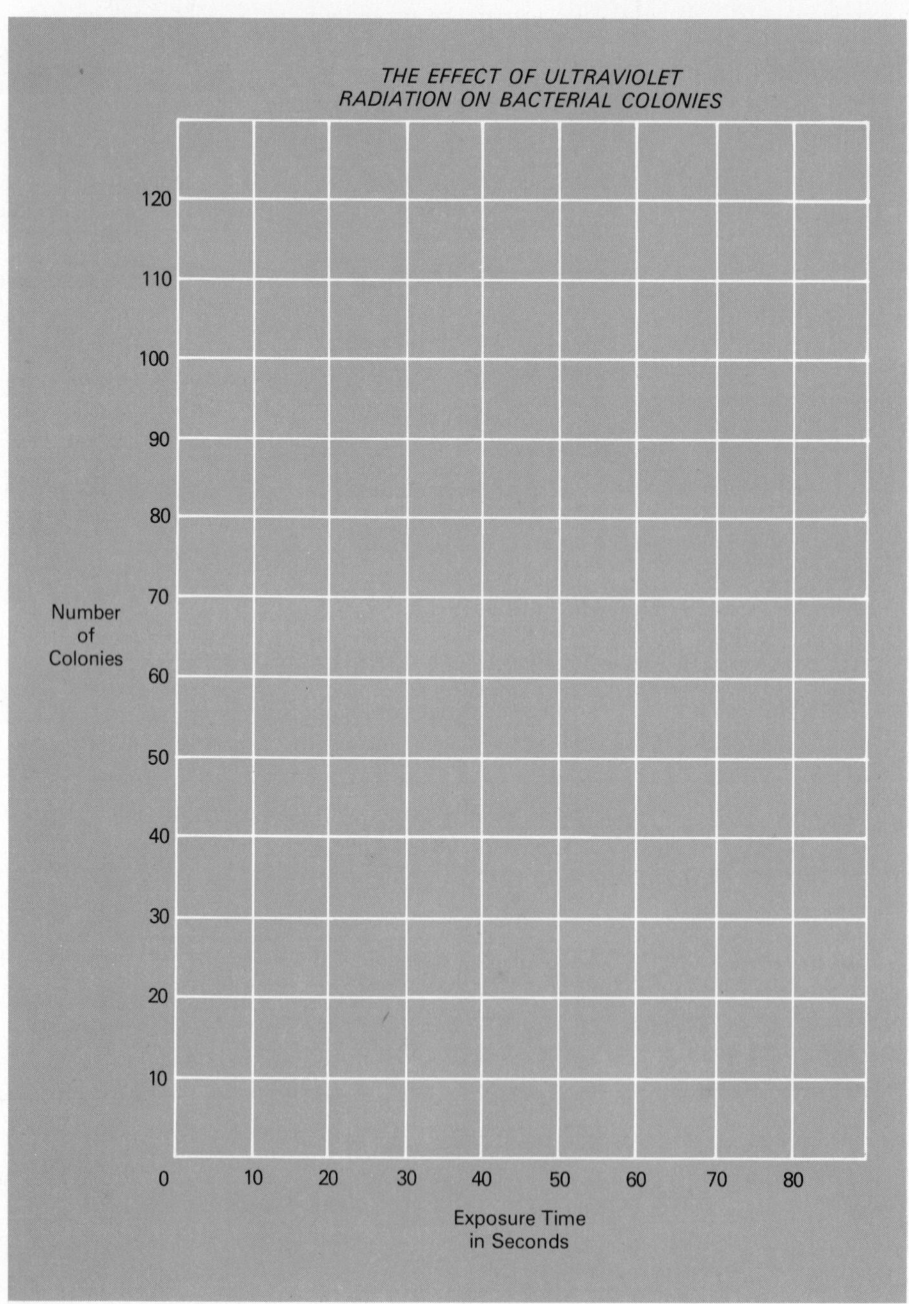

10-12. The effect of ultraviolet light on bacterial colonies.

8. Both lines curve downward to the right.

8. How would you describe the lines formed by the graph?

9. The number of bacteria decreases.

9. What happens to the number of bacteria as the exposure time increases?

10. About 20 colonies; about 8 colonies.

10. How many bacteria would you expect at 100 seconds of exposure in Tube C? In Tube D?

11. The control dishes had more because they received no treatment (no bacteria were killed). The dish for Tube C had more than the dish for Tube D because it started out with more after the serial dilution process.

11. Why did one petri dish have more bacteria than the other petri dishes?

When the genes of an organism are permanently changed, they are said to have *mutated.* They have undergone a mutation. Mutated genes produce permanent changes in the next generation.

12. Where do you think the white bacteria came from in the pure culture?

12. From mutated genes (caused by the ultraviolet radiation).

10-13. The top slice of bread was treated with ultraviolet radiation. The control slice was not, and is now overgrown with mold and bacteria.

You should now be able to

Describe the effect of ultraviolet light on the growth of the bacterium *Serratia marcescens.*

Determine the exposure time of ultraviolet radiation needed to kill most of the *Serratia marcescens* bacteria present.

Prepare a graph to show the relationship between exposure time and bacterial growth.

Determine the effect of dilution on the concentration of bacteria.

Science terms

asepsis
bacillus
bacteriologist
coccus
colony
flaming
inoculating loop
mutation
pasteurization
spirillum

Review questions

1. What are bacteria?
2. What is the difference between a bacterium and a bacterial colony?
3. List three things bacteria must obtain from their environment in order to live.
4. Sterilization kills all microorganisms. What process only frees an area from large numbers of microorganisms?
5. Name and describe three shapes of bacteria that may be seen under the microscope.
6. What process is used to kill harmful organisms in milk?
7. Who was the person given credit for the discovery of the aseptic technique?
8. What is the name for the change in the chemical makeup of a bacterium that may be caused by ultraviolet light?

1. Very small, single-celled protists known to have a cell membrane and a cell wall.

2. A bacterium is one organism, but a colony encompasses millions, perhaps billions, of organisms.

3. Food, moisture, acceptable temperature range, oxygen (in most cases). Accept any 3 of these.

4. Asepsis.

5. Coccus—round; bacillus—rod-shaped; spirillum—spiral-shaped.

6. Pasteurization.

7. Joseph Lister.

8. Mutation.

Check your understanding

See Teacher's Guide section for answers to Questions 9-22.

9. Describe the size and structure of a bacterium.
10. How is a bacterial colony formed?
11. What are three ways colonies of bacteria may look different from each other?
12. How would you tell the difference between a mold colony and a bacterial colony?
13. A pure culture of bacteria is easier to study than a mixture of bacteria. How would you explain this?
14. What does a serial dilution do to the numbers of bacteria in a culture?
15. Do you think pond water contains bacteria? Explain.
16. What conditions are necessary for bacterial growth?
17. Describe the process of pasteurization.
18. What conditions keep bacteria from reproducing to the point where they "overpopulate"?
19. State several ways in which bacteria may be killed.

20. Washing your hands removes many bacteria. Explain how this is part of the aseptic technique.
21. *Escherichia coli* is a harmless bacterium that lives in the human intestine. If you wished to grow this kind of bacteria, at about what temperature would you incubate the bacterial cultures? Explain.
22. Ultraviolet light can be used to kill bacteria. But human beings with bacterial infections are never treated by being exposed to ultraviolet light. Why not?

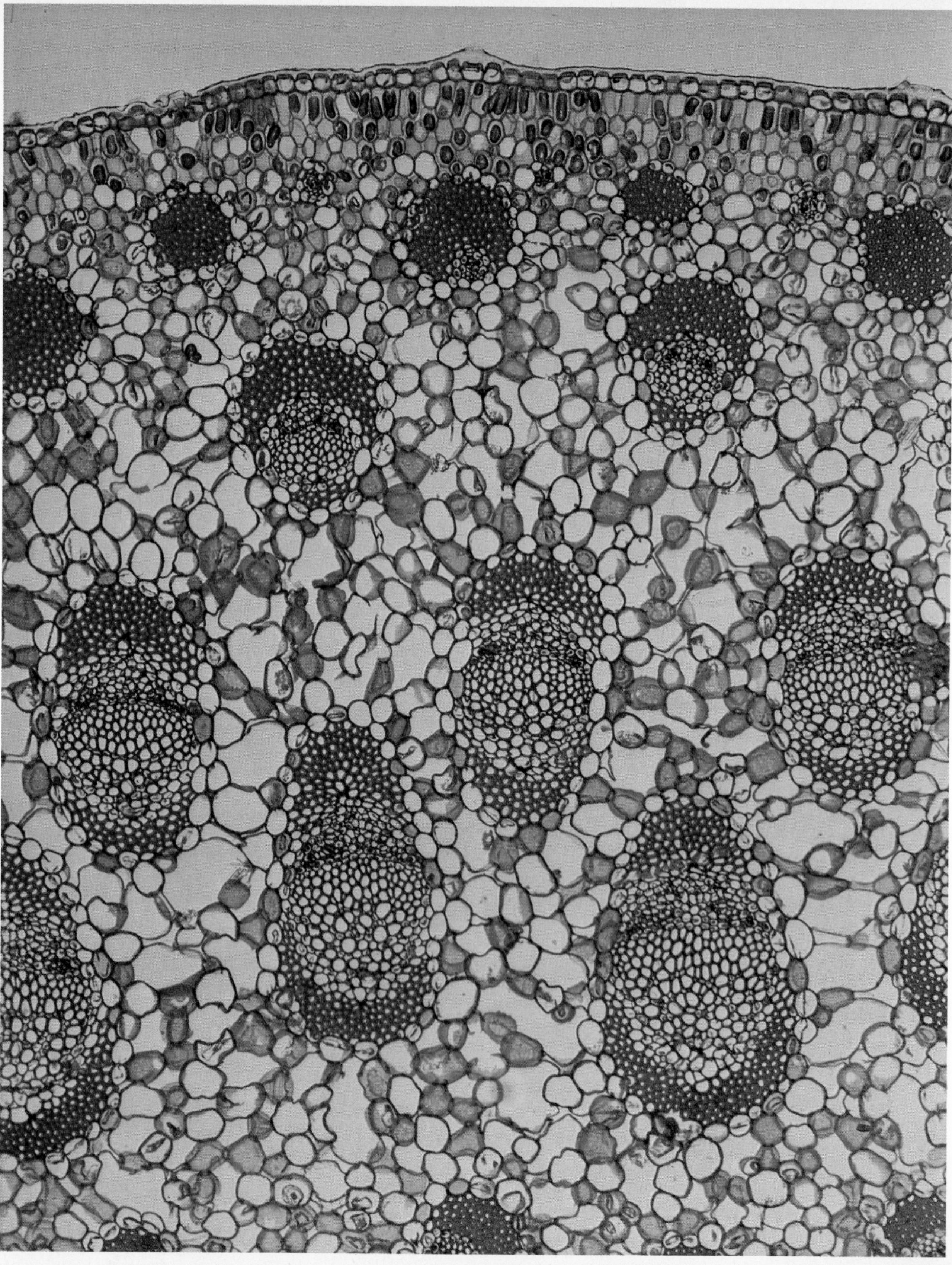

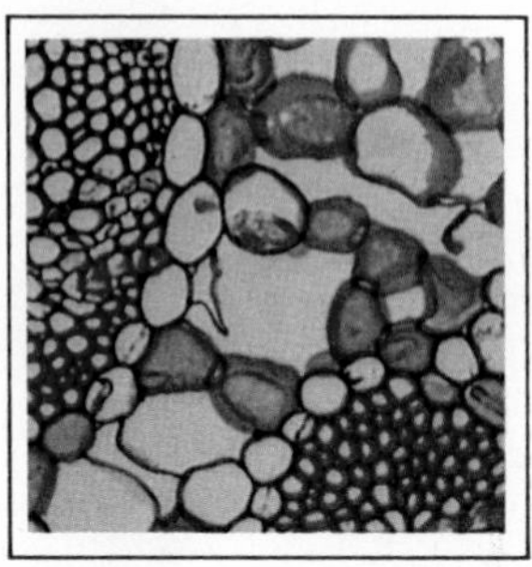

Unit 4

Plant structures and functions

Unit-opening photo shows a cross section through a yucca leaf. Having done Problem 7-2, students should be able to identify the various cells and tissues evidenced in this photo.

All living things begin life as single cells. Unlike protists, however, plants develop way beyond the single-cell stage. Plants are complex and many-celled. Their cells work together in such a way that they form a successful living organism.

Just how plants work is one of the many questions that challenge scientists today. Scientists are trying to understand the processes that control the development of young plants. Many kinds of experiments with many kinds of plants have been conducted. Much can be learned about the growth patterns of plants by studying how seeds change as they develop into young plants. You will get a chance to do this in Chapter 11.

(*Opposite page*) Cross section through a yucca leaf.

As a plant grows, its cells undergo a series of divisions and many chemical changes. The roots, stem, leaves, and flowers — all organs of the plant — are results of cellular growth. Many factors affect the

Chlorophyll enables green plants to manufacture their own food through the process of photosynthesis. Some plants, however, such as the white Indian pipes shown here, do not contain chlorophyll. Such nongreen plants depend on decaying organic matter for food.

growth of plants. These factors may come from outside the plant as external stimuli. Or they may come from inside the plant itself, as internal stimuli. Some plant movements, for instance, are caused by certain chemicals produced within the plant. You will test the responses of plants to internal and external stimuli in Chapter 12.

In Chapter 13 you will study the movement of materials into and through plants. Your work with plant organs in this chapter will be related to your earlier study of leaf structures. You'll examine how plant roots absorb water and minerals and transport them to the stem and leaves.

A living plant must obtain energy and raw materials to stay alive as well as to produce new cells, tissues, and organs. Green plants absorb energy from the sun. They use the energy to combine certain materials to produce food. In Chapter 14 you will learn about the factors that play important roles in this food-making process called photosynthesis. In another process (respiration), living cells release energy from food by a different series of chemical reactions.

Green plants are of vital importance to other living things on earth. Green plants, directly or indirectly, supply the world's food.

And green plants replenish the oxygen that they and other organisms use in respiration. Without green plants, the supply of oxygen in the atmosphere would be depleted. Most life as we know it would cease to exist.

Without some method of reproduction, a living species would soon become extinct. Plants reproduce by a variety of methods, but the most advanced method is by seeds. In Chapter 15 you will study the structure of the seed-producing organ, the flower. The development of the seed and the fruit of flowering plants will complete the unit.

As you begin your study of green plants, remember that the existence and well-being of the total plant depend on the activities of its individual cells.

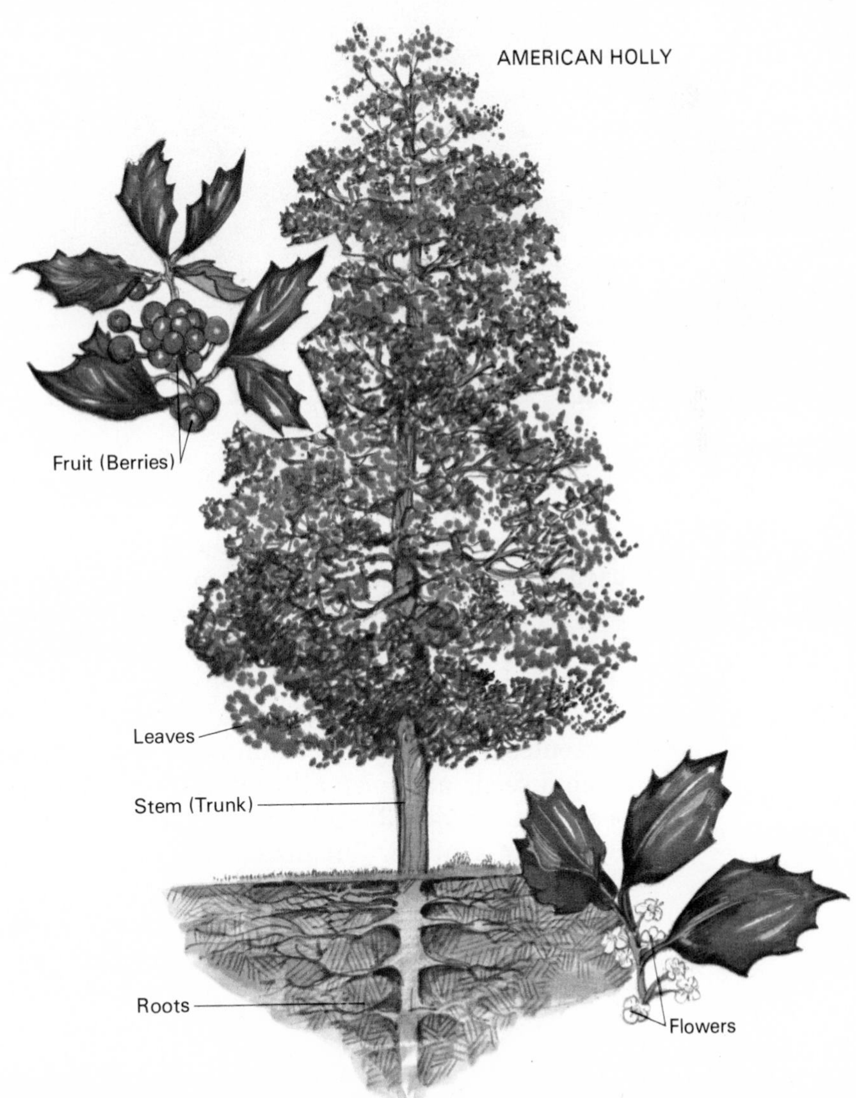

Essential organs of an advanced green plant include roots, stem, leaves, flowers, and fruits. The fruits contain the seeds for the next generation of the plant.

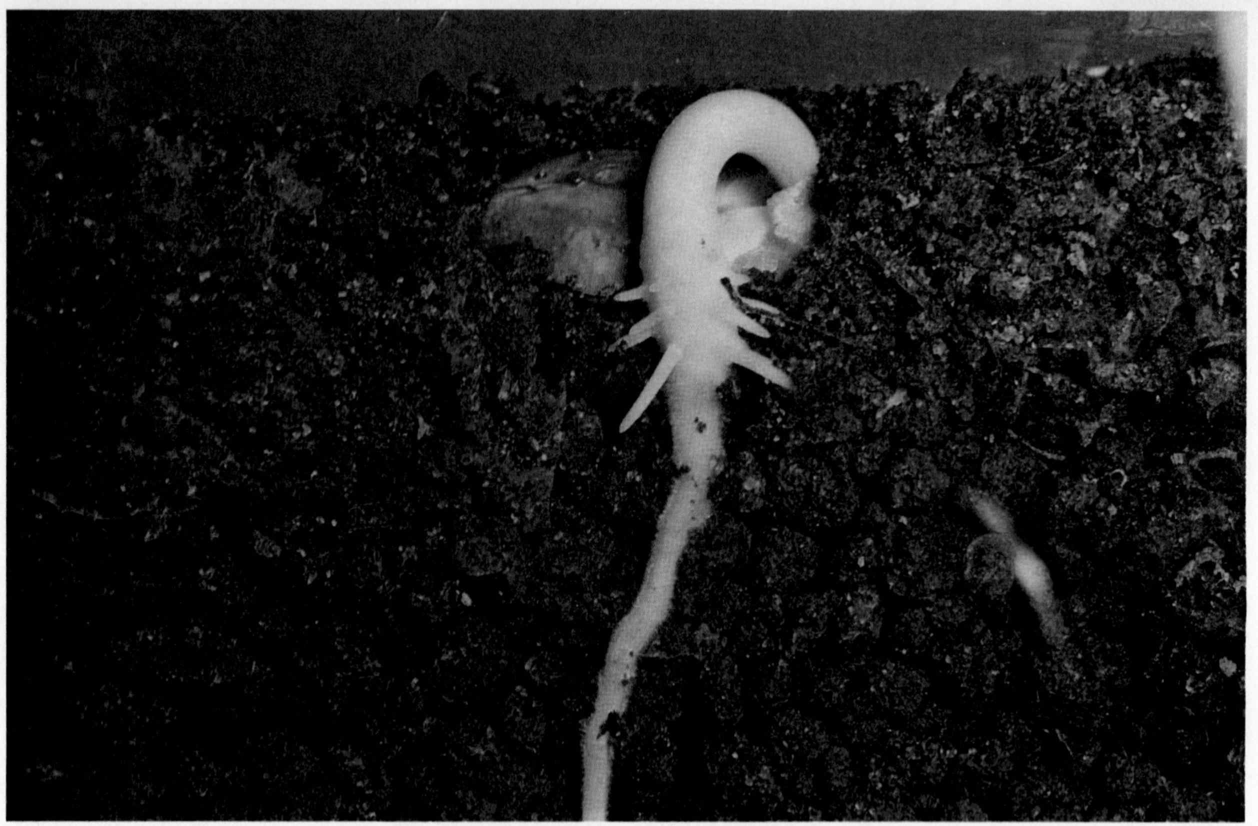

Chapter 11 Seed germination

Chapter-opening photo shows a bean seed in the process of germinating. Clearly visible are the cotyledons, root, and root hairs.

Early humans were food gatherers, not food growers. They hunted meat and collected wild fruits and grains. A seed was something to be used for food. What a great discovery it must have been when early people found that seeds could be used to produce new plants! With these remarkable little packages called seeds, people could supply their food needs by growing crops for themselves and their animals.

Seeds vary greatly in size, shape, and the arrangement of their contents. A coconut, for example, is one of the largest seeds known. Orchid seeds are so small that you would need a magnifying lens to see them. The small size of an orchid seed limits the amount of material it can contain. But inside every seed, no matter how small, are the parts needed to produce a new plant. In Problem 11-1 you will take a close look at the parts of seeds.

Seeds are important to people because they are the best method of growing new seed plants. Much of our food supply comes from the stored food in certain seeds. We eat the seeds of corn, wheat, rice, bar-

(*Above*) A germinating bean seed.

ley, rye, peas, beans, soybeans, peanuts, and oats. Some seeds also furnish oils, food flavoring, and medicines. The hairy covering of the cotton seed is used to make fabrics for clothes.

The undeveloped plant within a seed is called an **embryo.** When a seed sprouts, or **germinates,** the embryo begins to grow. Before **germination,** the cells of the embryo are resting, or **dormant.** During germination, the embryonic cells begin to divide and grow. The young plant emerges from the seed. (See Figure 11-1.) Plant organs such as the roots, stem, and leaves take form. The embryo is now a **seedling.**

Conditions needed for germination

Seed germination is controlled by conditions within the seed and outside the seed. If a plant embryo is alive and able to germinate, the seed is said to be **viable** [VY-uh-bul]. Seeds that contain dead or poorly formed embryos are called **nonviable.** In Problem 11-2, seed viability will be determined by how many seeds in a group germinate.

External conditions also affect seed germination. Such conditions include temperature, moisture, oxygen, and light. By knowing when to plant certain seeds, farmers can control the environmental conditions and expect better results. In Problem 11-3 you will investigate external conditions that affect germination. Since environments are not the same from place to place, the same kind of plants are not found everywhere.

When a plant embryo begins to grow, its cells need to use stored food for energy. To get the energy out of the stored food, the cells car-

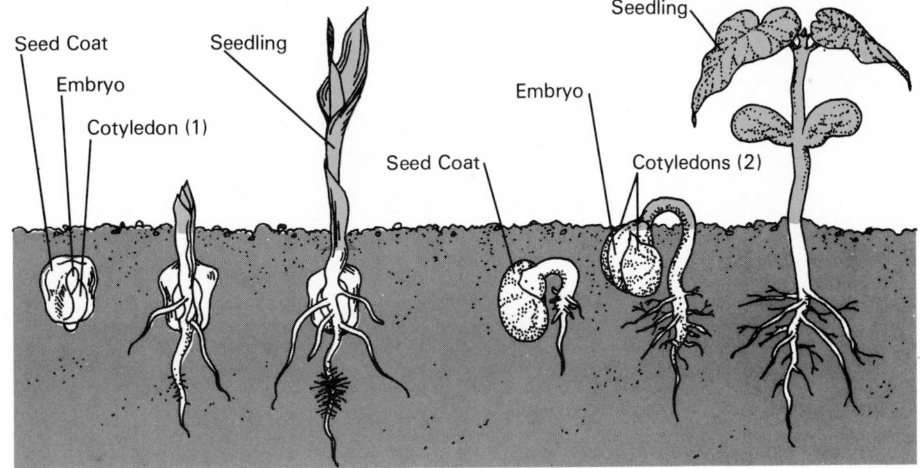

11-1. During germination, the seed coat is broken and the embryo plant begins to develop roots and stem. On the left is a corn seed, on the right a bean seed.

ry on a process called **respiration.** During respiration complex food materials are broken down to release energy. This process goes on in both plants and animals. It uses oxygen gas and produces carbon dioxide gas. In Problem 11-4 you will measure the carbon dioxide gas produced by respiring pea seeds.

Problem 11-1 What are the main parts of corn and bean seeds?

Purpose To locate and identify the main parts of a bean seed and a corn seed.

Materials

- dry bean seed
- water-soaked bean seed
- dry corn seed
- water-soaked corn seed
- razor blade, single-edged
- iodine solution

Procedure

Part One: The main parts of a bean seed

A. Obtain a dry bean seed and a soaked bean seed. Rub your finger over the dry seed and then over the soaked seed. The structure you feel is the **seed coat.**

1. Unsoaked seed coats are hard.

2. It softened and broke the coat.

1. Is the dry seed coat hard or soft?
2. What effect did soaking the bean seed have on the seed coat?

The seed coat provides a hard covering around the seed to protect the inner structures. The seed begins the process of germination by taking in water, swelling, and breaking the seed coat.

3. Yes, from the soaked seed.

Point out that the physical processes of water intake and swelling are necessary steps in the breaking of the seed coat in nature.

3. Can you break or remove the seed coat from the dry or the soaked bean seed?

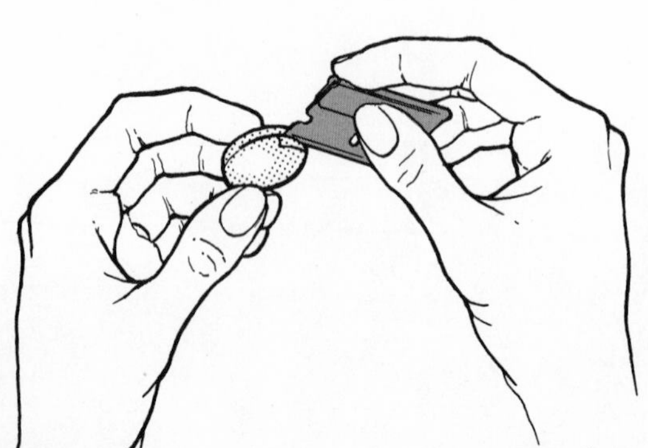

It will probably not be necessary to use a razor blade to remove the seed coat from a soaked seed. If it is, warn students to be careful with razor blades.

11-2. In Step B, if the seed coat does not peel off easily, *carefully* cut it with a razor blade.

Students will read about monocots (such as corn) vs. dicots (such as bean) on page 197, but you may also want to point it out here.

B. Remove the seed coat from the soaked seed. Separate the inner structure by gently prying apart the two halves. These two halves of the seed are called **cotyledons.**

C. Find a part of the seed that looks like a tiny plant. This tiny plant is the embryo. The embryo of the soaked seed has started to produce new cells by the process of mitosis. The production of new cells began with the absorption of water at a suitable temperature. The first part of the embryo to start to grow is the root.

4. What is the shape of the embryo's root?
5. The embryo also has leaves. How many leaves does the bean embryo have?
6. What is the shape of a bean embryo's leaf?
7. Where is the embryo attached to the cotyledons?

4. Like a banana or comma, with tiny fingerlike projections.

5. Two.

6. Broad at the base, narrow at the tip. (Triangular.)

7. The part of the embryo between the root and the leaves is attached to both cotyledons near one end of the seed.

D. For the embryo to continue to grow, it must have water and food. The cotyledons contain the stored food that the embryo needs. This food is in the form of starch. If iodine solution is added to starch, the iodine will change from golden to blue-black. Add two or three drops of iodine to the surface of the cotyledons. Then test the embryo.

8. Do the cotyledons contain stored starch?
9. Does the embryo contain starch?

8. Yes.

9. No.

In order for the embryo to use the stored starch as food, the starch must be changed to a simpler substance. A simple sugar is produced from the starch. The sugar is then used by the embryo to get the energy it needs for growth.

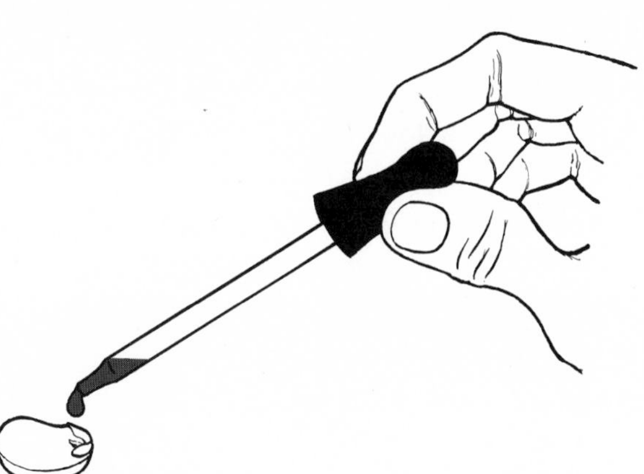

11-3. Test the seed for starch.

Part Two: The main parts of a corn seed

E. Obtain a dry corn seed and a soaked corn seed.

10. The unsoaked coat is hard.

11. From the soaked seed.

10. Is the dry seed coat soft or hard?
11. Can you remove the seed coat from the dry or the soaked seed?

F. With a single-edged razor blade, cut the soaked corn seed into halves. To do this, place the seed with the flat side on a cutting surface. (See Figure 11-4.) Push the razor blade through.

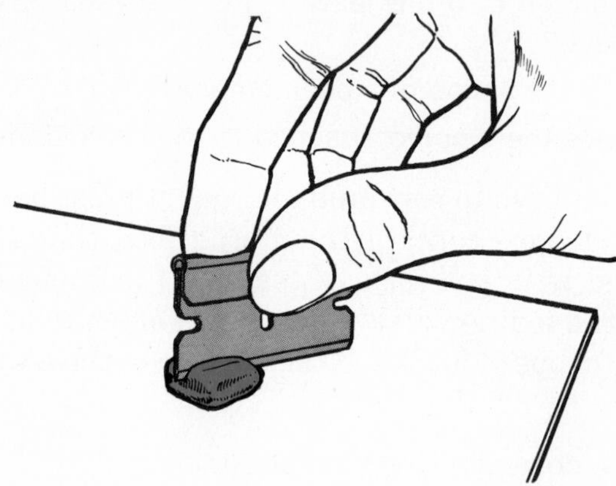

11-4. Carefully cut the soaked corn seed in half. It is best not to hold the seed while cutting it.

12. Yes.

13. The diagram should show starch present in the large fleshy portion called the endosperm. In a small area near the bottom of the seed, the brown color of the iodine solution should remain unchanged.

14. The embryo.

G. Add two or three drops of iodine to one-half of the seed.

12. Does the corn seed contain food in the form of starch?
13. In your notebook, draw a diagram of the cut surface of the corn seed. Shade in the area that contains starch.

The part of the corn seed that contains the stored food is called the **endosperm.**

14. What part of the seed would not be turned blue-black by the iodine? Label this clear area as the embryo.
15. In what ways does the corn embryo appear to be a tiny plant?

You should now be able to

15. It has tiny leaves and the beginnings of a root and stem.

Identify the three main parts of bean and corn seeds.
Locate the leaf and root regions of an embryo plant.
Describe the appearance of a plant embryo.
Describe changes in the seed as a result of soaking it in water.
Test for the location of starch in a seed.

Seed characteristics

Corn and bean seeds are alike in that each contains an embryo, seed coat, and stored food. The iodine test you performed in the last problem showed that cotyledons (or endosperm) contain food in the form of starch. Sugars and other food materials are also contained in the seeds. This food is used by the embryo as it starts to grow (germinates). Indeed, such seeds are included in our own diet because of their nutritive value.

A flowering-plant embryo has either one or two cotyledons. Plants that have one cotyledon are called **monocotyledons** [mahn-uh-kaht-ul-EED-uns] or **monocots.** Plants that have two cotyledons are called **dicotyledons** [dye-kaht-ul-EED-uns] or **dicots.** Grasses, corn, and orchids are examples of monocots. Dicot examples include beans, peas, and sunflowers.

As the embryo starts to develop, the parts of a mature plant are easier to recognize. The root, shoot (stem), cotyledons, and even the seed coat play important roles in the growth of the plant.

Several years ago, newspapers carried stories of seeds being found in tombs of ancient Egyptian kings. The accounts said that the seeds were alive and viable. Scientists do not understand how the seeds found in the tomb could be viable after 4,000 years. Seeds vary in their ability to remain viable over time. An orchid seed, for example, remains viable only for a few days or weeks. Indian lotus seeds have been shown to be viable after 200 years. Most seeds are viable for a period of four to ten years.

Problem 11-2 What is meant by seed viability?

Purpose To determine the percentage of seeds that will germinate in an ideal environment.

Materials

paper towels	tweezers	petri dish
scissors	seeds (15)	

Procedure

A. Obtain a paper towel and fold from end to end to make two double layers. Cut the two double layers of paper towel to fit the bottom of a petri dish. Put the toweling into the dish.

Remind students each day to add water to the paper toweling.

B. Cover the toweling with water and let it set for about one minute. Tilt the petri dish to pour off the excess water. This will leave the toweling saturated with water. Add enough water each day to keep the toweling saturated.

Handling seeds with tweezers will help prevent contamination by molds.

C. Use tweezers to sort out ten seeds that appear identical. Check that they are not cracked or broken in any way.

D. Use the tweezers to place the ten seeds on the saturated toweling in the petri dish. Add the cover and label it with your name and type of seed. Store the dish in the dark at room temperature.

E. Copy Table 11-1 into your notebook.

F. Record in your table the number of seeds that germinate until all have germinated or 10 days have passed. A seed has germinated when the root breaks through the seed coat.

G. Calculate the percentage of seeds that germinated out of the total number placed in the dish. See the sample problem that follows. If ten out of ten seeds germinated, 100% would have germinated. The percentage you find represents the relative number of seeds that are able to germinate under laboratory conditions. Seeds that are alive and capable of germinating are called viable.

Sample problem
Calculating the percentage of seeds germinated

If six seeds out of ten germinated, the percentage of the total would be calculated as follows:

Students may have difficulty computing the percentage of germination. Do several sample problems with the class.

$$\text{Percentage germinated} = \frac{\text{number germinated}}{\text{total number of seeds}} \times 100$$

$$= \frac{6}{10} \times 100$$

$$= 0.6 \times 100$$

$$= 60\%$$

1. Answers will vary. These seeds typically show 60-90% germination.
2. No.
3. Yes. The percentage would be lower because the seed coats had been damaged.

1. What percentage of your seeds germinated?
2. Do you think all types of seeds would show the same percentage of germination?
3. If broken or cracked seeds had been used, would this have changed the percentage of germinating seeds? Explain.

TABLE 11-1 SEED GERMINATION RESULTS

Seed Tested: ______________ *Date Packaged:* ______________

Total number of Seeds placed in dish	*Number of seeds germinated within Ten days*	*Percentage of seeds that germinated* $\left(\frac{\text{No. Germinated}}{\text{Total Number}} \times 100 = \%\right)$

4. Lack of moisture would lower the percentage of germination, since seeds require moisture to germinate. If there were no water at all, none of the seeds would germinate.

5. Freezing would inhibit the growth of the embryo, thus lowering the percentage of germination.

6. Various answers are acceptable. The manner in which the seeds were selected, storage conditions, exposure to frost, moisture conditions, and the age of the seeds could all affect viability.

4. How would a lack of moisture change the percentage of germination?
5. How might freezing the seeds change the percentage?
6. The viability that you found for your seeds could be greatly different from that listed on the package. Give one reason why the percentage expected to germinate, and the percentage that actually did germinate, may not be the same.
7. If seeds packaged in 1900 had 87% expected germination then, should you expect the same viability now?

Seeds that take five or six days to germinate can cause storage problems during germination tests. A slow germination rate also makes it difficult to tell exactly how many seeds are actually germinating.

To help eliminate this problem, scientists are trying a new method of determining viability. They know that a seed that is alive and growing needs energy. And to get energy, starch must be changed to sugar. So the embryo of a viable seed has sugar present. By testing a seed for sugar, scientists can determine viability before germination.

You should now be able to

Calculate the percentage of viable seeds in a given sample.

Predict some possible factors that could affect seed viability.

Recognize conditions of moisture and temperature necessary for maximum viability of the seed.

Recognize a seed that has germinated.

7. No. (Viability decreases with each passing year.)

Germination factors

When water enters a seed, the cotyledons start to swell. The seed coat, which has enclosed and protected the seed, splits open. This permits the root to grow out of the seed. This process of germination leads to the development of the young plant.

Why some seeds germinate and others do not has always been a puzzle. You know from the last problem that, even under ideal conditions, a plant embryo may not germinate. As with other living things, some plant embryos just may not have the ability to survive.

Even when an embryo is alive within a seed, it may remain dormant. There are many conditions that keep seeds dormant. Some seeds, for instance, have a very thick seed coat that keeps out water and oxygen. Until this seed coat has softened or rotted, the seed cannot germinate. Seeds of alfalfa have a seed coat that does not let water in. Once the seed coat is scratched, the seed germinates like any other seed.

Scratching the outside of some seeds is very important. So important, in fact, that a mechanical scratching process called **scarifying** is done before planting. Sweet clover and other important crops must also be processed in this way. For most seeds, however, soaking in water is enough to weaken the seed coat.

Besides the amount of water available, there are other external factors that affect seed germination. In the next problem you will investigate how heat and light affect germination.

In Problem 11-3, you may want to have several teams work jointly on each environment and pool results for the total data to be recorded in copies of Table 11-2 (p. 202).

Problem 11-3 What effect do light and temperature have on seed germination?

Purpose To observe and record changes in seed germination resulting from conditions of light and temperature.

Materials

- paper towels (4)
- scissors
- petri dishes (4)
- wooden splints (8)
- tweezers
- peas, presoaked (20)
- radish seeds (20)
- tomato seeds (20)
- grass seeds (20)
- aluminum foil
- masking tape
- marking pen
- plastic wrap

11-5. Divide each of the petri dishes into four sections.

Procedure

Remind students to moisten paper toweling every day.

A. Obtain a paper towel and fold from end to end to make two double layers. Cut the two double layers of paper towel to fit the bottom of a petri dish. Put the toweling into the dish.

B. Cover the toweling with water and let it soak into the toweling for about one minute. Tilt the petri dish to pour off the excess water. This will leave the paper toweling saturated with water. Add just enough water each day to keep the toweling saturated.

C. Divide the dish into four sections by fitting together two wooden splints as shown in Figure 11-5.

D. Repeat Steps A, B, and C to prepare the other three petri dishes in the same way.

E. Place five pea seeds into one section of each of the four petri dishes. (See Figure 11-5.) Place five radish seeds into a second section of each dish. Use tomato and grass seeds in the other two sections of each. Each of the four dishes should appear as shown in Figure 11-6. Replace the covers on the petri dishes.

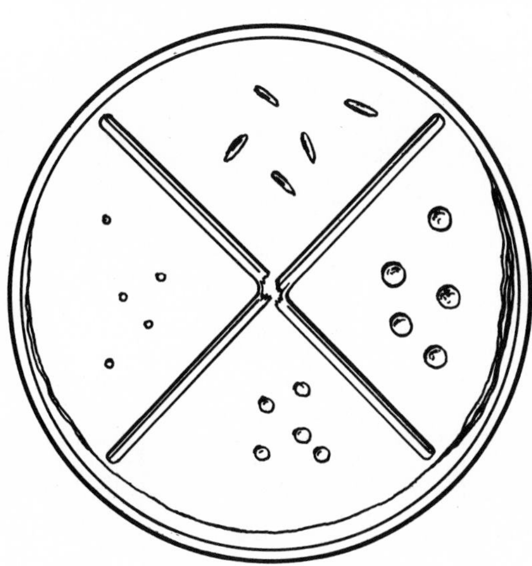

11-6. Petri dish containing four different kinds of seeds.

Foil-wrapped dishes may be stacked together in corners of the refrigerator away from the light. Plastic-wrapped dishes should not be stacked, so that they are all uniformly exposed to light.

F. Cover two dishes so they are light-tight. Aluminum foil can be molded to the dish to block out the light. Be careful not to disturb the positions of the seeds by tipping or shaking the petri dishes. Cover the other two dishes with clear plastic wrap.

G. Mark your group, class or section number, and type of environment on each dish. The environments are *cold-light, cold-dark, warm-light,* and *warm-dark.*

H. Place one foil-wrapped dish and one plastic-wrapped dish in a well-lighted part of the room. These are the warm-light and warm-dark dishes.

1. The presence or absence of light.

1. What is the only environmental difference in these two dishes?

I. Place the other foil-wrapped and plastic-wrapped dishes in a refrigerator. Be sure the refrigerator is equipped with a lamp that burns 24 hours a day.

TABLE 11-2 SEED GERMINATION RECORD

Kind of Seed	Cold-Light												Cold-Dark											
	Number of Seeds Germinated by Day										Total Germ.	Total Used	Number of Seeds Germinated by Day										Total Germ.	Total Used
	1	2	3	4	5	6	7	8	9	10			1	2	3	4	5	6	7	8	9	10		
Pea																								
Radish																								
Tomato																								
Grass																								

Kind of Seed	Warm-Light												Warm-Dark											
	Number of Seeds Germinated by Day										Total Germ.	Total Used	Number of Seeds Germinated by Day										Total Germ.	Total Used
	1	2	3	4	5	6	7	8	9	10			1	2	3	4	5	6	7	8	9	10		
Pea																								
Radish																								

2. The presence or absence of light.

3. Generally the warm, dark environment.

5. Darkness seems better for most kinds of seeds. Grass and lettuce germinate equally well in either environment.

Results of germination tests should be expected to vary somewhat.

8. Usually radish, but results may vary.

9. In the refrigerator, usually pea, but results vary. At room temperature, usually radish.

10. Pea seeds often have the highest overall germination.

11. Tomato seeds often have a very low percentage of germination, but results may vary.

Discuss the fact that there are many phenomena in nature that we know occur but cannot explain why. This is the reason for scientific investigation.

2. What is the only environmental difference in these two dishes?

J. Prepare a data table in your notebook like the one shown in Table 11-2.

K. Record the number of seeds that have germinated daily. (A seed has germinated when the root breaks through the seed coat.) Be sure to record the results of each petri dish, or environment, in the correct column.

3. In which environment did the most seeds germinate?
4. In which did the least seeds germinate? 4. Usually the cold, light environment.

L. Compare the total number of seeds that germinated in the dark with the total number that germinated in the light.

5. In general, is light or darkness better for germinating seeds?

M. Compare the number of seeds that germinated in the refrigerator with the number that germinated at room temperature.

6. In general, is room temperature or the refrigerator temperature better for germinating seeds? 6. Room temperature.
7. What type of seed had the highest percentage of germination in light? (If you forget how to find a percentage, review the Sample Problem on page 198.) 7. Usually grass.
8. What type of seed had the highest percentage of germination in darkness?
9. What type of seed had the highest percentage of germination in the refrigerator? At room temperature?
10. What type of seed had the highest percentage of germination in all four environments?
11. What type of seed had the lowest percentage of germination in all four environments?

Each type of seed has a set of conditions that must be present before the process of germination can begin. Some seeds germinate in a wide range of conditions. Others germinate in only a narrow range of conditions. This is one reason why certain plants are found in some areas of the country and not in others.

You should now be able to

Determine how different temperatures affect seed germination.

Determine how conditions of light and darkness affect seed germination.

Describe the change in appearance of a seed that has germinated.

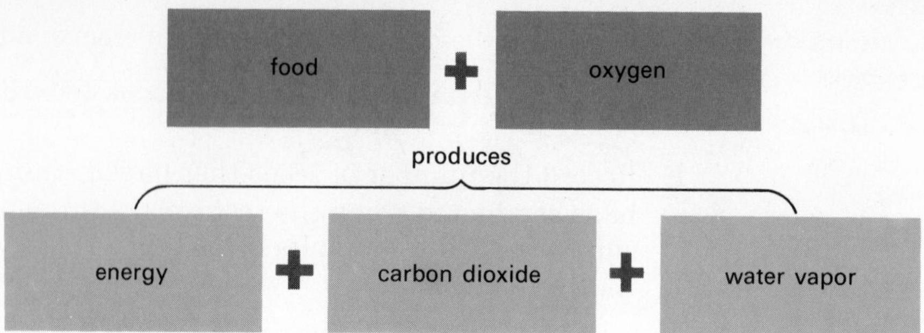

11-7. Respiration provides energy in a living cell.

Respiration

Dormant seeds are in a resting state. They require little energy. As soon as a seed germinates, however, the activity within the plant increases. And greater activity means a greater need for energy.

The process of **respiration** provides the energy needed for the activities of life. (See Figure 11-7.) When seeds absorb water, digestion of stored food begins. The rate of respiration increases. The energy released by respiration is used for cell division and other cellular needs.

Every living cell gets energy by breaking down food materials. This process involves the combining of food material, in the form of sugar, with oxygen. Living things combine sugar with oxygen to produce carbon dioxide gas, water vapor, and energy. In the next problem, you will measure the amount of carbon dioxide gas given off by seeds during the process of respiration.

Problem 11-4 How much gas do seeds release during germination?

Purpose To collect, measure, and test the gas given off by germinating pea seeds.

Materials

- rubber stopper, 1-hole
- glass tubing, 8 cm
- glass tubing, U-shaped (2)
- 400-ml beakers (2)
- rubber stopper, solid
- pea seeds (20)
- test tubes (2)
- wooden splint
- matches
- medicine dropper
- rubber band
- rubber tubing
- test-tube rack
- cloth
- limewater

Procedure

A. Place twenty pea seeds in a test tube. Then fill the test tube with water.

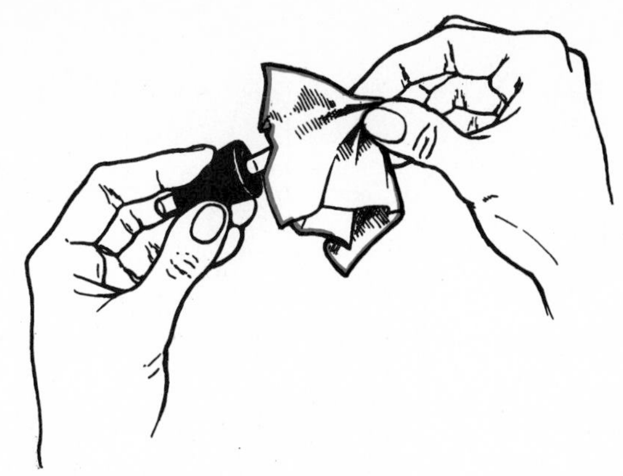

11-8. Gently insert glass tubing into stopper. Do not force it.

B. Assemble the stopper, glass tubing, and rubber tubing as follows. Wet the straight tube of glass and the hole of the stopper. Wrap the glass tube in a cloth. *Carefully* push the glass tube into the large side of the stopper. (See Figure 11-8.) Stop pushing when the end of the tube just shows on the other side. Connect the straight glass tube to the U-shaped tube with the rubber tubing. (See Figure 11-9.)

C. Insert the stopper with tubing into the test tube of pea seeds and water. Some water should enter the glass tube as you push the stopper firmly into the test tube.

D. Fill the rest of the tubing with water. Hold your finger over the end of the tubing so that the water does not escape.

E. Stand the test-tube apparatus in an empty beaker, as shown in Figure 11-9. Also as shown, place the unconnected end of the tub-

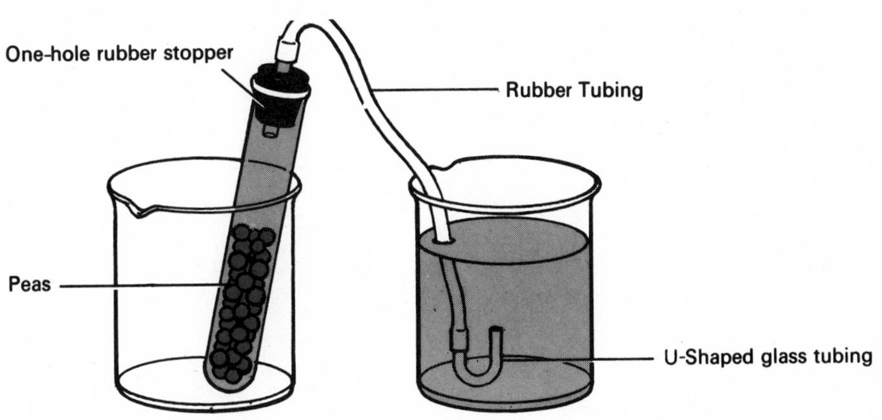

11-9. Place unconnected end of tubing assembly in a beaker containing water.

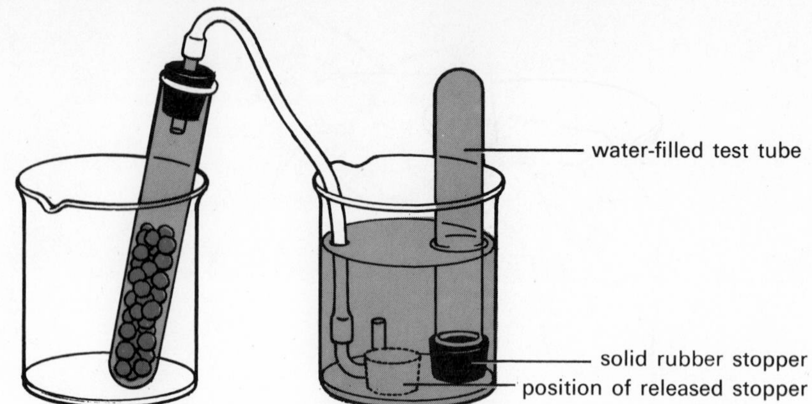

11-10. Remove the stopper of the water-filled test tube while the test tube is under water to avoid admitting air bubbles.

Make certain that all air bubbles are removed from the system, or the results will not be valid.

ing into a second beaker that is three-fourths full of water. Carefully jiggle the tubing to remove air bubbles.

F. Fill a second test tube with water until a small amount spills over. Hold the *large end* of a solid (no-hole) rubber stopper over the top. Hold the stopper in place while you invert the test tube and place the stoppered end below the surface of the water in the beaker.

G. Once you have the mouth of the test tube below the water surface, you may release the stopper. Allow the tube to rest on the bottom of the beaker. (See the dotted stopper in Figure 11-10.) Check to see if any air bubbles are present at the top of the test tube. If so, you will have to repeat Steps F and G.

H. As shown in Figure 11-11, connect the test tube with peas to the submerged test tube.

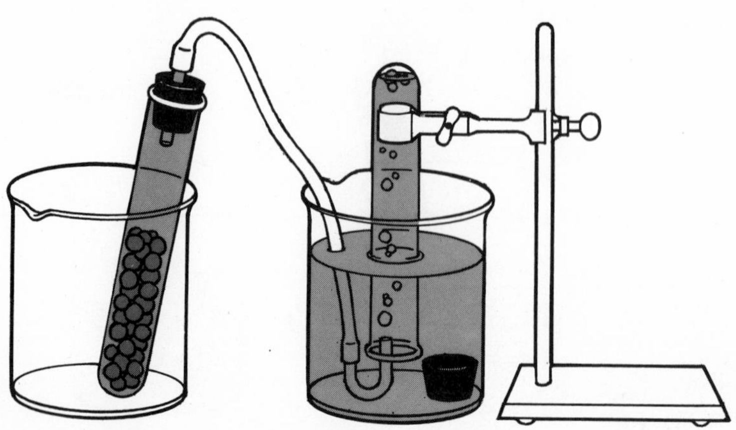

11-11. Collecting the gas produced.

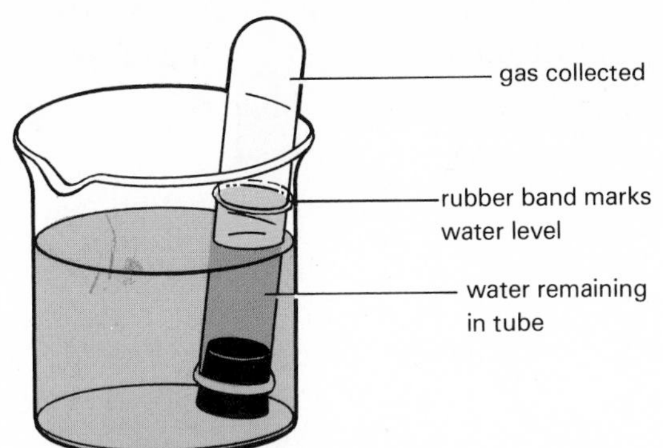

11-12. Trap the gas collected by inserting a stopper into the test tube, keeping the mouth of the test tube below the water surface.

1. At the top of the inverted test tube.

1. Where would a gas be collected if some is produced by the pea seeds?

I. Store your apparatus in a place where it will not be moved.

Do not allow seeds to remain in the container for more than 3 days. Decomposition produces disagreeable odors.

J. Observe after 24 hours. With the mouth of the test tube still below the surface, insert a solid rubber stopper to trap both the collected gas and the remaining water. With the stopper securely in place, remove the test tube from the beaker. *Before turning the tube upright,* mark the water level in the tube by using a small rubber band. This mark will also show the amount of gas collected. Place the stoppered and marked test tube upright in a test-tube rack.

All living things need energy to carry on the activity of growth. Most living things combine sugar with oxygen to get energy. When sugar is combined with oxygen, carbon dioxide and water are produced along with the energy. Respiring seeds oxidize sugar for energy. So respiring seeds give off carbon dioxide gas.

Review the tests for carbon dioxide gas (bubbling limewater) and for oxygen gas (glowing splint).

K. Test the gas in your test tube to see if it is oxygen gas. Light a wooden splint, then blow out the flame to produce a glowing tip

11-13. Test the gas with a glowing splint.

on the splint. Remove the stopper from the tube and insert the glowing splint into the gas at the top of the tube. If oxygen gas is present, the splint will flame up. Replace the stopper in the test tube.

2. No, since it does not cause splint to flame.

2. Is the gas produced by the germinating pea seeds oxygen?

You could use the overhead projector to demonstrate the technique of testing small amounts of gas in a medicine dropper.

L. Now you will test the gas to see if it is carbon dioxide. Carbon dioxide gas causes clear limewater to turn cloudy. Squeeze the bulb of a clean medicine dropper and draw up only enough limewater solution to fill the tip of the dropper. Keep the bulb of the dropper partially squeezed.

Remove the stopper from the test tube. Stick the tip of the medicine dropper into the gas at the top of the test tube. Release the rubber bulb so that bas bubbles through the limewater and up into the dropper.

Hold the dropper tip downward and observe the appearance of the limewater for thirty seconds.

3. It appears cloudy.

4. It behaves like carbon dioxide when reacting with limewater.

5. Respiration.

3. Describe the appearance of the limewater after thirty seconds.
4. What can you conclude about the nature of the gas produced by germinating pea seeds?
5. What seed germination process produced the gas collected in the tube?

6. Answers will vary. About 5-10 milliliters are usually produced.

7. You would get close to twice as much gas. To test, set up same experiment, using 40 seeds instead of 20.

M. Empty the water from the test tube. Use a graduated cylinder to fill the test tube to the rubber-band mark with water. This volume of water is the same as the volume of gas produced by the twenty pea seeds.

6. How many milliliters of gas were produced?
7. Do you suppose you would get twice as much gas with forty peas? How would you test to find out?

You should now be able to

Collect the gas that is produced by pea seeds during the process of germination.

Test a gas for the properties of oxygen and carbon dioxide.

Measure the amount of gas produced by the pea seeds when they germinate.

Relate the type of gas produced to the activity being carried on by the pea seeds.

Science terms

cotyledon
dicotyledon (dicot)
dormant
embryo
endosperm
germination
monocotyledon (monocot)
nonviable
respiration
scarifying
seed coat
seedling
viable

Review questions

1. List three main parts of a seed.
2. What term means the same thing as "sprouting"?
3. What term describes seeds in a resting state?
4. What are four kinds of seeds whose cotyledons furnish food for people?
5. List three external conditions necessary for seed germination.
6. What is meant when a seed is said to be viable?
7. What food material may be identified by the iodine test?
8. What process carried on by germinating seeds takes in oxygen and gives off carbon dioxide?

1. Seed coat, embryo, cotyledons.

2. Germinating.

3. Dormant.

4. Answers will vary. Coconut, corn, wheat, rice, etc.

5. Answers may vary. The factors of temperature, oxygen supply, moisture, and light all must be in the right condition if germination is to occur.

6. A viable seed has a live embryo capable of germinating.

7. Starch.

8. Respiration.

Check your understanding

See Teacher's Guide section for answers to Questions 9-20.

9. In what way are the seeds of monocots different from the seeds of dicots?
10. What do you suppose would happen to the embryo of a bean seed if its cotyledons were removed?
11. If 80 seeds germinated out of 100 seeds planted, what percentage of the seeds were viable?
12. Seeds stored in a cool place retain their viability longer than seeds stored at high temperatures. How would you explain this?
13. Under what conditions would it be an advantage for a plant seed to have a thick seed coat? When might a thick seed coat be a disadvantage?
14. How does light affect seed germination?
15. Do you think placing seeds in a freezer would affect their viability? In what way?
16. Describe a method you would use to determine how much heat is given off by respiring seeds.
17. A corn plant produces hundreds of seeds. What might prevent some of those seeds from germinating?

18. Why is it advantageous for a plant to produce a great number of seeds?
19. Suppose you have a garden and want to plant a particular kind of seed. What things should you consider in order to have as many of the seeds germinate as possible?
20. The instructions on some seed packages say that the seeds should be soaked in water overnight before being planted. Why is this necessary?

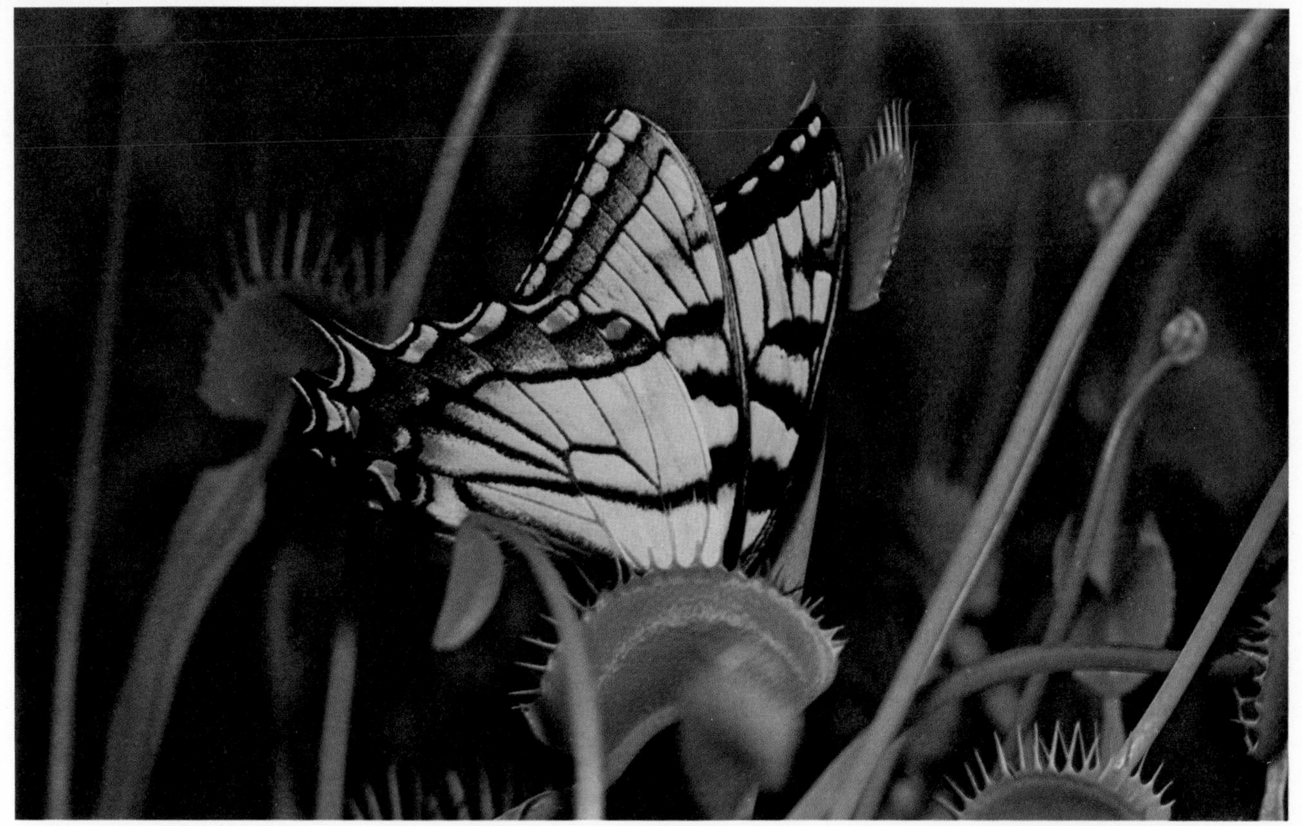

Chapter 12 **Plant responses to stimuli**

Chapter-opening photo shows the body of a swallowtail butterfly caught in a Venus's-flytrap. Students may not make the distinction between the showy wings of the butterfly and its arthropod body.

(*Above*) Butterfly caught by a Venus's-flytrap.

If you are startled by a loud noise, you may jump or react quickly. When your finger gets too close to a flame, you jerk your hand back. The noise and the heat are **stimuli** (singular *stimulus*). Your reaction to them is a **response.** Plants also respond to stimuli.

Most plant responses are very slow. This is due to the fact that the response usually depends on plant growth — a rather slow process. Organisms that do not move around but do respond to stimuli are said to show tropisms. A **tropism** is a growth response by a plant to certain stimuli.

In Problem 8-3 you observed the response of brine shrimp to stimuli. This response by a simple animal was called a *taxis* because it involved the movement of the animal from place to place.

In order for plants to survive, they must respond to changes in their environment. Roots have been found growing into underground water supplies. A tree will grow more branches and leaves on the side that receives more sunlight. How are plants able to do these things?

12-1. Plant roots shown growing toward water supply.

What are the stimuli that will cause reactions by parts of a plant? These are two questions you will try to answer as you do the problems in this chapter.

Plants do not have nervous systems or muscular systems. They cannot, therefore, receive stimuli and respond as animals do. Plants must depend on certain parts of themselves to grow, to cause bending away from or toward a stimulus. For instance, a plant stem will bend to one side if the cells on the other side grow more rapidly.

A fair comparison could be made to the lifting of a car on the grease rack at a service station. The whole car rises evenly as force is applied to all parts of the frame at once. But what happens when a jack raises just one side of the car? Since only one side goes up, the car tilts in the opposite direction.

Plant stems contain chemicals called **auxins.** When present, an auxin causes rapid cell growth. The concentration of auxin seems to be greater in cells away from direct light than in cells that are in direct light. The cells on the shaded side of a stem will thus grow faster than the cells on the illuminated side. This rapid, one-sided growth causes the tip of the stem to bend toward the light.

Roots also contain auxins. How a plant root grows has much to do with the success of the plant. The root must be able to hold the plant in the ground. The root must also go deep enough to reach moisture and dissolved minerals. Desert plants need very long roots to reach water deep in the ground. And desert winds can be very strong, so deep roots also help to anchor the plant.

In Problem 12-1 you will examine how the main root of a corn seedling grows. You will compare the growth rates of various parts of the root. You will need to work carefully if you are to get meaningful results.

Problem 12-1 Where does growth take place in a root?

Purpose To locate areas of rapid growth in a corn root.

Materials

corn seedling, two days old
petri dish
paper towels (2)
felt-tip pen, permanent ink
plastic window screening

Procedure

Stamp-pad ink could be used in place of a felt-tip pen.

The pattern of growth within a root may be observed by placing a series of evenly spaced marks on the root. The relative positions of the marks after a few days will show the growth pattern.

A. Obtain a corn seedling about two days old.

Wire screen may be saved and used again. Do not use water-soluble ink.

B. Place a plastic screen on a paper towel. Lightly ink a small section as shown in Figure 12-2. *Too much ink will give poor results.*

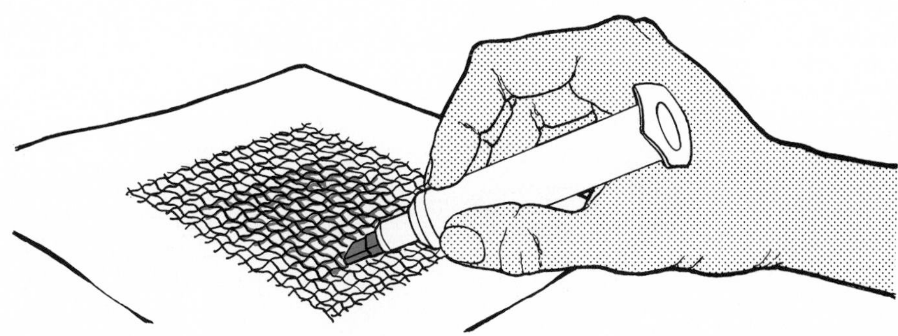

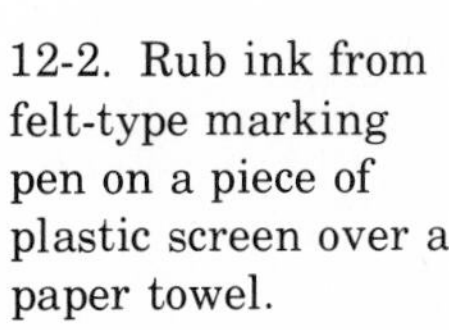

12-2. Rub ink from felt-type marking pen on a piece of plastic screen over a paper towel.

12-3. Mark the root of the corn seedling and allow the ink to dry.

C. Position the corn seedling so the root may be easily marked by the inked area. (See Figure 12-3.) *Gently* press the root onto the screen. Do not roll or smear the root across the screen. Allow the marks to dry.

Be sure students keep seedlings moist to allow growth to continue.

D. Place the seedling into a petri dish containing two double layers of moist (not wet) paper toweling. Keep the root dry or the ink will smear. Cover the dish.

E. Prepare a table like Table 12-1 in your notebook. Examine the root each day for the next 3 to 5 days. Record your observations in your table.

1. No.

2. The tip.

3. In the root tip about 2 mm from the end.

4. The horizontal marks would be longer and probably more diffuse. Yes, there was an increase in diameter.

5. Mark the stem with evenly spaced marks and observe relative changes in the marks and the spaces between them.

1. Did all the marks stay the same distance apart?
2. What part of the root has the greatest distance between the marks?
3. The marks move apart as a result of cell division producing more cells in that section. Where does the most cell division seem to take place in a root?
4. How would the marks change to show an increase in diameter? Was there an increase in diameter?

F. Your observations should indicate to you that the root grows in length only at the tip. The same growth pattern is followed by the stem.

5. How could you use a similar procedure to show where growth takes place in a stem?

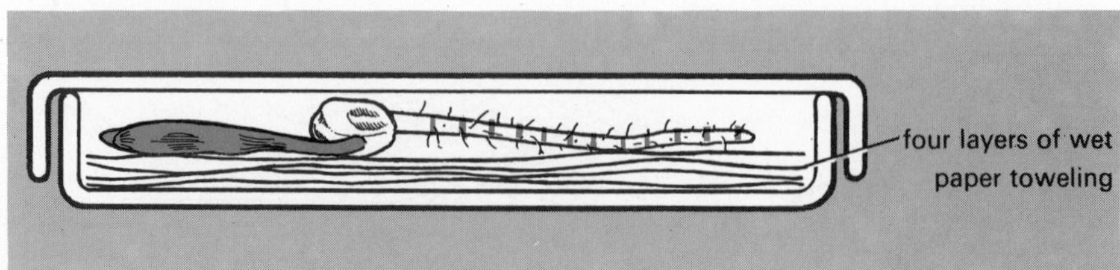

12-4. Cover the petri dish to prevent rapid evaporation of moisture.

TABLE 12-1 CORN ROOT GROWTH RECORD

Day	Observations of Root
1	
2	
3	
4	

You should now be able to

Determine where growth occurs in a corn root.

Suggest a way to determine where growth occurs in a stem.

Relate cell division to increase in length of a root.

Predict where the growth areas are located in a plant.

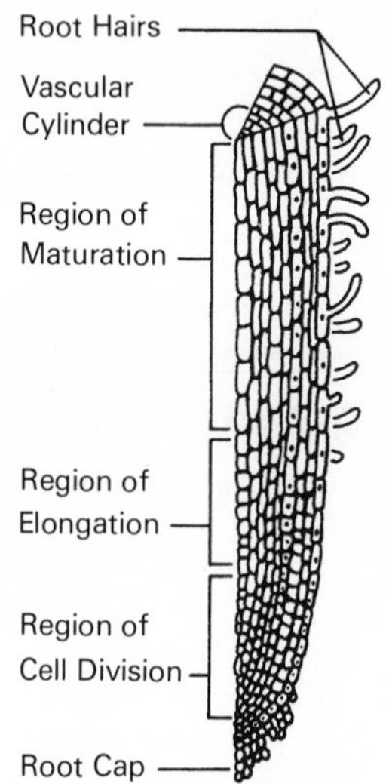

12-5. In most plant roots, the region of most active cell division is near the tip of the root.

Factors affecting direction of plant growth

In Problem 12-1 you probably found that the most rapidly dividing cells in a root were at its tip. This would suggest that roots increase in length by the addition of cells near their tips. And in most plants this is true. (See Figure 12-5.)

But what about the direction in which a root grows? What determines the path a root takes through the soil? There are three major factors that influence where a root will grow in the soil. These factors are gravity, water, and chemicals. All three factors act as stimuli to the roots.

Most roots will grow toward water, showing a **positive hydrotropism.** *Positive* means "toward" and *hydro-* refers to water. A positive hydrotropism is a movement of the organism toward moisture.

If there are beneficial minerals dissolved in the soil, the root will probably grow in that direction. It will display a **positive chemotropism.** If there are harmful chemicals, on the other hand, the root will probably grow away from them. That would be a **negative chemotropic** reaction.

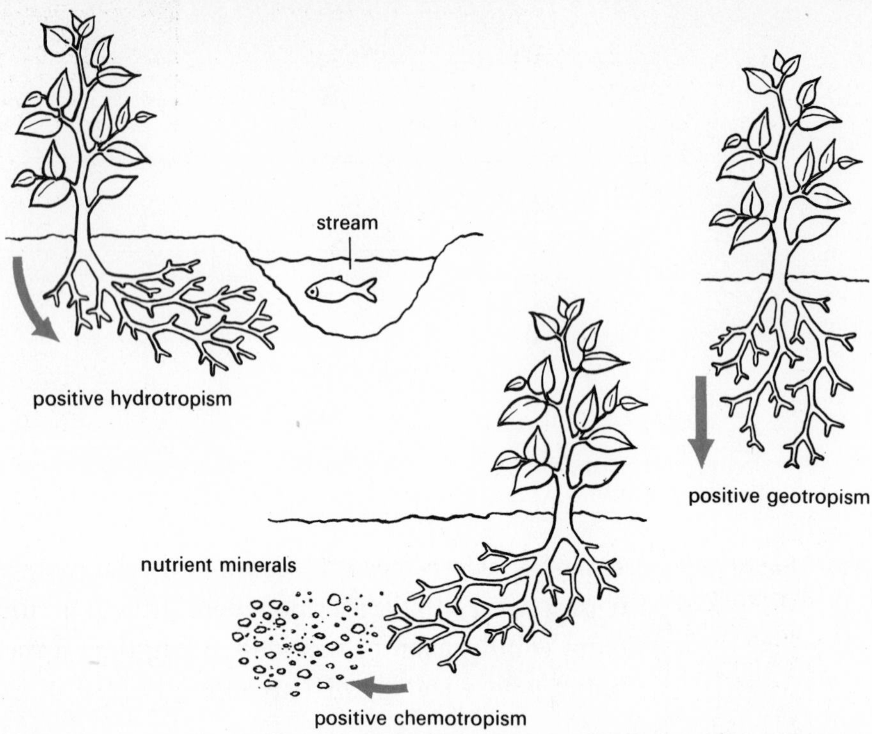

12-6. Root tropisms — positive responses to water, gravity, and chemicals.

Geotropism is the response of a stem or root to the stimulus of gravity. In most cases, the direction of stem growth is opposite to the direction of root growth. You will investigate geotropic reactions in the next problem.

Problem 12-2 What effect does gravity have on plant growth?

Purpose To observe how gravity affects the direction of stem growth.

Materials
corn seedlings (4)
test tubes, same size (4)
cardboard, 10 cm × 30 cm
flannel cloth
masking tape
scissors

Procedure

A. Cut four squares of flannel cloth. Make each square small enough to fit loosely into a test tube when rolled up.

B. Wrap a flannel square around each of four corn seedlings. Allow the roots and shoot to extend out of opposite ends of the cloth. (See Figure 12-7.)

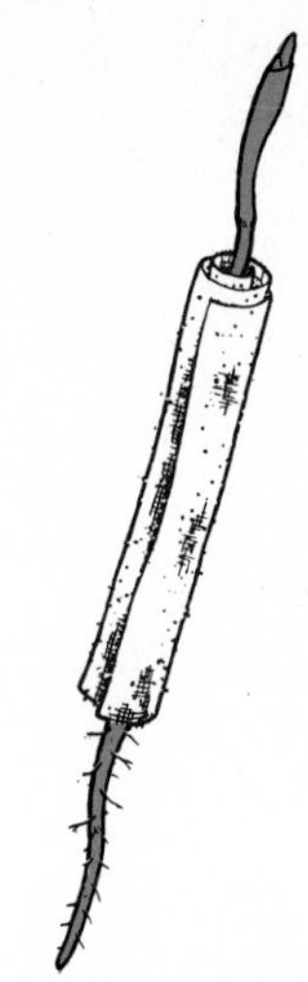

12-7. Corn seedling wrapped in flannel.

C. Dip the wrapped seedlings in water until they are dripping wet. Insert the wrapped seedlings, root downward, into the test tubes. The green part of each seedling should be sticking out of its test tube, as shown in Figure 12-8.

D. On the piece of cardboard, write the information shown in the lower left corner of Figure 12-8.

E. Using masking tape, fasten the four test tubes securely to the cardboard as shown below. Put Tube 1 mouth upward; Tube 2, mouth slanted 45° upward from the horizontal; Tube 3, mouth sideways (horizontal); and Tube 4, mouth downward. Tack the cardboard to a bulletin board or tape it to a hard surface as directed by your teacher. Each day, remove the board from the wall and use a dropper to wet the flannel. (While watering, you will need

Check to see that the tops of plants are extending from the test tubes.

Keep flannel saturated. If the air is dry, students may have to moisten the flannel twice daily.

A bulletin board is an ideal place to fasten cardboard sections.

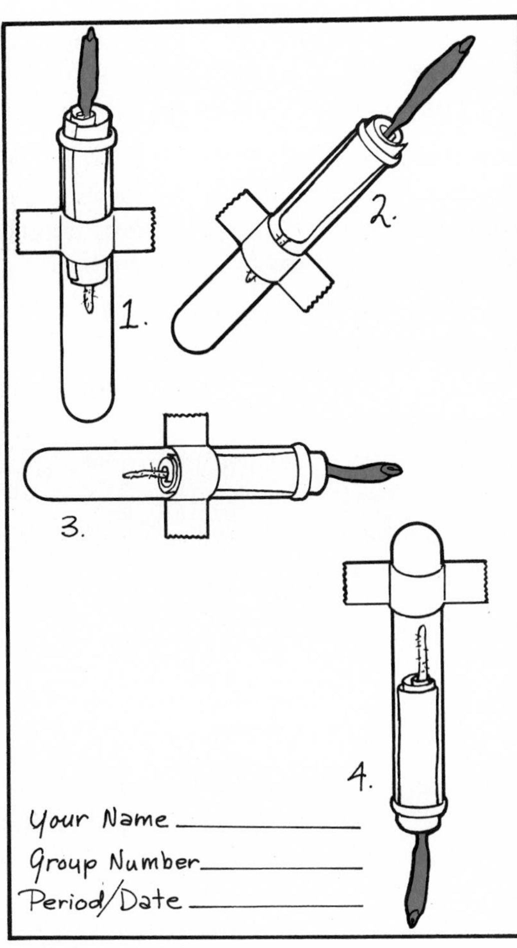

12-8. The test tubes containing the seedlings should be placed in these positions. To water each plant, rotate the cardboard until the tube is upright, and moisten the flannel with water from a medicine dropper.

to turn the cardboard so that Tubes 3 and 4 are in upright positions.) Replace the cardboard on the wall in its original position as soon as you are done watering.

F. Observe the direction of growth of the shoots each day for the next three to five days.

1. Draw a diagram in your notebook showing the final position of each stem.
2. Which tube acted as the control for this experiment?
3. Does each stem grow away from the mouth of the test tube in a straight line?
4. In which tube(s), if any, are the stems growing in a curved path?

If the stem changes the direction it is growing, one side of the stem must be growing faster than the other. If the stem grows in a straight line, then all sides must be growing at the same rate.

5. Does the position of the tube seem to affect something in the stem, which then causes a change in length of one side of the stem?
6. Which tubes show unequal growth on the sides of the stem?

The side of the stem that shows the greatest increase in length is located nearer the gravitational attraction of the earth. The only things that could explain the change in length on one side of the stem are more cells, or larger cells, or both.

7. Does gravity appear to affect the rate of cell division or growth of cells in the stem?
8. Which part of the plant stem — top, sides, or bottom — got longer in Test Tube 3?
9. Did the stems show a positive geotropism or a negative geotropism?
10. In question 8, what test tube did you use for comparison with Test Tube 3?

1. Drawings should show all four stems growing upward (negative geotropism), regardless of how the plant was oriented originally.

2. Tube 1 (right side up), since that is the direction in which plants normally grow.

3. No, only in Tube 1.

4. In Tubes 2, 3, and 4.

5. Yes. (The stem bends as a result of unequal growth.)

6. Tubes 2, 3, and 4.

7. Yes. (The side nearest the earth must be growing faster in order for the stem to bend and grow upward.)

8. One side.

9. Negative, since they grew in a direction opposite the pull of gravity.

10. Test Tube 1, the control.

You should now be able to

Describe how gravity affects the growth of a stem.

Predict the effect gravity would have on the direction of growth of a root.

Predict the effects of gravity on the rate of growth and cell division.

Light and chemical effects

Plants are rarely found growing upside down. But it is possible to see plants growing on a steep hill with their main trunks and branches curved upward. (See Figure 12-9.) This growth pattern shows the effect of gravity on the stems.

Although gravity is an important factor in the growth of roots and stems, light also influences the direction of stem growth. The response of a plant to light is called **phototropism.** In the next problem you will investigate how plants respond to the stimulus of light.

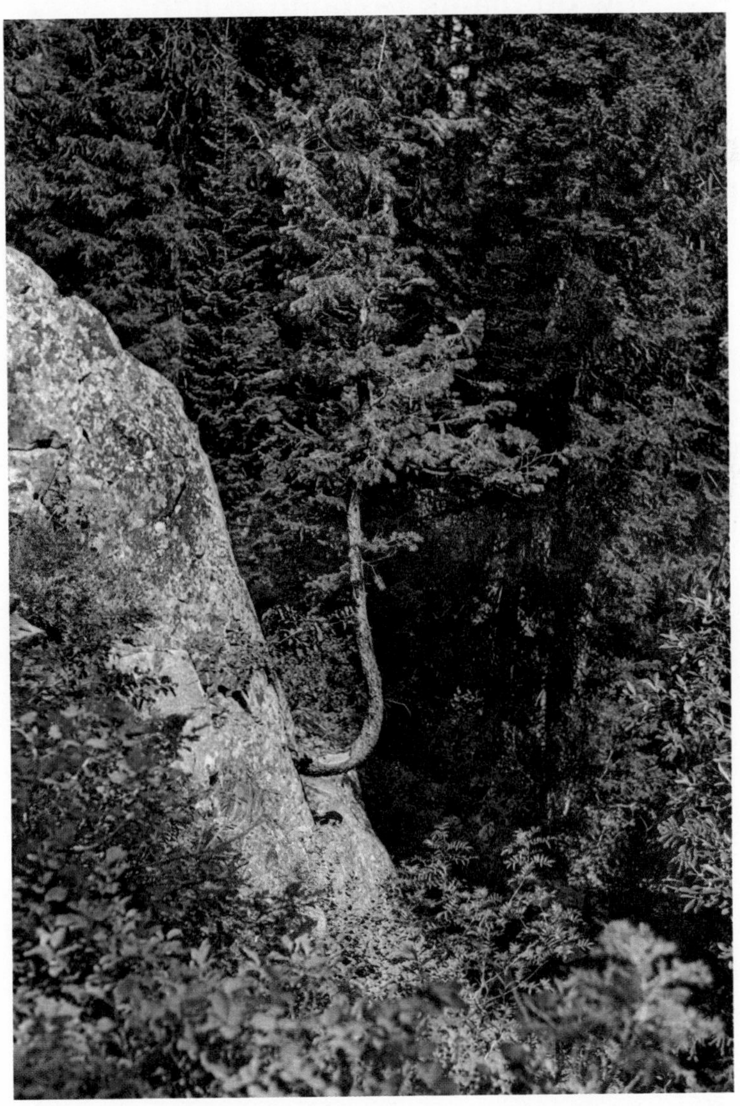

12-9. The growth of this plant demonstrates geotropism.

Plant hormones, or auxins, play an important role in the direction of stem growth. Light has an influence on the auxins that is not fully understood. It is thought that light may cause auxins to move to a darker part of the stem. Or light may prevent auxins from functioning. When an auxin is present, the cells divide rapidly and increase in length. This causes the stem to bend in the direction of the light.

The next problem should give you a better understanding of the influence of light on a plant stem. Keep in mind that the direction of stem growth is affected by gravity as well as light.

Problem 12-3 How do plants respond to light?

Purpose To observe how a controlled source of light affects the growth of a green plant.

Materials

- milk cartons, small (3)
- vermiculite or soil
- corn seedlings, 5 days old of equal size (3)
- aluminum foil
- masking tape
- graph paper
- scissors
- paper clip or stapler
- graduated cylinder

Juice cans or flower pots could be substituted for the milk cartons. Pumpkin seedlings could be used in place of corn seedlings.

Procedure

A. Cut around three sides of a small milk carton about 6 cm from the bottom. (See Figure 12-10.) Remove the lid and throw it away.

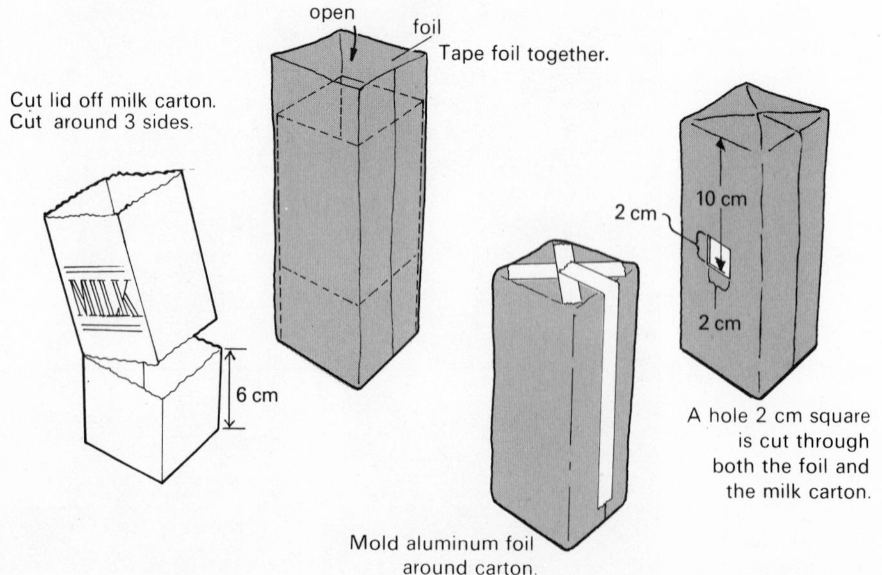

open
foil
Tape foil together.
Cut lid off milk carton.
Cut around 3 sides.
MILK
6 cm
2 cm
10 cm
2 cm
A hole 2 cm square is cut through both the foil and the milk carton.
Mold aluminum foil around carton.

12-10. Preparing the milk carton.

Prepare a light-tight cover by wrapping a piece of aluminum foil loosely around the carton, leaving the bottom open. Tape the edges of the foil together where they meet at the sides. Fold the foil over the top of the carton and tape it down.

B. Cut a 2-cm square hole on one side of the carton. The bottom edge of the hole should be about 10 cm from the top of the carton. Cut through both the foil and the carton to make the hole.

C. Repeat Step A with another carton. *Do not* cut any opening in the side of this second container.

D. Prepare a third carton by cutting the carton in half. Cut the top half along the edges to make four flat pieces of cardboard. You will use the bottom half of the carton in Step E. Save three of the four flat pieces for Step G.

E. Remove the foil covers from the two tall cartons. Put vermiculite in the bottom of all three cartons, to a depth of 4 cm. Choose three corn seedlings of equal size. Plant them in the middle of each carton. Try not to damage the roots as you cover them with vermiculite.

1. All cartons should have an equal amount of water so that water will not be a variable factor in the experiment.

F. Pour 50 ml of water into each carton.

1. Why is it necessary to add the same amount of water to each carton?

Remind students to keep vermiculite moist throughout the experiment.

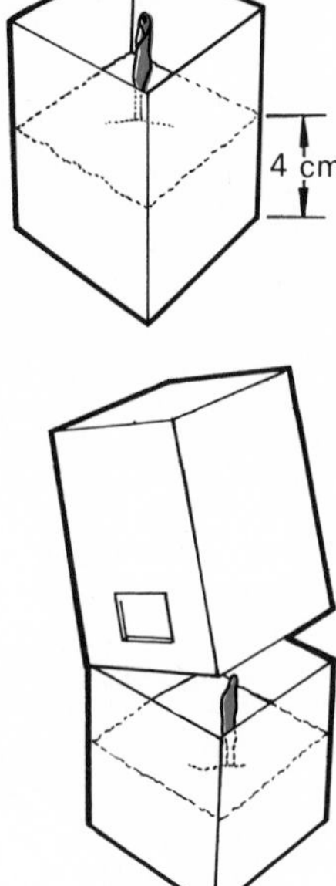

Put 4 cm of vermiculite into each carton and carefully plant one corn seedling in each of three cartons.

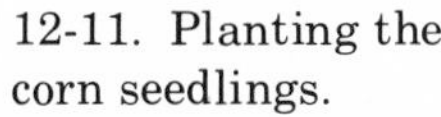

12-11. Planting the corn seedlings.

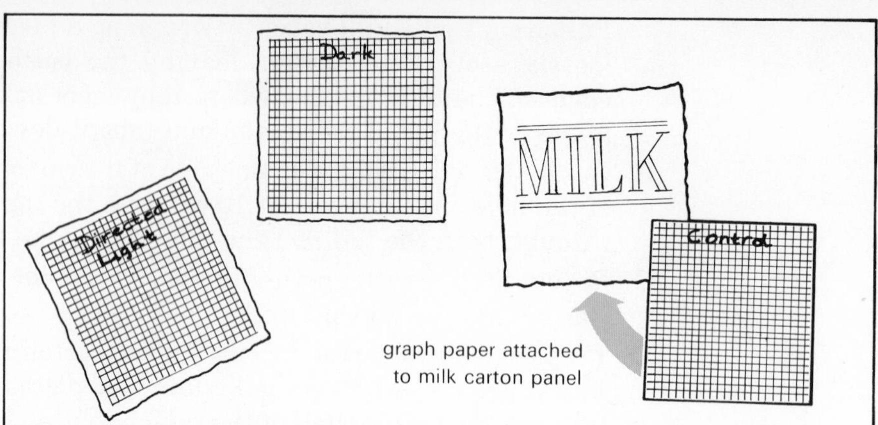

12-12. Graph papers labeled "directed light", "dark", and "control" are attached to milk carton panels.

Instruct students to trim edges off cardboard so that graphs will fit easily into the cartons.

G. Obtain the three pieces of cardboard saved from Step D. Trim the side edges so that the pieces will fit easily into the milk cartons. Cut three pieces of graph paper the same size as the three pieces of cardboard. Clip or staple one piece of graph paper to each piece of cardboard.

Label one graph "control", the second "dark", and the third "directed light."

H. Place the "control" grid behind the plant seedling in the *open container*. (See Figure 12-13.) Put a dot on the graph paper at the point where the tip of the plant hits it. Draw a line on the graph paper to mark the level of the vermiculite. Do the same thing with the "dark" and "directed light" containers.

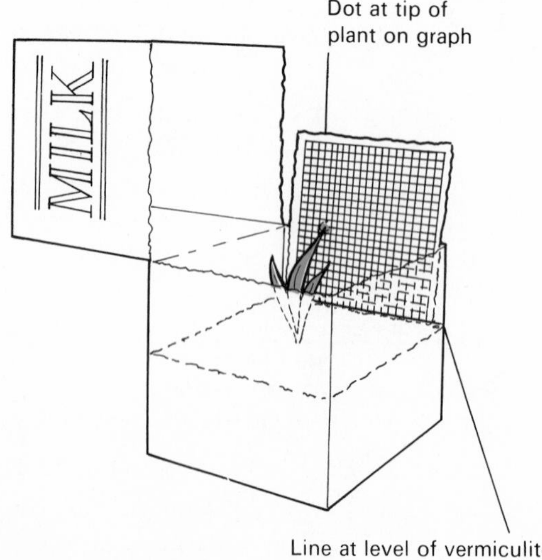

12-13. The dot is placed on the graph paper at the tip of the seedling.

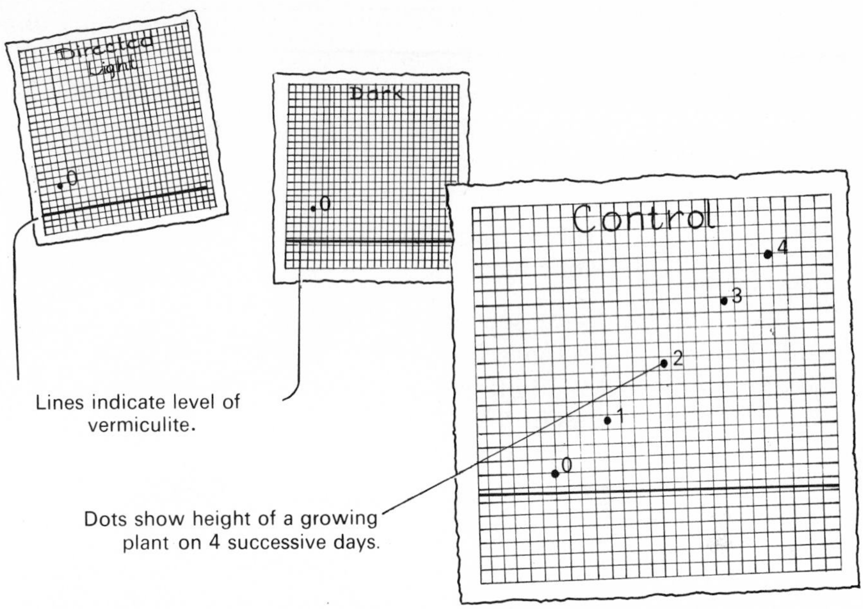

12-14. Graphing the growth of the corn seedlings. When marking the graph each day, be sure the graph paper is always put in at the same depth.

I. Remove the graph paper after making each measurement. Label the dot on each graph *O*. (See Figure 12-14.)

J. Replace the foil covers on the two tall cartons. Check to see that, in the "directed light" carton, the holes in the carton and foil line up. *Foil covers are to be kept in place* except when you are measuring the plants. Make sure the "directed light" container has the hole toward a direct source of light.

K. The next day, remove the foil covers and insert the graph paper in each carton as you did before. Be sure the vermiculite lines on the grids line up with the vermiculite levels in the cartons. Mark the new location of the tip of each plant with a dot on the grid. Label this new dot *1* on each graph. Repeat these measurements for the next three days, labeling the other dots *2*, *3*, and *4*. Remove the graph paper and replace the foil after each measurement.

2. Straight.

3. Nearly straight. It may lean somewhat.

4. The dark.

5. Plants grown without light will usually be taller than those grown in the light.

2. Is the stem of the "control" plant curved or straight?
3. Is the stem of the "dark" plant curved or straight?
4. Which plant is taller, the "control" or the "dark"?
5. How is lack of light related to plant height?

6. Whitish-yellow or yellow-green.

7. No. The side away from the light is longer.

8. A decrease.

The *absence* of light causes plants to grow faster, yet plant stems exhibit a *positive* phototropism. Discuss the relationship between these two phenomena, and make sure that students understand the difference between them.

6. Plants do not develop chlorophyll in the dark. What color is the plant that grew in the dark?
7. Did the stem of the "directed light" plant grow in a straight line? If not, which side of the stem is longer, the side facing the light or away from the light?
8. Compare the size of the "control" plant with the size of the "dark" plant. Does light seem to cause an increase or a decrease in the size of a plant?

Light seems to affect some substance in a stem that results in a decrease in the rate of growth. The side of a plant that is toward the light probably has less of this substance and, therefore, grows slowly. The cells on the other side, *away* from the light, grow faster. They probably contain more of the substance. The unequal growth rates of the sides of the stem cause the stem to bend.

9. Does the "directed light" stem show a positive or a negative phototropism?

You should now be able to

Describe how light from only one direction affects the growth of a plant.

Describe how total darkness affects the rate of plant growth.

Identify a plant that has been grown in the dark by the color of its leaves.

Predict the effect of light on the rate of growth and cell division.

9. A positive phototropism, since the stem grows toward the light.

Plant growth hormones

Are light and gravity the only factors that affect plant growth? In the last problem you grew a plant in the dark. You saw how much faster and taller it grew than the plant in the light. Scientists have found that unusually tall plants contain an abnormal amount of *plant growth hormone*.

Plant growth hormones are not completely understood. When certain growth hormones are placed on a plant, they cause the plant to grow rapidly, and to a height greater than normal. But these plants are usually weak. They will fall over unless supported. Botanists (plant scientists) are trying to find ways to take advantage of the rapid plant growth caused by hormones. In Problem 12-4, you'll be using a plant growth hormone called **gibberellic acid.**

Problem 12-4 What effect does gibberellic acid have on plant growth?

Purpose To determine the effect of gibberellic acid on the rate of growth of corn seedlings.

Materials
corn seedlings of equal size (10)
flower pots, 4-inch (2);
or milk cartons, half-gallon (2)
graduated cylinder
gibberellic acid solution
metric ruler
graph paper
vermiculite or soil

Procedure

You might want to assign some students to look up information on gibberellic acid and report to the class.

A. Line the inside of two flower pots with paper toweling. Then fill the pots with vermiculite to 2 cm from the top.

B. Select ten corn seedlings about the same size.

C. Place five seedlings, stems up, around the outside of each pot on top of the vermiculite. (See Figure 12-15.) Further cover the plants with vermiculite to about 0.5 cm from the top of the pot.

D. Add enough water to saturate the vermiculite in both flower pots. This is best done by placing the flower pots in a tray and covering the bottom of the tray with water. Leave the pots in the tray for 10 to 15 minutes. Then remove the pots and let the excess water drain out.

E. Label one of the pots "experimental." In that pot, pour 5 ml of gibberellic acid solution around each plant. Rinse the graduated cylinder.

12-15. Planting corn seedlings in vermiculite or soil.

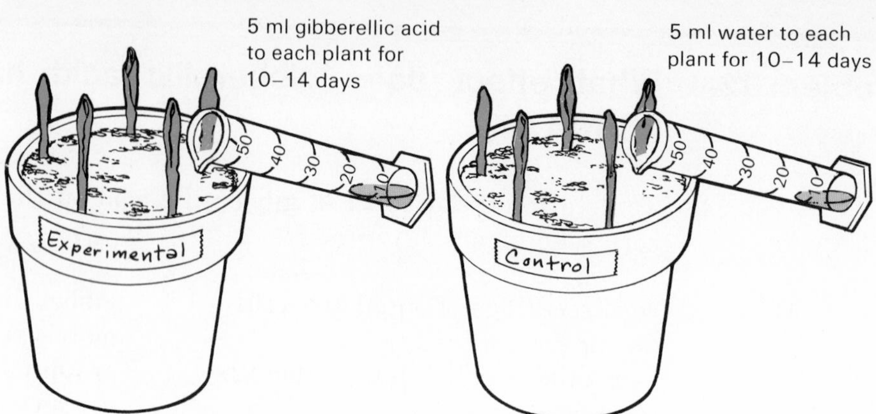

12-16. Treating the plants with gibberellic acid and water.

F. Label the second pot "control." In that pot, add 5 ml of water around each plant.

G. Place both pots in sunlight or under fluorescent growing lamps. Keep the lamps burning 24 hours a day.

The sample data given here suggest what students might expect for results in the average growth figures.

TABLE 12-2 SEEDLING GROWTH WHEN TREATED WITH GIBBERELLIC ACID

	Plant number	*Starting height*	*Measurement on day number:*													
			1	2	3	4	5	6	7	8	9	10	11	12	13	14
Plants treated with Gibberellic acid	1															
	2															
	3															
	4															
	5															
	Average	2.5	2.7	3.5	5.5	7.0	9.5	13.5	14.5	15.5	16.5	17.0	17.0	17.0	17.0	17.0
Plants with just water added	1															
	2															
	3															
	4															
	5															
	Average	2.5	3.0	3.5	4.0	4.5	6.0	7.5	8.5	9.0	10.5	11.5	13.0	13.2	13.5	13.5

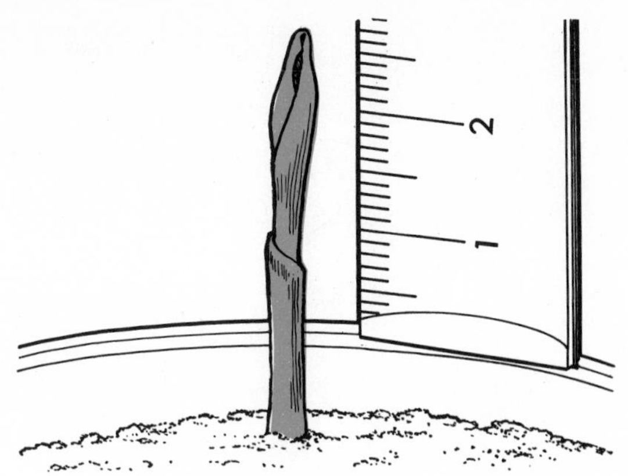

12-17. A metric ruler, carefully placed on the top edge of the flower pot, is used to measure the height of each plant.

Students should not add more water to the plants than the daily 5 ml stipulated.

H. Add 5 ml of gibberellic acid to each "experimental" plant each day for 10-14 days.

I. Add 5 ml of water to each "control" plant each day for 10-14 days.

J. Prepare a table similar to Table 12-2 in your notebook.

K. Measure and record the heights of the five plants in each pot every day for 14 days. To make the measurements as uniform as possible, always place the ruler on the top edge of the pot opposite the plant. (See Figure 12-17.) Measure the height that each plant grows above the edge of the pot. Measure to the nearest millimeter.

L. Each day, calculate and record the average height of the plants in each pot. (Add the heights of the five plants in the pot, then divide the sum by 5. See the sample below.)

M. Prepare a graph similar to Figure 12-18. Each day, plot the average growth of the "control" and "experimental" plants. Use cir-

Sample Computation of Average		
Plant 1	=	14.0 mm
Plant 2	=	13.5 mm
Plant 3	=	12.5 mm
Plant 4	=	16.0 mm
Plant 5	=	14.0 mm
Total		70.0 mm
70.0 mm ÷ 5	=	14.0 mm (Average)

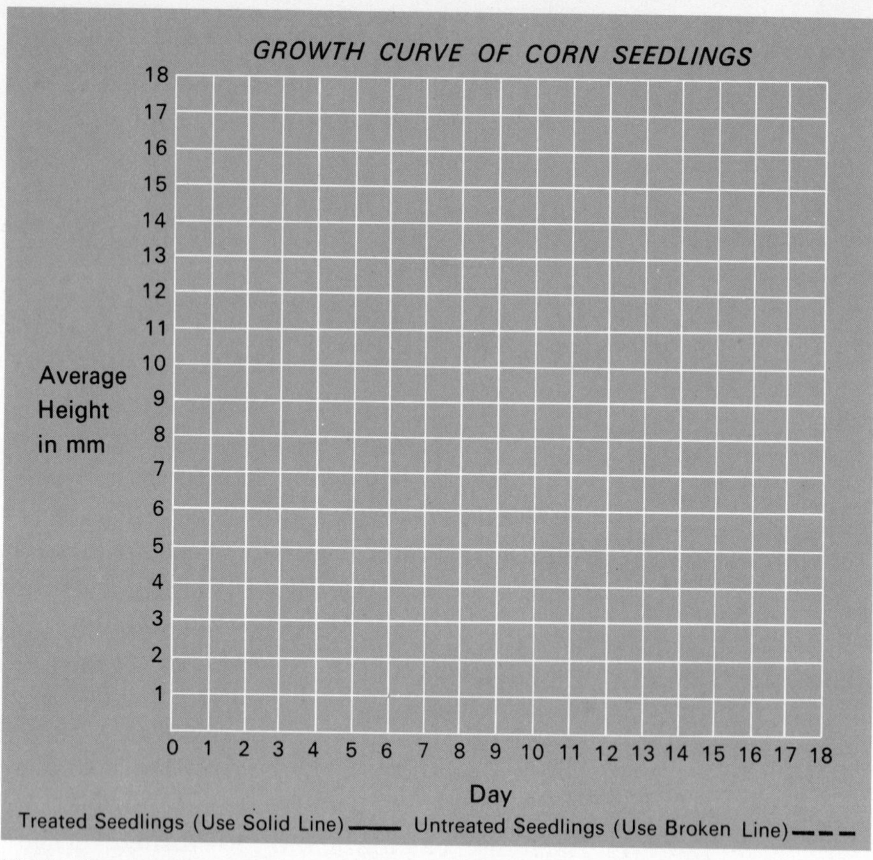

12-18. Graphing the effects of gibberellic acid on corn seedlings.

cles to plot the average heights of the "control" plant. Use squares to plot the average heights of the "experimental" plant. After 14 days, connect the plot points. Use a dashed line to connect the circles, and a solid line to connect the squares.

1. Which group of plants, "control" or "experimental", had grown higher by the end of the experiment?
2. According to your graph, which group of plants grew at the faster rate?
3. What substance must have caused the faster growth?
4. Did these plants show a tropism by growing in a special direction?

1. The experimental plants should be noticeably larger.

2. The experimental group.

3. Gibberellic acid.

4. No.

The growth rate of the seedlings was affected by the gibberellic acid. However, when gibberellic acid is exposed to light it seems to lose its ability to increase a plant's growth rate.

5. No. Gibberellic acid causes cells to grow more rapidly. If placed on one side of a plant, that side would grow faster.

6. The stem would bend in even more, since the most rapid growth takes place on the side away from light, and gibberellic acid would be increasing growth there.

5. Do you think the corn plants would grow straight if gibberellic acid were placed only on *one side* of the stem? Explain your answer.
6. What would happen to the corn plant if a light were directed at the side opposite where the gibberellic acid was placed?

By changing the growth pattern of the cells in a stem, the direction of growth can also be changed. A substance that seems to cause this change is gibberellic acid, a plant growth hormone.

You should now be able to

Prepare a graph to show the growth curve of a plant.

Determine the growth rate of a plant from a graph.

Predict the role of chemicals in plant tropisms.

Predict the effects of gibberellic acid on the rate of growth and cell division.

Science terms

auxin	gibberellic acid	response
chemotropism	hydrotropism	stimulus
geotropism	phototropism	tropism

Review questions

1. What substance produced in a plant causes the plant roots and stem to grow?
2. What is the name of the tropism in which light acts as the stimulus?
3. What is a chemotropism?
4. Name a substance that is an acid and is used as a growth hormone by plants.
5. When a plant seedling is grown in a horizontal position, what stimulus causes the stem to grow upward?
6. What are three stimuli that cause tropisms in plants?
7. Where does the most rapid growth occur in a root?
8. Which side of a plant stem will become longer — the side toward the sun or away from the sun?

1. Auxins, or plant growth hormones.

2. Phototropism.

3. Response of a plant to chemicals.

4. Gibberellic acid.

5. Gravity.

6. Light, gravity, and chemicals.

7. Near the tip.

8. The side away from the sun.

Check your understanding

See Teacher's Guide section for answers to Questions 9-14.

9. What chemicals in the soil might cause a root to react, showing a negative chemotropism?
10. Suppose sunlight is striking a plant from the side. How could you set up the plant so that the stem would grow straight up, rather than toward the light?
11. Do you think that a constantly blowing, strong north wind would affect the direction of growth of tree branches?
12. Why do you think a plant grown in the dark grows faster and taller than one grown in the light?
13. Why is vermiculite often used to grow seedlings in lab experiments?
14. How would you set up an experiment to see if a plant root will respond more strongly to minerals or to water?

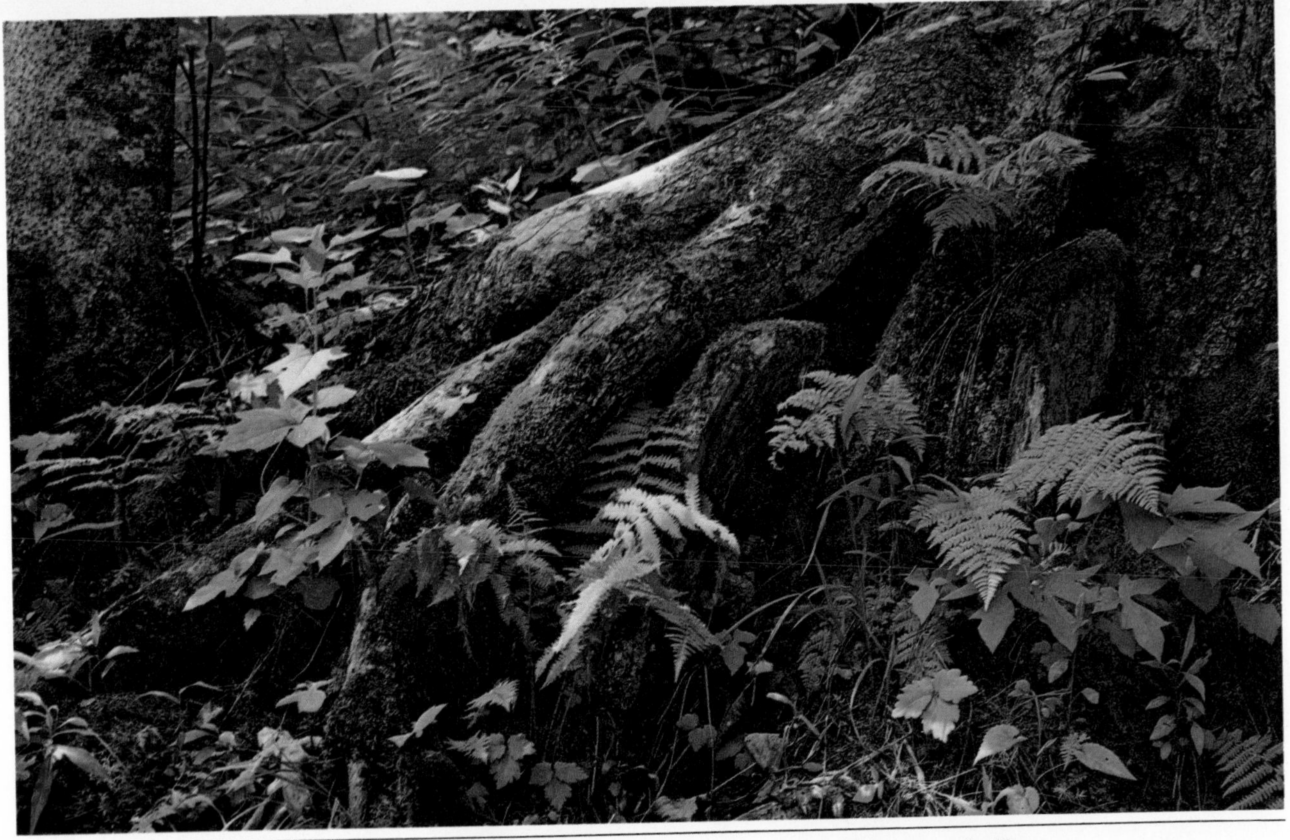

Chapter 13 Movement of liquids in plants

Chapter-opening photo shows several varieties of green plants. Whether ferns or trees, they all have similar methods of internal liquid transport. The large roots serve as a visual emphasis on the main route by which water enters a plant.

The liquid most vital to the growth and development of plants is water. Water makes up much of the material found in living plant cells. It is also needed to dissolve essential substances and to transport them throughout the plant. Also, a large amount of water in plant cells gives rigidity and support to the plant. In this chapter you will investigate the processes by which water and dissolved materials move through plants.

Water enters the plant at the roots. It moves upward through the stem to the leaves. And it brings dissolved substances from the soil with it. In the leaves, the water may be used in some life function such as food-making. Or it may be given off to the air.

It is estimated that ninety-eight percent of the water taken in by a plant is lost through the stomata (tiny openings) of the leaves. This

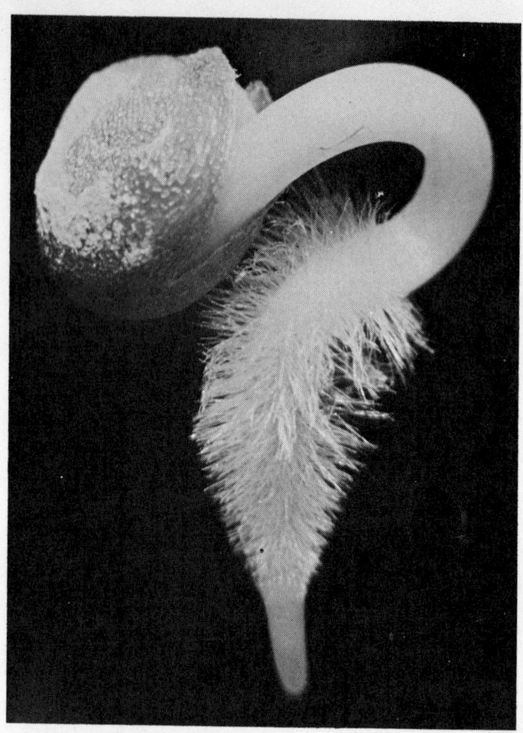

13-1. Water enters a plant or seedling through projections in epidermal cells called root hairs.

loss of water vapor from plants is called **transpiration**. You will use a leafy stem of a living plant to study this process in Problem 13-6.

Transpiration

How much water a large plant will lose by transpiration varies with the kind of plant. A single corn plant loses almost 200 liters of water during its growing season. And mature red maple trees may lose as much as 230 liters in a single day. You can see why plant roots must receive large amounts of water if the plant is to survive.

The rate at which water is lost from a plant depends on several factors. These include the temperature of the air, the moisture in the air (humidity), and the movement of air around the plant. The size of the stomata in the leaves also affects the rate of transpiration. If the stomata are wide open, the rate of water loss will be more rapid than if the stomata are closed.

The continual loss of water at the leaves means that water must be continually taken in at the roots. This water helps carry dissolved substances from the soil to other parts of the plant where they are used to make food or build cells.

Water intake at roots

Water enters a plant through epidermal cells in the roots. Some of these cells have tiny threadlike projections called **root hairs**. (See Figure 13-1.) These increase the amount of water that may be absorbed from the soil. Water enters the epidermal cells by **osmosis.** (You will learn about this process as you read about the diffusion of water into a carrot root in Problem 13-4.)

Water passes through the epidermal cells of the roots. It goes on through neighboring cells. It finally enters special cells in the center of the root. These special cells, called **xylem** cells, form long tubes with thick walls. (See Figure 13-2.) These tubes transport water and dissolved substances upward into the stem of the plant. Xylem cells are found in the stem and leaves as well as in the roots.

Liquid movement through plant stems

You have read that water is lost by transpiration at the leaves, and that water enters by osmosis at the roots. How are these two events related to each other? As water leaves the xylem and surrounding cells in the leaves, more water must be taken in at the roots to take its place. There is a continuous flow of water up the plant from the roots, through the stem, and out the stomata. This water that is lost to the air must somehow be replaced.

Consider the problem of moving water upward through the entire length of the stem (trunk) of a giant California redwood tree 110 meters tall! Biologists believe the upward movement of water and dis-

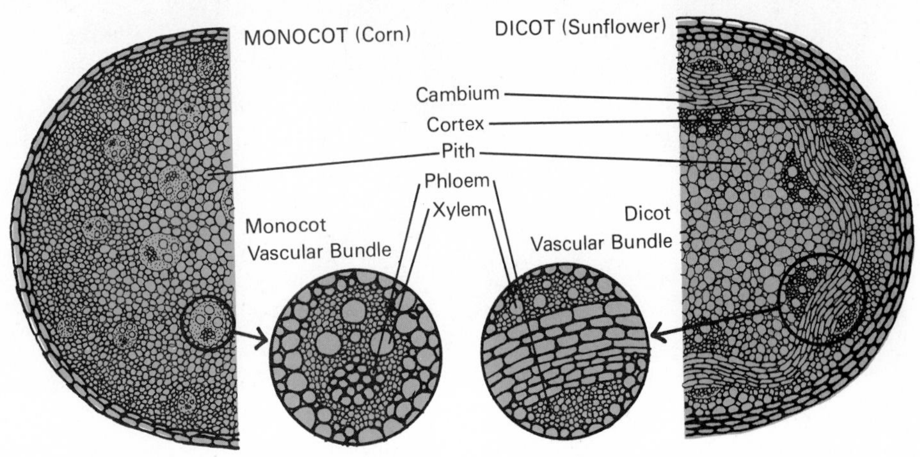

13-2. Cross sections of typical monocot and dicot stems. Note the different arrangements of vascular bundles and of the phloem and xylem cells within the bundles.

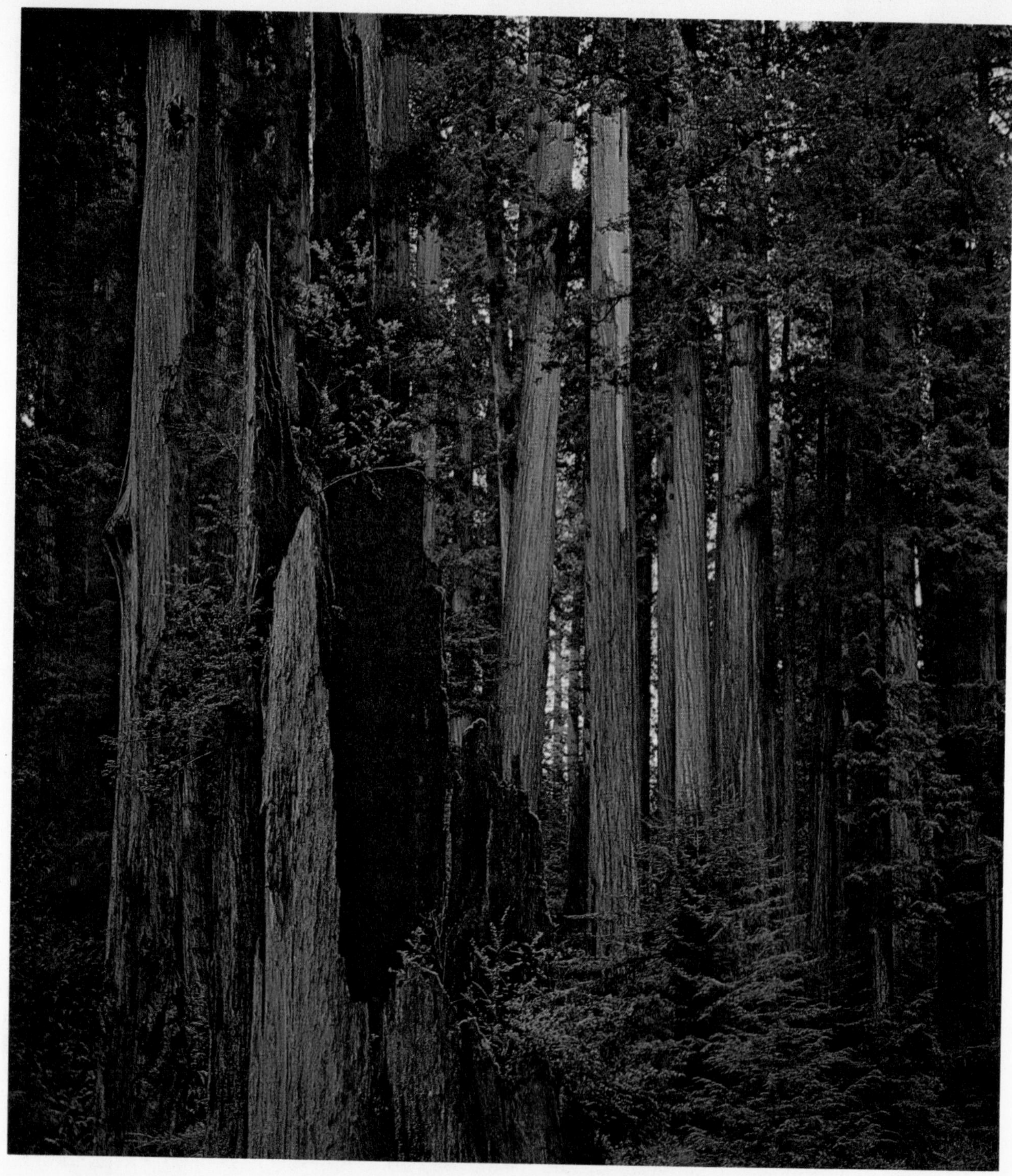

13-3. Imagine the force necessary to lift water to the height of the tallest California redwood (Sequoia), some 110 meters high!

solved materials in plants depends upon several forces. One force is *root pressure*. Root pressure results when water moves into the root by osmosis and forces water upward through the xylem tubes. Another lifting force is *capillary action*. This is the attraction of water to the walls of the narrow xylem tubes.

The most likely explanation for most of the movement of water in plants is the loss of water in the leaves. Remember that a continuous column of water exists from roots to leaves. As water evaporates from the stomata, water must enter the roots, or the water column will be pulled apart. Since water molecules show a strong attraction for each other, they do not pull apart, and the column remains continuous from root to leaf.

Downward liquid movement in plants

There is also downward liquid movement in plants. The food (sugar and starch) made in the leaves must be transported elsewhere in the plant for use or storage. Another kind of conducting cells, called **phloem** cells, serves this purpose. The xylem and phloem tubes are usually grouped as bundles. In some plants, the bundles are arranged in rings. In others, they are scattered throughout the stem. (See Figure 13-2, page 233.) In a leaf, the same bundles make up the veins.

As you learned earlier, leaves are only a few cell layers thick. When held to the light, the veins in a leaf can easily be seen. Veins contain thick fibers that provide support for the leaf. The tubes of xylem and phloem, plus supporting fibers, make up the wood.

Diffusion of particles in solution

To understand other movements of liquids into and within plants, you need to know something about molecules. **Molecules** [MAHL-uh-kyuls] are very small particles of matter. Scientists believe molecules of liquids and gases are always moving about and bouncing into each other.

The molecular motion of perfume can be detected easily. When a bottle of perfume is opened, its molecules move away from an area (in the bottle) where they are closely packed, or **concentrated**. They move to an area (outside the bottle) where they are not closely packed. You detect their aroma quickly.

The movement of particles, such as molecules, from an area of high concentration to an area of lower concentration is called **diffusion**. Remember that the movement is due to the bouncing around of the molecules themselves. It is not due to any external force acting on the molecules.

Problem 13-1 How do dissolved materials diffuse in solution?

Purpose To observe the movement of dye particles in a water solution.

Materials beaker, 400-ml; potassium permanganate; white paper (2)

Procedure

Caution students to be careful when using poisonous potassium permanganate. Warn them to keep it away from their mouths and eyes.

A. Start this problem at the beginning of the period. Fill the 400-ml beaker three-fourths full of water. Place a sheet of white paper under the beaker and another sheet behind the beaker. (See Figure 13-4.)

B. Wait until the water appears to be motionless. Then drop a crystal of potassium permanganate into the water. Observe the crystal from time to time while you are setting up Problem 13-2.

1. Does the crystal seem to move around in the beaker?
2. Describe how the color moves away from the crystal.

1. No.

2. The purple color spreads slowly through the water. It may be described as "drifting," "swirling," etc.

Since the water appears motionless, the dissolved dye particles must be moved by something too small to see. Studies have shown that the molecules of liquids and gases are in a constant back-and-forth motion. The constant motion of the water molecules causes the dye particles to spread out, or diffuse, through the liquid.

3. Is the color of the water the same from top to bottom?
4. Where is most of the color located after an hour?
5. Where were most of the colored dye particles located in the beginning of the experiment?

3. No. In the early stages, the color will be darker at the bottom.

4. It should be fairly evenly distributed throughout the beaker.

5. In the immediate area of the crystal.

The molecules of liquids and gases are always moving. The motion of the molecules in a liquid will cause dye particles to

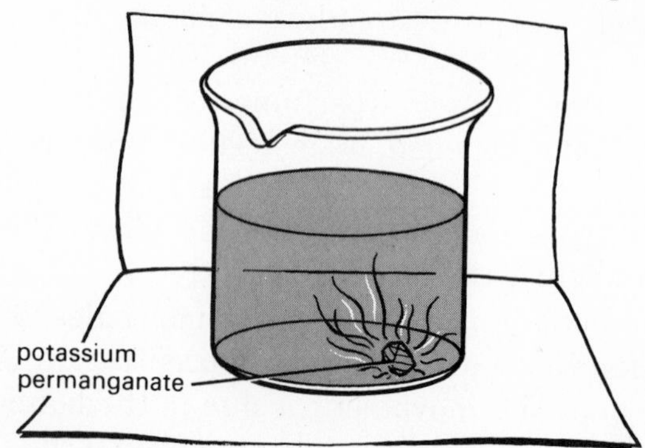

13-4. A crystal of potassium permanganate in a beaker of water illustrates diffusion.

6. Yes. Molecular movement is continually going on but its effects cannot be seen since the dye is by this time evenly distributed throughout the water.

spread out. In spreading out, they form a random pattern. The final result appears as a uniform purple color. And this represents complete mixing due to the action of moving molecules.

6. After an hour's time, do you think the purple dye particles are still being moved about the beaker by the action of the water molecules? Explain your answer.

You should now be able to

Describe movement of molecules in a solution.

Relate the movement of dye particles to the motion of the molecules of water.

Predict the diffusion of dye particles away from an area of high concentration to an area of low concentration.

Diffusion

The dissolving of the dye potassium permanganate in water shows how particles spread out in a water solution. The same thing happens when a sugar cube is placed in a cup of water. The sugar dissolves and spreads evenly throughout the water.

By diffusion, molecules spread out from an area of high concentration to an area of low concentration. Diffusion depends on the continuous movement of molecules. Raising the temperature increases the molecular motion, causing diffusion to take place at a faster rate.

When tea is made using a tea bag, the tea dissolves and passes through the holes in the bag. Tea molecules would not be able to escape the bag if the holes were too small. A thin layer or membrane, such as the tea bag, which allows molecules to pass through it is called **permeable** [PUR-me-uh-bul]. An **impermeable** membrane allows nothing at all to pass through it. (See Figure 13-5.)

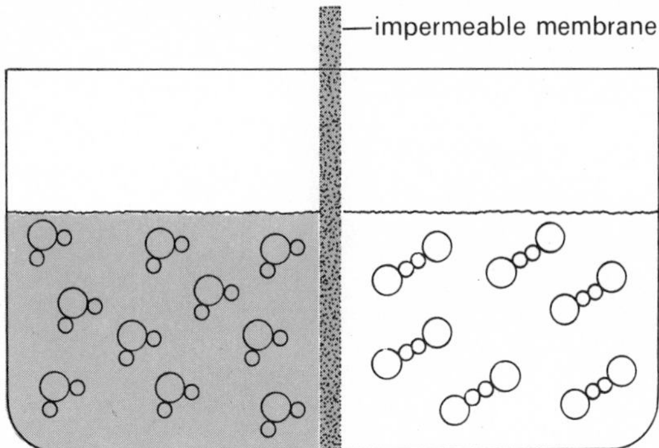

13-5. The impermeable membrane does not allow the molecules to spread out evenly in the container.

If a membrane allows *some* materials to pass through but not others, it is called **semipermeable**. It is selectively permeable. Living cells have membranes that regulate the kinds of materials that can enter or leave the cell. The movement of water through a semipermeable membrane is called **osmosis**. In the next problem, you will study the screening effect of a semipermeable membrane.

Problem 13-2 What materials can diffuse through a semipermeable membrane?

Purpose To study the effects of a semipermeable membrane on the movement of starch and sugar.

Materials

Soak dialysis tubing before class. If tubing has not been soaked, it will be very difficult to open.

- dialysis tubing, 15 cm (2)
- beakers, 250-ml (2)
- cotton string, 15 cm (2 pieces)
- starch and water mixture, 20 ml
- graduated cylinder
- Bunsen burner
- test-tube holder
- glucose solution, 20 ml
- Benedict's solution
- marking pen
- paper clips (2)
- iodine solution
- rubber bands (2)

Procedure

Part One: Preparing a semipermeable membrane

A. Obtain a piece of cellophane dialysis tubing that is soaking in water. Tie one end of the tubing shut with five turns of the string

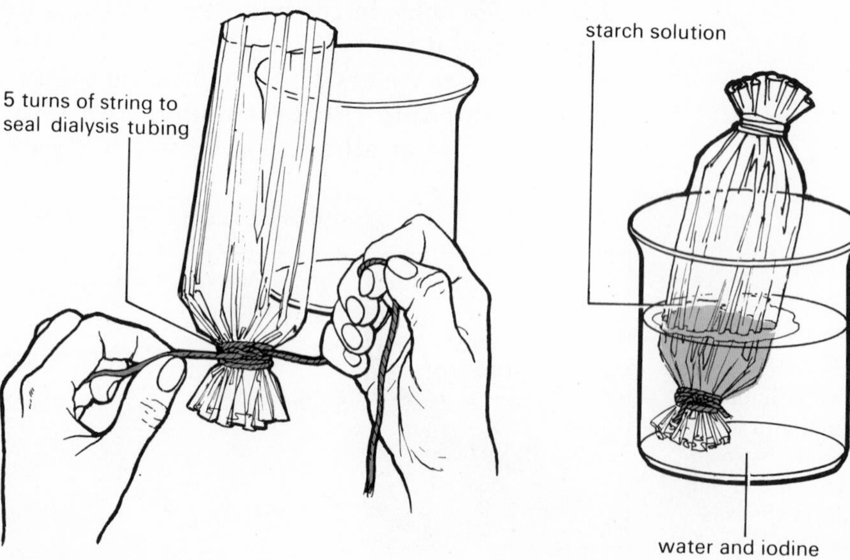

13-6. Preparing a semipermeable membrane.

about 1 or 2 cm from the end of the tubing. Draw the string as tight as possible and secure it with a tight knot. Rub the untied end between your thumb and forefinger to open it up.

B. Pour 20 ml of starch and water mixture into the tube. This should leave several centimeters empty at the top. Close the tube with a rubber band. Rinse the outside of the tube under running water to wash off any starch. Check for leaks.

C. Place the tube in a 250-ml beaker. Add water to the same level as the starch mixture in the tubing. (See Figure 13-6.) Then add about 5 drops of iodine solution to the water in the beaker, enough to turn the color a pale yellow. Label this beaker "starch."

Iodine, you remember, turns blue-black in the presence of starch. If the iodine changes color at once, the tube has a leak and both liquids must be discarded. Repeat the procedure until there is no leak. Set this beaker aside for later examination in Step J.

Caution students to use the proper technique for heating liquid in a test tube. They should wear safety goggles for this activity.

D. Make an identification test for the presence of glucose sugar. To get a positive test for glucose, put 5 ml of glucose in a test tube and add 5 drops of Benedict's solution. Use a test-tube holder to put the test tube in a flame. Move the tube back and forth

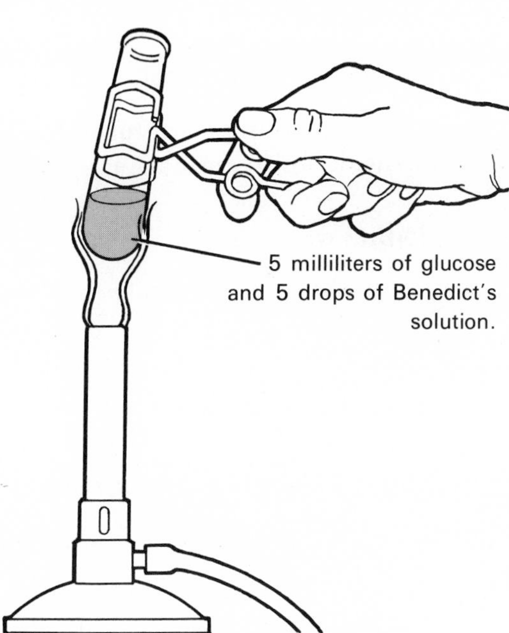

13-7. Heat Benedict's test solution at a low boil for at least three minutes. Be sure to keep the test tube pointed away from you and others.

through the flame until the solution boils. Keep the solution at a low boil for at least three minutes.

CAUTION: Keep the test tube pointed away from you and other people.

1. From blue to yellow-green to yellow-orange to red-orange.

1. What colors did the blue Benedict's solution turn as you heated the glucose solution?

Instruct students to be careful when handling the tube containing glucose, so that they do not spill any. They should return it to the beaker as soon as the water sample has been taken from the beaker.

E. Obtain another piece of dialysis tubing. As before, tie one end with string and open the other end. Pour 20 ml of glucose solution into the tube. Fold over the top and close with a rubber band. Rinse the outside in running water. Be sure to check for leaks around the string.

F. Put the tube in an empty 250-ml beaker. Add water to a level even with the solution in the tube. *Do not add iodine* to this beaker. (Iodine is not a test for glucose.) Mark this beaker "sugar."

G. Test the water at the bottom of the beaker for glucose right away. (Follow the procedure in Step D, but put water from the bottom of the beaker in the test tube instead of glucose.) A positive test will indicate a leak in the tube. If a leak is discovered, discard the contents and repeat Steps E, F, and G.

H. Allow the tubes to sit in their beakers for about twenty minutes. Then remove the tube of glucose but *do not discard*. Pour about 10 ml of the water from the beaker into a test tube. Test for the presence of glucose.

2. Yes.

2. Was glucose sugar present in the water you tested?

I. Return the tube containing the glucose solution to the beaker. Set the beaker aside for examination again after 24 hours (Step M).

J. Observe the iodine water in the "starch" beaker.

3. Is the color of the water in the beaker still the pale yellow color of iodine and water?

3. Yes.

Have students put their names on beakers so that they will know which ones to claim the next class.

K. Place both beakers, "starch" and "sugar" in a spot where they will be undisturbed for 24 hours.

Part Two: Testing for diffusion through a membrane

L. After 24 hours, again observe the "starch" tube and beaker.

4. The color inside the tube is now blue-black.

4. How does the color inside the "starch" tube compare with the pale yellow color of iodine and water?

5. No.

6. Iodine.

7. They are too large to fit through the holes in the membrane.

5. Did the starch particles pass through the membrane?
6. What molecule must be small enough to pass through the porous membrane?
7. Suggest a reason why starch particles could not get through the porous membrane.

By diffusion, molecules of dissolved material tend to move away from areas where they concentrated to areas where they are less concentrated. However, if a porous membrane separates them, the movement is determined by the size of the molecules as well as by concentration.

M. Test the water outside the tube in the "sugar" beaker after 24 hours.

8. Red-orange.

9. Yes.

10. Glucose molecules must be smaller than starch molecules.

8. What color is Benedict's solution after heating?
9. Did glucose move out of the sealed tube?
10. How does the size of glucose molecules compare to the size of starch particles, according to your results?

The cellophane dialysis tubing acts in somewhat the same manner as a living cell membrane. It selects materials on the basis of size, letting small molecules pass through but stopping larger ones.

You should now be able to

Test for the presence of starch with iodine.

Test for the presence of glucose with Benedict's solution.

Relate size of particles to their movement through a semipermeable membrane.

Compare the size of a starch particle to a glucose molecule.

Osmosis in living cells

The results of the last problem showed that a cellophane membrane allows some materials to pass through but not others. Membranes of living cells act much the same way. They prevent large molecules from entering or leaving the cells. They let smaller molecules come and go.

Certain large molecules must be broken down before they can enter individual cells. Chemical substances called **enzymes** are produced by cells for this purpose. Enzymes break up large starch mole-

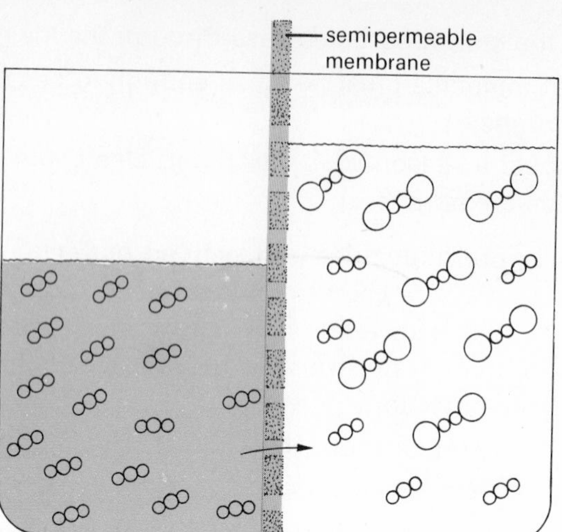

13-8. Membranes of living cells allow some molecules to pass through while stopping others.

cules into small sugar molecules. The sugar molecules may then enter the cell. There they are combined with oxygen molecules to release energy through respiration. Membranes play a very important role in cells.

In the next problem you will observe how different concentrations of salt affect the water content of cells. The effect occurs because cell membranes allow water molecules to pass through them by the process of osmosis.

Problem 13-3 How does the concentration of a salt affect osmosis in a plant cell?

Purpose To observe the effect different concentrations of salt solution have upon the water content of a cell.

Materials
freshly cut potato slices, 0.5 cm thick (3)
marking pen
distilled water
salt
beakers, 250-ml (3)

Procedure

A. Label the three beakers "1", "2", and "3."

B. To Beaker 1, add 100 ml of distilled water.

C. To Beaker 2, add 100 ml of a 1% salt-water solution. (One gram of salt dissolved in 99 ml of water.)

D. To Beaker 3, add 100 ml of a 5% salt-water solution. (Five grams of salt dissolved in 95 ml of water.)

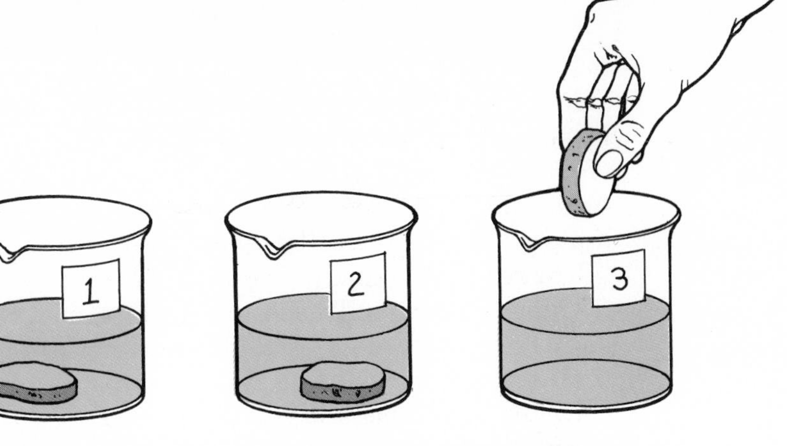

13-9. Place a slice of potato into each of three beakers.

E. Place a slice of potato in each beaker. Use slices about the same thickness. After ten minutes, feel each slice.

1. Which beaker is the control for this experiment?
2. Do the potato slices in Beakers 2 and 3 feel the same as the control?
3. Are the slices in Beakers 2 and 3 spongy or more rigid than those in Beaker 1?
4. The only difference between Beakers 2 and 3 is the amount of salt added. Do the different concentrations of salt have any effect on the slices?

If water leaves a plant cell, the cell becomes more flexible. A plant wilts when this happens. This change in the rigidity of the plant is a measure of the **turgor pressure**.

5. Based on its flexibility, which slice seems to have *less* water in the cytoplasm?
6. Which slice seems to have *more* water in the cytoplasm?
7. What effect does the concentration of salt solution around cells have on water content within the cells?

1. Beaker 1, containing only distilled water.

2. No. Both slices in Beakers 2 and 3 feel softer than the slice in Beaker 1.

3. Spongy.

4. Yes. (The higher the concentration of salt, the spongier the slice becomes.)

5. The slice in Beaker 3.

6. The slice in Beaker 1.

7. The higher the salt concentration around cells, the less water remains within the cells.

You should now be able to

Determine the effect of salt on the flexibility of potato slices.

Relate the concentration of salt solution around cells to the changes that occur in the cells of a potato.

Relate the rigidity or stiffness of a plant to the amount of water present in the cells of the plant.

Effects of osmosis on cytoplasm

Osmosis takes place when water molecules diffuse through a thin membrane. In Problem 13-3, you put a high concentration of salt outside some cell membranes. The solution inside the cells had a very low concentration of salt. The cells contained a higher concentration of water. So water molecules left the cells by osmosis. They diffused from a place (inside the cells) where they were more concentrated, to a place (outside the cells) where they were less concentrated.

The result was that water left the cytoplasm of the cells faster than it entered the cells. This loss of water from a cell is called **plasmolysis**. The cells that lost great amounts of water felt rough because very little besides the cell wall was present.

Living cells constantly exchange water with the outside environment by osmosis. High concentrations of salt and sugar stop bacterial growth on food. When bacterial cells land on heavily salted fish, or on jelly containing much sugar, water leaves the cytoplasm of the bacteria. The bacterial cells die. This is the same action that took place on the potato slices.

Osmosis into and out of cells depends on the number and kind of molecules present on both sides of the membrane. The next problem deals with osmosis in a plant root.

Problem 13-4 How may osmosis in a plant root be measured?

Purpose To determine the rate of osmosis in a carrot root from sample data and graphs.

Materials None. You will be provided with the results of an experiment that has been previously completed.

Procedure Some young scientists wanted to find out how long it took water entering the roots of a plant to reach the leaves through the stem. These scientists carried out the following procedure to gather information to answer their question.

A. A carrot was hollowed out and filled with molasses. A rubber stopper, with a glass tube, was inserted into the opening and sealed. (See Figure 13-10.)

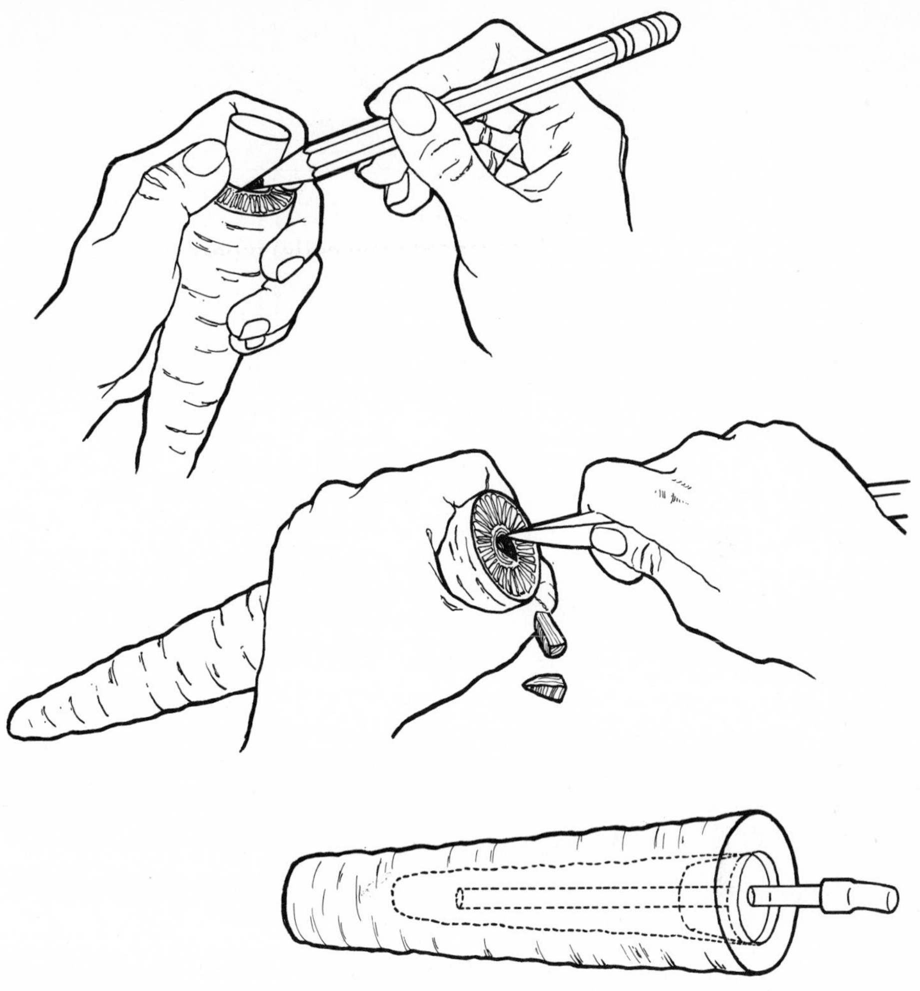

13-10. Preparing a carrot for osmosis experiment.

B. The carrot with tube was placed in a beaker of water and observed for 72 hours. The experimental setup is shown in Figure 13-11 (page 246).

C. The results of the experiment are shown in Table 13-1 (page 247).

1. Water.

1. Molecules of what substance must be moving through the carrot to cause the liquid to rise in the tube?

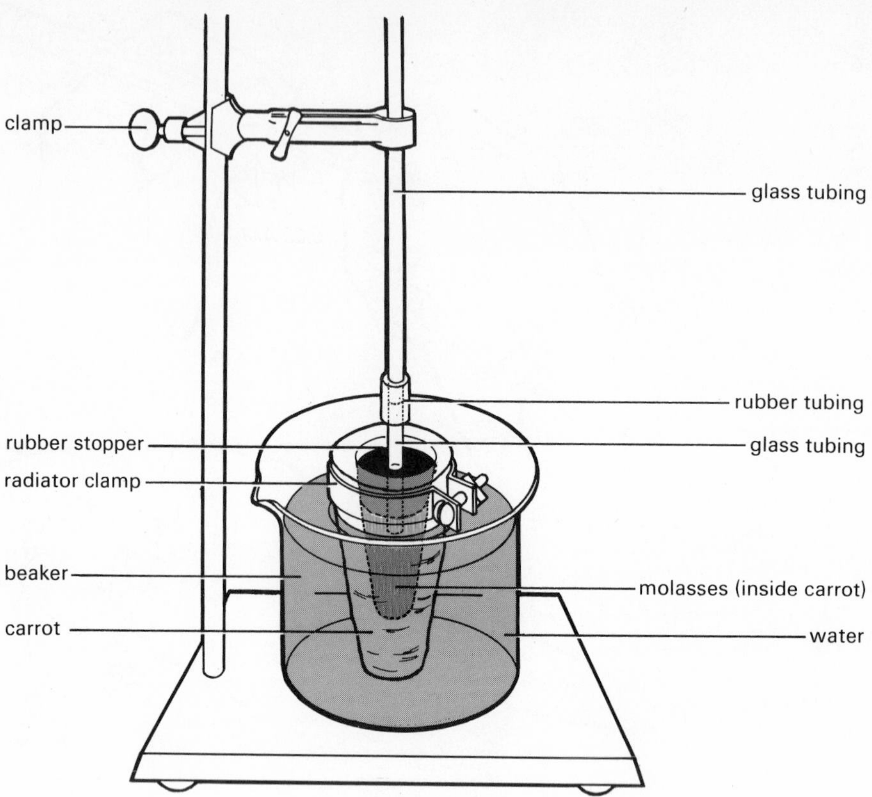

13-11. Carrot assembly in beaker, supported with a ring stand.

D. In your notebook, prepare a line graph to show the rate of osmosis. Label the horizontal axis "Time in Hours" and the vertical axis "Height in Centimeters." Use Figure 13-12 (page 248) as a model for your graph.

2. Not quite at the same rate.

2. Did the molecules move through the carrot at the same rate throughout the experiment? (If the line connecting the points on the graph is nearly straight, the process of osmosis occurred at about the same rate throughout. A curved line would show a changing rate of osmosis.)

3. It got slower.

3. Did the rate of osmosis stay the same, get faster, or get slower over the three days of the experiment?

4. 150 cm; 230 cm; 280 cm.

4. How many centimeters did the fluid rise the first 24 hours? After 48 hours? After 72 hours?

5. $280 \div 72 \cong 3.9$ cm/h.

5. What is the rate of osmosis (in centimeters per hour) over the 72 hours?

TABLE 13-1 RECORD OF LIQUID MOVEMENT IN A CARROT

Date	*Time*	*Hours*	*Liquid Height in cm*
Nov. 20	*8:00 AM*	*0*	*0*
	9:00 AM	*1*	*6*
	10:00 AM	*2*	*13*
	11:00 AM	*3*	*21*
	12:00 Noon	*4*	*27*
	1:00 PM	*5*	*35*
	2:00 PM	*6*	*41*
	3:00 PM	*7*	*48*
Nov. 21	*8:00 AM*	*24*	*150*
	9:00 AM	*25*	*154*
	10:00 AM	*26*	*159*
	11:00 AM	*27*	*162*
	12:00 Noon	*28*	*166*
	1:00 PM	*29*	*169*
	2:00 PM	*30*	*173*
	3:00 PM	*31*	*178*
Nov. 22	*8:00 AM*	*48*	*230*
	9:00 AM	*49*	*232*
	10:00 AM	*50*	*235*
	11:00 AM	*51*	*237*
	12:00 Noon	*52*	*239*
	1:00 PM	*53*	*240*
	2:00 PM	*54*	*243*
	3:00 PM	*55*	*245*
Nov. 23	*8:00 AM*	*72*	*280*
	9:00 AM	*73*	*281*
	10:00 AM	*74*	*281*
	11:00 AM	*75*	*283*
	12:00 Noon	*76*	*284*
	1:00 PM	*77*	*285*
	2:00 PM	*78*	*285*
	3:00 PM	*79*	*285*

6. $14{,}000 \div 3.9 \cong$ 3590 hours; or about 149 days.

7. Yes. (The water became brown colored.) Test with Benedict's solution.

6. Using your answer to question 5, how long would it take to reach the top of the General Sherman sequoia tree at 140 meters (convert to centimeters)?

7. Do you see any evidence that molasses molecules passed through the carrot into the water in the beaker? How could you test the water for molasses?

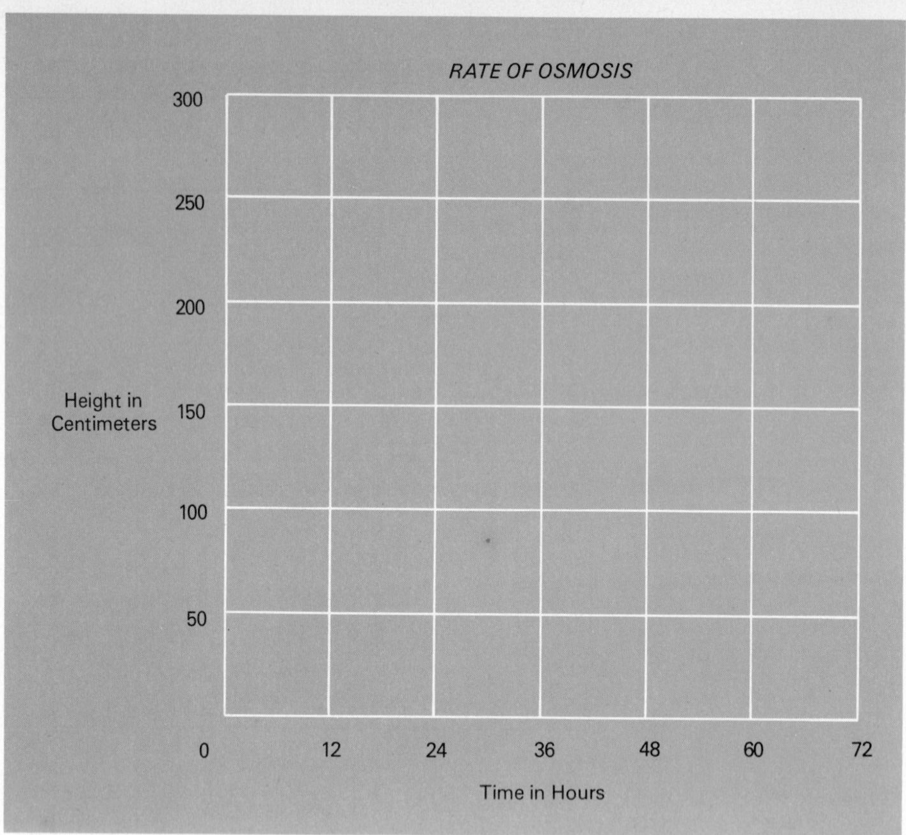

13-12. Prepare a graph to show the rate of osmosis in a carrot.

8. Water.

8. Based upon the number of each kind of molecule that gets through the carrot cell membranes, which molecule (molasses or water) must be smaller?

9. Less concentrated.

9. Did the molasses inside the carrot become more concentrated or less concentrated?

10. It decreased very much.

10. Concentration of molecules determines the rate of diffusion and also the rate of osmosis. Suppose the rate of osmosis became very slow. What must have happened to the concentration of molasses inside the carrot compared to outside the carrot?

You should now be able to

Calculate the rate of osmosis in a carrot root.

Prepare a graph to show the rate of osmosis.

Determine the direction of movement of molasses and water molecules in an osmosis experiment.

Movement of liquids in plant stems

There is a constant exchange of dissolved food and waste materials into and out of cells. When water molecules are outside a cell membrane and sugar molecules are inside, both molecules try to move through the membrane. But the sugar molecules are slowed down by the cell membrane more than the water molecules are. So the water molecules move inward more rapidly than sugar molecules move outward. As a result, a pressure develops.

Root pressure is brought about by this osmotic movement of water molecules. It helps make liquids rise in plants. The stem acts as a pipeline to deliver water, food, and minerals to the leaves. It also transports food materials from the leaves to the rest of the plant.

The functions of xylem and phloem tissues mentioned earlier have been identified by experiments with live plants. When xylem cells are destroyed at a particular spot, water and minerals accumulate *below* the destroyed cells. Destroying phloem cells causes a buildup of food materials *above* the spot. In this way the main functions of xylem and phloem cells were determined. In Problem 13-5 you will examine some of the cells through which water moves in a celery stem.

Problem 13-5 Where is water transported in a celery plant?

Purpose To observe the upward movement of liquids in a celery stem and to locate the tube cells that carry the liquid.

Materials

celery stalk, large	microscope	dropper
red ink, washable	razor blade, single-edged	glass slide
beaker or jar	pan	cover glass
paper towel		

Procedure

Part One: Preparing the celery stalk

A. Select a fresh celery stalk with several leaves on it.

B. Place the lower part of the stalk in a pan of water with the end of the stalk under water.

Instruct students to cut the celery stalk under water for best results.

C. As shown in Figure 13-13, cut about 2 cm from the bottom of the stalk. Add water to a depth of about 3 cm in the beaker or jar. Now add 2 droppersful of washable red ink to the water.

D. Put the celery stalk into the colored water. Let it stand for 24 hours.

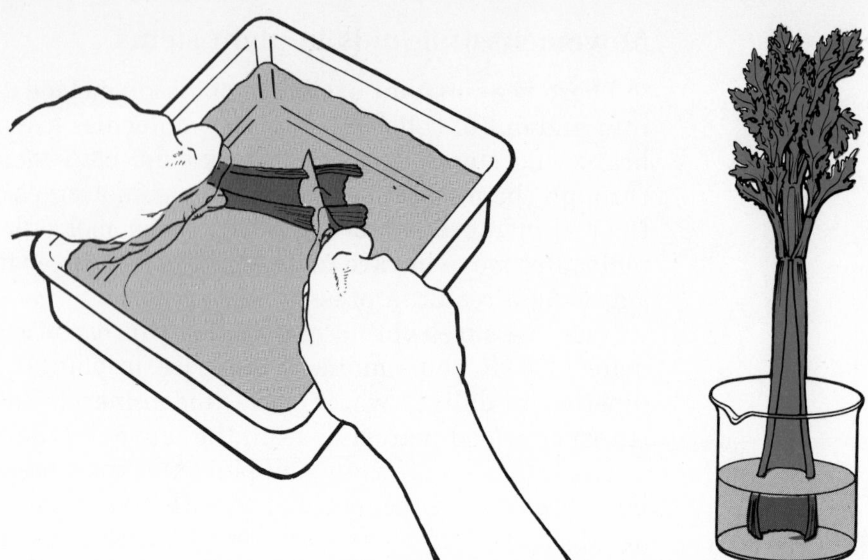

13-13. With the end of the celery stalk under water, cut off about 2 centimeters from the bottom. Then place the stalk in red ink solution.

Part Two: Examining the stem

E. Examine the stem and leaves after 24 hours.

1. Did the ink move up the stem?
2. What evidence is there that the ink reached the leaves?

1. Yes.
2. Red (or other) color in leaf veins.

F. Cut the stalk in half — that is, cut the top leaves off the stem. Examine the cut end of the stem section.

3. Are the colored areas located throughout the stem or only in small areas?
4. Are these colored areas located near the center or near the outside of the stem?

3. Only in small areas.
4. Near the outside.

G. Cut off a slice of stem about 2 cm long. With your fingernail or a razor blade, carefully separate one of the colored tubes from the slice. Place the colored tube on a damp paper towel.

H. Use a razor blade to split the colored tube lengthwise. (See Figure 13-14.) Make the lengthwise cut so that a wedge of the tube is obtained.

I. Prepare a wet mount slide of the thinnest section of the tube.

J. Observe the thinnest section of the tube under both low power and high power.

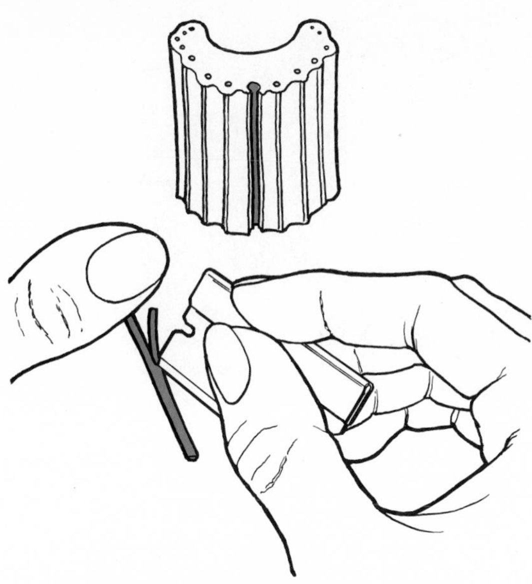

13-14. Using a razor blade, split a tube containing ink lengthwise.

5. Drawings should be similar to Figure 13-15 (p. 252) for xylem cells.

5. Draw the tube cells as they appear under high power.

In a plant, fluids move up and down the stem in tubelike cells. The water from the roots must be moved to the leaves for use in food-making. Then the food produced by the plant must be moved from the leaves to all other cells in the plant.

6. Thick.

7. These xylem cells have thick walls to keep the water from leaking out.

8. Students may be able to find the thin-walled phloem cells.

6. Do the tube cells containing the red color have thick or thin outer walls?

7. How are the walls of these cells specialized to conduct water upward through the stem of the plant?

8. Did you find any thin-walled tube cells under the microscope? These cells transport food made in the leaves to other parts of the plant.

You should now be able to

Trace the path of water through a celery plant.

Prepare a wet mount slide to show the conducting cells of a celery stem.

Identify the cells that transport liquids in plants.

Relate the structure of cells to their function.

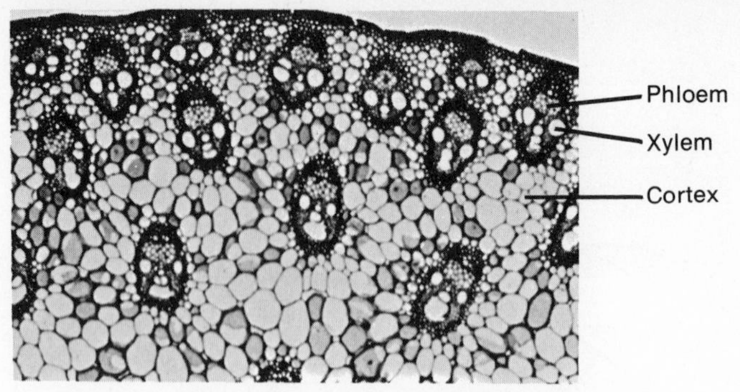

13-15. Cross section of a celery stem.

Courtesy Carolina Biological Supply Company

Capillary action in plants

Like soda straws bundled together, xylem and phloem cells transport materials in plants. When water is contained in a narrow tube, it moves upward through a process called **capillary action**. Capillary action occurs when molecules of a liquid are attracted to the sides of a tube and are lifted higher than the liquid surface. The smaller the tube size, the higher the water rises. (See Figure 13-16.) Narrow tube cells in plant tissues help lift water and dissolved materials upward through the stem.

When water evaporates from a leaf by transpiration, the pressure in the xylem cells is reduced. The reduced pressure at the leaves permits the greater pressure in the roots and stem to raise the column of water even more. Transpiration, osmosis, and capillary action all work to move large amounts of water through the stem and leaves and into the air. In Problem 13-6 you will observe the amount of water lost by a plant through transpiration.

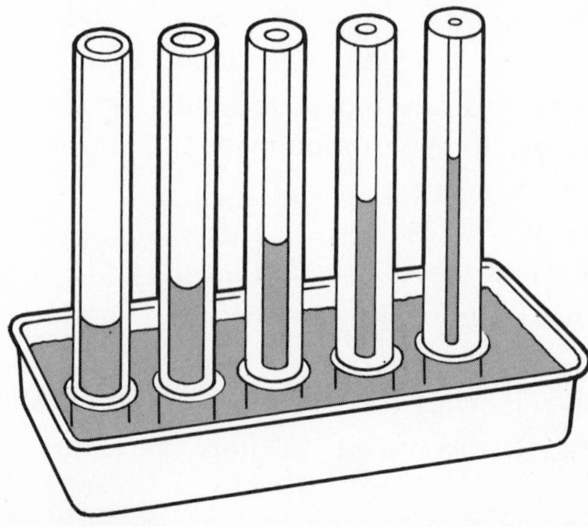
13-16. Water in a narrow tube rises through a process called capillary action. The narrower the tube, the higher the water rises.

Problem 13-6 How much water is lost to the air by a plant?

Purpose To measure the amount of water lost by a leafy plant stem.

Materials

leafy plant stem	metric ruler	burner stand
rubber tubing, 30 cm	masking tape	test-tube clamps (2)
glass tubing, 30 cm	pan, large	test tube, small

Procedure

A. Fill the large pan with water. Select a leafy plant stem large enough to fit tightly into the rubber tubing to be used. Place the stem end of the leafy plant below the surface of the water. Cut off a thin section, keeping the stem below the water. Leave the stem in the pan and discard the thin section.

B. Carefully connect the length of glass tubing to one end of the rubber tubing. Put the other end of the rubber tubing below the surface of the water in the pan. Move the tubing through the water to be sure all air bubbles are out.

C. Keeping the stem and tubing under water, attach the rubber tubing to the stem. (See Figure 13-17.)

D. As you remove the plant and tubing from the water, hold the end of the glass tubing above the plant. This will help to remove any air bubbles that may still be left in the rubber tubing.

Remind students to take the care necessary to remove all the air from the glass tubing.

13-17. Attach the rubber tubing to the plant stem, keeping it under water.

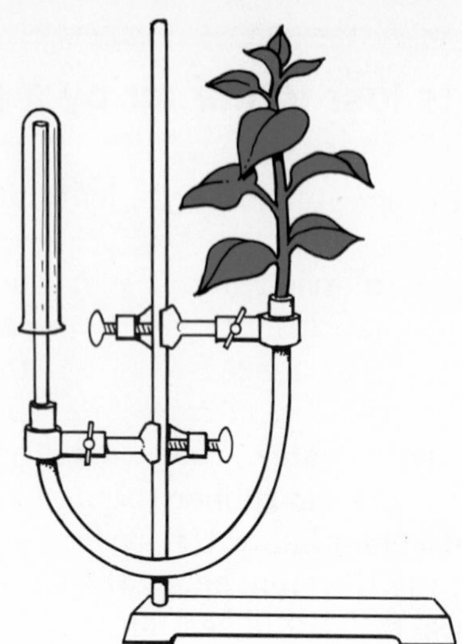

13-18. Setup showing plant stem and leaves with tubing attached.

E. Attach the plant to a stand as shown in Figure 13-18. If a stand is not available, tape the plant to the wall. Be sure that the glass tubing is in a vertical position.

F. Use a piece of tape to mark the water level in the glass tubing.

G. Put a small test tube over the end of the glass tubing to reduce evaporation. Put the setup aside overnight.

H. Observe the setup after 24 hours.

1. Did the level of water in the tube change?
2. Where do you think the water went?

1. Yes. (The water in the tube decreased.)

2. Into the plant through the stem.

A living plant always has enough sugar in its cells to bring in water by osmosis. This absorbed water is used in the leaves to make food during the daylight hours.

3. What cells are used to carry the water from roots to the stem and on to the leaves?

3. Xylem cells. (Students may simply call them tube cells.)

Day and night, the plant continuously moves water to the leaves. Since the plant absorbs more water at the roots than it can possibly use, some must be lost.

4. What structures found in the leaf epidermis could let this excess water out?
5. From the amount of water the leafy plant stem absorbed from the glass tube, only a small amount was used to make food. What do you think happened to the rest of the water that was absorbed and transported to the leaves?

4. Stomata.

5. Some of it was used for cellular activities. A lot of it was released into the air by the stomata.

You should now be able to

Measure the amount of water lost by a green plant.
Relate absorption of water to osmosis in the stem.
Relate water loss to the stomata of the leaves.
Predict the type of cells used for the movement of water in a plant stem.

---

1. (a) Diffusion is the movement of materials from an area where they are highly concentrated to an area where they are less concentrated. (b) Osmosis is a special kind of diffusion in which water moves through a membrane separating solutions of unequal concentration, equalizing the concentration of water molecules on both sides of the membrane.

2. Xylem.

3. Phloem.

4. The stoma.

5. Cell membrane.

6. Salt.

7. Epidermal cells.

8. Closely packed together; condensed.

9. Capillary action.

10. Transpiration is the process by which leaves release water into the air. Water is taken into the plant through the stem to the leaves, where some of it is released by the stomata.

Science terms

capillary action
concentrated
diffusion
enzymes
impermeable
molecule
osmosis
permeable
phloem
plasmolysis
root hairs
semipermeable
transpiration
turgor pressure
xylem

Review questions

1. Define the following:
   a. Diffusion
   b. Osmosis
2. What tissues provide the tubes necessary for the transporting of water in plant stems?
3. Through what tissue is manufactured food transported downward in plants?
4. Through which leaf structure does evaporation occur?
5. What structure keeps the contents of a cell inside the cell?
6. Name one substance that may cause the contents of a cell to undergo plasmolysis (water loss).
7. In which cells are root hairs found?
8. What does it mean when molecules are called concentrated?
9. Name the process by which water rises in a narrow tube.
10. Explain the process of transpiration.

Check your understanding

See Teacher's Guide section for answers to Questions 11-20.

11. Describe how the process of diffusion causes particles in solution to spread out.
12. How is diffusion related to osmosis?
13. How does a cell membrane function in the process of osmosis?

14. Does osmosis always continue at the same rate? Explain.
15. The cytoplasm within a plant cell will shrink if the cell is placed in a concentrated salt solution. Why?
16. What is meant by permeable and semipermeable membranes?
17. Celery in water becomes firm and crisp. By what process does water enter the celery cells?
18. Of what importance are root hairs?
19. When plants are transplanted, a ball of soil should be kept around the root system. How does this procedure protect the root hairs?
20. What would happen if the large amount of water lost by the leaves of a plant were not replaced in the plant?

Chapter 14 Photosynthesis

Chapter-opening photo of fern fronds provides a macrocosmic view of the "photosynthesis factory."

In early Greece, the scholar Aristotle said that plants received all their food directly from the soil. That idea seemed so logical that it was accepted for hundreds of years and may still be believed by many people today. But scientists' understanding of how plants get their food has been greatly clarified since the days of Aristotle.

In the 1800s a Belgian scientist, Jan van Helmont, decided to test Aristotle's ideas. Twenty centuries had passed since Aristotle had made his statement before anyone tried to test it scientifically!

Van Helmont planted a 5-pound tree in 200 pounds of soil that he had carefully dried in an oven. Five years later the tree weighed 164 pounds. It had gained 159 pounds. But the soil weighed only 2 ounces less than it had to begin with!

The gain in weight of the tree was obvious. But where the additional material had come from was a mystery to van Helmont. And for almost another 200 years, no one understood. Then scientists discov-

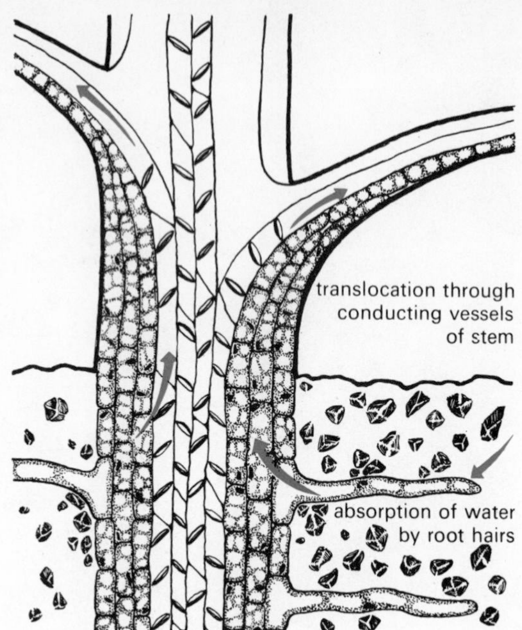

14-1. Water, one of the raw materials of photosynthesis, enters the roots by osmosis.

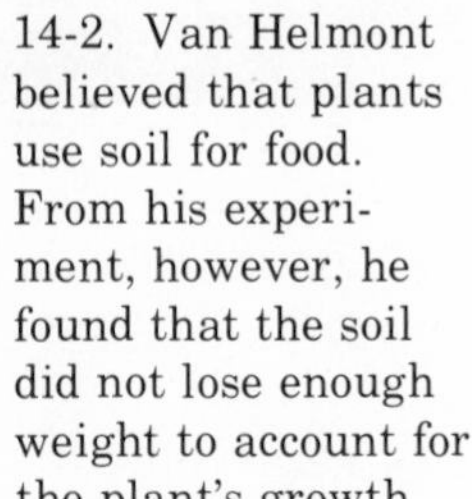

14-2. Van Helmont believed that plants use soil for food. From his experiment, however, he found that the soil did not lose enough weight to account for the plant's growth.

ered what plants had been doing for millions of years. Plants had been making food by a process called **photosynthesis** [fote-uh-SIN-thuh-siss].

Photosynthesis in green plants makes use of two simple compounds. These are water and carbon dioxide. Both compounds are found in large quantities on the earth. Water enters the plant by osmosis through the roots and is carried through the stem to the leaves. Once the water reaches the leaves, it moves into the cells by osmosis. In the leaf cells, it is used in the photosynthetic process.

Carbon dioxide is found in the air. It accounts for about 0.03 percent of dry air. In Problem 7-1, you examined the stomata in leaves. These tiny openings permit air containing carbon dioxide gas to enter the leaf. The carbon dioxide then enters the cells.

Thus, two compounds necessary for photosynthesis are brought together in a leaf cell. But no photosynthesis can occur without the presence of one more ingredient. That is the chemical compound called **chlorophyll** [KLOR-uh-fill].

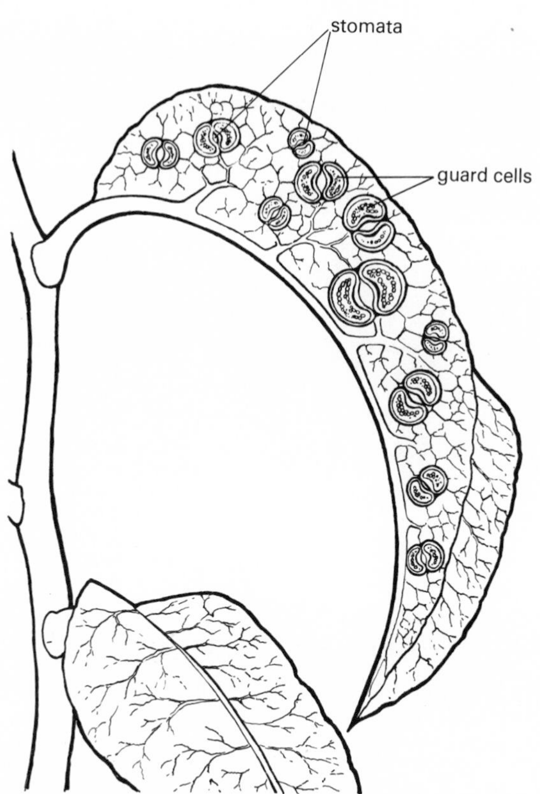

14-3. Air containing carbon dioxide enters the leaf through stomata.

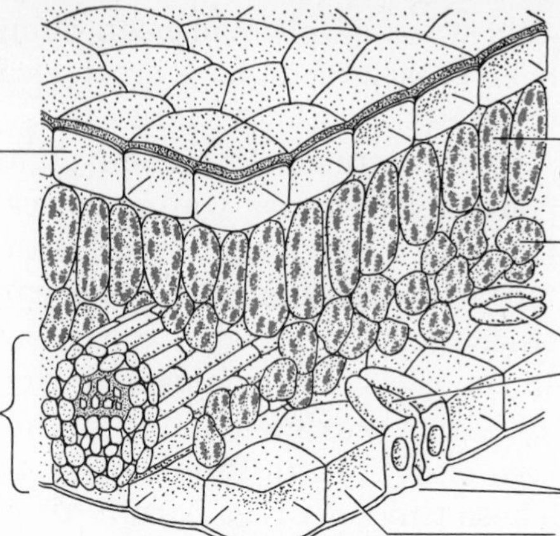

14-4. Cross section of a leaf showing the many chloroplasts of the palisade layer. The palisade layer is where most photosynthesis occurs.

Chlorophyll is the green pigment found in the chloroplasts of a cell. You examined the palisade cells of leaves in Problem 7-2. You saw that those cells contained many chloroplasts. It is in the palisade cells that most photosynthesis takes place.

Photosynthesis takes place only in the presence of light. Light energy must be absorbed by the leaves before they can make sugar and other compounds from carbon dioxide and water.

Sunlight is composed of all colors of the spectrum. When you see a color, such as the green of a plant, it means that the plant has absorbed all colors *except* the green. The green is reflected back. You could try growing plants under different color lights. The plant that grows the best would indicate which color in sunlight is used to best advantage by the plant during photosynthesis.

If students are unfamiliar with chemical symbols and equations, you will need to spend some time explaining what the equations mean.

Photosynthesis, then, is the interaction of carbon dioxide (CO_2) and water (H_2O) in a cell. The process is assisted by chlorophyll in the presence of light. One of the products is sugar ($C_6H_{12}O_6$), a substance the plant can use for food. Here is the equation commonly used to describe the process —

$$6CO_2 + 6H_2O \xrightarrow[\text{chlorophyll}]{\text{sunlight}} C_6H_{12}O_6 + 6O_2$$

Six molecules of carbon dioxide unite with six molecules of water in the presence of sunlight and chlorophyll. One molecule of glucose sugar and six molecules of oxygen gas are produced. Scientists now know that several other products are produced at the same time. Photosynthesis is much more complicated than the above equation shows.

Most green plants make more sugar during the day than they need. The excess sugar is changed to starch, which is then stored. At night, photosynthesis cannot be carried out. So, at night, some of the starch is converted back to sugar, which the plant can use for energy.

A plant requires oxygen for the process of respiration. In this process, sugar is combined with oxygen, and carbon dioxide, water, and energy are released. Respiration in green plants goes on all the time, day and night, just as it does in animals. Happily, the oxygen produced by photosynthesis is more than plants need for their own respiration. The extra oxygen is used by nongreen plants and animals. Most of the oxygen in the air surrounding earth was probably produced by the algae in the oceans during the process of photosynthesis.

Problem 14-1 What is one kind of food produced by green plants?

Purpose To test for the presence of glucose in a green plant.

Materials

Benedict's solution	test tubes (2)	green onion tops
glucose test solution	test-tube holder	Bunsen burner

Procedure You will be testing green plants for the simple sugar called glucose. Review Step D in Problem 13-2 before you begin.

1. What color change occurs when blue Benedict's solution is heated in the presence of glucose?

1. Color changes from blue to green to red-orange.

A. Cut four small pieces from the top of a green onion. Put the four pieces into a test tube. Add enough water to cover the pieces. Add

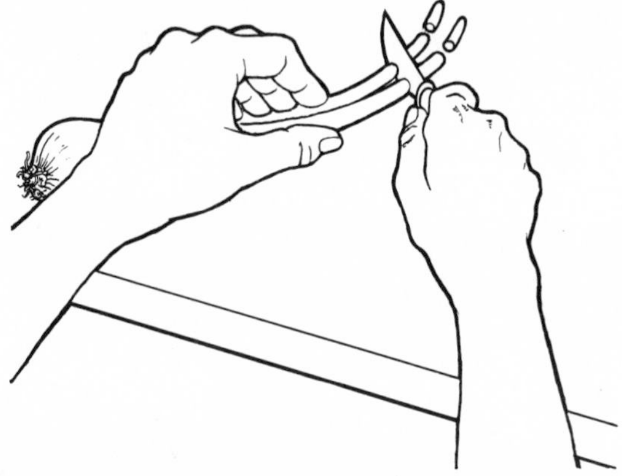

14-5. The green tops of onions are cut off and tested for the presence of simple sugar.

Warn students to be careful when heating liquids in a test tube. Remind them to point the test tubes away from themselves and others.

2. Light blue.

3. Probably red-orange.

4. Yes.

5. Light blue.

6. It should again be red-orange.

7. Yes (though not as much as the leaves). A number of answers are possible for how it got there—through the tubes of the plant, by diffusion, or a combination of these.

8. Glucose was present in the white part of the onion.

9. Diffusion is the best answer, since the term osmosis refers only to the movement of water through membranes.

5 drops of Benedict's solution to the test tube. Bring to a boil, then continue boiling for about 3 minutes. Remember to keep the test tube pointed away from you and other people.

2. What was the color of the solution inside the test tube before heating?
3. What is the color of the solution inside the test tube after heating?
4. Glucose is the simple sugar produced in green plants by photosynthesis. Do the cells of the green top of the onion contain glucose?

B. Now cut four small pieces of the white part of the onion and put them into a test tube. Add water and Benedict's solution as directed in Step A. Boil for 3 minutes.

5. What was the color of the solution inside the test tube before heating?
6. What is the color of the solution inside the test tube after heating?
7. Do the cells of the white part of the onion contain glucose? If they do, how do you think the glucose got there?

Roots of plants are unable to produce food because they do not contain chlorophyll and are not exposed to light. But glucose is able to move easily through cell membranes, so it is found in all living cells. The cell uses the glucose as food by breaking it down into smaller compounds. This process produces energy.

8. What evidence did you find that shows that glucose is able to pass through cell membranes and move to different parts of the plant?
9. What is the process that involves the movement of materials through cell membranes?

You should now be able to

Test various parts of a green plant for the presence of glucose.

Relate the presence of glucose to the process of photosynthesis.

Describe the processes by which glucose is transported from the leaves to other parts of the plant.

Use of food in plants

The food made by a green plant is used by the plant for energy, growth, and tissue repair. The plant needs food in order to produce new leaves, stems, and roots. You have observed the rapid growth of cells at the tips of stems and roots. Many plants also produce new leaf buds every fall. All the food that is needed to produce fully developed leaves is stored in the plant all winter. The buds develop into leaves in early spring.

Most of the food stored in a leaf bud is in the form of starch. Compared to a starch molecule, glucose molecules have a simple structure. Hundreds of glucose units are linked together to form a starch molecule.

The potato, carrot, or onion that you eat is the part of the plant where food is stored. They taste different because each plant adds different chemicals to the stored food. People take advantage of the ability of plants to make and store food. They grow the plants and harvest them for their own needs.

Figure 14-6 shows an electron micrograph of a chloroplast, the food-making structure in green plants. Notice the labeling of *grana* (singular *granum*). These are the layered structures within a chloroplast where the chlorophyll is concentrated. Each granum contains several million molecules of chlorophyll.

In the next problem, you will test plants for one type of stored food. You will try to determine where and in what form the food is stored.

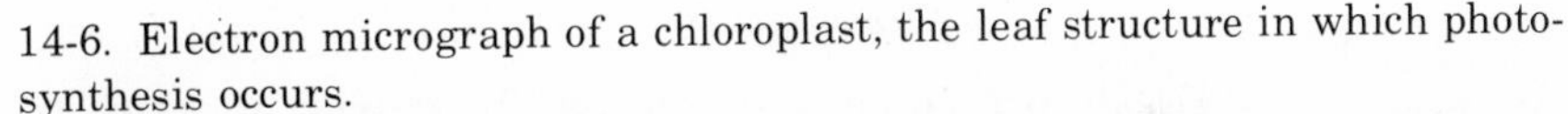

14-6. Electron micrograph of a chloroplast, the leaf structure in which photosynthesis occurs.

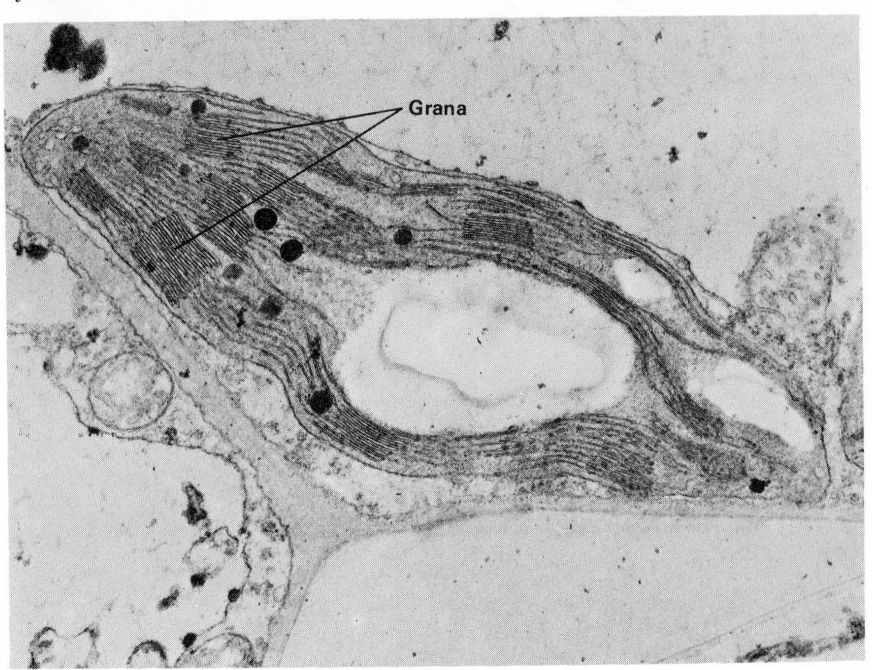

Problem 14-2 When do plant leaves contain starch?

Purpose To determine the effect of light on the presence of starch in leaves.

Materials

starch and water mixture	test tubes (4)	iodine solution
hot plate or hot-water bath	plants (2)	sugar solution
beakers, 250-ml (2)	petri dish	alcohol
test-tube rack	forceps	vegetable oil

Procedure

A. Review the iodine test for starch used in Problems 11-1 and 13-2. Repeat the test by adding about 5 drops of iodine solution to 2 ml of starch mixture.

1. Blue-black.

1. What color is found with a positive test for starch?

B. Test the effect of iodine on some other liquids. Test sugar solution, alcohol, water, and vegetable oil.

2. They shouldn't.

2. Do these other materials give positive tests for starch?

C. Select a healthy leaf from a plant that has been growing in the light for 24 hours.

D. Before you can test a leaf for starch, you need to remove the green pigment (chlorophyll). Put the leaf in a beaker, cover with about 2 cm of water, and boil. This boiling is necessary to soften the leaf by breaking down the cell walls.

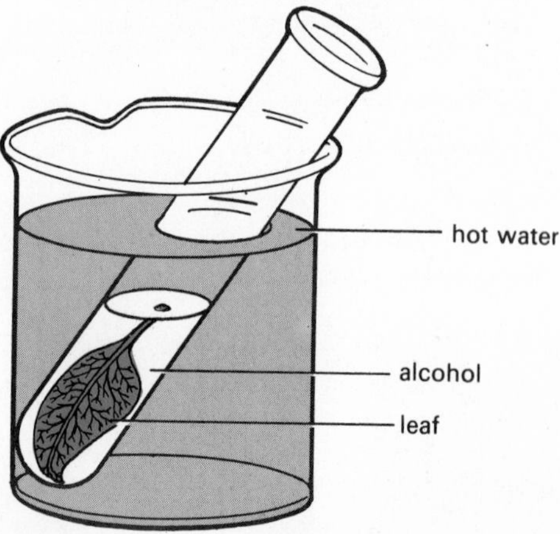

14-7. Removing the chlorophyll from a leaf by using alcohol.

Have *no* open flames around when using alcohol. Alcohol is highly flammable.

The leaf will not be destroyed by boiling in alcohol. Tell students to make sure that most of the green color is removed before taking the leaf out of the alcohol.

3. The leaf may be drawn in a rather mottled way. Parts of it could be black, indicating the presence of starch, while other parts may be the golden color of the iodine solution.

4. Yes. Blue-black color, due to the presence of starch.

5. Glucose.

6. They are too large to pass through the pores in the cell membrane.

7. Almost the entire leaf will be the yellow-brown of the iodine.

8. Yes. In darkness most starch disappears.

9. This permits the plant cells to store manufactured food for later use.

10. Glucose.

11. Light.

CAUTION: In Step E, be sure that you are in a well-ventilated area and away from all open flames. Alcohol fumes are highly flammable.

E. Remove the boiled leaf with forceps. Put it in a large test tube one-third full of alcohol. Warm the test tube in a beaker full of hot water. The water need not be boiling. (See Figure 14-7.)

F. Allow the leaf to stay in the alcohol about 5 minutes. The leaf should be almost white before you remove it.

G. Lay the leaf flat in an open petri dish. Cover the leaf with a small amount of iodine solution. After a few minutes, rinse the leaf with water and examine it for the presence of starch.

3. In your notebook, draw the leaf and shade in the areas that are the golden color of the iodine solution.
4. Is any color other than that of the iodine present? What is this color, if any?
5. A starch molecule is formed when hundreds of smaller molecules of a certain substance are linked together. What substance produced by photosynthesis might have been changed to starch in the leaf?
6. Recall the experiment you did in Problem 13-2, with starch and sugar in the dialysis tubing. Why do you think starch particles cannot move out of the cells?
7. In your notebook, draw the leaf and color the areas that are either yellow-brown or blue-black.

H. Select a healthy leaf from the plant that has been growing in the dark for 24 hours. Remove the chlorophyll and test for starch as directed in Steps D, E, F, and G.

8. Does the absence of light seem to change the amount of starch in a leaf?
9. Starch is unable to leave living cells. In what way might this be useful to the plant?
10. What smaller molecules, used to make the giant starch molecule, can be used for food by the plant grown in the dark?

Plants grown in the dark cannot undergo photosynthesis. So they lack glucose. In the dark, the stored starch is broken down and used to produce energy.

11. What factor tested in this experiment must be present for a green plant to carry out food-making activity?

You should now be able to

Test for the presence of starch with iodine solution.

Relate production of starch to exposure to light.

Predict whether glucose is being produced as indicated by the presence of starch.

Relate light to the process of photosynthesis.

Carbon dioxide and photosynthesis

What would happen to a plant if one of the factors needed for photosynthesis were removed? Take water, for example. Most people realize that if a plant is not watered it will wilt and die. The plant takes in water through its roots by osmosis. It transports the water to the leaves where it is used in photosynthesis or, if not needed, released into the air. What about carbon dioxide, the other compound necessary for photosynthesis?

In the next problem, you will remove most of the carbon dioxide from the air around a plant. Around a second plant, you will add more carbon dioxide than is usually found in the air. You will then test each plant for stored starch. The results should tell you which plant was carrying out photosynthesis and which one was using its stored starch.

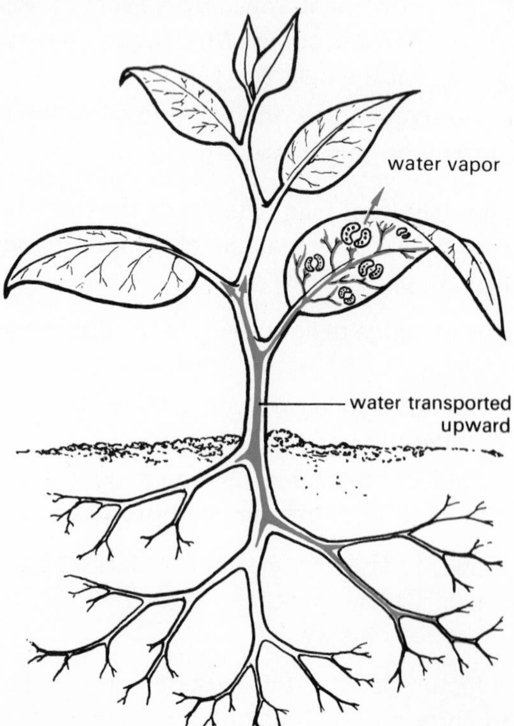

14-8. The passage of water from the soil, up through the stem to the leaves, and into the air.

Problem 14-3 How does carbon dioxide affect the production of starch?

Purpose To observe the effect of carbon dioxide on the production of starch in plant leaves.

Materials

In place of the gallon jars, you could use cardboard boxes. Just cut off the top and 2 sides, and cover with plastic wrap.

plants (2)
sodium hydroxide pellets
spoon or scoop
baby-food jars (2)
gallon jars, wide-mouth (2)
marble chips
iodine solution
dilute hydrochloric acid
test tubes
test-tube rack
alcohol
hot plate or hot-water bath
petri dish
graduated cylinder

Procedure

A. Obtain two of the plants kept in the dark for 24 hours.

CAUTION: In Step B, do not touch the pellets or let them come in contact with your skin. Wash your hands if you touch the pellets.

Caution students to be careful when using hydrochloric acid and sodium hydroxide. Students should wear aprons when they handle these materials.

B. Use a spoon or scoop to put 15 to 20 sodium hydroxide pellets in a baby-food jar. Replace the lid on the sodium hydroxide supply bottle immediately after removing the pellets. Place the jar with the pellets near one of the potted plants.

The sodium hydroxide will appear to be moist, shortly after air hits it. Through a chemical reaction, sodium hydroxide removes carbon dioxide from the air inside the jar. Carbon dioxide is a gas normally found in the air.

C. Cover both the jar and the plant with a wide-mouth gallon jar. (See Figure 14-9.) Label the gallon jar "1."

CAUTION: In Step D, do not get any acid on your hands. Wash your hands immediately if you do.

D. Put 15 to 20 marble chips in a second baby-food jar. Cover the chips with 10 ml of dilute hydrochloric acid (HCl). The hydrochloric acid reacts with the marble chips to release carbon dioxide gas.

E. Place the jar containing acid and marble chips next to the second potted plant. Cover both with another gallon jar. Label that gallon jar "2."

1. What substance is found in large amounts in Container 2, but removed from Container 1?

1. Carbon dioxide gas.

2. The drawing of the leaf from Container 2 should show the presence of more starch than the leaf from Container 1.

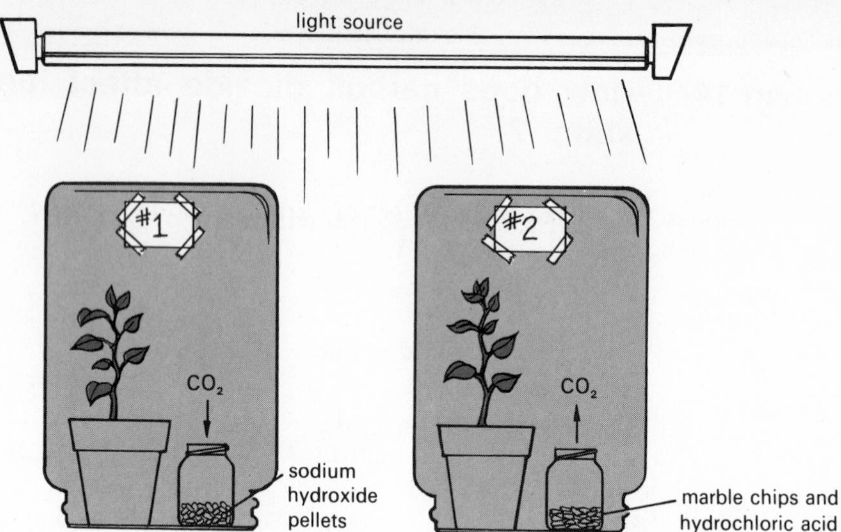

14-9. Setup to test the effect of carbon dioxide gas on the production of starch in a plant.

3. The most starch should be found in the leaf from Container 2; however, a trace may be found in Container 1. Students' answers may vary.

F. Place both of your inverted containers, with their contents, in the light for 24 hours. (See Figure 14-9.)

G. After 24 hours, select a healthy leaf from each plant. Cut a small notch out of the leaf from Container 1 to identify it. (See Figure 14-10.)

H. Remove the chlorophyll and test for starch in both leaves. (See Steps D, E, F, and G in Problem 14-2.)

14-10. Leaf from Container 1 with a notch cut out.

4. Yes.

5. Carbon dioxide.

2. Draw both leaves in your notebook and shade in the areas that show the presence of starch.
3. Is starch found in both of the leaves you tested?
4. Does carbon dioxide aid in the formation of starch?
5. What gas seems to be necessary for photosynthesis to take place?
6. When a plant produces more glucose than it can use, the excess is changed to starch and stored. Would you expect the plant in Container 1 to have large amounts of glucose after 48 hours?

6. No. (The absence of starch suggests that glucose is not being produced in large amounts.)

You should now be able to

Relate the presence of carbon dioxide to the formation of starch.

Locate starch in a leaf with the iodine test.

Relate carbon dioxide to the process of photosynthesis.

Control the amount of carbon dioxide in an experimental environment.

Light and photosynthesis

If plants are to carry out photosynthesis, several factors must be present. In the last problem you learned some things about the role of carbon dioxide. Light is another factor that is needed for photosynthesis.

In Problem 14-4, you will read about testing for the effects of different amounts of light on photosynthesis. Because oxygen is released during photosynthesis, it is possible to test for oxygen to see if photosynthesis is taking place. This is the test used in the next problem.

Sunlight is a mixture of all the colors in the light **spectrum.** Those colors are red, orange, yellow, green, blue, indigo, and violet. (See Figure 14-11.) Are all the colors able to supply the energy needed by the plant during photosynthesis? You may wish to investigate this question with an experiment of your own. You would need several plants. You would also need several different colored lights. Or you could use regular light bulbs covered with colored transparent paper. Remember, if you try this, to include one plant under white light in addition to the various colored lights.

Other factors, such as temperature and light intensity, affect food-making in plants. Scientists still do not understand all the factors involved. They know what goes into the reaction and what the products are, but some of the processes in between are still unknown.

14-11. Sunlight is a mixture of all the colors in the light spectrum. The process of photosynthesis is affected by different colors of light. Do you think that leaves "turning color" in the fall has anything to do with the light spectrum?

Students will learn about color changes in leaves on page 273. What actually happens is that the destruction of chlorophyll by cold temperatures allows other leaf pigments to show up.

Problem 14-4 What is the effect of light on the production of oxygen by green plants?

Purpose To learn about the gas produced by a green plant.

Materials None. You will be provided with the results of an experiment that has been previously completed.

Procedure Some students wanted to find out how different amounts of light affected the production of oxygen by a green plant. They used a water plant called *elodea.* These students carried out the following procedure to gather information to answer their question.

A. Equal amounts of elodea were placed in four test tubes. The test tubes were then inverted in large beakers of water. No air was left in the test tubes.

B. One of the beaker setups was placed in the dark. The other three setups were each placed in a growth chamber with a light source. One chamber had a 20-watt bulb. The second chamber had a 60-watt bulb. The third chamber had a 100-watt bulb.

C. The tubes were left in the chambers for four days and were then observed. They appeared as shown in Figure 14-12.

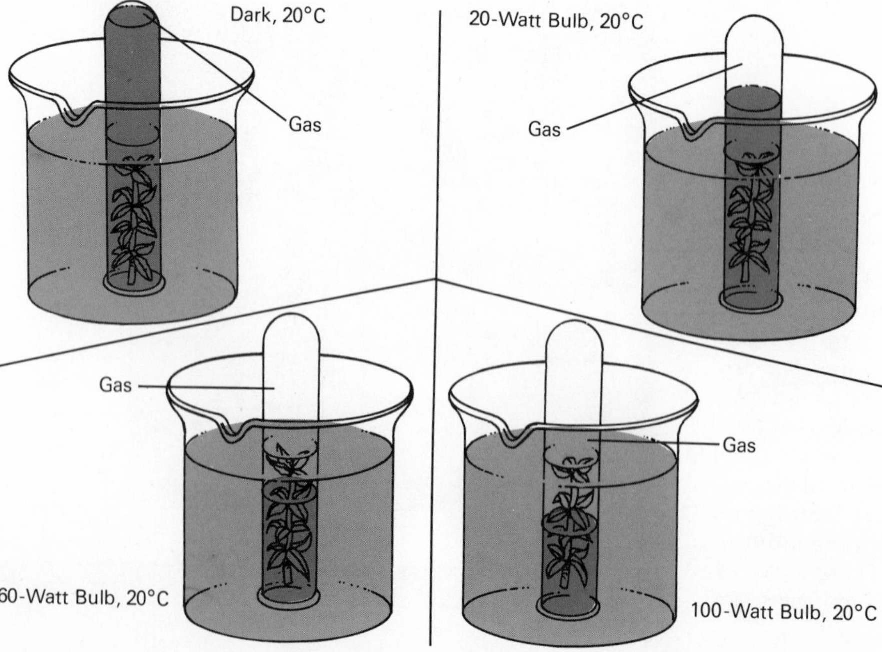

14-12. Water-filled test tubes containing elodea leaves were placed in different light environments but at a controlled temperature. Here you can see the different amounts of gas produced.

TABLE 14-1 GAS PRODUCED BY ELODEA WITH DIFFERENT AMOUNTS OF LIGHT

Trials	*Dark*	*20-Watt Bulb*	*60-Watt Bulb*	*100-Watt Bulb*
	ml gas	ml gas	ml gas	ml gas
1	0	5	15	24
2	1	7	17	26
3	0	4	14	23
4	0	6	16	25
5	0	8	13	27
Total	1	30	75	125
Average	0.2 ml	6 ml	15 ml	25 ml

D. The students performed the experiment a total of five times and recorded their results as shown in Table 14-1.

1. Did all the tubes have gas in them?
2. Which tube had the greatest gas production?
3. Which tube had the least gas production?
4. Did all the tubes in the light produce the same amount of gas?
5. What light source produced the greatest amount of gas?

1. No.
2. The tube with the 100-watt bulb.
3. The tube in the dark.
4. No.
5. The 100-watt bulb.

E. Prepare a line graph to show the effect of light on the production of gas by a green plant. Use "Light in Watts" along the x-axis and "Gas Produced in Milliliters" as the y-axis. (See Figure 14-13.)

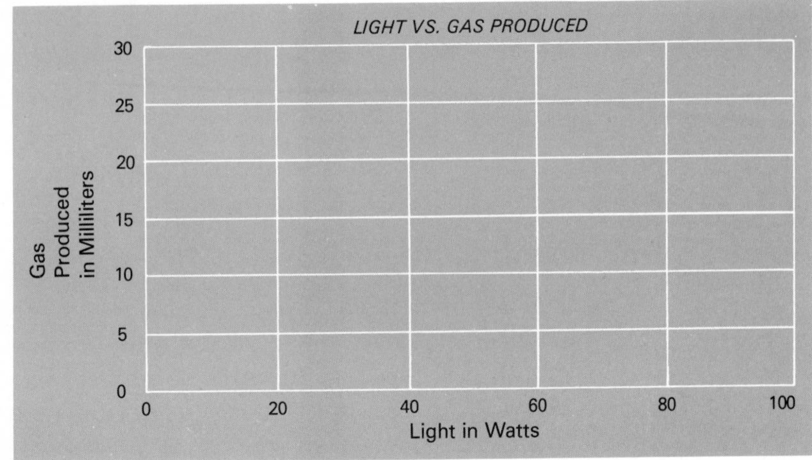

14-13. Graphing the volume of gas produced by elodea with different amounts of light.

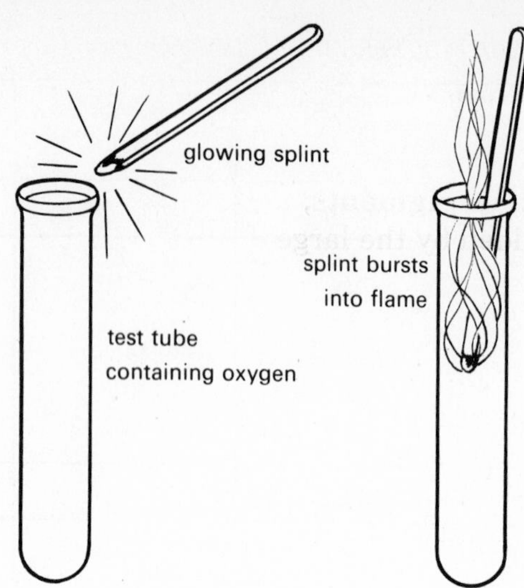

14-14. Oxygen causes a glowing splint to burst into flame.

6. More light causes more gas production.

7. Yes; yes.

8. It would burst into flame.

9. Yes. Because oxygen is a by-product of photosynthesis, and the splint test showed that oxygen was the gas being produced by the plants.

6. How does the increase in light affect the production of gas?
7. Is light *directly* related to gas production? (Is yours a straight-line graph?)

F. The glowing-splint test was used on the gas in the tubes. (See Figure 14-14.) The test was performed to see if oxygen was the gas produced by the plants. When the tubes were tested, it was found that they contained oxygen.

8. What would happen to the glowing splint when placed in these tubes?
9. Is there reason to believe that the elodea plants were carrying out photosynthesis? Explain your answer.

You should now be able to

Identify the gas that causes a glowing splint to burn.
Name the gas produced by a plant grown in the light.
Relate the importance of light to the production of oxygen by a water plant.
Relate oxygen to the process of photosynthesis.

Chromatography

Chloroplasts in leaves absorb light energy. This energy helps to split the water molecule into hydrogen and oxygen. The hydrogen is used by the plant when it manufactures glucose. The oxygen is released. As you can see, light energy is a vital factor in the process of photosynthesis.

Looking around in parks and gardens, you may notice some plants whose leaves are not green. There is one type of maple tree that has dark red leaves. Other plants have yellow parts, and many plants have brown, red, and pink sections.

These colors, or **pigments,** are present in many plants. But they are usually hidden by the large quantities of green chloroplasts. The red pigment is not always present, but it will appear in the leaves of some plants as a result of temperature and light changes. When leaves start to die in the fall, the colors change. The green chloroplasts are destroyed by the change in temperature, permitting the other colors to be seen. Thus, when leaves "turn color" in the fall, it is really that the colors are revealed because the green is destroyed.

The various colors in a leaf can be separated in the lab. The process used is called paper **chromatography** [kro-muh-TAHG-ruh-fee]. It works because different pigments in leaves, when dissolved, diffuse at different rates as they are absorbed by paper.

The leaf pigments are dissolved in a special solvent and then absorbed by a special kind of filter paper. The colors move up the paper at different rates. Moving at different rates, they separate from each other. This is something like a car race. When you remove the filter paper, you stop the action for a "photo finish." Since each compound has its own color and is deposited at a different level, it is easy to identify each one.

Problem 14-5 How may the different pigments in leaves be separated?

Purpose To separate and identify plant pigments by chromatography.

Materials

clover, grass, or spinach
mortar and pestle
chlorophyll solvent "A"
filter paper
large test tube
cork stopper
wire cutters
round toothpick
paper clip
chromatography solvent "B"
funnel or thistle tube
scissors
test-tube rack
magnifying glass

Procedure

A. Obtain some clover, grass, or spinach leaves. Chop up the leaves and put the pieces in a mortar. Pour in about 6 ml of chlorophyll solvent "A." Grind the mixture to a paste. Add more solvent if necessary.

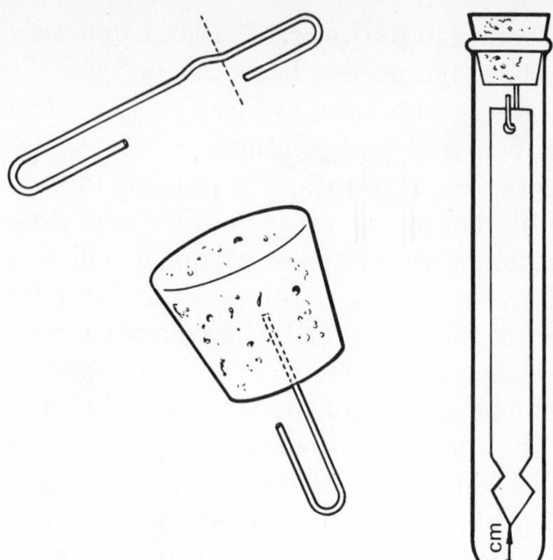

14-15. Cut the filter paper to the proper length and notch it near the bottom.

B. Open up a paper clip and cut one end off. (See Figure 14-15.) Attach the paper clip to the bottom of a cork as shown. Hook a strip of filter paper to the paper clip.

C. Slide the paper into the test tube and fit the cork on snugly. Note the length of the paper strip, then remove and trim to about 1 cm from the bottom of the test tube. Cut a triangular notch on two sides near the bottom and cut the end to a point. (See Figure 14-15.)

D. With a round toothpick, place a drop of the paste from Step A between the two notches on the filter paper. Allow the drop to dry, then place another drop on the same place. Do this four more times for a total of 6 drops.

E. Pour chromatography solvent "B" into the empty test tube to a height of 1.5 cm. Use a funnel or thistle tube *to keep the sides of the test tube dry.*

The paper should not touch the test-tube walls or solvent may rise unevenly along the edge of the paper, distorting the results.

F. Stand the test tube in a test-tube rack. Carefully lower the filter paper into the test tube and cork it. (See Figure 14-16.) *Be sure the paper does not touch the sides.* The paper must be in the solvent, but the level of the solvent should be below the notches. Keep the test tube in an upright position.

G. Observe the solvent moving up the filter paper.

1. It slowly seems to dissolve and disappear.

1. What happens to the spot as the solvent rises?

H. Remove the cork and filter paper when the solvent is about 1 cm from the top. Allow the paper to dry.

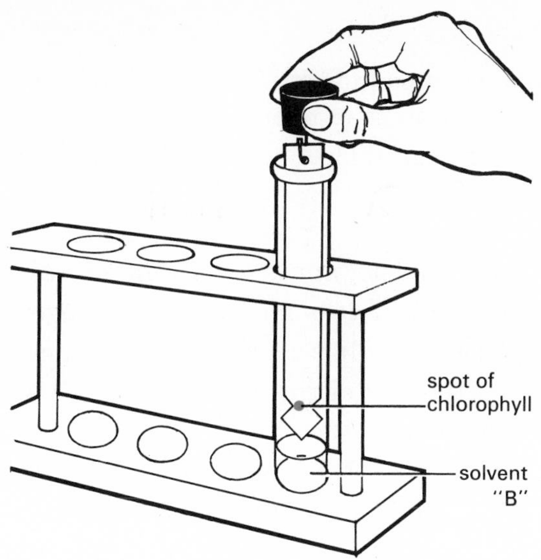

14-16. Filter paper is lowered into solvent "B."

2. Yes.

3. Blue, yellow, green, and red may all be reported. Other intermediate shades may be described. Answers will depend on types of leaves used.

4. The green pigment is usually nearest the top.

5. Blue, if present, or possibly yellow.

6. It diffuses into the paper at the fastest rate.

7. Green (chlorophyll).

2. Did the original spot of pigment contain several different colors?
3. Use the magnifying glass. What different colors (pigments) did you find on the filter-paper strip?
4. Which color is located nearest the top of the filter paper?
5. Which color is located closest to the notch in the paper?
6. Why does one color go higher than the others?
7. Which pigment found in a green plant is always necessary for photosynthesis to take place?

Using chromatography and other techniques, scientists have further separated the green pigment into several pigments. Two of these pigments are called chlorophyll *a* and chlorophyll *b*. Chlorophyll *a* is found in all higher plants that are able to carry on photosynthesis.

You should now be able to

Separate several different pigments by paper chromatography.
Recognize the individual pigments removed from a green plant.
Relate chlorophyll to the process of photosynthesis.
Predict the relationship of different pigments to color of leaves.

Science terms

chlorophyll	glucose	pigment
chromatography	photosynthesis	spectrum

Review questions

$$6CO_2 + H_2O \xrightarrow[\text{chlorophyll}]{\text{sunlight}} C_6H_{12}O_6 + 6O_2$$

1. What two compounds are used by a green plant as "raw materials" in the process of photosynthesis?
2. Name four ingredients necessary for plants to carry out photosynthesis.
3. Write the summary equation for photosynthesis.
4. What materials do plants use in the process of respiration?
5. Where in the leaf does most of the photosynthesis take place?
6. What process supplies much of the oxygen in our atmosphere?
7. When testing for sugar with Benedict's solution, what color change is seen?
8. List some of the ways that a plant uses glucose sugar.
9. What green plant pigments are necessary for photosynthesis?
10. If you used another plant in your chromatography experiment, do you think the colors would be the same? Explain.
11. When does a plant use its stored starch?
12. What are the colors of the visible spectrum?
13. What process is used to separate the various plant pigments from each other?

1. Carbon dioxide and water.

2. Carbon dioxide, water, light, and chlorophyll.

3. See annotation at top of page.

4. Glucose and oxygen.

5. In the palisade cells and spongy cells of the mesophyll tissue.

6. Photosynthesis.

7. Solution changes from blue to green to red-orange.

8. Largely for energy. From this substance plants build other materials, such as starches, fats, oils, proteins, and vitamins.

9. Chlorophyll *a* and *b*.

10. Probably not. The same pigments are not always found in different plants.

11. When its energy needs are not met by available glucose. This is usually during the dark hours and winter, when no or little photosynthesis is taking place.

12. Red, orange, yellow, green, blue, indigo, violet.

13. Paper chromatography.

Check your understanding

See Teacher's Guide section for answers to Questions 14-20.

14. Water was the only material added to the potted tree in van Helmont's experiment. Where did the added weight come from?
15. How does the process of photosynthesis differ from respiration?
16. Explain how the pigments in leaves may be separated by chromatography.
17. Where does the yellow or red color in autumn leaves come from?
18. Why is it necessary to remove the chlorophyll from a leaf before testing it for starch?
19. There are a number of factors necessary for photosynthesis to take place. The presence of carbon dioxide, water, light, and chlorophyll are all important. Choose one of the four factors and tell why you think it is the most important.
20. In Problem 14-4, the experimenters had to keep the test tubes containing elodea completely full of water when inverting them into the beakers of water. Why?

Chapter 15 Flowers, seeds, and fruits

Chapter-opening photo shows the flowers and fruits of the tomato plant.

The final chapter in our study of plants deals with structures familiar to most everyone. These structures are the flowers, fruits, and seeds common to so many plants. Flowers come in all sizes, shapes, and colors. People use the more showy flowers for decorations and gifts. But what use do we make of flowers such as bean flowers, corn flowers, or tomato flowers?

Such flowers are not very decorative, but they play an important role in the life of the flowering plant. Plain or showy, all flowers perform the same general function. Their function is the production of seeds used to reproduce the plant.

In Chapter 11 you studied the conditions under which corn seeds, bean seeds, and grass seeds will produce seedlings. In this chapter you will study how the seeds are produced. Each part of a flower serves a reproductive function, from attracting insects to forming the complete seed. Brightly colored petals are the most noticeable parts, but they are only the beginning of the process.

The water lily (*right*) contains both pistil and stamens for reproduction. The flowers of a cactus (*left*) are not only decorative, but also, like all flowers, serve a reproductive function.

Bananas, grapes, avocados, oranges, pears, and apples are all fruits. Fruits develop from the ovaries of flowers.

Parts of flowers

We have already noted that flowers show a great deal of variation. Roses often grow in clusters or blossoms. Plants such as tulips grow flowers that are separate from each other on the plant. Regardless of growth pattern, each flower is basically the same thing. Each is really a shortened stem that contains several structures involved in producing seeds.

The essential parts of a flower are the stamens and the pistil. (See Figure 15-2.) These parts are common to all flowers. In addition to these essential parts, several other structures may be found. The other structures depend on the particular kind of plant being studied. These parts include the sepals and the petals, also shown in Figure 15-2. A flower that contains all four structures — stamens, pistil, sepals, and petals — is called a **complete flower.**

Of the four parts of a complete flower, the outermost are the sepals. The **sepals** are green leaflike structures that protect the other parts of the flower in the bud. The **petals** form the next inward structure. They are usually the most colorful part of the flower.

Just inside the ring of petals are the stamens. The **stamens** are the male reproductive parts of the flower. Each stamen consists of a slender stalk, the **filament,** with a knobby top, the **anther.** (See Figure 15-3.) **Pollen grains** are produced within the anther. The pollen grains contain the male reproductive cells, the **sperm cells.** Complete flowers usually contain several stamens.

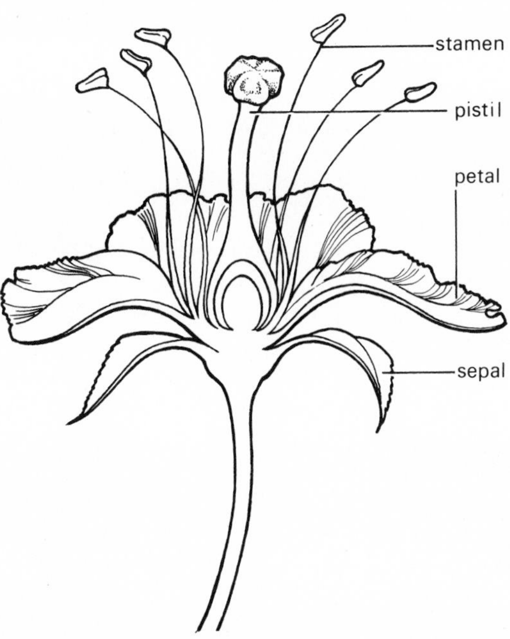

15-1. A complete flower contains stamens, pistil, petals, and sepals.

15-2. The corn tassel, although not very decorative, is a reproductive organ of the corn plant.

The fourth structure, found nearest the center of the complete flower, is the pistil. (See Figure 15-3.) The **pistil** is the female part of the flower. It produces the **ovules,** or **egg cells,** which eventually form the seeds.

The pistil is composed of three main parts. The lower part, which is attached to the stem, is the ovary. The **ovary** contains the egg cells.

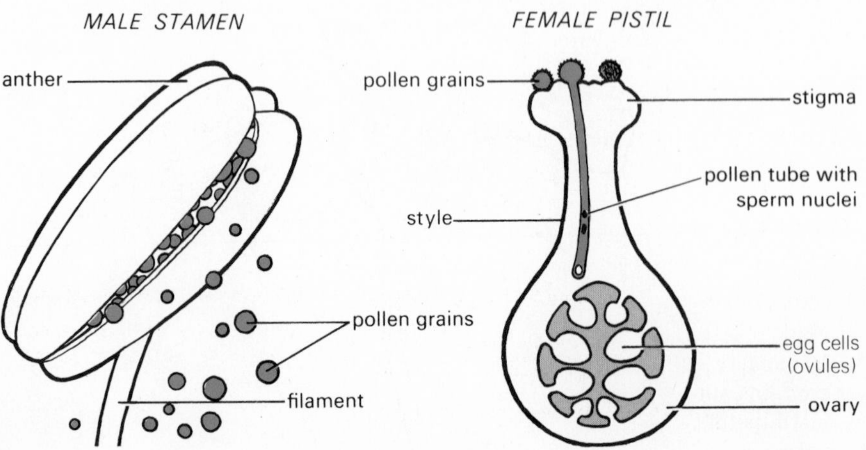

15-3. Reproductive parts of a flower.

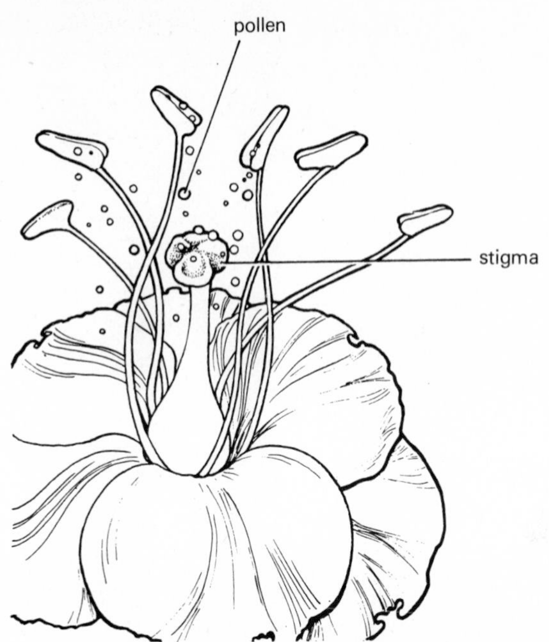

15-4. In self-pollination, the pollen falls onto the sticky stigma of the pistil of the same flower or plant.

Above the ovary is the **style,** shaped like the neck of a vase. At the top of the style is an enlarged area called the stigma. The **stigma** is covered with a sticky substance that is useful for collecting pollen grains.

Seed development

Before an ovule in the ovary can develop into a seed, two events must take place. The first event is **pollination.** This occurs when pollen grains are transferred from the stamen to the pistil. The second event, **fertilization,** occurs when a sperm cell nucleus from the pollen grain unites with an ovule.

When the pollen grains from one flower land on the pistil of another flower, the process is known as **cross-pollination.** Cross-pollination is often accomplished with the aid of insects, wind, or birds. When people purposefully transfer pollen from one plant to another, it is called *artificial* cross-pollination. When the pollen from one flower lands on the pistil of the *same* flower, or on a flower of the same plant, **self-pollination** has taken place. (See Figure 15-4.)

In many flowers, self-pollination cannot occur. The petals may be arranged in such a way as to prevent the pollen from falling on the pistil of the same flower. Or, the pollen may mature at a different time from the rest of the flower. Both cases prevent self-pollination.

Milkweed

Witch Hazel

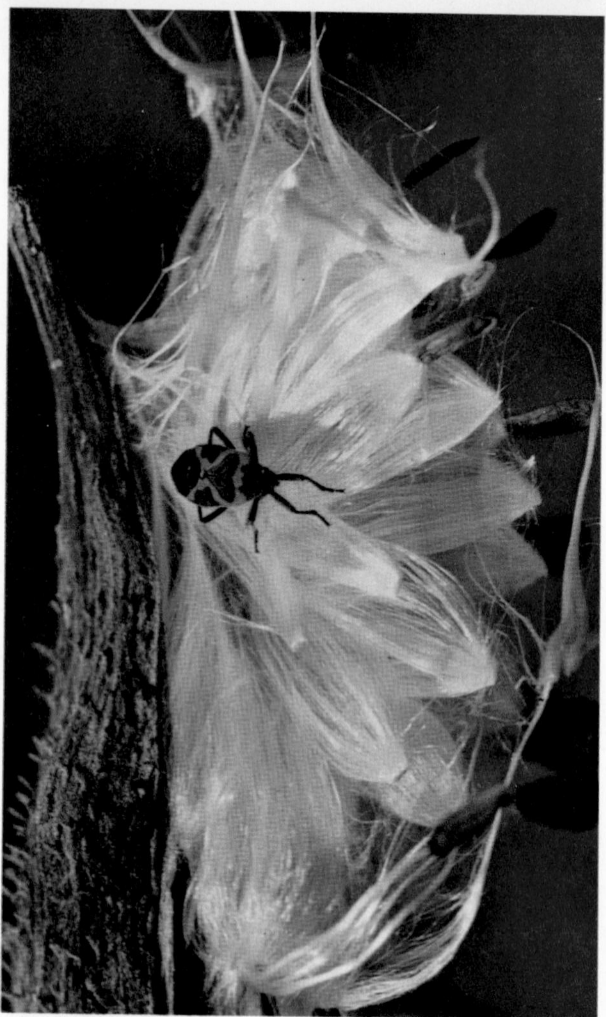

Seed dispersal

Seeds can be dispersed in a number of ways as shown here. The common burdock has prickly seeds that attach themselves to animals passing by, and drop off later in a new location. The milkweed's seeds are carried away by the wind. The seeds of witch hazel "explode" out of their casing and fall a ways from the plant.

Common Burdock

Some plants depend on wind to carry pollen through the air. Such plants must produce large numbers of pollen grains. This increases the chances that at least one grain will land on the pistil of an identical plant.

Before fertilization can occur, sperm cells contained in pollen grains must travel through the pistil down to the ovules at the base of the pistil. The sperm cells are able to do this by means of a special **pollen tube.** A pollen tube develops from a part of the pollen grain after it lands on the stigma. (Look back at Figure 15-3, page 280.)

Each pollen grain actually forms two sperm nuclei. In the ovary, one of the nuclei unites with an ovule. This starts the development of the **embryo**, or young plant, within the seed. The second sperm nucleus unites with other nuclei in the ovule. This starts the production of the endosperm within the seed. The **endosperm** is the fleshy part of a seed, used for food by the embryo as the seed germinates. The seed is complete when the embryo and the endosperm are enclosed in a protective covering called the **seed coat.**

Seed distribution

If all the seeds produced by a plant were to fall close to the plant, most of the seeds would not survive. There would probably not be enough water, minerals, or light available for all the seedlings. Many plants have special structures that help to disperse their seeds. The seeds of some plants, such as dandelion and milkweed, have feathery attachments that enable them to float through the air. Others, like the seeds of the touch-me-not, are shot out of the plant with great velocity. A maple seed has a winglike attachment that twirls like a propeller in the wind. The wind thus carries the seed away from the parent plant.

The study of plants can be fascinating. A lot of careers are associated with plants. Your activities in this chapter may start you on a career as a botanist, florist, or landscape architect. A great deal of research is still needed to develop new varieties of plants that will be more resistant to disease, insects, and drought.

In this chapter you will examine the parts of a flower and learn the function of each part. Your investigations should help you to appreciate the importance of flowers as essential to the life cycle of plants. The study of flowers, seeds, and fruits is another step leading to the understanding of living things.

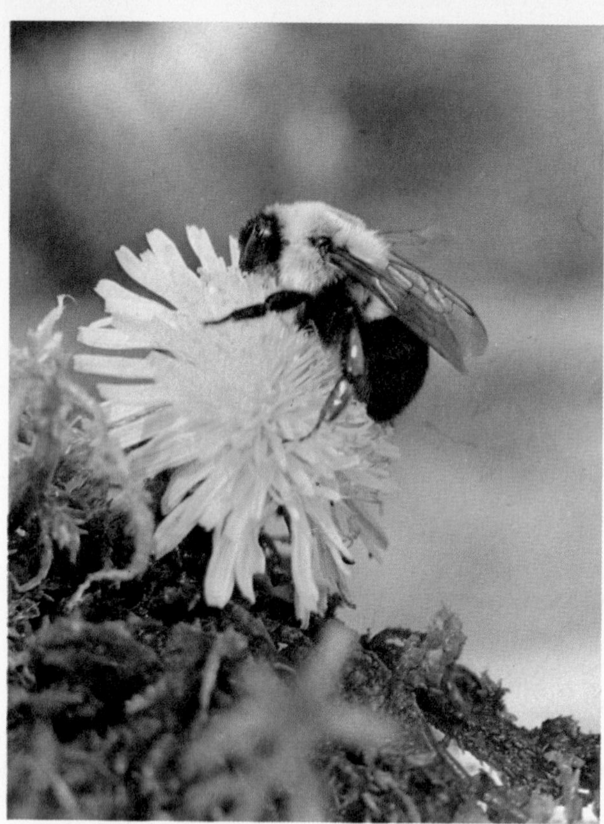

15-5. Insects help in pollination.

Problem 15-1 What are the parts of a flower?

Purpose To identify the parts of a flower and learn their functions.

Materials

selection of flowers	cover glass	microscope
scissors or razor blade	medicine dropper	cardboard
microscope slide	tweezers	hand lens

Procedure

You might want to display charts or models to help clarify the location of flower parts.

A. Observe a typical flower and locate the stalk that attaches it to the plant. The enlarged base of the flower is called the **receptacle.** Directly above this section are the green, leaflike structures called sepals. Above the sepals there are usually brightly colored structures called petals. (See Figure 15-1, page 279.)

1. How many sepals are found on the flower you examined?
2. Does the flower have the same number of petals as sepals?

1. The number will depend on the variety of flower.

2. Probably not, but this may vary.

3. This will depend on the variety of flower.

4. The saclike structure is able to hold large amounts of pollen, which then may be blown or brushed off. (Any answer that indicates that the structure of the anther is suitable for the storage and release of pollen is satisfactory.)

5. Sketches will vary, depending on flower. Most grains will be round, oval, or lobed.

6. Sizes will vary, but will probably be less than 70 microns.

7. Students should sketch the flowers that they have examined. They should show the different parts in approximately the same locations as shown in Figures 15-1 and 15-3.

8. Sketch should show ovary with several egg cells inside.

B. Locate the stalklike structures inside the petals. These are the stamens, the male parts of the flower. The stamens contain the pollen grains. The pollen grains contain the male sperm cells, which may fertilize egg cells in another part of the flower.

3. How many stamens can you find in your flower?
4. How is the upper part of the stamen, the anther, well suited for holding pollen grains?

C. Gently crush a stamen on a microscope slide. Examine the pollen grain with your microscope using high power.

5. Sketch the shape of the pollen grains in your notebook.
6. Estimate the size of a pollen grain in microns. (You may need to review the microscope measuring techniques in Problem 5-4.)

D. Locate the single thick structure at the very middle of the flower. This is the female part of the flower, called the pistil. The pistil produces the egg cells of the flower, which eventually become seeds. The pistil and the stamens are the essential parts of the flower, since one structure produces the egg cells and the other produces the sperm cells.

E. Gently cut out the pistil with pointed scissors or a razor blade. Place the pistil on a piece of cardboard and examine it with a hand lens. The stigma is the sticky upper surface of the pistil which holds pollen grains that may touch the surface.

The narrower portion of the pistil below the stigma is the style. Sperm cells from the pollen grains move down through the style in a pollen tube. (See Figure 15-3, page 280.) The enlarged lower part of the pistil is the ovary. The ovary produces the female sex cells, or egg cells.

When the pollen tube growing down through the style reaches the ovary, the two sperm nuclei enter the ovary. There, one nucleus unites with an egg cell to produce the embryo plant. The other nucleus unites with other material in the ovary to form stored food within the seed. The embryo plant plus the stored food (endosperm) make up the seed.

7. Sketch the pistil in your notebook. Label the stigma, style, and ovary.

F. Slice the pistil in half lengthwise. Use a hand lens to examine the sections you have cut.

8. Sketch and label the structures found in the ovary portion of the pistil.

You should now be able to

Identify the male and female parts of a flower.
Observe and measure pollen grains with the microscope.
Identify the parts of a complete flower.

Flower structures

There is variety in the structure of flowers. Some flowers, such as tulips, form cuplike bodies. Others have numerous frilly petals, as in roses. The snapdragon has a flower that has the female parts enclosed, while the male stamens are visible. This arrangement of stamens helps pollination, since an insect will brush the pollen off the stamens as it crawls between the petals to get the **nectar.** Insects are attracted to flowers by the odor of the nectar as well as by the bright color of the petals.

Plants usually have the male stamen and the female pistil in the same flower. If both reproductive parts are present in a single flower, it is called a **perfect flower.** Some plants have only the male or female parts in a single flower. These are called **imperfect flowers.**

It is possible to find two types of flowers on the same plant. One flower will have only the male parts and another flower on the same plant will have only the female parts. The plum tree is an example of such a plant. Other plants, like the date palm, have flowers of only one sex on each plant.

In the next problem, you will look at several types of flowers and study their structures. Keep in mind that, in spite of the variety you will see in shapes and structures, all flowers have the same basic function. All flowers produce seeds that will reproduce the plant.

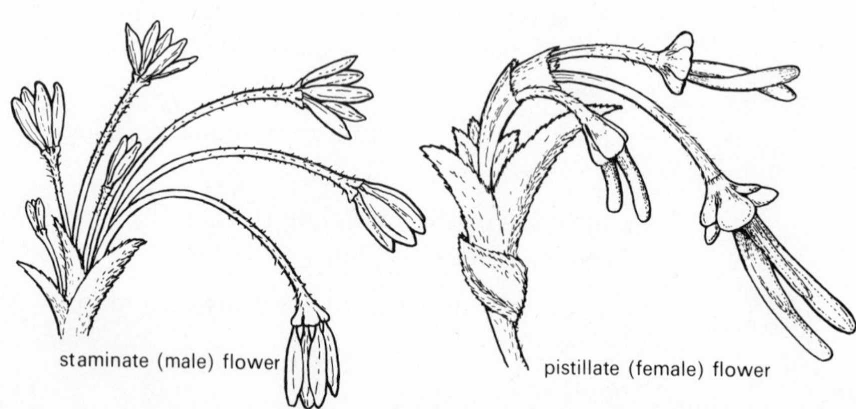

15-6. Imperfect flowers of the box elder tree. Like the date palm mentioned above, each type of flower grows on a different tree.

Lady's Slipper

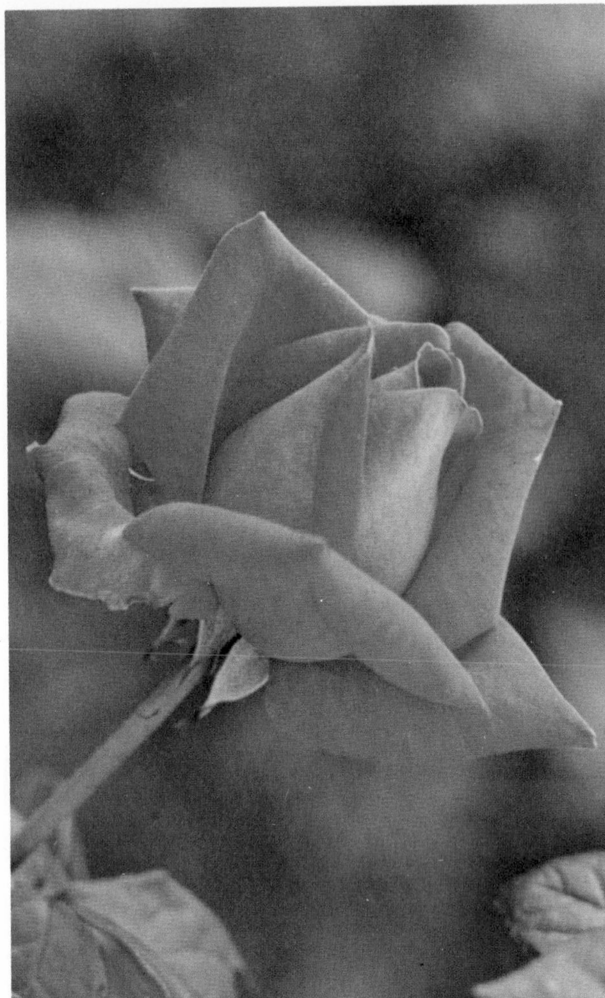
Rose

Morning Glories

The lady's slipper, rose, morning glory, and dahlia display a variety of petal shapes.

Dahlia

Problem 15-2 How are flowers different?

Purpose To investigate the structures in flowers that aid in pollination.

Materials selection of flowers toothpick

Procedure

A. Observe the parts of three of four different kinds of plant flowers. Find the male parts (stamens) and female part (pistil).

1. Are both parts found in one flower?

If both parts are present, it is called a **perfect flower.** If the flower contains only male or only female parts, it is called an **imperfect flower.**

2. Which of your flowers are perfect flowers?
3. Which are imperfect flowers?
4. Which flowers would be capable of self-pollination? (Self-pollination requires both stamens and pistil present in the same flower.)
5. Which flowers must depend on cross-pollination if seeds are to develop? 5. Possible examples: corn, wheat, grasses.

B. Observe the petals and sepals of the different flowers.

6. Which flowers would attract insects by the bright color of their sepals or petals? 6. Examples include rose, snapdragon, tulip, nasturtium.
7. How would insects help cross-pollinate flowers with brightly colored petals or sepals?

C. Examine the central part of several flowers near the base of the ovary. Scrape any liquid from around the base of the pistil with a toothpick.

8. Can you detect any odor from the liquid removed from any flower? This liquid is the nectar. 8. Answers will vary.
9. How would the presence of nectar help bring about the cross-pollination of a flower? 9. It attracts insects, who carry pollen.
10. Which of the flowers you examined had neither brightly colored flowers nor sweet-smelling nectar?
11. Were the flowers you listed in question 10 perfect or imperfect flowers?
12. Would the flowers you listed in question 10 probably be self-pollinated or cross-pollinated? Explain.

12. Cross-pollinated, probably, since most of them were imperfect. Since the flowers are not scented or brightly colored, pollination would probably depend on agents such as wind and water.

1. Answers will depend on the flowers being used.

2. Answers will depend on the kinds of flowers used—possible examples are iris, tulip, rose, snapdragon, lily, sweet pea.

3. Answers depend on kinds of flowers—possible examples are willow, corn, cottonwood, and buffalo grass flowers.

4. Answers depend on kinds of perfect flowers used—possible examples are pea, sweet pea, rose, snapdragon.

7. Bright colors attract insects to flowers where they can brush against pollen, which sticks to their bodies. If the insects move to other flowers, the pollen could be transferred.

10. Examples are wheat, grasses, corn, cottonwood, willow.

11. Most will probably be imperfect.

13. They could be transported by wind or water.
14. Large numbers would be necessary, since the chances of any one pollen grain reaching a flower are very small.

13. How could pollen grains be transported long distances without the aid of insects?
14. Why would large numbers of pollen grains be necessary for this method of pollen transfer?

You should now be able to

Predict the type of pollination that occurs in a flower by examining the stamens and pistil.

Determine whether cross-pollination or self-pollination is probable.

Fruits and their function

Do you remember the last time you ate a fresh, juicy peach? The tasty flesh of the peach encloses a hard seed, which you probably threw out. Like the bean and corn seeds studied in Chapter 11, the seed of the peach contains the embryo plant and endosperm. But un-

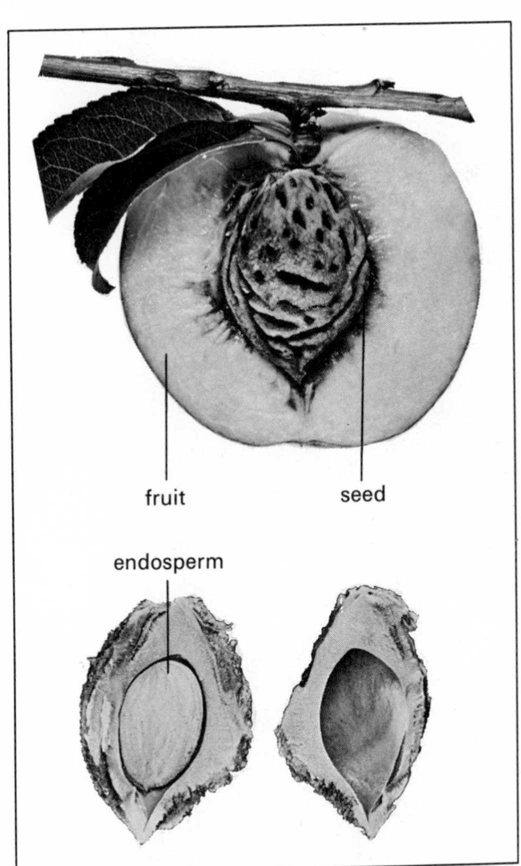

15-7. The peach seed is enclosed by a fruit. The embryo and endosperm develop inside the hard pit.

like the bean and corn seeds, the peach seed is surrounded by an edible, fleshy covering called a **fruit.**

A fruit develops from the ovary of a flower. In some plants, when sperm cells fertilize egg cells within the ovary, certain tissues of the ovary begin to develop into a fruit. As the fertilized eggs develop into embryo plants inside the ovary, the outer portion of the ovary grows and ripens as a fruit. You will try to find some of the remains of the ovary wall in the fruit of the apple tree in the next problem.

The presence of an edible fruit around a seed is often an advantage in distributing the seed. Birds eat berries and other fruits. The seeds often pass undamaged through the digestive tract of the animals. Unharmed, the seeds are thus deposited long distances from the plant that produced the fruit. And they are still viable when conditions for germination are favorable.

Inedible fruits such as cockleburs also help in dispersing the enclosed seeds. The barbs or hooks catch on the fur of animals and may fall off some distance from where they were picked up.

Many plants are cultivated for their crop of fruit. Just remember that the fruit you eat is only a covering for the seed that is so necessary for a plant's reproduction.

15-8. The spiny fruit of cockleburs may catch on the fur of animals and be carried away from the parent plant.

15-9. Cut your apple in half as here.

Problem 15-3 What are the different parts of a fruit?

Purpose To identify the parts of a fruit.

Materials pear or apple | green bean pod | pea pod | knife

Procedure

A. Obtain an apple and cut it in half. You should have a section as shown in Figure 15-9.

B. Locate the seeds in the center of the fruit. The hard, fleshy structure around the seeds is the ovary wall. The part that you usually eat is the enlarged base of the flower.

1. The ovules inside the ovary.
2. Receptacle.

1. What part of the flower produced the seeds?
2. What is the name of the base of the flower?

C. Observe the side that is opposite the stem on the fruit.

3. Sepals.

3. What is the name of the dried, leaflike structures of the flower that remain attached to the fruit?

D. Find the center of these green, leaflike structures. This was the sticky surface of the flower pistil.

4. Pollen.

4. What was deposited on the sticky surface of the pistil that caused the formation of the seed and fruit?

E. Examine a fresh green bean or green pea pod with seeds inside.

7. Because the fleshy portion of the pod developed from the ovary wall, and it encloses the seeds.

8. The fruit is mainly useful in helping to disperse the seeds.

5. How many seeds are contained in the bean or the pea pod (fruit) you examined? 5. Numbers will vary.
6. Are there any dried leaflike structures at one end of the fruit? What are these structures called? 6. Yes, sepals.
7. Why is it correct to call a bean pod or a pea pod a fruit?
8. Fruits are used for food by people and other animals. What is the main function of fruits in the life cycle of a green plant?

You should now be able to

Locate a seed in a fruit.
Identify the food portion of a fruit.
Relate the fruit to the female parts of the flower.

---

1. Cross-pollination.

2. Imperfect flowers.

3. The stamen.

4. Seed production.

5. The cotyledons and endosperm, if present.

6. Examples include grasses, corn, wheat, barley, rye, cottonwood.

7. In the ovary.

8. Color of petals and scent of nectar.

9. The fleshy part of the apple was the receptacle, the seed was an ovule within the ovary, and the core was the wall of the ovary. Stamens, sepals, and other structures have dried out but are not greatly changed in other respects.

Science terms

anther
complete flower
cross-pollination
egg cell (ovule)
embryo
endosperm
fertilization
filament
fruit
imperfect flower
nectar
ovary
perfect flower
petal
pistil
pollen grain
pollen tube
pollination
receptacle
self-pollination
sepal
sperm cell
stamen
stigma
style

Review questions

1. Name the process that involves the landing of pollen from one flower on the pistil of another.
2. What word describes flowers that have only stamens (male parts) or only pistils (female parts)?
3. Which part of a flower produces pollen?
4. What is the major function of a flower?
5. Name the part of the seed that contains the stored food.
6. Name at least three kinds of plants that do not have petals as part of their flower.
7. Where are the egg cells located in a flower?
8. How are the insects attracted to flowers?
9. Name the parts of an apple and tell the part of the flower from which each part came.

Check your understanding

See Teacher's Guide section for answers to Questions 10-15.

10. Some foods that we call vegetables are called fruits by a botanist. Why?
11. Describe three methods by which plants distribute seeds.
12. Explain the events that occur when a pollen grain lands on the pistil of a flower.
13. Describe two conditions that would prevent self-pollination in flowers.
14. How would you set up an experiment to discover if certain plants could self-pollinate?
15. What parts of a flower are essential for the flower to be able to produce seeds?

Unit 5

Unit-opening photo shows a frog in its natural, swampy habitat.

Animal organs and systems — the frog

People's curiosity has caused them to study everything in their environment. The questions people ask are often the springboards to long and rewarding investigations. People seek to answer such questions as: What is it made of? How is it put together? How does it work? The organization within living things has always been of interest.

You have studied the tissues, organs, and systems of some plants and animals. The structure of a living thing is called its **anatomy**. The study of how tissues and organs function is called **physiology**. Knowledge about an organism is gained through a study of its anatomy and physiology.

Learning about a complicated subject does not always depend on the use of precise scientific instruments. The most important tool that any scientist can have is an open and curious mind.

In 1543, Andreas Vesalius [vuh-SAY-lee-us] published a book on the structure of the human body. He had been dissatisfied with ancient anatomy books, which were accepted without question. He examined the human organs. Others in his day might have seen the same things if they had taken the trouble to look. When Vesalius published his book, more than two hundred of the errors in previous books were corrected. Vesalius taught us to search for evidence, rather than to rely only on what had been written before.

In the next two chapters, you will study the anatomy and physiology of the frog. The frog is an animal whose body shows many similarities to the human body. To learn about structure and function in the frog, you will observe both a living and a preserved frog.

There are many differences between a frog's body and your body, of course. But there are also many likenesses. Frogs and humans actually belong to the same subphylum in the classification system of animals. They are both vertebrates. And all vertebrates have certain things in common. Through the study of the frog, you can learn more about the human.

When you have finished this unit, you will know some things about a living animal that even the greatest of scientists did not know a few centuries ago.

There are seven classes of vertebrates. Five of those classes (the ones shown) are well known to you. The other two classes are less familiar. They include the jawless fishes such as the lamprey and the cartilagenous fishes such as rays and sharks.

Chapter 16 Observing the living frog

Chapter-opening photo shows a bullfrog in a typical floating position—with its eyes, ear membranes, and nostrils above the water surface.

The frog belongs to a group of animals that have never entirely left their water environment. Frogs and the other animals in this group are called **amphibians**. Amphibian comes from the Greek words *amphi* (which means "dual" or "both") and *bios* (which refers to life).

Amphibians spend part of their lives in water and part on land. A frog lays its eggs in water. From these eggs, a fishlike form called a **tadpole** develops. This form has gills and a tail. After a short time, the tadpole absorbs its gills and tail. In the meantime, it has developed lungs and legs. The tadpole thus becomes an adult frog.

The series of changes from egg to tadpole to adult is called **metamorphosis** [met-uh-MOR-fuh-siss]. In addition to frogs, amphibians also include toads and salamanders. All amphibians undergo metamorphosis. The process is shown in Figure 16-1 on page 299. Notice the gradual absorption of the tail as the tadpole develops into a frog. There is also a gradual disappearance of gills as lungs take over the breathing process.

The frog (*left*) is the most aquatic of the amphibians, spending most of its life around a water environment. The toad (*above*) looks very much like a frog, but it is more *terrestrial*, or land-dwelling.

The developing embryos (*right*) of salamander eggs are protected by a jellylike substance. At lower left is an adult spotted salamander.

16-1. The metamorphosis of a frog from egg to adult.

It is not surprising that some people confuse toads and frogs, since they are very much alike. However, they also differ in many ways. A frog has teeth in its upper jaw. Toads have no teeth. Frogs feed in the daytime. Toads feed at night. The eggs of a frog are found in round masses. Toads lay their eggs in stringlike strands. The tadpoles of toads are small and black. Frog tadpoles are lighter in color and larger in size than toad tadpoles.

The area in which an organism lives is called its **habitat**. A frog's habitat is the pool, marsh, or stream in which it lives. Like many other amphibians, a frog feeds on insects and worms. In addition to providing food, an animal's habitat must protect it from enemies and unfavorable weather. The rocks and vegetation of a pond give a frog places to go when danger threatens. Snakes, turtles, and raccoons are the frog's chief enemies.

Frogs, like all living things, need water to live. Instead of drinking water, amphibians absorb water directly through their skins. As a result, most amphibians cannot live in salt water or in desert regions.

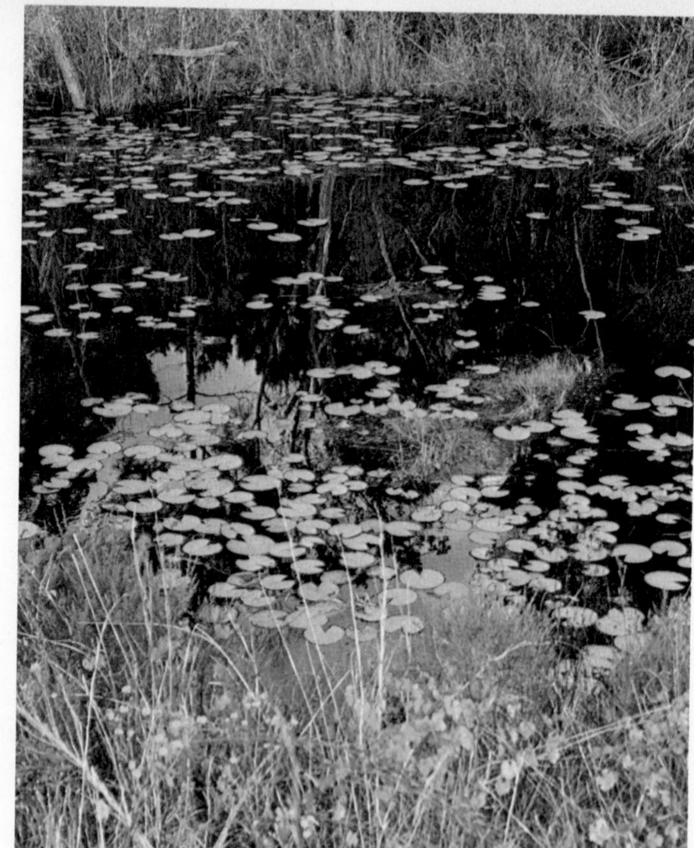

This marsh scene (*right*) is typical of the frog and toad habitats where eggs are laid in the spring. Toad eggs (*lower left*) appear as long, stringy masses. The adult toad (*lower right*) is a land-dweller, but must lay its eggs in water.

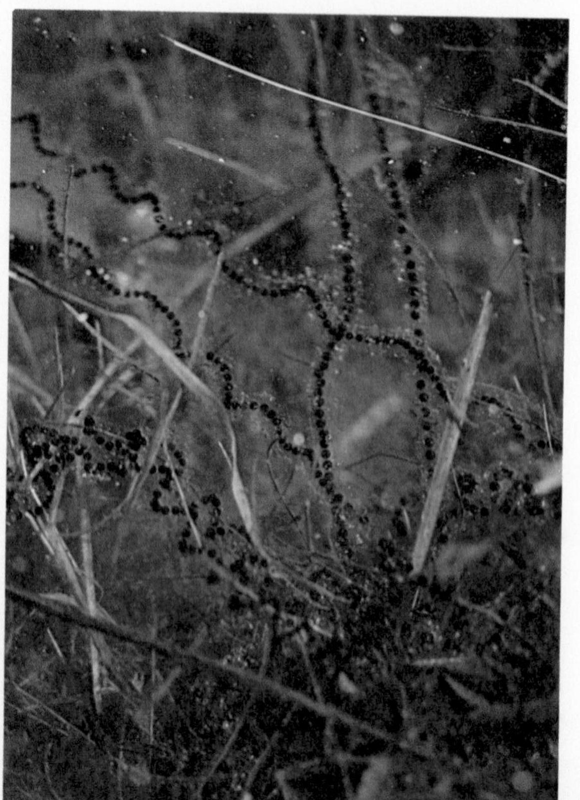

Frog eggs form a jellied mass (*left*). They begin to hatch into tadpoles after 10-14 days. An adult leopard frog (*right*) is also shown below, in size relationship to a tadpole.

In winter, when temperatures are low, a frog burrows into the mud of a pond. This "winter sleep" is called **hibernation**. It is a reaction to cold weather. During hibernation, the body activities go on at a much slower rate than usual. At this slowed rate, little food or oxygen is required for the life processes. The frog appears motionless.

Animals whose body temperatures are regulated by the outside temperature are called **cold-blooded**. The term cold-blooded is not really correct, because a frog's blood is not really cold. The term means that the blood temperature of the frog is the same as the temperature of its environment. When you touch a frog, it feels cold because your body temperature is higher.

A frog's skin coloration permits it to blend with its environment. The spotted color provides **camouflage**, which keeps the frog from being seen easily. The dark color of the frog's back, when viewed from above, blends in with the darkness of the ground or pond. The underside of the frog is light in color. When viewed from the bottom, the frog blends in with the brighter light from the water surface.

Problem 16-3 (pages 309-313) is recommended for demonstration. it would be a good idea to save a frog specifically for that problem. You might also decide to demonstrate (or have students do) Problem 16-3 first, before Problems 16-1 and 16-2, to ensure the frog is fresh.

The frog's skin also plays a very important part in underwater breathing. Tiny, thin-walled blood vessels are located near the surface of the frog's skin. These vessels absorb oxygen directly from the water. In this way, a frog is able to breathe under water. In the next problem you will study the external structure of an adult frog. You will see how it is adapted to live its dual existence — on land and in water.

Keep frogs in damp environment whenever possible. A moist paper towel under the frog serves this function.

Problem 16-1 How is the frog adapted to live on land and in water?

Purpose To observe the external body features that enable the frog to live in its environment.

Materials live frog; meter stick; chalk; aquarium, small

Procedure

Have students tie a 100-cm length of soft string to the frog's leg to enable them to catch the frogs with greater ease. To avoid injuring the frog's leg, do not leave string attached more than one day.

A. Mark a small circle with chalk on an open area of the floor. Obtain a live frog and place it in the middle of the circle. When the frog jumps, mark an "x" on the spot where it lands. Place the frog back in the circle. Mark the length of two more jumps. Observe how the frog uses its front and hind legs when jumping.

4. They support the frog and absorb the impact of landing.

5. The humps become level with the frog's back. (They are the articulation between the pelvic girdle and the vertebrae.)

6. Folded under the body.

7. The legs are folded (flexed) under the frog's body. The extending of the legs propels the frog forward.

8. Not quite. The first act of swimming is usually like the jumping motion, in that the legs are extended simultaneously. Swimming may also be accomplished by rapid flexing and extending of one leg and then the other.

9. The skin that forms a webbing between the toes and hind legs.

11. The frog swims by flexing and extending the legs. People usually swim by kicking their legs with an up-and-down motion. People sometimes use the "frog kick," however, which is very similar to the motion of a swimming frog.

13. They are usually above the surface to permit breathing.

1. Most frogs will jump from 5 to 30 cm; longer jumps are possible.

1. Measure the distance from the circle to each "x" and find the average. Record the average jump length in centimeters.
2. Measure and record the body length of your frog in centimeters. (Do not include legs in measurements.) 2. Generally 5 to 9 cm.
3. How many times the length of your frog's body was the length of its average jump? 3. Answers will vary. Jumps may equal 3 to 4 times body length.
4. What function do the front legs serve as a frog jumps and lands?
5. The two humps on the back of the frog are part of its skeleton. How do these humps change when the frog's body straightens during the process of jumping?
6. Describe the position of the hind legs when a frog is sitting.
7. In what way does the position of the hind legs prepare the frog to jump?

B. Place the frog in water and observe its method of swimming.

8. Does the frog use its legs in the same manner for swimming as for jumping?
9. What structures on the frog's hind legs aid it in swimming?
10. Are these structures also found on the front legs? 10. No.
11. How do the swimming motions of the hind legs of a frog differ from those of a person?

C. Wait for the frog to float quietly in the water. Then observe the positions of its eyes and its ear membranes. (The ear membranes are the round areas just behind the eyes.)

12. Where are the eyes and ear membranes located in relation to the surface of the water? 12. They are located at the surface or above it.

The locations of these sense organs, the eyes and ear membranes, help the frog to keep aware of its environment.

13. Locate the nostrils of the frog. Are the nostrils above, below, or at water level as the frog floats?

D. Hold the frog under the water for about three minutes.

14. Did your frog drown? 14. No.

E. Frogs are able to absorb oxygen dissolved in the water through their skin. This is made possible by many tiny blood vessels just under the skin. When the frog is at the surface of the water, notice that the nostrils are again opening and closing as air enters and leaves.

F. Frogs have a rather special structure associated with their eyes. While the frog is floating, slowly move your finger toward its eyes.

15. How does the frog blink its eye?
16. What is the color of the frog's eyelid?

15. Two lids may be brought together to cover each eye. There is also a transparent membrane attached to the lower lid that may be used to cover the eye.

16. The two external lids are usually the color of the frog's body. The third membrane is transparent.

G. While the frog is completely under water, observe its eyes.

17. Are the eyes open or closed? 17. Open, with the transparent membrane covering them.
18. What useful function could transparent eyelids serve while the frog is under water? While on land?

18. It protects the eye, yet allows the animal to see under water. On land, the transparent membrane keeps the eye moist and clean.

H. Store the live frog as directed by your teacher. See annotation below for proper storage of live frogs.

You should now be able to

Relate the structures of the hind legs to swimming and jumping.

Locate the nostrils and explain how they are adapted for use in the frog's environment.

Locate the clear eyelid and explain how the frog uses this structure both on land and in water.

Relate the structure of the frog's legs to jumping and swimming.

Procedure for storing frogs that must be transported from one area to another: Place each frog in a quart fruit jar containing a moist paper towel. Lids should have holes punched in them for ventilation. The last class using frogs each day should return them to the refrigerated storage area.

16-2. By throwing its sticky, forked tongue forward, a frog is able to capture flying insects. Note that the tongue is attached at the front of the mouth.

16-3. A frog swims by flexing and then extending its legs.

Special frog structures

The frog has many adaptations that allow it to survive in its environment. A large mouth permits the frog to capture insects and swallow them whole. Its sticky tongue can be thrown forward to capture the insects. The sense of smell and sight work together to locate food. Most frogs are farsighted. This aids them in catching flies and gnats. The frog's clear eyelids keep the eyeballs moist in air and protect them under water.

The jumping and swimming movements of a frog are very different from those of a human. A frog swims by flexing and then extending the hind legs. Broad webs between the toes on the hind legs push against the water, driving the frog forward. When a frog jumps, it lands in such a way that the front legs absorb the impact of landing. Immediately upon landing, the hind legs fold, ready to jump again. A frog's hind legs are large and powerful. They propel the body forward rapidly when they are extended.

When frogs float, they expose just the tip of the nose while the hind legs are left hanging down. When the frog is disturbed and wishes to dive, the hind legs are flexed and drawn up close to the body. This jerks the head and body. The front legs guide the frog downward as the hind legs are extended again.

As you breathe out, muscles in your chest and ribs contract to force the air out of your lungs. The number of exhaled breaths in a minute is known as a **breathing rate.** A frog has no ribs or chest muscles to force air out of its lungs. As a result, the frog breathes in a manner different from you. In the next problem you will investigate the method and rate of breathing in a frog.

Problem 16-2 How does a frog's method and rate of breathing differ from a person's?

Purpose To compare the breathing patterns of frogs and humans.

Materials live frog paper towel

Procedure

A. In your notebook, prepare a table similar to Table 16-1 to record your observations.

B. Obtain a live frog and place it on a wet paper towel. Gently hold the frog with your hand to prevent it from jumping. Observe the nostrils, located on the upper surface of the head.

TABLE 16-1 BREATHING RATE DATA

Trials	*Frog*		*Person*
	Nostril Counts	*Throat Movements*	*Breaths per Minute*
1			
2			
3			
4			
5			
Average	Up to 25	0-5 times the nostril count	15-30

Values shown for averages represent what ranges can be expected in students' tables.

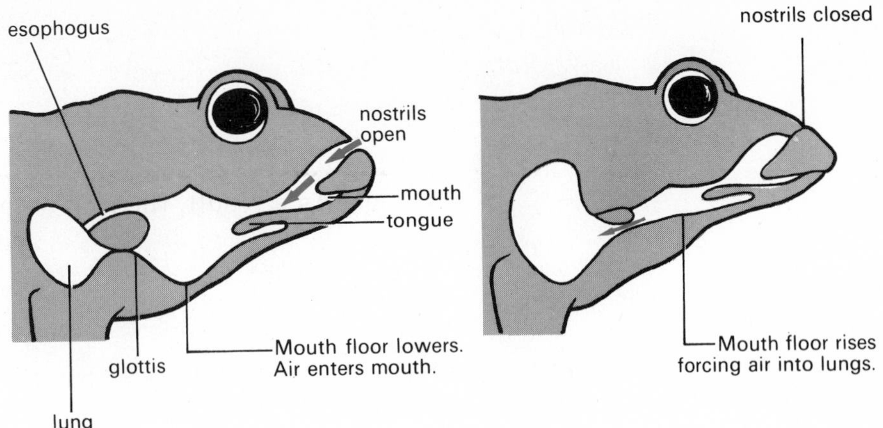

16-4. A frog forces air into its lungs by changing the volume and pressure in its mouth cavity.

C. Count and record in your notebook the number of times the nostrils open and close in one minute. Repeat the one-minute count four more times.

1. Students might record up to 25 nostril movements per minute.

1. What was the average number of times your frog's nostrils opened and closed in one minute?

D. Now observe the movements of the flap of skin under the chin. This flap of skin is involved in the breathing process of the frog. Count the number of times that this flap of skin moves up and down in one minute. Repeat the one-minute count four more times. Record your readings in your table.

Skin flap movements will range from 0-5 times the number of nostril movements.

2. Yes, as a rule.

3. Yes.

2. On the average, does the flap of skin move more times per minute than do the nostrils?
3. Does the flap of skin move when the nostrils are closed?

When the nostrils close, movements of the flap force air into the lungs. When the nostrils are open, air enters the mouth. The oxygen may also pass directly into the bloodstream through the skin lining the mouth.

E. Close your mouth and breathe naturally through your nose. Place your finger under your nose to feel your exhaled breath. Count the number of times that you exhale in one minute. Repeat the one-minute count four more times and record the results in your table.

4. From 15-30 breaths per minute can be expected for this age group.

4. What was the average number of times you exhaled in one minute?

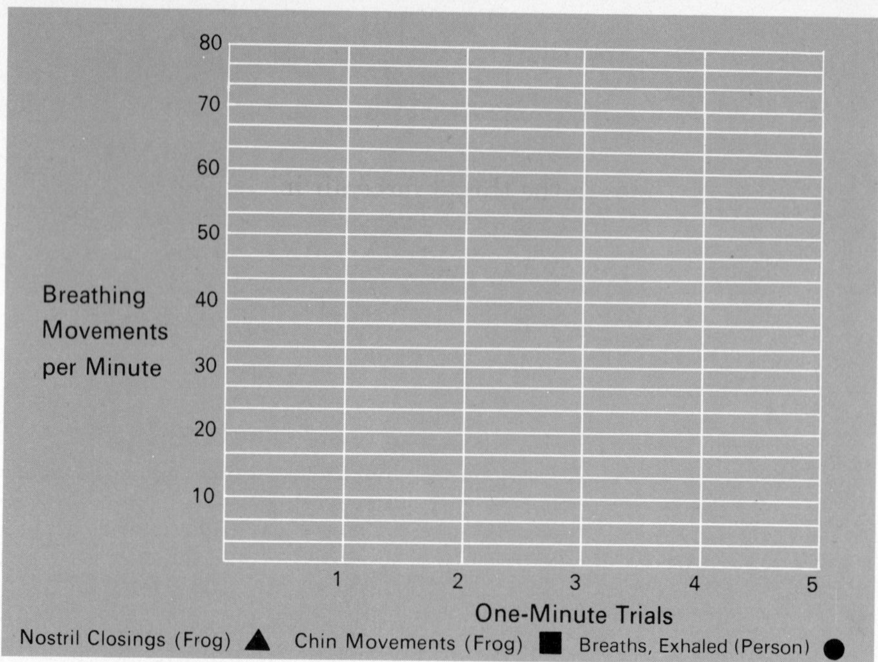

16-5. Graph for comparing the breathing rate of a frog to that of a person.

5. Students' graphs should agree with their data and show that a person's breathing rate is faster and fluctuates less than the frog's rate.

6. Yes. Rate may range from 0-30 breaths per minute.

9. Yes. Activities such as swimming or jumping would be accompanied by an increased breathing rate. (A person's breathing rate is affected by exercise, fear, anger, sleeping, etc.)

F. You will need to prepare a graph to compare the breathing rate of the frog to your own breathing rate. Refer to the sample graph in Figure 16-5. Use a different mark to plot each type of breathing movement on your graph. Use a triangle, a square, and a circle as keyed in Figure 16-5. Connect each plot point for the same type of movement with a smooth line.

5. Copy the graph into your notebook. Complete the graph using the data in your table.
6. Did the frog's breathing rate change? (Compare the number of nostril movements taken by the frog each minute during the five-minute period.)
7. Did your breathing rate change? 7. No.
8. How does the average number of nostril movements per minute of the frog compare with the number of times you breathed per minute? 8. Usually it is less.
9. Do you think the frog's breathing rate would be related to its activity? (Is yours?)

You should now be able to

Determine the breathing rates of a frog and a human.
Compare the breathing rates of a frog and a human.

Frog breathing and vocal cords

A frog has no chest muscles to force air out of its lungs. So its method of breathing is quite different from that of a human. In the frog, valves in the nostrils close to prevent air from escaping while muscles in the throat force air into the lungs. It is impossible for a frog to take air into its lungs while its mouth is open. The constant movement of a frog's throat is a sign that it is swallowing air.

Air that is forced backward over the vocal cords in the throat may produce a noise or a "croak." Male frogs have well-developed vocal cords. Frogs croak the most during their breeding season. They also croak at other times, especially in the evening. A frog can even croak under water by moving the air back and forth between the lungs and the throat.

During hibernation, the frog's breathing rate changes as the temperature becomes colder. Frogs, you remember, are called "cold-blooded." Their bodies do not have the ability to regulate their body temperatures. Humans, however, are **warm-blooded**. A human's body temperature normally remains steady at 37°C (98.6°F). In the next problem you will determine how changes in temperature affect the breathing rate and body temperature of a frog.

RECOMMENDED FOR DEMONSTRATION

Problem 16-3 How does a change in temperature affect the breathing rate and body temperature of a frog?

Purpose To determine how changes in temperature affect both the breathing rate and internal temperature of a frog.

Materials

Use a fresh frog for best results.

- live frog
- insulated chests (3)
- ice
- Celsius thermometers (2)
- water at room temperature

Procedure

Review the correct procedure for reading a thermometer precisely and handling it safely.

A. Copy Table 16-2 (next page) into your notebook for recording your observations.

B. Put room-temperature water in an insulated chest to a height of about 15 cm. Record the temperature of the water. It should be between 20° and 25°C. Place your frog in the water.

Values shown represent what ranges can be expected for averages.

TABLE 16-2 BREATHING RATE AND BODY TEMPERATURE OF A FROG

Water Temperature	*Room Temp.* 20-25°C	*Cold Temp.* 5-10 °C	*Warm Temp.* 35-40 °C
Nostril Movements	1		
	2		
	3		
	4		
	5		
	Average 15-20	Average 5-10	Average 25-30
Internal Body Temperature	1		
	2		
	3		
	Average 20°-25°	Average 5°-10°	Average 35°-40°

Review procedure for finding average, if necessary.

C. Count the number of times the nostrils open and close in one minute. Repeat the one-minute count four more times. Record the five counts in your table.

1. Should be 16-20 per minute.

1. What is your frog's average number of nostril movements per minute when the water is at room temperature?

Demonstrate proper procedure for inserting thermometer. Care should be taken to avoid injuring the frog.

D. Look at Figure 16-6. Hold the frog in the water and *gently* insert a thermometer into its mouth. Go through the gullet and into the stomach. This is a distance of only about 2 or 3 cm in most frogs. Take three readings, at one-minute intervals, of the frog's internal temperature. Record the readings in your table.

2. Should be about the same as the environmental temperature, 20-25°C.

2. What is your frog's average internal temperature when the frog is in room-temperature water?

E. Remove the frog from the room-temperature water and place it in an insulated chest containing ice water. Measure the temperature of the water with a thermometer other than the one you will use on the frog in Step F. Record the temperature of the ice water.

F. Take three readings, at one-minute intervals, of the frog's internal temperature. Hold the frog in the ice water while measuring the frog's temperature. Record the readings in your table.

3. Should be same as ice water, about 5-10°C.

3. What is your frog's average internal temperature in ice water?

G. Count the number of times the nostrils open and close during one minute while the frog is in the ice water. Repeat the one-minute count four more times. Record the five counts in your table.

4. Most averages will fall between 5-10 breaths per minute.

4. What is your frog's average number of nostril movements per minute while in the ice water?

Be careful that students do not use water at temperature above 40° C. High temperatures may kill the frog.

H. Now put the frog in an insulated chest containing warm water (35°-40°C). Measure and record the temperature in your table.

I. Take three readings, at one-minute intervals, of the frog's internal temperature. Hold the frog in the water while taking the readings. Record the readings in your table.

5. Internal body temperature should go up towards the warm temperature, 35-40°C.

5. What is your frog's average internal temparature in warm water?

J. Count the number of nostril movements during one minute while the frog is in warm water. Repeat the one-minute count four more times. Record the five counts in your table.

6. Around 25-30 per minute.

6. What is your frog's average number of nostril movements while in the warm water?

16-6. Gently insert a thermometer through the frog's mouth into its gullet to observe its internal body temperature.

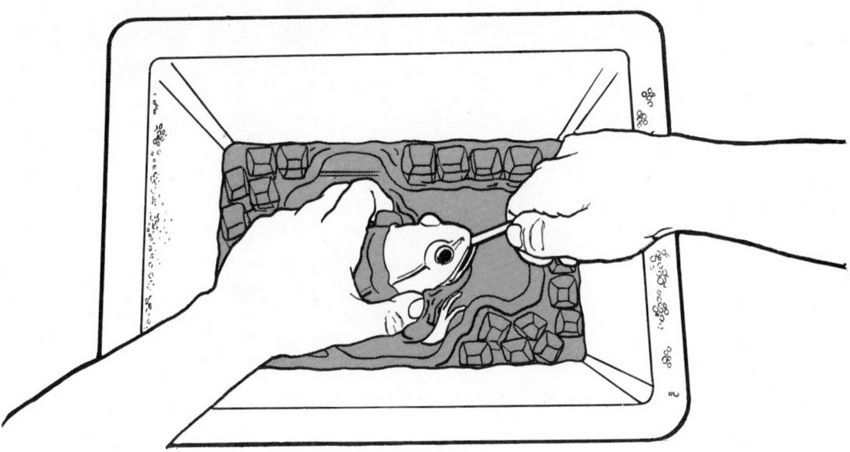

You may want to review steps in preparing a line graph.

K. Remove your frog from the warm water. Store the frog as directed by your teacher.

L. Prepare line graphs to compare nostril movement and body temperature changes to water temperature changes. Use Figure 16-7 as an example.

7. Graphs should show a direct relationship between water temperature and internal temperature, and between breathing rate and nostril movement.

7. In your notebook, graph the data recorded in your table.
8. How did the breathing rate of the frog change as the temperature increased?
9. How did the internal body temperature of the frog change with the environmental temperature?

8. It also increased.

9. There was a direct relationship between the body temperature and environmental temperature.

16-7. Line graphs to compare nostril movement and body temperature changes to water temperature changes.

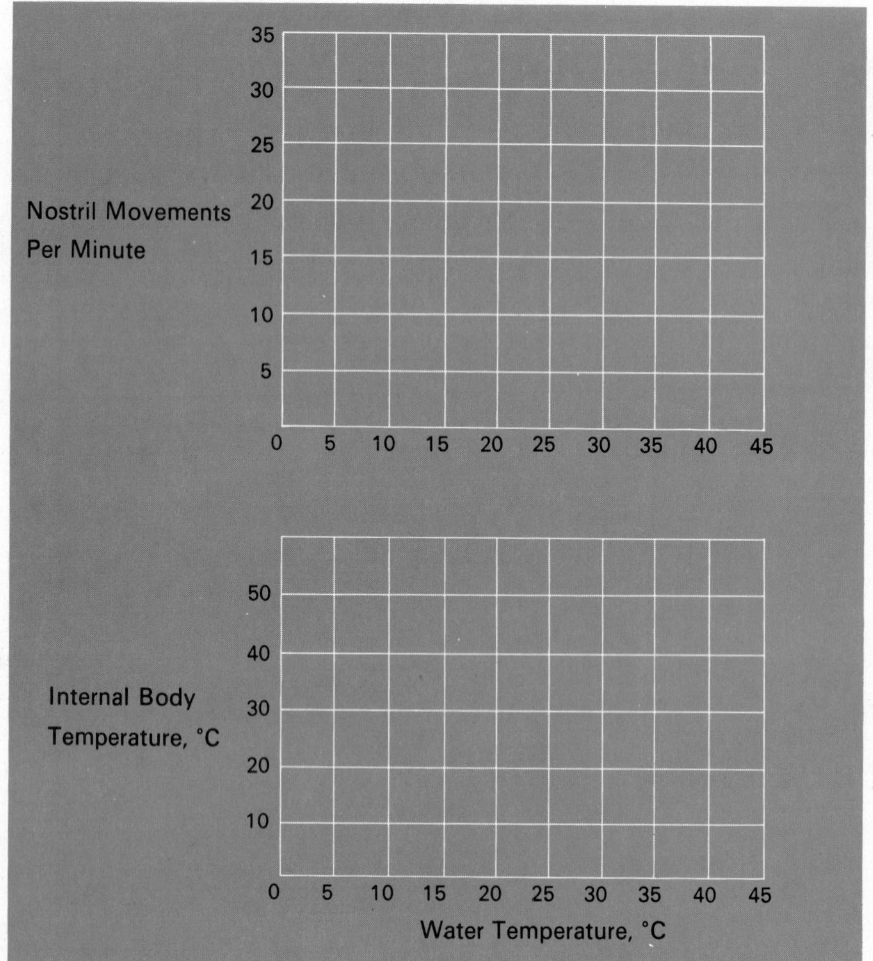

*TABLE 16-3 BREATHING RATE AND BODY TEMPERATURE OF A HUMAN**

Air Temperature	*Normal Body Temp.* 37°C	*Cold Temp.* 5°C	*Warm Temp.* 50°C
Breaths Per Minute	14 16 15 Average 15	18 18 18 Average 18	22 21 23 Average 22
Internal Body Temperature	37° 37° 37° Average 37° C	37° 38° 36° Average 37°C	39° 37° 38° Average 38° C

* Data given is for a person 15 years old.

When the internal temperature of an organism changes with the environmental temperature, the organism is said to be cold-blooded. If kept at a low temperature, the frog will hibernate.

10. It decreased.

10. What happened to the breathing rate of the frog as the temperature was changed to 0°C?

In Table 16-3, the average temperature and breathing rate of a fifteen-year-old person has been recorded.

11. It stays the same.

11. What happens to the person's body temperature as the environmental temperature increases or decreases?

12. It increases slightly.

12. What happens to the person's breathing rate as the environmental temperature decreases?

When the internal temperature of an organism stays about the same while the environmental temperature changes, the organism is said to be warm-blooded. That takes energy, however. Energy is used to prevent the internal temperature from changing with the environment.

You should now be able to

Compare the internal body temperature of a frog with the environmental temperature.

Relate a frog's breathing rate to the environmental temperature.

Relate the constant body temperature of a human, as a warm-blooded organism, to the environmental temperature.

1. A "cold-blooded" animal that spends part of its life in water and part on land.

2. An immature, fishlike form of a frog. The stage of metamorphosis between the egg and the adult.

3. Metamorphosis.

4. Cold-blooded animals have body temperatures that are regulated by the environmental temperature. Warm-blooded animals maintain an even body temperature, not regulated by the temperature of the environment.

5. The area in which an organism lives.

6. Food, shelter, oxygen, favorable temperature, etc. (Accept any 3.)

7. Mouth, nostrils, skin.

8. Hibernation.

9. Insects and worms.

10. Webs of skin between the toes on the hind legs, large hind-leg muscles, and a smooth skin. The frog also uses its front legs to help guide it. Other assets are the location of the mouth, eyes, nostrils, etc.

Science terms

amphibian	cold-blooded	physiology
anatomy	habitat	tadpole
breathing rate	hibernation	warm-blooded
camouflage	metamorphosis	

Review questions

1. What is an amphibian?
2. What is a tadpole?
3. What word indicates the changes that occur as a frog egg develops into an adult?
4. Define the terms cold-blooded and warm-blooded.
5. What is a habitat?
6. Name three things a frog needs from its environment.
7. In what three ways does a frog breathe?
8. What word indicates a frog's condition of "winter sleep"?
9. Name two kinds of organisms eaten by a frog.
10. What special structures assist a frog in swimming?

Check your understanding

See Teacher's Guide section for answers to Questions 11-19.

11. Describe how a frog catches an insect.
12. What structures help the frog to jump the way it does?
13. Describe how a frog swims.
14. How does the color of a frog's skin protect the frog from its enemies?
15. Describe how a frog swallows air.
16. What happens to the body temperature of a cold-blooded animal when the environmental temperature changes?
17. How does a frog breathe when it hibernates?
18. Of what value is a frog's clear eyelid?
19. Why does a frog feel cold to the touch?

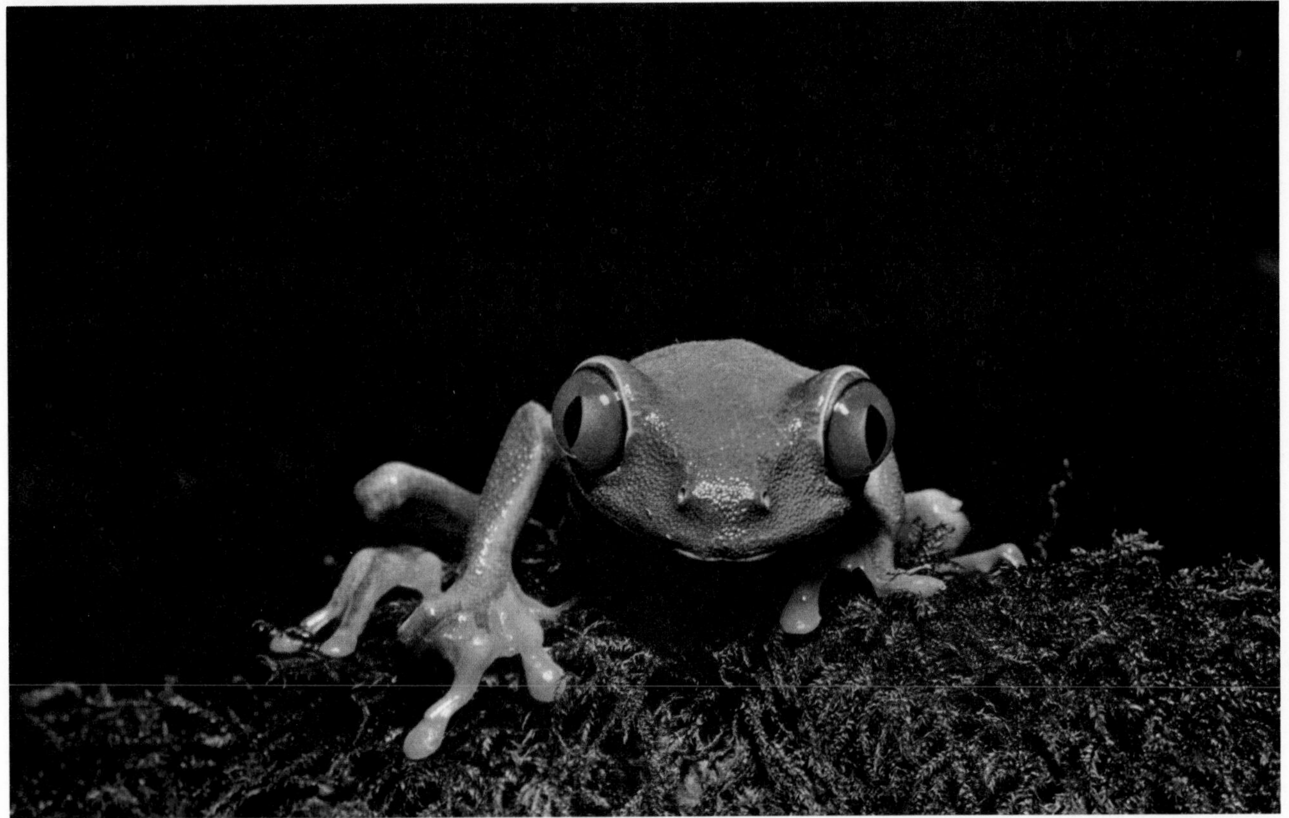

Chapter 17 Comparing the frog's organ systems to the human's

Chapter-opening photo shows a frog that can't be seen in this country, but serves to illustrate the variety of forms a given group of animals can take. Point out that although the frog looks very different in many ways from the bullfrog, for instance, it is still the same in other, anatomical ways.

Two of the factors that determine the success of an organism are where it lives and what it needs for food. Humans can adjust to almost any kind of condition. People are found in humid tropical areas, in cold polar regions, and in dry deserts. Humans can adapt to different environments because they are able to modify hostile conditions. They are also aided by their constant body temperature. Lower forms of life, such as frogs, can exist only where the conditions necessary for their life are favorable.

Humans can clothe their bodies against the cold. Frogs can only bury themselves in mud and hibernate. Humans can produce and eat a wide variety of foods. Frogs must stay in areas that provide them with the only foods they can eat — insects and worms.

The differences between frogs and humans are fairly obvious. This chapter is about some of the similarities that exist as well.

(*Above*) A red-eye tree frog from Central America.

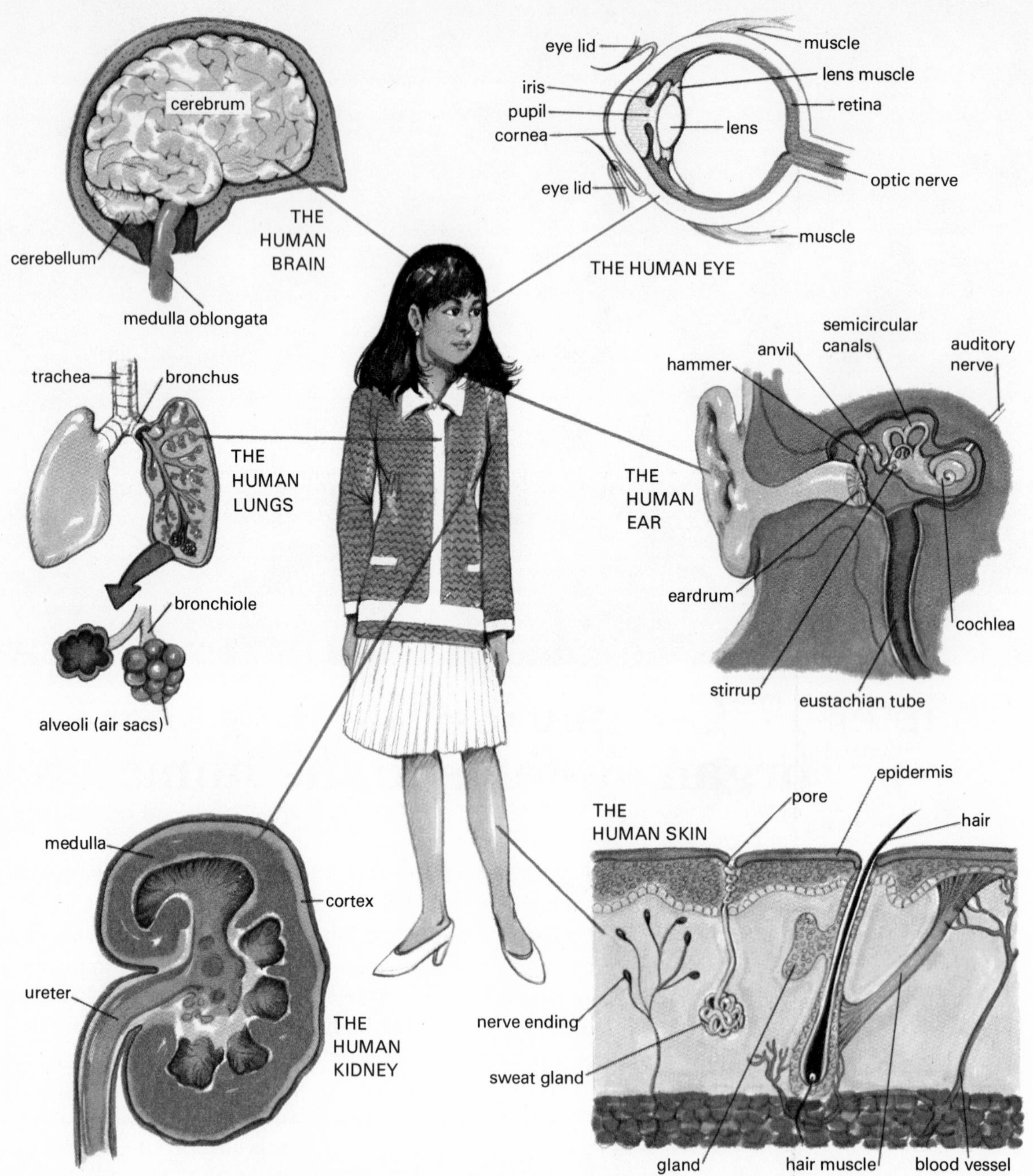

17-1. Some of the major organs in the human organism include the lungs in the respiratory system; the kidneys and skin (perspiration) in the excretory system; the brain, eye, and ear in the nervous system.

Comparing digestive systems

A frog captures insects and worms with the help of its fast-moving, sticky tongue. The food is swallowed whole. All digestion must take place in the stomach and small intestine. You will study the frog's digestive tract in Problem 17-4.

Humans can chew their food, thus speeding up the process of digestion. Your **incisors**, the front teeth, are constructed to bite food. Next to the incisors are the **canine** teeth. These can tear food into small pieces. Your mouth also contains a number of teeth called **molars,** which grind food into tiny pieces before it is swallowed. (The human teeth are shown in Figure 17-7, page 322.)

Working with the teeth is the tongue, which is used to push the food around inside the mouth. (See Figure 17-2.) When the food is ready to be swallowed, the tongue pushes it back toward the **glottis**, the opening in the back of the throat. As you swallow, a little flap of muscle, the **epiglottis**, covers the opening to the lungs. Without this protection the food would "go down the wrong way" and cause you to cough and choke.

You also use your teeth and tongue in cooperation with your lips, mouth, and throat for speaking. Thus it is clear that your mouth serves a double function. It begins the digestive process and is a vital part of the speech process.

In the frog, the process of digestion starts as food enters the stomach. Digestion is the process of breaking down complex foods into simpler compounds. Since the frog's teeth are not used for chewing, the food must be broken down mechanically in the stomach. You will study the internal structure of the frog's stomach in Problem 17-4.

From the stomach, the broken pieces of food enter the small intestine. In the small intestine of both frogs and humans, digestive chemicals from the liver and the pancreas help to digest the food. Re-

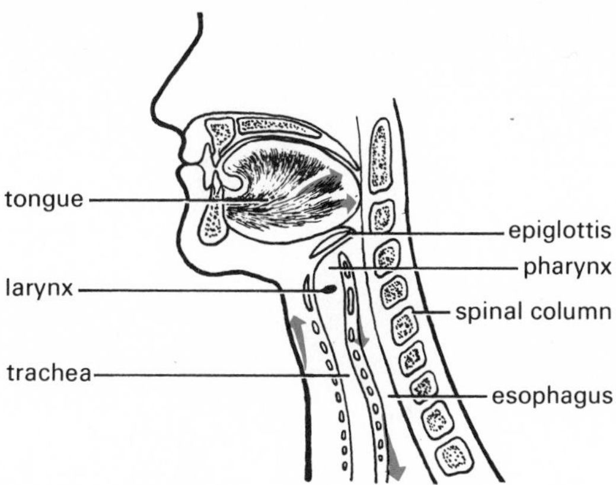

17-2. The muscular epiglottis covers the top of the windpipe during swallowing.

call your study of the process of diffusion in Problem 13-2. The dialysis membrane permitted small sugar molecules to pass through. But it did not allow more complex materials to pass through. The intestine could be compared to the dialysis tubing. The intestine permits only small molecules to pass through it by the process of diffusion.

Once the molecules of digested food pass through the walls of the intestine, they enter the bloodstream. The circulatory system then carries the food to all the cells in the body. The blood flows because of the pumping action of the heart. The regular contraction of the heart muscles forces the blood through the arteries, capillaries, and veins.

It is in the capillaries where one of the most important functions of the blood takes place. The capillaries are tubes just one cell layer thick. This thinness allows materials to pass between the capillaries and the cells of the body. The movement of highly concentrated food from the blood to a body cell is the beginning of the final phase of digestion. (See Figure 17-3.)

Oxygen, which entered the blood at the lungs, will also diffuse through the capillary wall and enter the cell. In the cell, the food is either used for growth or oxidized for energy. The oxidizing of food in the cell is called **internal respiration**. Carbon dioxide, water, and other waste products of cell respiration diffuse back into the bloodstream. The kidneys remove some wastes from the blood and the lungs remove other wastes. Taken together, the total chemical processes of the body are called **metabolism**. Metabolism includes digestion, cell respiration, and the elimination of wastes.

There are other systems that help to keep organisms functioning properly. The nervous system, which includes the brain and spinal cord, receives stimuli from the external environment. Messages may then be sent to the part of the body that will respond. The muscles, stimulated by nerves, move the organism. (See Figure 17-4.)

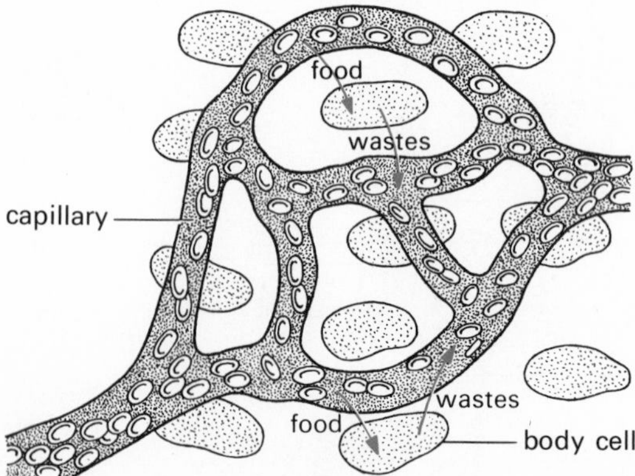

17-3. The exchange of materials between capillaries and cells of the body.

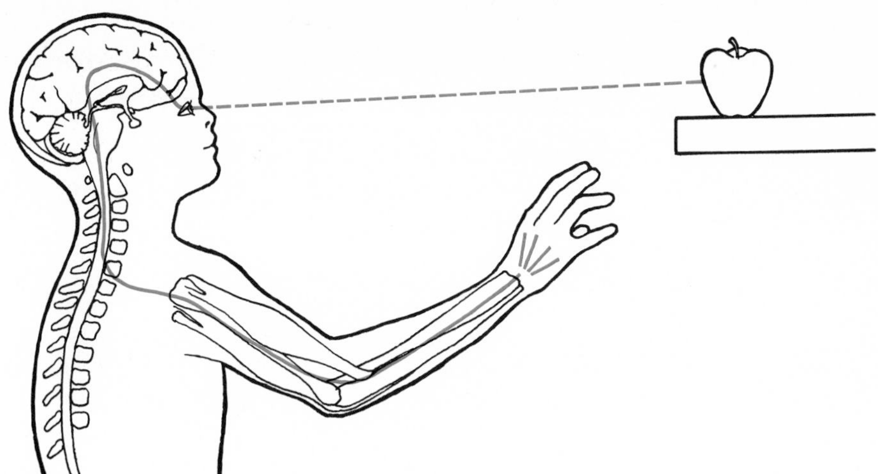

17-4. The stimulus is received by the eye and is sent to the brain, which then directs the muscles to respond.

Many sensory organs are located near the brain. The brain is usually located in the **anterior** (front) part of an animal. In the frog, the powerful jumping legs are in the **posterior** (rear) of the animal. The underside of the frog is its **ventral** side, while the top (back) is its **dorsal** side. This is shown in Figure 17-5.

In this chapter you will examine the internal structures of the frog. The organs will be compared to similar organs in humans. When you have finished this chapter, you will not only be familiar with the internal structures of the frog, you will also have a better understanding of your own body and how it is organized.

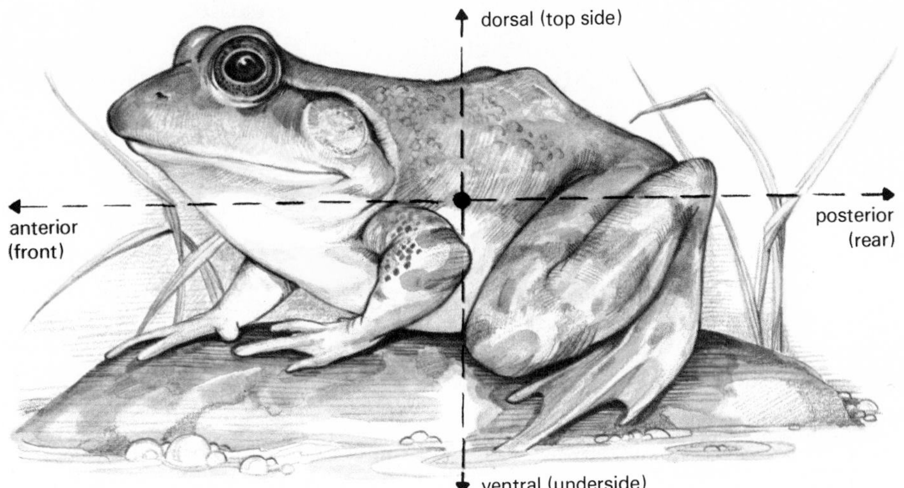

17-5. With the frog used here as an example, all animals have an anterior and a posterior end, a dorsal and a ventral side.

Problem 17-1 How does the structure of your mouth compare with the structure of a frog's mouth?

Purpose To compare mouth parts of frogs and humans to discover similarities and differences.

Materials

preserved frog	dissecting needles (2)	plastic bag
scissors	tweezers	paper clip
dissecting pan	medicine dropper	masking tape

Procedure

Dissecting pins may be used to hold the mouth open.

A. Open the preserved frog's mouth and make a 1-cm cut in each corner of the mouth with your scissors. This procedure will allow the lower jaw to move freely. (See Figure 17-6.)

B. With the mouth open, locate the tongue. Lift the tongue with the tweezers to find where it is attached.

1. Where is the tongue attached in the mouth of a frog? The frog uses its sticky tongue to catch insects.
2. How does the attachment of your tongue prevent you from extending it full length from your mouth?
3. How is your tongue used in the eating process?
4. Your tongue has some specialized cells that help you to taste the food you eat. What surfaces of your tongue have these specialized taste buds?

1. The front part of the lower jaw.

2. It is attached to the back floor of the mouth.

3. The tongue is used to move the food around as it is chewed, and to push the food to the back of the mouth where it is swallowed.

4. Top and sides.

C. Use the blunt end of a dissecting needle to probe near the center of the frog's mouth. Probe for the opening of the digestive tube. This opening is called the **gullet**. (See Figure 17-6.)

D. Find the glottis, below the gullet in the lower jaw. The glottis controls the movement of air from mouth to lungs. Use a dropper to force air into the opening.

5. What change of the body wall do you notice?
6. Is the glottis open or closed in your frog?
7. Can the gullet also be opened and closed?

5. The body wall below the front legs moves slightly outward and seems to enlarge somewhat.

6. The glottis is normally closed, but it may remain open after being forced open by the dropper.

7. Yes.

E. In humans, the single opening in the mouth leads to both the stomach and the lungs. The epiglottis is a small flap of muscle tissue that can be moved to direct the path of material toward stomach or lungs. (See Figure 17-2 on page 317.) The epiglottis is located in the back of your throat, an area called the **pharynx**.

Students may have to raise the upper lip of the frog in order to feel the teeth on the upper jaw.

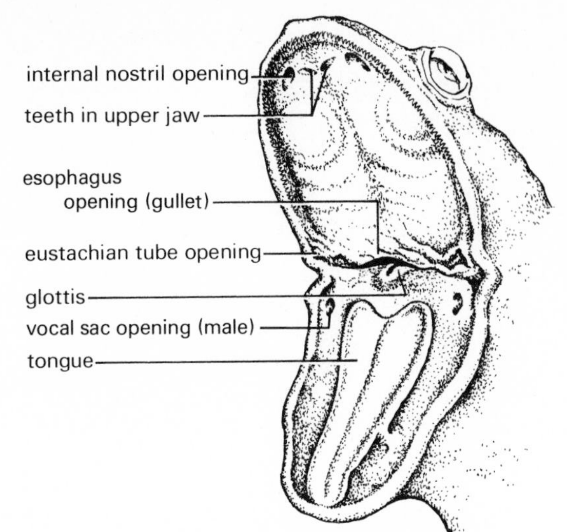

17-6. When the preserved frog's mouth is cut so it can be opened wide, the internal parts of the mouth can be easily seen and identified.

8. Open.

8. Would your epiglottis open or close to allow air to enter the windpipe on the way to the lungs?

The similar function of the eustachian tubes in the frog and human should be emphasized.

F. In humans, the **eustachian** [yoo-STAY-shun] **tube** connects the middle ear with the mouth. This allows air pressure within the middle ear to stay equalized. Locate the opening to the frog's eustachian tube, on the upper jaw near the corner of the mouth. (See Figure 17-6.) Gently insert the point of the dissecting needle into the opening and follow the path of the eustachian tube.

9. Yes.

10. Yes.

9. Is the eustachian tube connected to the frog's ear?

10. Do humans have a separate opening into the mouth from the eustachian tube?

G. Locate the two internal nostril openings near the front of the frog's upper jaw. (See Figure 17-6.) With a dissecting needle, gently follow one of the openings to the outside. These openings to the outside are used by the frog to bring oxygen into the mouth, where it is absorbed directly through the linings. The glottis remains closed except when the lungs are used in breathing.

11. External nostrils (nares).

11. What external structures are connected to the internal nostril openings?

H. Locate the frog's large teeth, between the two internal nostrils on the upper jaw.

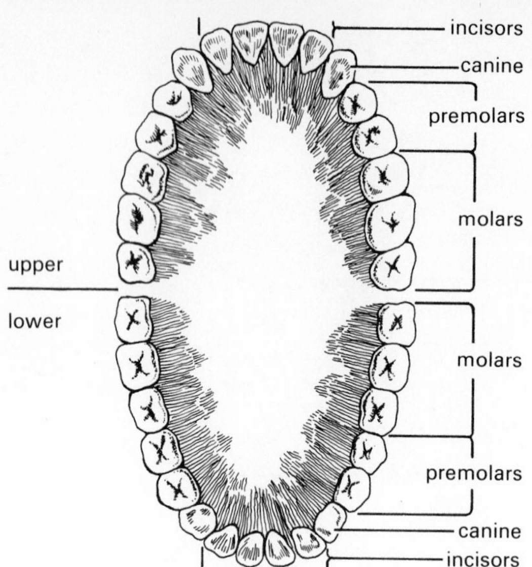

17-7. Teeth of a human adult. The incisors are used for biting food, the canine teeth for tearing, and the premolars and molars for grinding food.

12. Two.

12. How many hard projections are visible?

I. The frog also has teeth located on the upper jaw bone. To find these teeth, run your finger over the surface of the upper jaw.

13. Rough, due to the presence of many fine teeth.

13. Does the upper jaw feel smooth or rough?

J. The frog is unable to chew food with its teeth. The frog only uses its teeth to hold the prey while it swallows the organism whole. Notice the two large bulges in the lining of the upper jaw. These bulges in the upper jaw, along with the two sets of teeth, help the frog hold the prey during swallowing. Gently push on the frog's eyes.

14. Yes.

14. Do the eyes seem to push the roof of the mouth down?

K. Figure 17-7 shows a complete set of human teeth. The shapes of human teeth are specialized for different jobs. This makes them more useful for the biting, chewing, tearing, and grinding of food.

15. Usually 32.

15. How many teeth are there in an adult human mouth?

16. Incisors.

16. Which teeth have a sharp knifelike edge for cutting?

17. Molars.

17. Which teeth are used to grind the food?

18. Large, rough, irregular surfaces.

18. What type of surface do the grinding teeth have?

L. Canine teeth are best suited for piercing and tearing food. They are greatly enlarged in animals such as tigers that hunt and kill their prey.

M. *Storage Procedure:* Place a piece of masking tape on a small, plastic bag. Write the name of your team and class or section number on the masking tape. Place the preserved frog in the bag and seal it with a paper clip or rubber band. Store the bag containing the frog in the container designated by your teacher. You will use the same frog in Problems 17-2, 17-3, and 17-4.

You should now be able to

Relate the attachment of the tongue to its function in frogs and humans.

Locate the openings to the digestive tube, lungs, and middle ear in the frog.

Locate the teeth of a frog and compare number and type with those of a human.

Locate internal and external nostril openings in a frog.

Protection and support of internal organs

When you handled the frog, you may have noticed one obvious difference between its head and the rest of its body. The head is very hard. The reason for this is that almost the entire top of the head is a bone. This bone, called the **skull**, protects the brain from injury. (See Figure 17-8.) The center of all the senses — sight, touch, smell, taste, and hearing — is located in the brain.

The internal organs of the rest of the frog's body are also protected. Extending from the back of the head down the center of the dorsal surface is the backbone. It consists of many interlocking and movable **vertebrae**. These bones protect the organs in the body cavity, but are flexible enough to allow the frog to move. The human has a similar structure that protects the spinal nerve cord and also helps the human stand erect.

The frog's heart lies in the middle of the body almost directly beneath the hard bone of the shoulder girdle. Other organs are also protected against damage. The two kidneys are attached to the inner muscle wall on the posterior dorsal (rear upper) surface. You may be able to see them in Problem 17-2 if you push the intestines aside.

The lungs of the frog are deep within the center of the body. They are protected on the dorsal side by the bony vertebrae. They are protected on the ventral side by the liver. As you dissect your frog in Problem 17-2, notice how the other organs are protected.

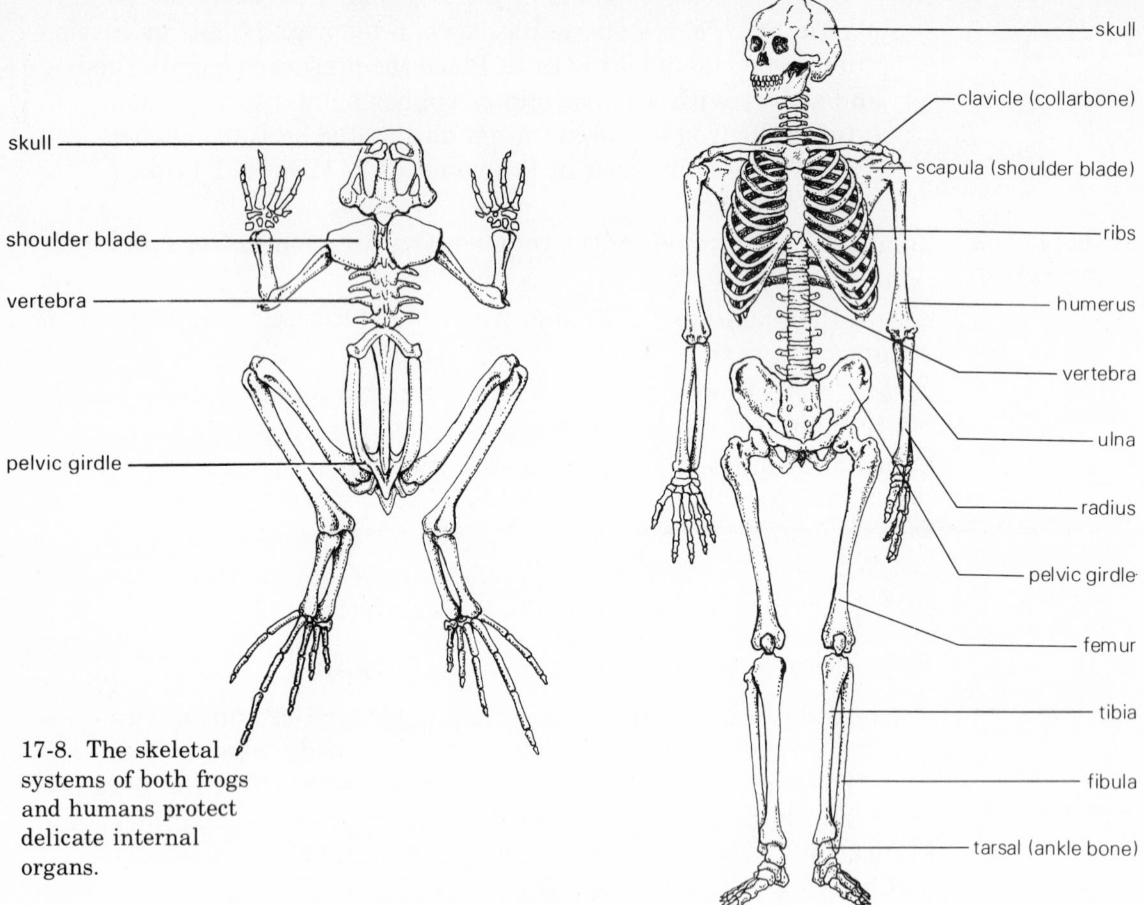

17-8. The skeletal systems of both frogs and humans protect delicate internal organs.

Human organ protection

Humans have more protection for their internal organs than frogs do. (See Figure 17-8.) The heart and lungs are surrounded by hard ribs as well as by a strong, flat bone in the center of the chest. This flat bone is the **sternum**, or breastbone. The **pelvic girdle**, just below the hips, serves to protect the intestine and reproductive system.

However, several vital organs in the human are not protected by bone. The two kidneys, for example, lie on the dorsal side of the body just above the pelvic girdle and on either side of the backbone. Because of their exposed position, a punch to the kidneys has been declared illegal in professional boxing.

In both frogs and humans, all of the internal organs are attached to each other or to bones by tough membranes. You will see these membranes when you remove the digestive system of your preserved frog.

Problem 17-2 What organs are found in the body cavities of frogs and humans?

Purpose To locate some of the organs of a frog and compare them with the organs of humans.

Materials

Each team should use the same frog they used in Problem 17-1.

preserved frog (from Problem 17-1)
dissecting pins
dissecting pan
scissors
tweezers

Procedure

If this is students' first experience with dissecting a frog, demonstrate the dissection procedure before allowing students to try it.

A. Obtain your preserved frog. Place it in the pan with the ventral surface up and the head pointed away from you.

B. Cut through the skin layer *only*, starting at the point where the hind legs are attached to the body. (See Figure 17-9.) Continue the shallow cutting up to the curve of the lower jaw. Pull the skin away from the underlying muscle layer. Use the blunt end of your tweezers to separate any tissue holding the skin to the muscle layer.

C. Carefully cut through the muscle layer. Use just the points of your scissors, cutting with an upward stroke. This procedure pre-

17-9. Slit the skin from the angle of the rear legs to the curve of the lower jaw (colored dotted line on frog at left). Then carefully cut through the muscle layer.

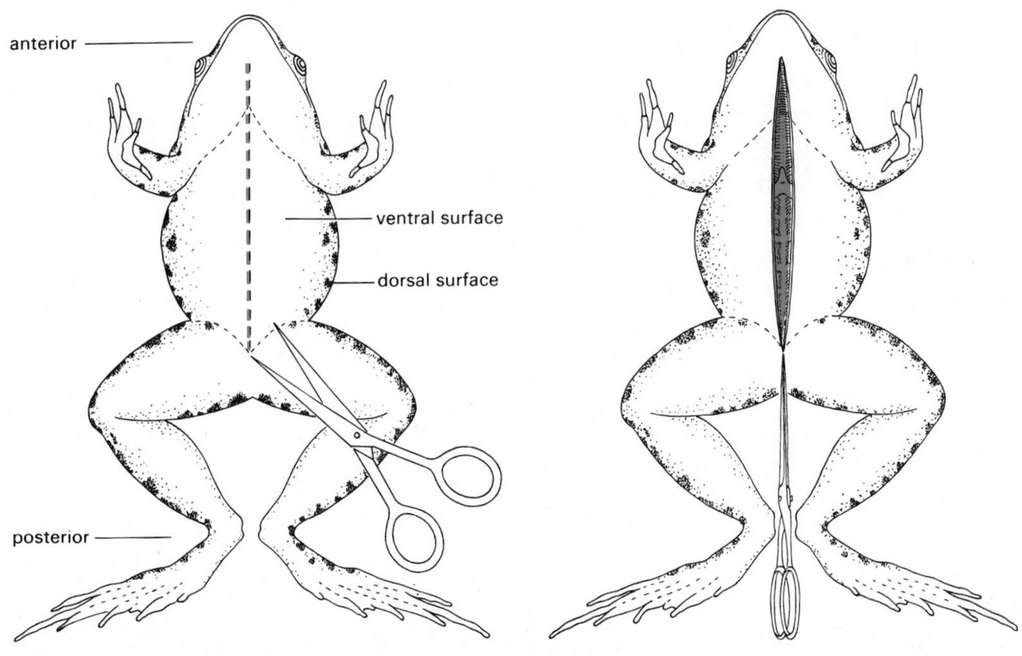

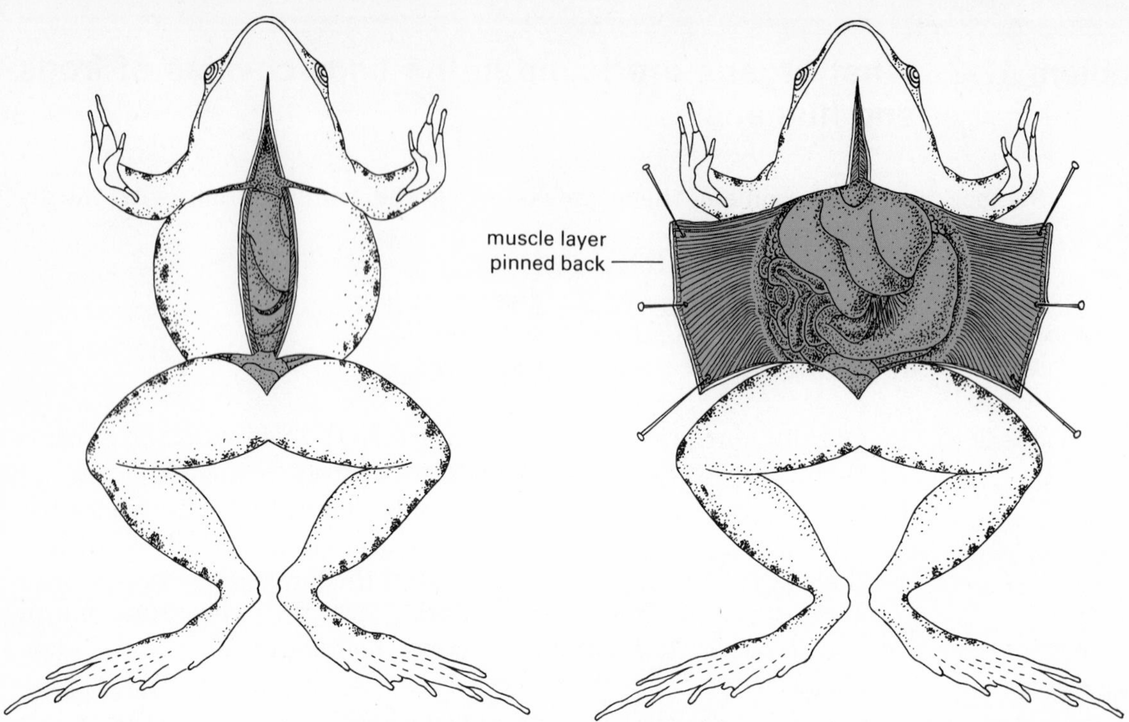

17-10. When you have finished making the incisions, pry the front legs of the frog apart to expose the internal organs. Pin back the layers of muscle and skin.

vents cutting and damaging the internal organs. Cut the muscle layer as indicated in Figure 17-9.

At the front legs you will have to cut through the bones of the shoulder girdle. Turn the scissor blades *parallel* to the table, to cut almost sideways rather than up-and-down. Cutting down may destroy the heart. As you complete this cut, the scissors will snap shut. Then cut through the skin and muscle layers around the front and hind legs, as indicated by the black dotted lines in Figure 17-9.

D. With your thumbs, pry the front legs apart to expose the internal organs as shown in Figure 17-10. Use dissecting pins to keep the skin and muscle layers pulled away from the internal organs. If you have a female frog, the body cavity may contain a mass of black and cream-colored eggs. You should also be able to find the mass of coiled white tubes that are part of the female reproductive system.

E. Figure 17-11 identifies the internal organs visible when the body cavity of the frog is open. In your frog, locate each of the labeled

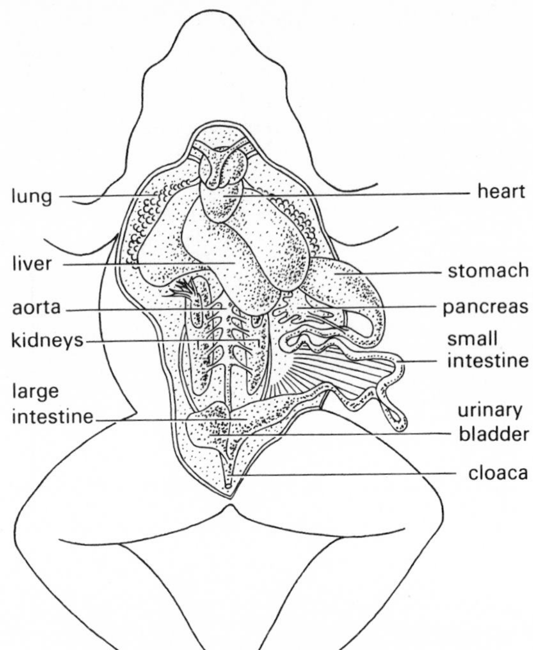

17-11. The internal organs of a frog.

Remind students that the internal organs of the frog should not be removed during this problem.

organs. After you have done this, compare the frog's organs with the human organs in Figure 17-12. To locate the organs in the frog's body cavity, you must work very carefully. The triangular heart is located at the surface of the opened frog, between the

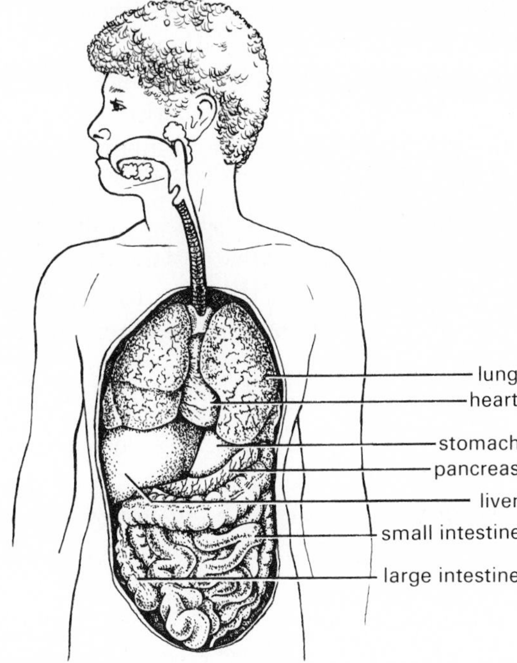

17-12. The internal organs of the human body are similar to those of a frog.

Tally marks indicate how students' tables should be completed.

TABLE 17–1 FROG ORGAN IDENTIFICATION

Frog Parts	*Digestive System*	*Circulatory System*	*Respiratory System*
Liver	x		
Heart		x	
Small Intestine	x		
Large Intestine	x		
Pancreas	x		
Stomach	x		
Lungs			x

front legs. The liver is composed of three flat lobes, next to and posterior to the heart. (Refer to Figure 17-11.) The lungs are found below and on each side of the heart and liver. The stomach is the yellow-white organ under the liver, on the right side of the body cavity as you look at it. Follow the stomach until it narrows into the coiled small intestine. The small intestine connects to the shorter, enlarged area called the large intestine. Other organs of the body cavity will be identified as you complete Problems 17-3 and 17-4.

F. Copy Table 17-1 into your notebook. For each organ, check the column that tells to what system the organ belongs.

G. *Storage procedure:* Return the frog to the plastic bag with your group name on it. Store as your teacher directs.

You should now be able to

Identify the major organs found in the body cavity of a frog.

Organize the organs found in the frog's body cavity into the systems to which they belong.

Compare the organs found in the body cavity of a frog with those of a human.

Relate the structures of some organs to their functions.

The heart and circulatory system

The circulatory systems of the frog and the human are very similar. Both systems are composed of blood vessels that take blood to all parts of the body. The **arteries** are the vessels that carry blood away from the heart. As the arteries branch to different parts of the body, they get smaller and smaller. They finally become the **capillaries**. From the microscopic capillaries the blood flows into the **veins**. The veins carry the blood back to the heart.

Both frogs and humans also have hearts. Not all animals do. The earthworm, you may recall, has five pumping arteries instead of a heart. (See the aortic arches in Figure 7-10, page 121.)

You located the frog's heart in the last problem. In the human body, the heart is located in the center of the chest, under the sternum. Both the frog and human hearts have several large blood vessels connected to them. (See Figure 17-13.) Some of these vessels bring "used" blood from the body to the heart. Some carry blood to or from the lungs. And the largest vessel of them all leaves the heart carrying blood to the body.

The human heart is about the size of a fist. It begins to beat months before birth. Proper care of the heart is important. Certain diseases, such as rheumatic fever, can damage it. Many drugs, such as the nicotine in cigarettes, interfere with the flow of blood through the circulatory system. This puts a strain on the heart.

Medical science has done some dramatic things with the heart. The valves that control blood flow through the heart can be replaced with synthetic devices. Entire hearts have been transplanted. Scientists are working to make a completely artificial heart.

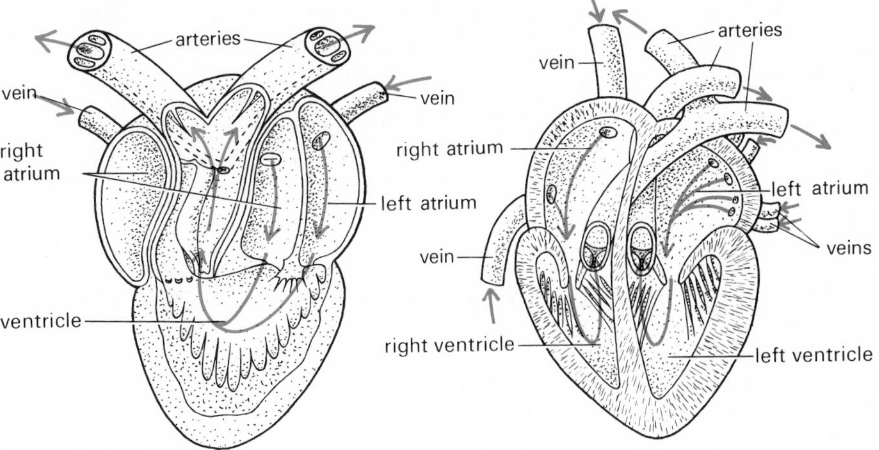

17-13. Comparing a frog's heart (*left*) to a human heart (*right*). Arrows show the direction of blood flow through the hearts.

Problem 17-3 How is the human heart different from the frog's heart?

Purpose To locate and name the chambers of the frog's heart. To compare the frog heart with the human heart.

Materials

preserved frog (from Problem 17-1)
dissecting needle
razor blade, single-edged
dissecting pins
dissecting pan

Procedure

Each team should use the same frog they used in Problems 17-1 and 17-2.

Demonstrate the proper procedure for removing the heart without damaging it.

Part One: The frog's heart

A. Remove the heart from the preserved frog as follows. Use the end of a blunt pencil to lift the triangular-shaped section as shown in Figure 17-14. Find the thin membrane and blood vessels that hold the heart in position. With the dissecting needle, carefully start to tear the tissues that keep the heart in place. Continue to lift and tear the tissue until you have removed the heart from the

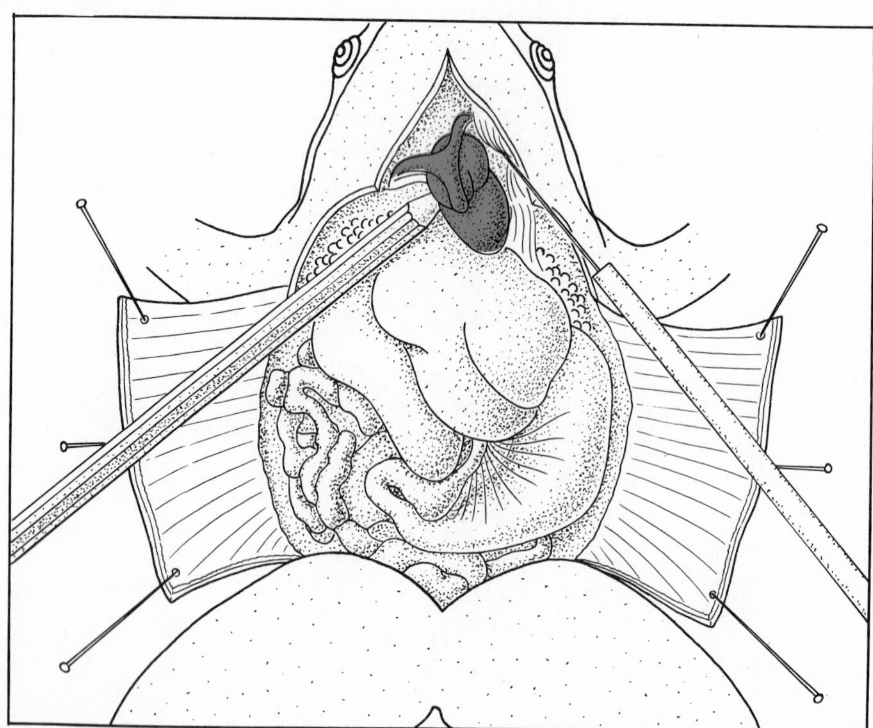

17-14. Carefully remove the frog's heart from the body cavity.

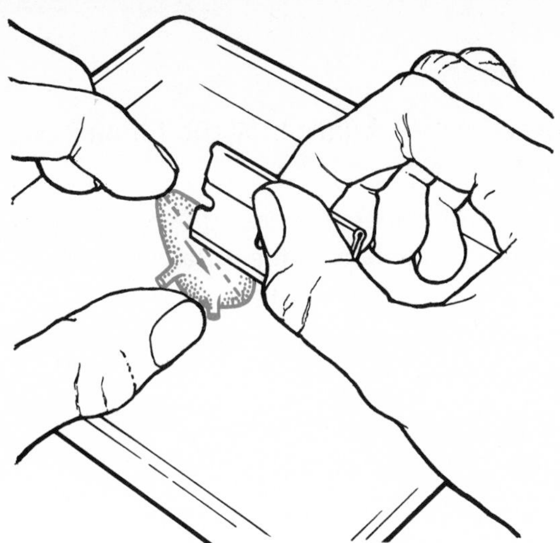

17-15. Place heart in dissecting pan and cut heart in half.

body cavity. Be careful not to miss the large saclike sections connected to the triangular portion of the heart.

Caution students to be careful with razor blades.

B. Use a razor blade carefully to cut the heart into two equal halves. Cut from the pointed end to the wider end as shown in Figure 17-15. The lower, pointed section of the heart is called the **ventricle**. The saclike sections above the ventricle are the **atria** (singular *atrium*).

1. It is thicker.

1. How is the wall of the ventricle different from the walls of the atria?

Emphasize the muscular nature of the heart.

C. The heart consists of a special type of muscle cell. The function of the heart is to pump blood through the circulatory system to all parts of the body. The section of the heart that has the thickest, strongest wall is able to pump blood the longest distances. Examine the frog's heart that you have dissected.

2. The ventricle.

3. One.

4. The atrium.

5. Two.

2. What section of the heart has the structure that would enable it to pump blood long distances?
3. How many chambers, or cavities, are found in the more muscular section of the heart?
4. What is the name of the section of the frog's heart that has thin walls and pumps blood to the thick-walled section?
5. How many chambers are located in the thin-walled section of the heart?

D. *Storage procedure:* Return the frog to the plastic bag with your group name on it. Store the bag as directed by your teacher.

Part Two: The human heart

E. Look again at the diagram of the human heart in Figure 17-13 (page 329).

6. Two; two.

6. How many chambers are found in the ventricle section of the human heart? How many in the atrial section?

7. The ventricles.

7. Which section of the heart has the thickest wall?

8. The atrial section.

8. Which section pumps blood within the heart and not to other parts of the body?

F. Refer to Figure 17-13 as you read this description of blood flow through the human heart. The blood is returned to the right atrium from the general body circulation. It is then pumped to the right ventricle, which pumps the blood to the lungs. In the lungs, the blood absorbs oxygen and releases carbon dioxide (a waste product from the body cells).

From the lungs, the blood returns to the left atrium of the heart. The left atrium pumps the blood to the left ventricle. The left ventricle pumps the blood to all parts of the body. When the blood returns from the body to the heart, it enters the right atrium again.

9. To the right ventricle.

9. Where does the right atrium pump the blood?

10. The right ventricle.

10. What section of the heart pumps blood to the lungs?

G. When blood returns from the lungs, it has been *oxygenated,* or supplied with oxygen. Because the human heart has two atria and two ventricles, the oxygenated blood can be kept separate from the blood that contains carbon dioxide.

11. The left atrium.

11. What chamber of the heart receives blood from the lungs?

12. To all parts of the body except the lungs.

12. Where does the left ventricle pump the blood?

H. The portion of the human heart that does the most work in pumping blood to the body has a different structure from the part that receives the blood.

13. It has thicker walls and is more muscular.

13. How is the left ventricle different from the rest of the human heart?

You should now be able to

Identify and name each chamber in the heart of a frog and a human.

Relate the structure of the heart to its function in the circulatory system.

Trace the circulation of blood through the heart of a frog and a human.

The functions of the intestine

The function of the digestive system is basically the same in all animals. Food enters through an opening in the anterior end and, in most cases, is mechanically broken up. In the earthworm, hard grains of sand in the gizzard break up the food. In much the same way, the frog's stomach is constructed to do the mechanical breaking up of food. In humans, the teeth serve that function.

Once food has been ground into small pieces, chemicals called digestive **enzymes** [EN-zimes] complete the job. Large, complex molecules of carbohydrates (sugars and starches) are chemically changed to the simple sugar glucose. (See Figure 17-16.) Glucose molecules are small enough to pass through living membranes. In this form, digested foods enter the circulatory system.

The length of the intestine is very important. Animals that live on a diet of plants need longer intestines than do meat-eating animals. Plant material takes longer to digest than meat. There is a difference between the diameters and lengths of the small and large intestines in any animal. In the human, the small intestine is about 5.5 meters long, but the large intestine is only about 1.5 meters long.

The major function of the large intestine is to reabsorb water used during the process of digestion. If the water were not returned to the body, the animal would *dehydrate* and die. In many animals the large intestine is also a storage place for solid wastes. Some have a specialized sac at the end for this function.

In both frogs and humans, the internal organs are neatly packaged in and around the digestive tract. If an engineer tried to design a machine to perform all the functions of a digestive tract, it would probably be very large, extremely heavy, and not nearly as efficient. When you examine the digestive system of the frog, pay close attention to the organs that produce and send digestive enzymes into the small intestine. Similar organs do the same thing for humans.

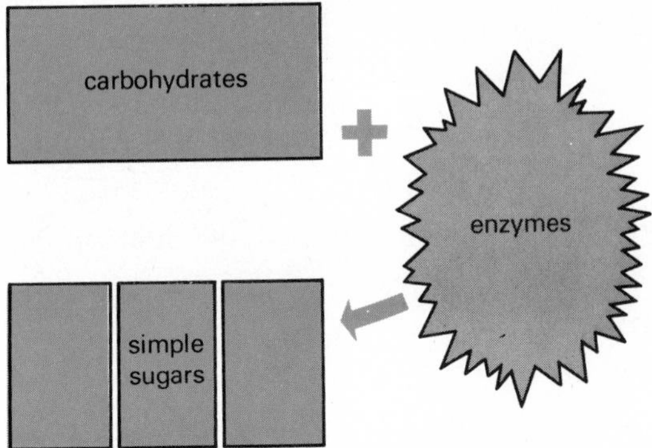

17-16. With the aid of digestive enzymes, large, complex food molecules are broken down into simpler substances.

Problem 17-4 How are the digestive systems of frogs and humans different?

Purpose To locate the organs of the digestive system of a frog. To compare the digestive organs of frogs and humans.

Materials

preserved frog (from Problem 17-1)
dissecting needle
dissecting pins
scissors
metric ruler
dissecting pan

Procedure

A. Use the dissecting needle to separate the digestive system from the body cavity of the preserved frog. (See Figure 17-17.) Carefully lift the liver with your fingers and use the needle to tear the tissue that holds the organ in the frog.

1. Three.

1. The human liver has four lobes. How many lobes are found in the frog's liver?

17-17. Separate the entire digestive system from the body cavity. Gently tear the connecting membranes with a dissecting needle.

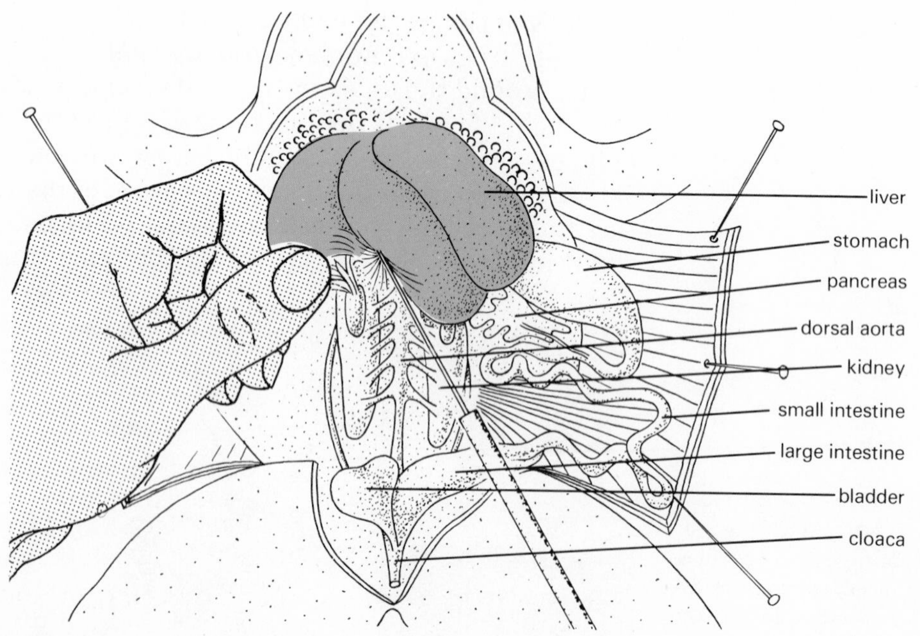

2. The bile has to get from the liver to the gall bladder for storage, and from the gall bladder to the intestine to work on the food.

Some students may need help in locating the frog's pancreas in the curve of the stomach.

3. The human esophagus is comparatively longer.

4. The inside is ridged and undulated while the outside is comparatively smooth.

5. The ridges rub together, crushing the food.

Make sure the students understand that the small intestine, rather than the large intestine, is attached to the stomach. The designations "small" and "large" refer to diameter, not length.

6. About 10-15 cm, depending on size of frog.

7. The human intestine is relatively longer.

8. The human's, due to its greater relative length.

B. The liver in both frogs and humans produces digestive juices, or enzymes. **Bile** is produced by the liver and stored in the **gall bladder**. The bile gives the gall bladder a greenish color. Search for a small, greenish sac between the middle and right lobes of the liver in your frog.

2. In humans and frogs, the gall bladder is attached to both the liver and the beginning of the small intestine. Why is this double attachment necessary? (Remember the function of bile and where it is produced.)

C. Locate the creamy-white **pancreas**. In both frogs and humans, it is found along the inside curve of the stomach. The pancreas produces digestive enzymes that pass through the same tube as the bile into the small intestine.

D. Trace the digestive tube from the stomach to the mouth of the frog. The stomach is connected to the mouth by a short tube called the **esophagus**.

3. How does the relative length of the frog's esophagus (compared to size of body) compare with the length of the esophagus in a human?

E. Use the scissors to cut into the stomach to observe the inside wall. In humans, teeth grind food before it reaches the stomach. But frogs swallow their food whole.

4. How is the inside of the frog's stomach different from the outside?
5. How is the inside wall of the frog's stomach adapted to help grind food?

F. Separate the small and large intestines from the tissue that holds them in the body cavity. Start by lifting the stomach. Gently use the dissecting needle to separate the tissues.

6. What is the length of the frog's small intestine in centimeters?

G. In both frogs and humans, the small intestine is specialized to absorb digested food. Absorption is a slow process. The length of the intestine indicates that a great deal of time is needed for this process. The large intestine, on the other hand, is adapted to absorb most of the water used in the digestive process.

7. Compare the relative length of your frog's large intestine (compared to size of body) with that of a human. (Refer to Figure 17-12.)
8. Which large intestine would appear to be able to absorb more water, the frog's or the human's?

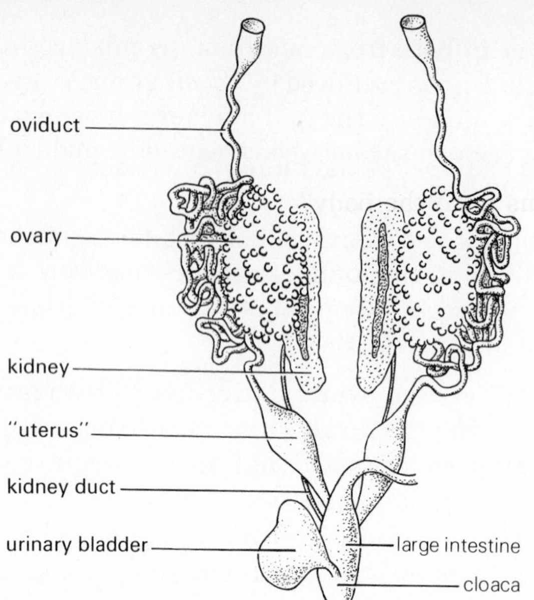

17-18. The excretory organs of a frog. Also shown are the female reproductive parts.

H. In humans, the **anus** is the opening at the end of the large intestine. In frogs, the large intestine empties into a muscular sac called the cloaca [klo-A-kuh]. The **cloaca** collects materials from the large intestine, bladder, and reproductive system. (See Figure 17-18.) From this sac the materials leave the frog through an opening in the dorsal surface between the hind legs.

9. Only one.

9. How many excretory openings are found in the frog?

You should now be able to Identify and compare the organs found in the digestive systems of frogs and humans.

Science terms

anterior
anus
arteries
atrium
bile
canine teeth
capillaries
cloaca
dorsal
enzymes
epiglottis
esophagus
eustachian tube
gall bladder
glottis
gullet
incisors
internal respiration
metabolism
molars
pancreas
pelvic girdle
pharynx
posterior
skull
sternum
veins
ventral
ventricle
vertebrae

Review questions

1. Front—anterior; rear—posterior; top—dorsal; bottom—ventral.
2. Right atrium.
3. Eustachian tube
4. Gall bladder.
5. The sternum.
6. Capillaries.
7. The ventricle.
8. Metabolism.
9. Enzymes.
10. Vertebrae.
11. Mouth, esophagus, stomach, small intestine, large intestine, anus.

1. When describing parts of an animal's body, what terms are used to describe the front, rear, top, and bottom of the animal?
2. Which chamber of the human heart does the blood enter when it returns from the body?
3. What is the name of the tube that connects the mouth and the ear of a frog?
4. What is the name of the sac where bile from the liver is stored in both frogs and humans?
5. What flat bone in your body protects your heart?
6. What are the tiny blood vessels called that exchange food, oxygen, and waste materials with the cells?
7. Which section of the heart has the more muscular walls in vertebrate animals?
8. What term describes the total body processes of an organism?
9. What are the chemicals called that help the process of digestion?
10. What are the individual bones of the human backbone called?
11. List the parts of the digestive tract of a frog in the same order that food would pass through them.

See Teacher's Guide section for answers to Questions 12-17.

Check your understanding

12. Discuss the reasons why humans are better able to adjust to different environments than frogs are.
13. Why do you think the human's large intestine needs to be much longer, in relation to body size, than the large intestine of the frog?
14. What structures are found in the mouth of a frog that are not found in the mouth of a person?
15. In what way is the human's heart structured to circulate blood more effectively than the frog's heart?
16. What is the basic relationship between the lungs and the circulatory system in both humans and frogs?
17. Why is it necessary for food to be ground in a frog's stomach before it passes into the small intestine?

Unit 6

Humans and their environment

Unit-opening photo illustrates one of the more challenging ways that humans interact with their environment.

The world we live in contains a huge variety of living things. Previous units in this book have explored the structure and function of organisms very different from each other. Yet protists, plants, and animals have all been found to exhibit some of the same life processes. They all have many of the same requirements for life. Several human body systems were compared to similar systems in the frog. This helped you to understand the human body and how it functions.

It is not enough to learn only about a single organism. Each living thing may be only one of several thousand kinds that inhabit a given area. Each organism, directly or indirectly, depends on the other living (and nonliving) things that make up its community. This fact points out the serious consequences that often follow people's tampering with their environment. Some examples of the interrelations between plant and animal populations will be studied in this unit.

To better understand humans and their relationship to the rest of the world, you will study some of the traits that are inherited from previous generations. The same trait may vary quite a bit among organisms of the same kind. In Chapter 18 you will observe the variation in one such physical feature among your own classmates. You and your classmates make up the human population in a science classroom.

The food needs of a population are critical to the success of that organism in any area. You have learned in previous units that every organism except green plants must obtain food from its surroundings. The limitation of the food supply is usually the limiting factor on the growth of a population. In this unit you will identify the different kinds of nutrients found in the food you eat. You will also calculate the energy value of one kind of food.

The food needs of humans are not the only element in their environment that they depend on. Clean air and fresh water are just as important as an adequate food supply. As the human population increases, the protection of the environment, including food, air, and water, must be a chief concern for all of us. Regulations on waste disposal and pollution must be enforced before our environment is changed so much that we cannot survive in it.

Examples of unwise use of natural resources, resulting in the poisoning of the environment, are given in the final chapter of this unit. You may want to participate in a survey of the problems in the community where you live. You will have that opportunity in the last chapter.

Chapter 18 Variations in a human population

Chapter-opening photo, with its peripheral blurring and small area of sharp focus, is a visual reminder that populations are composed of individuals.

The term *population* is often used to refer to the number of people in a certain city or state at a certain time. It could also be used to describe the number of students in your school. Even the members of your class make up a population.

However, many groups other than people can make up populations. A farmer might be interested in the bird population, the tree population, or the mammal population of a certain wooded area. These groups could be further divided into kinds of birds, trees, or mammals if this much detail were desired. Biologists define **population** as a particular kind of living things in a given area at a given time. In this chapter you will study some variations that are found in the human population of your classroom.

During your study of populations, you'll learn ways to collect, organize, and interpret data about them.

Presenting data in histograms

Data obtained from studies of human populations must be organized in a way that can be understood. It is often useful to present data on populations in the form of a histogram. A **histogram** is a bar graph that shows information about a population.

Figure 18-1 is a histogram. It shows the heights of students from one classroom. Inspection of the histogram shows that more students are between 158 and 162 centimeters than any other height. The histogram also shows that the tallest person in the student population is between 193 and 197 centimeters. And the shortest person is between 123 and 127 centimeters. The purpose of a histogram is the same as for any graph. A histogram presents the main patterns or trends, which numbers alone may not reveal.

On the histogram in Figure 18-1, each bar represents a range, or *interval*, of 5 centimeters in heights. The bar for the shortest student includes the height interval from 123 to 127 centimeters. A student in that group could be any height included in that interval. Notice that the total range of numbers along the horizontal axis extends from 118 to 197 centimeters. The total range is large enough to include the heights of all the members of the class.

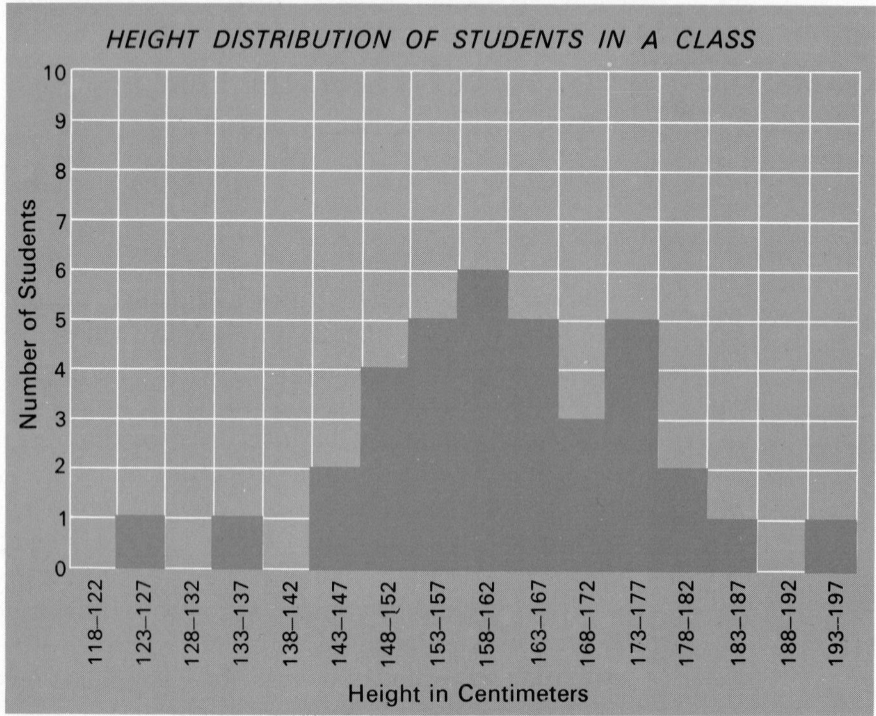

18-1. A histogram showing a possible distribution of student heights within a class.

In Problem 18-1 you will make a histogram. You will be graphing the variation in hand spans among your classmates.

Normal curves

Most of the student heights shown in Figure 18-1 were clustered around the 158-162 cm interval. Only a few students measured very tall or very short. Many characteristics of a population will show this same spread — most of the individuals will be grouped near the middle of the range.

Figure 18-2 shows the distribution of scores on a test taken by students across the United States. The scores resulted in a normal distribution curve. A **normal curve** is a distribution that shows only a few persons (or scores) at each end and an increasing number of persons toward the middle of the range. The average value in a normal distribution is always near the middle of the range.

Many human traits show a normal distribution when the traits are measured in a large, random sample. A **random sample** is one in which the participants are chosen by chance. Numbers drawn out of a hat by a blindfolded person would be a random sample of all the numbers in the hat.

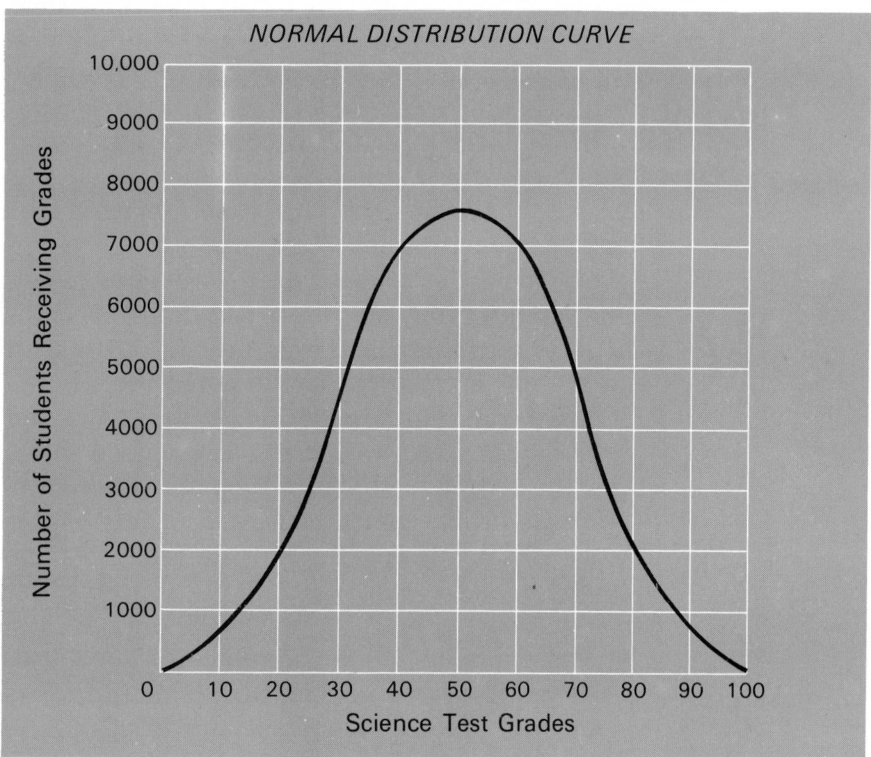

18-2. Distribution of grades received on a nationwide test.

Inherited traits

Genetics is the branch of science concerned with the characteristics, or *traits*, that are passed on from one generation to the next. What you are like depends in part on your **heredity**, on what you inherited from your parents. You have also been affected by your environment. Height and hand span are two inherited traits. Other inherited traits are eye color, hair color, hair texture, shoe size — almost every physical trait you possess.

The study of heredity began about 100 years ago. That was when the inherited traits of certain plants were studied. Later the study of animals, notably the fruit fly, gave us insights into how one generation inherits physical traits from preceding generations.

Within the nucleus of each cell are a number of chromosomes. These contain most of the material needed for the duplication of traits in the young, or offspring, of an organism. The particular structures within the chromosomes that control the development of traits are called **genes**.

Careful study of genes has revealed that they contain certain chemicals. It is the chemicals in the genes that cause traits to be transmitted from one generation to the next. There is one chemical in particular that is thought to be responsible for much of the duplication of features. It is called **deoxyribonucleic acid**, or simply **DNA**. DNA duplicates its structure before cell division takes place. This process is the key to understanding the pattern of inheritance.

The genes in the chromosomes of each human cell determine the inherited traits of an individual. Each parent passes on a set of genes to his or her offspring. Thus, each inherited trait is influenced by at least one gene from each parent.

Sometimes the gene for a trait from one parent masks or hides the gene for the same trait from the other parent. When this happens, the gene that controls the production of the trait is said to be **dominant**. The trait that can be hidden by the other is called **recessive**. A recessive trait may remain hidden for several generations. But when genes for such recessive traits are passed to a child from both parents, the recessive characteristic may appear in the offspring.

Certain traits seem to be passed on only by the male parent or only by the female parent. Such traits are said to be **sex-linked**. Colorblindness and certain speech and hearing defects are sex-linked traits.

Some scientists think the tendency to contract certain diseases is inherited. Research in this area of heredity is going on today as we seek causes and cures for such illnesses as cancer and heart disease.

Problem 18-1 How do you measure the variation in one characteristic in a population?

Purpose To determine the variation of a characteristic within a group of individuals.

Materials metric ruler paper graph paper

Procedure In populations of the same species, each organism may seem like all the rest. Actually, each individual is different in many ways from all the others. In this problem you will measure a particular human characteristic. You will measure the length of your hand span. Then you will prepare a histogram to show the distribution of the measurements in your class.

A. Measure the hand span of the hand you usually write with. Spread your hand as shown in Figure 18-3. Put your spread hand down on a piece of paper. Mark the paper at the tip of the thumb and at the tip of the little finger. Do not include the length of fingernails. Measure the distance between the pencil marks.

1. Hand spans will cover a wide range.

1. What is your hand span to the nearest millimeter?

B. Record your hand span on the chalkboard with the measurements of the other students. Then record all the hand spans in your notebook.

C. To organize the class data, prepare a data table in your notebook similar to Table 18-1 (next page). The intervals should be 5 mm

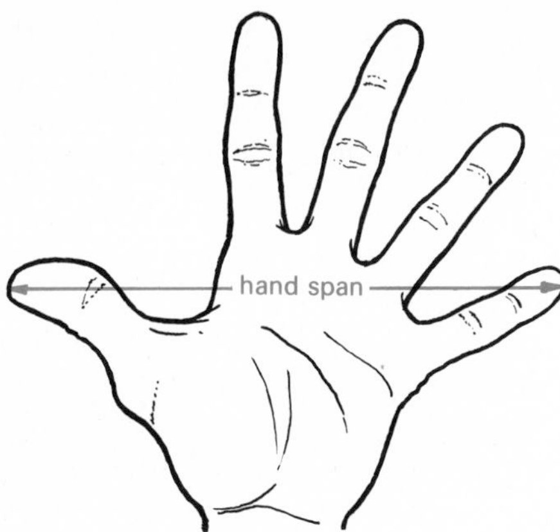

18-3. Measuring your hand span.

TABLE 18-1 HAND-SPAN MEASUREMENTS

Intervals in Millimeters	*Number of Students in Interval (Use a tally mark to record each hand-span measurement.)*
Less than 142 mm	
143–147	
148–152	
153–157	
158–162	
163–167	
168–172	
173–177	
178–182	
183–187	
188–192	
193–197	
198–202	
203–207	
208–212	
213–217	
218–222	
223–227	
228–232	
233–237	
238–242	
More than 242 mm	

each. The first interval should include lengths small enough to record the shortest span measured in the class.

2. Students should tally all hand spans in the class.

2. Record each measurement in your data table. Use a tally mark, such as an "x", in the correct interval for each hand span.

D. The next step is to prepare a histogram of the variation in your class. You will use the information in your data table to construct a bar graph similar to Figure 18-4. Make a copy of Figure 18-4 in your notebook. Under the horizontal axis, mark the intervals that you have chosen. The intervals should be marked directly under spaces on the graph so that bars may be drawn above them.

Label the vertical axis "Number of Students." Construct a number scale along this axis. The numbers should be evenly spaced, starting with zero and continuing as high as the largest number of students to be recorded in any interval. If, for instance, ten were the largest number of students in any interval, ten would be the highest number needed on the vertical scale.

Students' completed graphs should correspond with their data tables.

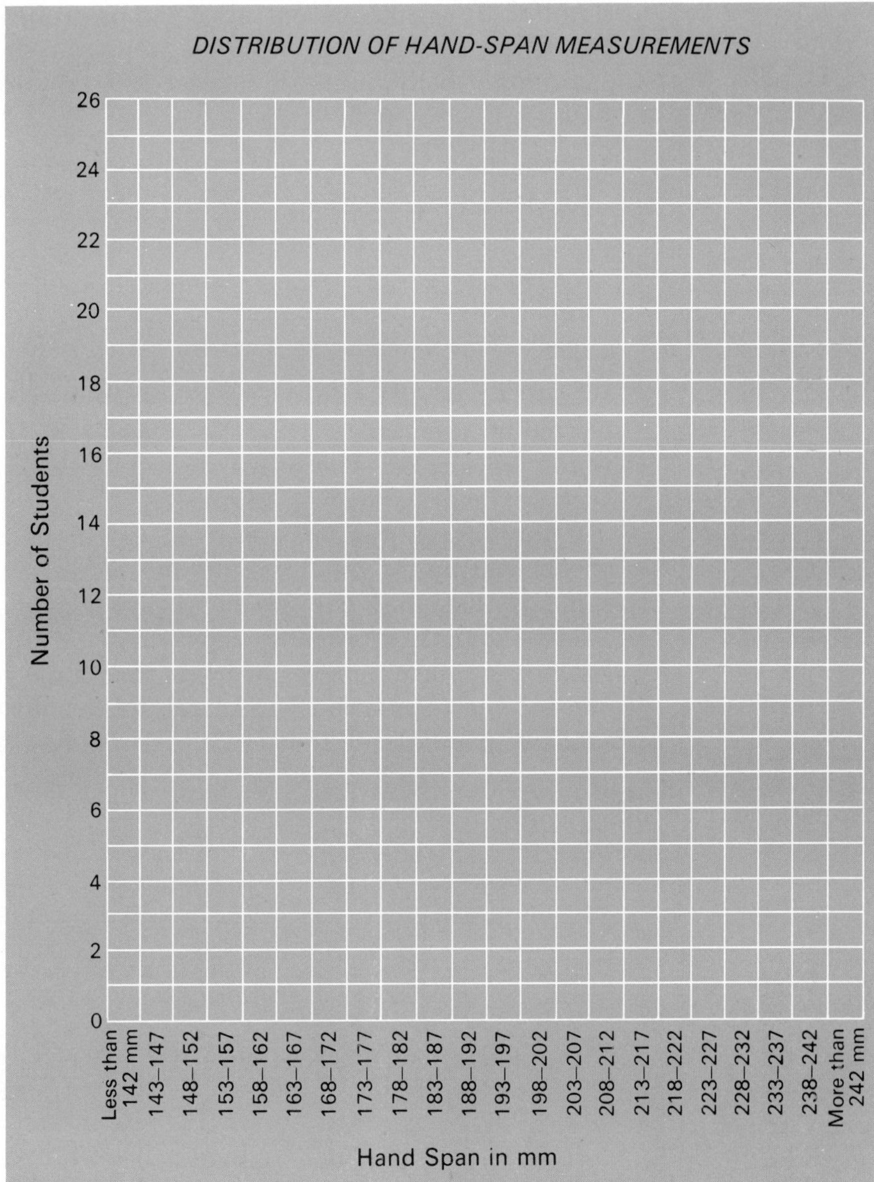

18-4. This histogram, when completed, will show the distribution of hand-span sizes for your class.

3. Data from Question 2 should be plotted on graph.

3. For each interval, make a mark opposite the number of students in that interval. Construct bars from the horizontal axis up to the marks. (See Figure 18-1 on page 342 for a similar type of graph.)

4. Answer varies from class to class.

4. Into which interval do most of your classmates' hand spans fall?

5. Probably a normal (bell-shaped) curve, but this may vary.

5. How would you describe the shape of the distribution shown in the histogram?

E. Suppose the hand spans of newborn babies were obtained from a hospital. These measurements could be grouped and plotted on a histogram like the one you have just prepared. The smallest hand span might be 80 mm, the largest 120 mm, and the average 100 mm.

6. Normal (bell-shaped).

6. What shape of curve would you expect from the histogram of infant hand-span measurements?

7. There would be two distinct curves.

7. Suppose you made one graph that included both infant hand-span measurements and the measurements from your class. (The horizontal axis would have to be extended so that the shorter hand-span measurements could be recorded.) What pattern might you see?

F. When two sets of measurements of the same characteristic are plotted on the same graph, the curves may be close together or widely separated. There are three main relationships between such curves, as shown in Figure 18-5.

If the two curves appear at about the same location on the graph, you might assume that the measurements are from the same population. If the two curves are widely separated, you can assume that they probably represent two different populations. Finally, if the two curves overlap, that could mean that they represent one population with much variation. Or, it could represent two populations that are closely related.

GRAPHS OF POPULATION STUDIES

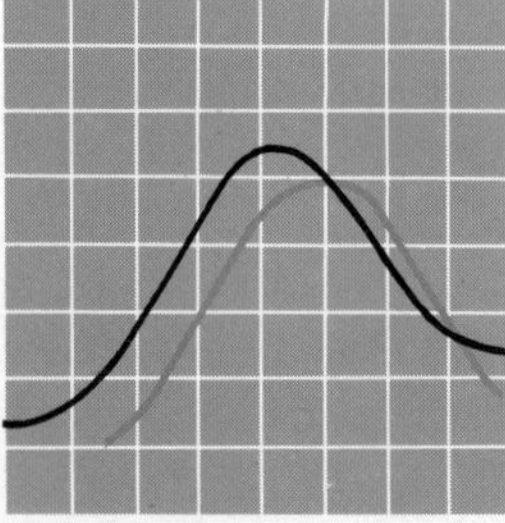

A. Two curves almost exactly alike

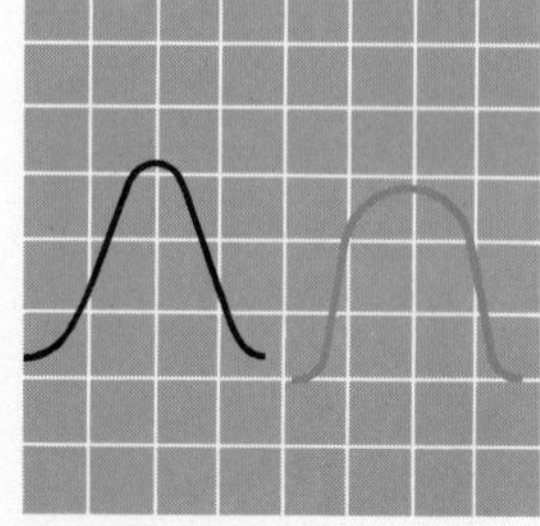

B. Two separate and distinct curves

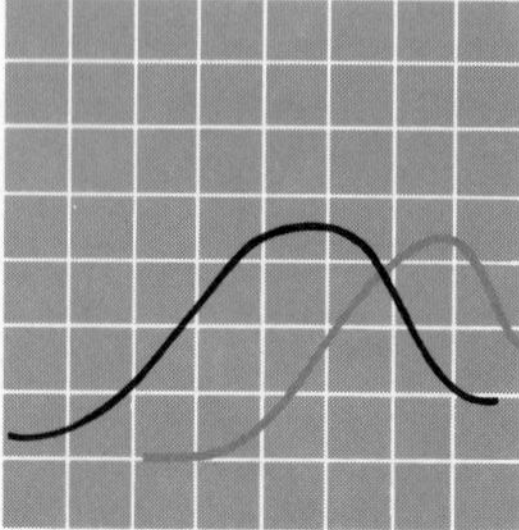

C. Two curves overlapped

18-5. Which graph probably represents data from two different populations?

You should now be able to

Obtain data to show the variation of one characteristic in a population.

Present data in the form of a histogram.

Use the shape of the curve on a histogram to explain what values are most likely to be expected for a particular trait within a population.

Comparing inherited traits

When population traits such as height, hand span, or shoe size are measured, they usually fall into the distribution of a normal curve. They are inherited traits that show a wide variation when measured in a large population sample. The hand spans in your class may have varied more than 100 millimeters from shortest to longest.

There is another kind of inherited physical trait. This type does not lend itself to the variations that result in normal curves. It doesn't vary, because it is an "either-or" trait. It is either present in an individual or it is not. For example, a person is either color-blind or not color-blind. A person has either attached earlobes or free-hanging earlobes. Such characteristics will be investigated in the next problem.

Since the traits that you will be observing are either present or not present, you can use Knit-Pick cards to record and retrieve the information. Only questions with yes-or-no answers may be used with this system. (You may want to refer to Problem 1-3 for review.)

Problem 18-2 What traits are visible in a human population?

Purpose To identify certain traits in a human population.

Materials

index cards, 3″ x 5″	scissors	P.T.C. paper
paper punch	ruler	knitting needle

Procedure

A. Prepare the index card for use in a Knit-Pick system. Refer to Steps A-D of Problem 1-3 for directions. A punched and numbered card is shown in Figure 18-6 on the next page.

B. Answer the following questions 1 to 10 on your Knit-Pick card. If your answer to a question is yes, darken the space next to that

Name	Period	Series
1		6
2		7
3		8
4		9
5		10

18-6. A punched and numbered Knit-Pick card.

number, between the hole and edge of the card. If your answer to a question is no, leave the card unchanged. Test yourself for the following traits and record the answer to each question opposite the same number on the Knit-Pick card.

1. Can you taste P.T.C.?
2. Can you roll your tongue? (See Figure 18-7.)
3. Do you have naturally straight hair?
4. Do you have brown eyes?
5. Do you have attached earlobes? (See Figure 18-7.)
6. Are you a female?

18-7. The ability to roll your tongue, and whether your earlobes hang free or are attached, are determined by heredity.

7. Are you less than 120 centimeters tall?
8. Do you have red hair?
9. Are you color-blind?
10. Is your vision good without glasses?

C. With the scissors, open the hole to the edge of the card for each question that you answered yes (the numbers with blackened spots beside them). Be sure you have labeled your card with your name, science period or division, and the letter "B" for the card series.

D. The Knit-Pick cards may now be collected and used to determine how often each trait appears in your science-class population. Copy Table 18-2 into your notebook to record the number of individuals that have each trait.

TABLE 18–2 INHERITED TRAITS RECORD FROM KNIT-PICK CARDS

Inherited Trait	*No. of Students Having the Trait*
1. Taste P.T.C.	
2. Roll your tongue	
3. Naturally straight hair	
4. Brown eyes	
5. Attached earlobes	
6. Female	
7. Less than 120 cm tall	
8. Red hair	
9. Color-blind	
10. Good vision without glasses	

1. Answers will vary.
2. Probably color-blindness, but variations can be expected.
3. Probably not.
4. Possibly.

1. Which trait occurs most often in the population?
2. Which trait occurs least often in the population?
3. Are any of the traits found in all of the individuals?
4. Are any of the traits absent in all individuals?
5. Are any two traits always found together in the population?

You should now be able to

5. Possibly. In any population there may be two or more traits that usually appear together.

Store information about inherited traits on Knit-Pick cards.
Retrieve information stored on Knit-Pick cards.
Determine the number of individuals in your class that have a specific trait.
Determine the number of individuals in a population that have two or more specific traits in common.

---

1. A group of the same kind of organisms living in an area.

3. One way would be to draw a metric scale on the floor measured out from the wall. Have each student put his or her heel against the wall while standing on the metric scale. Read length of foot at end of big toe.

4. In the middle section.

8. It is a recessive trait and will not appear as long as the dominant trait is present.

9. Color-blindness and hemophilia are examples.

10. One that is manifested in the individual even if a corresponding recessive trait is present in the individual's genetic makeup.

Science terms

deoxyribonucleic acid (DNA)
dominant
genes
genetics
heredity
histogram
normal curve
population
random sample
recessive
sex-linked

Review questions

1. What do biologists mean when they use the term population?
2. What type of bar graph would help you to understand information gathered from population studies? 2. A histogram.
3. How would you measure the length of each person's foot in your physical education class?
4. In what section are most of the scores found in a normal curve?
5. What is meant by a random sample? 5. A sample chosen by chance.
6. Which branch of science studies traits passed on from one generation to another? 6. Genetics.
7. Name three inherited human traits. 7. Height, eye color, hair color, etc.
8. What do we mean when we say that a trait is "hidden"?
9. Name one human trait that is sex-linked.
10. What is meant by a dominant trait?

See Teacher's Guide section for answers to Questions 11-21.

Check your understanding

11. How could you discover whether tasting P.T.C. was a dominant or a recessive trait?
12. How could you select a random sample of the students in your school to answer a list of questions?

13. How does a random sample of a population compare to the entire population?
14. Explain why some traits appear very seldom in some families.
15. How many curves might be found on a graph showing the same trait measured in three different populations?
16. Look back at Figure 18-1, page 342. Would you say that the majority of students in the class were tall, short, or somewhere in between? Explain your answer using the numbers in the graph.
17. How would you use the Knit-Pick cards to find out how many people in your class have brown eyes *and* naturally curly hair?
18. Based upon your class data, does tongue-rolling seem to be a dominant or a recessive trait? Use numbers to justify your answer.
19. Name two physical traits, besides height and hand span, that would probably show a normal distribution curve.
20. What advantage do you see in recording heights or hand spans in intervals, rather than as individual numbers?
21. What human traits can you think of that would be influenced by both heredity and environment?

Chapter 19 Relationships within a community

Chapter-opening photo shows a predator-prey relationship. But note the asphalt surface on which the deer fell. An added feature here is the presence of humans in the community. A car hit the deer, so the eagle didn't have to work for this meal.

People usually think of a community as a town or part of a city in which a number of people live. But biologists refer to a **community** as all of the populations living in a certain area. Using this definition you can see that quite a few populations would be included in one community.

In Chapter 18, humans were described as one type of population that might be found in an area. Other populations in the same place might include birds, dogs, and insects. All of the different populations found in a given area make up a community. How these different populations within a community affect each other is the subject of this chapter.

To understand the relationships among living things in a community, you also need to consider the nonliving things in the environment. The **environment** is all of the conditions that surround an organism. It includes such things as water supply, temperature, and food supply. It includes all the factors that affect the survival of living things. Conditions in the environment have much to do with the sizes and kinds of populations that exist in a community.

Sampling a community

Sometimes it is important to know the total number of organisms in a community. To count each one would be almost impossible. Instead, scientists have developed ways to *estimate* the number of individuals. Their method of estimating the size of a population is called **sampling**.

To sample the populations in a community, a small area is chosen and each kind of living thing within it is counted. Often the small area is based on a *square meter*. This is the area inside a square that is one meter on each side. In practice, the organisms in several square meters may be counted. Then the average number per square is determined.

Now the sampler has an average figure for populations per square meter. He or she then decides what the total area of the community is. The sampler multiplies the average for 1 square meter times the total number of square meters in the community. This gives an estimate of the total number of the various kinds of living things in the community.

The sampling technique can also be used to count only one kind of organism within a community. Suppose you found an average of 12 dandelions per square meter in a given area. And suppose the total area of the community were 260 square meters. You would estimate a total of 12 × 260, or 3,120 dandelions in the community. Of course, an organism such as the dandelion may thrive in one community but be unsuccessful in another.

Measuring the biomass of a community

Sometimes it is desirable to know just how much living material an area produces. This measure is called the **biomass**. It includes the mass of all the plants and animals within the community. To find the biomass of a community, the organisms in a sample plot are weighed. The total biomass of the entire area is then estimated from this measurement. You will make such a measurement in Problem 19-1.

Consumers and producers

One way to classify the organisms in a community is based on how they get their food. Do they produce their own, or do they depend on other organisms for their food? You know that green plants produce their own food in the photosynthetic process. Green plants are therefore called **producers**. Organisms that depend on producers for their food are called **consumers**. Consumers include organisms that eat green plants as well as organisms that eat other animals.

The food relationship between producers and consumers is sometimes called a **food chain**. Such a relationship might exist between a hawk, a field mouse, and the grass in which the mouse lives. (See Figure 19-1.) Grass is the only producer in this group, since it is the only organism that can make its own food. The mouse eats the grass, and the hawk eats the mouse. So both the mouse and the hawk are consumers. Eventually the consumers die. Bacteria break up the animal tissues and return material to the soil and the atmosphere. There it may be used again by the producers.

Consumers change the food they eat into their own body tissue. However, a pound of grass or meat does not become a pound of tissue. There is always a portion of the food that becomes waste material and a portion that is used for energy. For instance, about 1,800 kilograms of alfalfa are needed to raise one 250-kilogram cow. Because of this loss, more producers than consumers are needed to support the community. In areas where the soil is poor or there is little rainfall, the number of consumers is limited. The total number of organisms in any food chain is limited by the producer or consumer that is least abundant.

There are other factors that limit a community. Fire or flood sometimes destroys an entire community. Humans contribute to the destruction of communities by leveling forests, plowing fields, and pol-

19-1. A food chain in a community.

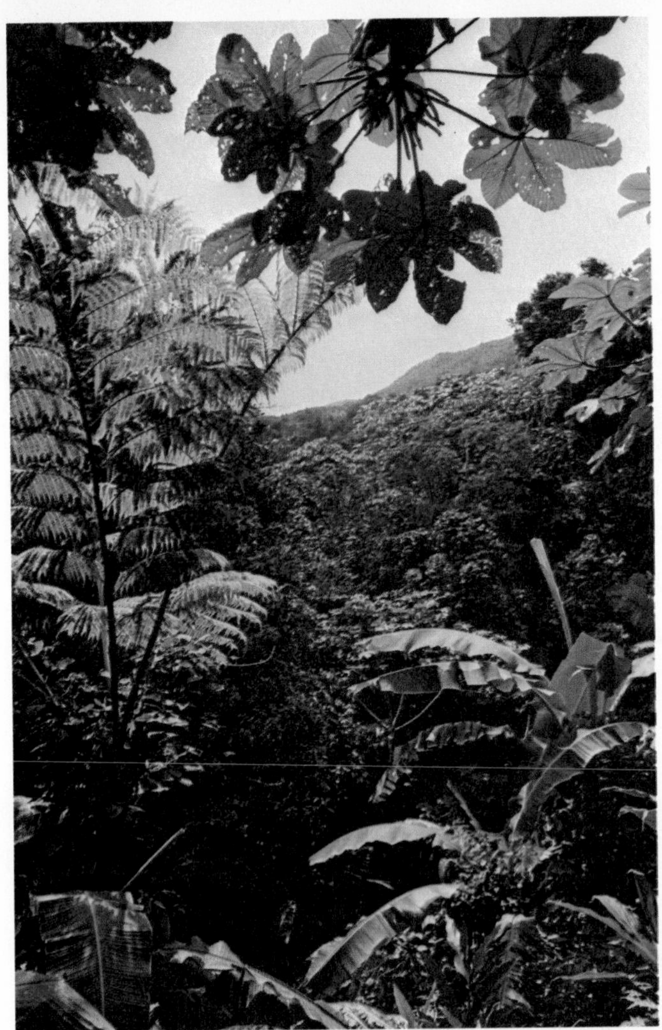

In the desert where there are only a few plants, consumers are limited. In contrast, the abundant vegetation of the tropics and many underwater environments can support large consumer populations.

luting the environment. Poisons that kill insects or rodents may kill such large numbers that the balance that previously existed in the food chain may be destroyed.

In Problem 19-1 you will investigate methods of sampling and learn how to find the biomass of a community.

Problem 19-1 How do you determine the number of different populations in a community?

Purpose To use a sampling technique to determine the number and kinds of organisms in a community.

Materials coat hanger balance paper bag

Procedure

Part One: Population sampling

Suppose you were asked to determine the number and kinds of plants found in a vacant lot. Counting every plant could be a long and tiresome job.

1. What method would you use to obtain the data?

One of the first steps would be to identify the kinds of plants. A plant identification book would help. Or you might ask a person who is familiar with plants. Suppose that you identified the following plants in a lot: dandelion, plantain, crab grass, white clover, blue grass, foxtail, and shepherd's purse.

2. How would you determine the total number of each kind of plant in the lot?
3. If you knew the average number of plants per square meter, how would you calculate the total number of each kind of plant in the entire lot?
4. How would you identify the organisms in the lot, as producers or as consumers? 4. Producers, since they all make their own food.
5. Suppose the mass of all the plants in the lot was 441 kilograms. What additional information would you need about the community to determine the entire biomass? 5. The mass of all the animals in the lot.

1. Suggestions may range from counting the organisms in a small area to counting every living thing in the lot. Discuss logical and practical sampling techniques.

2. Identify each kind of organism in the lot. Tally on a chart the numbers of each kind found in a sample plot and multiply by the number of plots in the lot.

3. Multiply the average by the total number of square meters to estimate the total number of plants.

Part Two: Sampling organisms in the field

A. Collect all the living plants and animals found in a small, plant-covered area. Use a coat hanger made into a square to select the

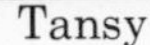

Tansy

Mullein

Thistle

Pokeweed

Many weeds, such as those listed on page 358, are harmless. Some plants, however, may cause irritation or even be poisonous. The stems and leaves of tansy and the roots and berries of pokeweed are poisonous to eat. Mullein's woolly, light-green leaves and the *wet* leaves of Queen Anne's lace can cause skin irritation. Thistle spines break off and easily embed themselves in skin. Pollinating ragweed should be avoided by hay-fever sufferers.

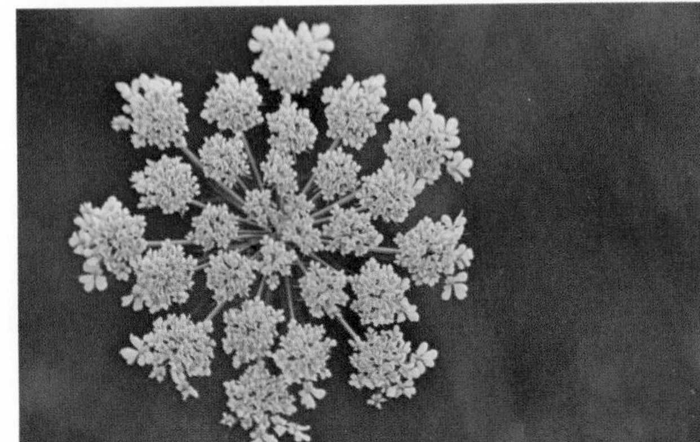

Queen Anne's Lace

Ragweed

19-2. A wire coat hanger made into a square to select the sample.

sample. (See Figure 19-2.) Lay the hanger on the ground and collect all the living material enclosed by the hanger. Place the material in a paper bag and bring it to class.

B. Separate the living material you collected into two piles, producers and consumers.

6. Which group, producers or consumers, is found in greater numbers in your sample? 6. Usually producers.

C. Group the producers further by putting together those that appear to be the same type.

D. On the balance provided, find the total mass of the producers. Then do the same with the consumers.

7. What is the total mass of the producers?
8. What is the total mass of the consumers?
9. What is the total mass of producers and consumers in your sample? This is the biomass of your sample. 9. Sum of answers to Questions 7 and 8.

7. Mass will vary from a few hundred grams in sparsely-covered areas to several kilograms where high weeds are found.

8. Answers will vary, but mass of consumers will usually be much less than the mass of producers.

It would take about 500 squares the size of your sample to cover an area the size of an average living room. Assume that the field from which you took your sample was exactly equal to the area of an average living room.

10. What would be the biomass of the total area from which your sample was taken? 10. Multiply answer to Question 9 by 500.

You should now be able to

Obtain a sample of the number of organisms in a community.

Classify organisms as producers or consumers.

Identify members from a community that belong to the same population.

Estimate the biomass of a community from a sample of the biomass.

Interdependence within a community

Living things in a community depend on all of the factors in the environment, living as well as nonliving. This relationship is called **interdependence**. You have seen this interdependence in the food chains discussed earlier. Each organism depends on the next member of the chain for its food supply. If something happens to one link in the chain, each succeeding organism will be limited. When the number of each kind of organism in a food chain reaches a constant level, a balance has been reached. As long as no important change is made in the environment, the populations within the community will usually continue at a constant level.

A community has been defined as all of the populations living in a certain area. This definition is not very restricting. In some cases, organisms are constantly moving into and out of an area. An ocean or a prairie are examples of such **open communities**, where the inhabitants may come and go. The populations that exist in a small pond are much more limited in their movement. Thus, a small pond may be called a **closed community**. In the next problem you will consider some of the relationships in the closed community of a pond.

Problem 19-2 How do different populations in a community affect each other?

Purpose To show the interdependence of populations in a community.

Materials None. You will be provided with the results of a study completed previously.

Procedure The study of population interrelationships in a community is called **ecology**. Ecology classes often take field trips. They need to visit communities to sample the different populations there.

A. The ecology classes at one school visited the same pond community for many years. After each visit, the students made a careful record of the number of organisms found in each of several populations. The populations of frogs, grasshoppers, and rye grass were recorded. The data were presented in a graph as shown in Figure 19-3 on the next page.

1. The grasshoppers eat the rye grass, and the frogs eat the grasshoppers.

2. Producer: rye grass. Consumers: grasshopper, frog.

3. 1962.

4. 1965.

5. 1966.

1. Considering only the three organisms mentioned, what food-chain relationship probably exists among them?
2. Which members of the chain are producers and which are consumers?
3. In what year was the number of producers greatest?
4. In what year was the grasshopper population at its greatest?
5. In what year was the frog population at its greatest?

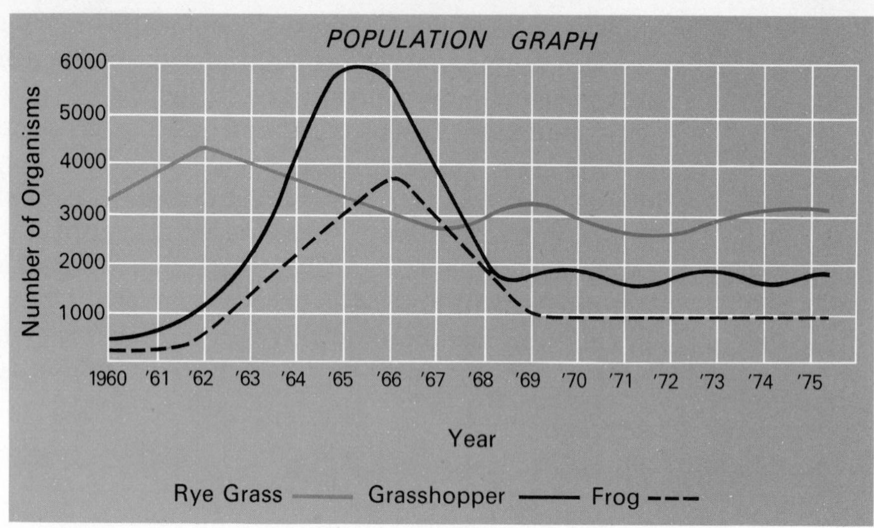

19-3. This graph shows the growth in population of three organisms in a pond community.

6. The grasshoppers depended on the rye grass for food. An abundant food supply meant that more grasshoppers could survive and perhaps produce more offspring.

7. Each frog requires many grasshoppers for food, so the frog population will always be much smaller than the grasshopper population.

8. Rye grass.

9. A balanced condition was reached.

10. The rye grass (followed by an increase in the grasshopper population).

11. Rye grass.

B. Reproduction of living organisms is a continuous process. But environmental conditions often reduce the number of organisms that survive to become adults and reproduce. When conditions for growth and reproduction are favorable again, more adults will survive to reproduce. Thus the population increases again.

6. Why did the grasshopper population reach a peak immediately after the rye grass population peaked?
7. Why was the frog population never as large as the grasshopper population?
8. The population of which organism seems to control all of the populations in this food chain?
9. Why were all three populations nearly constant during the last five years shown on the graph?
10. What population would have to be increased first in order to have an increase in the frog population?

C. The ecology class noticed that, just after their last visit to the pond, an extra amount of fertilizer was added to the land near the pond. This fertilizer will cause the grass to grow better and produce more seeds.

11. Which of the three populations will probably show an increase next year?

13. First the grasshoppers would die, and then the number of frogs would decrease because of decreased food supply. The grass would possibly increase, because fewer insects are eating it.

12. Which population will probably be the last to show an increase due to the addition of the fertilizer? 12. Frog.
13. What populations would be affected if an insect-killing chemical were applied to the grass around the pond? Explain your answer.

You should now be able to

Explain how one population in a community depends on other populations in the community.

Relate the success of one member of a food chain to the success of other members of the chain.

Identify some of the factors that control the growth of a population.

Predict the changes in populations that will result from various changes in the environment.

---

1. The best method would probably be to sample a small area that is representative of the entire area, then multiply by the number of small areas it would take to equal the total area. This is called sampling.

2. Examples include: sampling the popularity of television programs; sampling opinions about political candidates and issues.

4. An organism that produces its own food—mostly green plants.

6. The number of producers (food supply) that exists there.

7. Environmental conditions such as moisture, temperature, soil fertility, and the number of consumers present in the area.

Science terms

biomass	ecology	open community
closed community	environment	producer
community	food chain	sampling
consumer	interdependence	

Review questions

1. What indirect method is used to estimate the number of organisms in a community?
2. Name at least two areas of investigation, other than life science, in which the sampling method could be used to gather data.
3. What term means the total mass of living material that exists in a community? 3. Biomass.
4. What type of organism is known as a producer?
5. Would you classify mice as producers or consumers? 5. Consumers.
6. What factor limits the number of consumers in a community?
7. What factors would limit the number of producers in a community?
8. Name at least two things that could upset the balance in a community. 8. Drought, fire, insecticides, pollution, etc.
9. What is the term that is used to describe how each living thing in a community relies on all the other living things? 9. Interdependence.
10. What condition exists in a community when the number of living things remains constant each year? 10. It is balanced.

See Teacher's Guide section for answers to Questions 11-14.

Check your understanding

11. Make a list of four different types of communities found in the world. Name several different populations in each and tell how the populations are dependent on each other.
12. Describe the method by which you would figure the biomass of a pasture area.
13. How would the amount and quality of fertilizers in the soil affect the mouse population in an area? How might it affect the owl population?
14. Suppose you were given an assignment to set up a balanced fish aquarium. Tell what materials you would include and why you would include each one. When would you know if the aquarium were balanced?

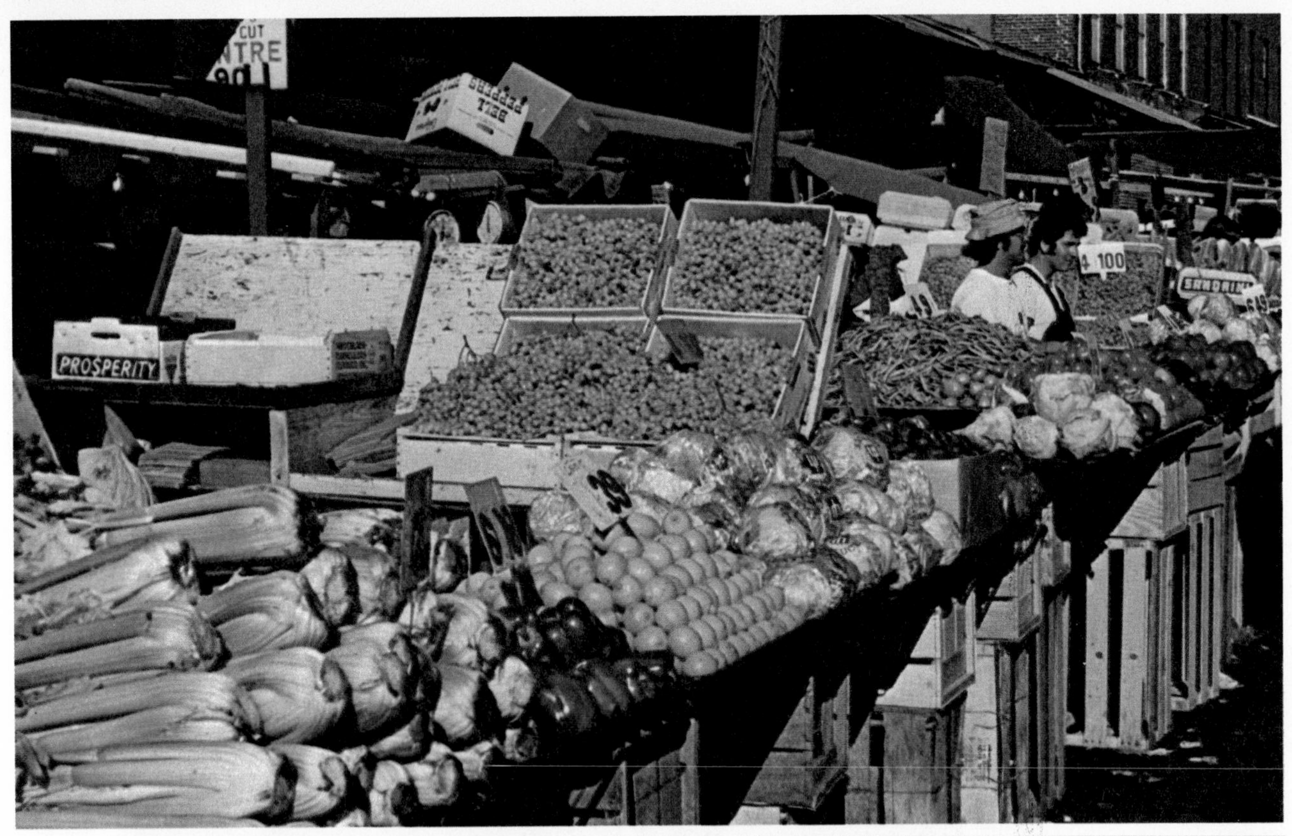

Chapter 20 The food we eat

Chapter-opening photo shows an open-air market. You might mention that this photo also shows a classification system, and thus tie in an earlier chapter of study.

A critical problem in the world today is how to provide food for an exploding population. The human population has filled its environment to a point where the number of people to be fed is rapidly exceeding the ability of the world to feed them. As a result, much of the human population of the world has insufficient food, with many people on a starvation diet. Your studies of plant growth in Unit Four should help you to understand the problem of increasing the food supply for a hungry world.

Diets in different parts of the world include some very different foods. People eat rattlesnakes, grasshoppers, octopus, seaweed, and snails to supplement the more common cereal grains and meats. Diets that depend heavily on rice and fish might seem unappetizing to people who are used to a more varied diet. But in countries where starvation is a constant threat, any kind of food is usually welcome.

Food supplies the **nutrients** needed by the body for energy, growth, repair of tissues, and other body activities. These nutrients include **carbohydrates, fats, proteins, minerals, vitamins,** and **water**. Carbohydrates include **sugars** and **starches**. Carbohydrates and fats are used by body cells to produce energy. Proteins supply the materials that the body needs for growth and repair. In Problems 20-1 and 20-2, you will apply identification tests to some foods to see if they contain fats, proteins, or carbohydrates.

20-1. Rats can be raised in large numbers in laboratories and may be fed many of the same foods that humans eat.

Vitamins and minerals are important for the prevention of certain **deficiency diseases**. A lot is now known about the body's nutritional requirements. Much of this knowledge came from controlled experiments with animals. Animals that have the same basic food requirements as humans may be used to determine the specific nutrients needed in the human diet.

Scientists have been able to solve many problems about nutrition with studies using white rats. Rats can be raised in large numbers and may be fed many of the same food items that humans eat. Through experiments with different diets, information about human nutrition needs as well as possible new foods can be evaluated.

Our daily diet should include foods that give us essential nutrients. A **balanced diet** is one that includes all of the essential nutrients. To help us maintain a balanced diet, the United States Department of Agriculture has classified food into four groups. We are advised to eat something from each of the four groups each day. These groups are:

1. *The milk group:* milk, cheese, and ice cream.
2. *The meat group:* meat, fish, eggs, peas, beans, and nuts.
3. *The bread-cereal group:* bread, cereal, crackers, and other grain products.
4. *The vegetable-fruit group:* fruit, citrus fruit, berries, green vegetables, and yellow vegetables.

Sometimes we include more carbohydrates and fats in our diets than our bodies need. The portion that is not used is changed into a kind of fat that our body can store until it is needed for energy. To measure the energy value of foods, a heat unit called a calorie is used. One **small calorie** (small c) is defined as the amount of heat needed to raise the temperature of one gram of water one degree Celsius. A **large Calorie** (capital C) is equal to 1,000 small calories. In Problem 20-4 you will see how the number of small calories released by a food can be measured.

Now, more than ever, people are concerned with the number of Calories and vitamins in their diets. The proportion and amount of nutrients required in a diet vary somewhat with a person's age, physical condition, and activity. Often, advertising implies that taking extra vitamins will mean better health. But if a person eats a well-balanced diet, vitamin and mineral supplements are not necessary. For the most part, unless your doctor prescribes supplements, a well-balanced diet will provide the nutrients you need.

In Problem 20-1 you will perform a series of tests to establish the presence of carbohydrates, fats, and proteins in foods.

Problem 20-1 How do you identify food nutrients?

Purpose To learn tests that identify fats, proteins, and carbohydrates.

Materials

starch solution
iodine solution
test tubes, 18 × 150 mm (2)
test tube, 25 × 200 mm
Benedict's solution
Bunsen burner
graduated cylinder
test-tube holder
glucose sugar solution
sodium hydroxide solution, concentrated
copper sulfate solution, dilute
egg white, raw
brown wrapping paper
butter
medicine droppers (3)

Procedure

Part One: Carbohydrates (starches and sugars)

A. In your notebook, prepare a table similar to Table 20-1 to record the results of your identification tests.

B. *Testing for starch:* Pour 1 ml of starch solution into a small test tube. Add 1 or 2 drops of iodine solution. Record the results in your table.

1. Blue-black.

1. What color appears when iodine is added to starch? This occurs only when iodine and starch are both present.

C. *Testing for simple sugar:* Pour about 5 ml of glucose sugar solution into a test tube. Add 5 drops of Benedict's solution. The solution should turn a light blue color.

CAUTION: In the next part of the test, keep the open end of the tube pointed away from you and others.

Hold the tube with a test-tube holder and heat slowly over a burner. Move the tube back and forth through the flame until the liquid boils. Keep the liquid at a low boil for at least three minutes. Record the results in your table.

2. Blue to green to yellow to orange to red.

2. What color changes occur as heat is added to the solution of simple sugar (glucose) and Benedict's solution?

Part Two: Proteins

D. *Testing for proteins:* Put a small amount of raw egg white into a large test tube. Add an equal amount of concentrated sodium hydroxide solution to the tube.

TABLE 20–1 IDENTIFYING NUTRIENTS IN FOODS

Check to make sure that students are performing tests correctly and are making correct conclusions based on observations.

Class of Foods	*Tested With*	*Results*
Carbohydrates Starches	Iodine	Blue-black color
Carbohydrates Simple Sugars	Benedict's solution	Color change from blue to light green to yellow to orange to red.
Proteins	Copper sulfate and sodium hydroxide	Color change to violet.
Fats and Oils	Brown paper	Translucent appearance of spot.

CAUTION: Sodium hydroxide is harmful to the skin, eyes, and clothing. If spilled, wash immediately with plenty of water.

After adding the sodium hydroxide, add 5 drops of copper sulfate solution to the test tube. Record the results in your table.

3. Color changed to purple or violet.

3. What color change occurred in the tube as the copper sulfate solution was added?

Part Three: Fats and oils

E. *Testing for fats or oils:* Rub some butter on a piece of brown wrapping paper. Hold the brown paper to the light and observe the stain. Record your observations in your table.

4. The paper becomes translucent and "oily" looking.

4. How does butter change the appearance of brown wrapping paper?

You should now be able to

Identify three basic food nutrients found in common foods.
Test for the presence of carbohydrates.
Test for the presence of proteins.
Test for the presence of fats or oils.

Testing foods

The tests you used on carbohydrates and proteins caused certain color changes. These color changes can be used to identify specific food materials. Tests of this type are useful, since they supply you with information about the nutrient content of foods. For the sake of simplicity, you can assume that the tests you performed on foods with only one kind of nutrient will identify that same nutrient even when others are present. In the next problem you will use the tests you have just learned to identify the contents of several foods.

Problem 20-2 Which foods contain carbohydrates, fats, and proteins?

Purpose To test some common foods for the presence of carbohydrates, fats, and proteins.

Materials foods — bread, butter, lettuce, bacon, apple, carrot, peanut, grapes, hard-boiled egg, cheese, potato, banana

razor blade, single-edged
medicine droppers (3)
iodine solution
Benedict's solution
Bunsen burner
graduated cylinder
test-tube holder
test tubes, 18 × 150 mm (3)
test tube, 25 × 200 mm
sodium hydroxide solution, concentrated
copper sulfate solution, dilute
brown wrapping paper

Procedure In this experiment you will test a number of foods for the presence of carbohydrates (starch and sugar), proteins, and fats. You will compare the results of these tests with the tests that you completed in Problem 20-1.

Perform Steps A, B, and C for each kind of food being tested. If there is not enough time to complete all of the tests, arrange to test one-half of the foods and share your results with another group. The other group may then do the other half and share their results with your group.

Before you begin, copy Table 20-2 (page 372) into your notebook to record all your observations.

To interpret and record the results of your tests for starch, use the following method. If the food shows the blue-black color found in the

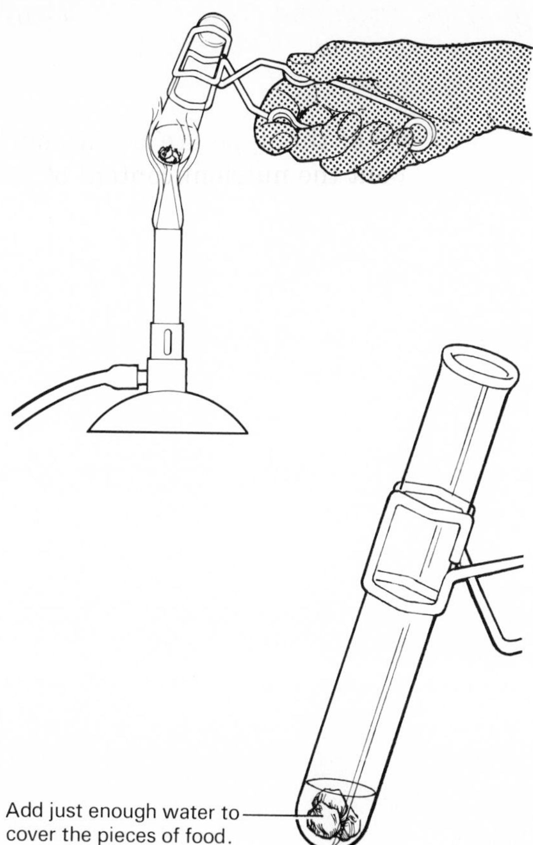
Add just enough water to cover the pieces of food.

20-2. Heat *only* until the water boils, to avoid drying the sample. Be sure the mouth of the test tube is pointed away from yourself and others.

test for starch, rate it with three plus marks (+ + +). If the test for starch causes only a slight color change, rate the food with a single plus mark (+). If the results are completely negative, without any indication of starch present, rate the food with a minus sign (−).

A. Obtain a small sample of one of the foods listed in the materials for this problem. Cut the small sample into many fine pieces. Put the cut-up pieces into a large test tube along with any juices that may have been released as you cut the food up.

B. Add just enough water to cover the food. (See Figure 20-2.) Heat the contents until the water boils. Boiling will dissolve material from the food.

CAUTION: In Step C, be sure to aim the test tube away from people during the test for sugar. And be careful not to spill the sodium hydroxide during the test for proteins.

Amounts of each nutrient will vary with the age, condition, and portion of the food selected for sampling.

TABLE 20–2 TESTING FOODS FOR STARCH, SUGAR, PROTEIN, FATS AND OILS

Food Tested	*Results of Tests for*			
	Carbohydrate Starch	*Carbohydrate Sugar*	*Protein*	*Fats and Oils*
Bread	+++	+	+	-
Butter	-	-	+	+++
Lettuce	-	+	-	-
Apple	+	+++	+	-
Bacon	-	+	+++	+++
Carrot	-	+	-	-
Grape	-	+++	-	-
Egg	-	-	+++	-
Cheese	+	-	+++	-
Potato	+++	-	-	-
Peanut	+	-	+	+++
Banana	+	+++	-	-

1. Of the foods listed, butter, bacon, and peanut contain the most fat.
2. Egg, cheese, bacon, and possibly bread.
3. Bread, potato, peanut.
4. Bread, banana, lettuce, grape, carrot, apple.
5. Peanut.
6. Of the foods listed in table, apple, carrot, grapes, and banana could be eaten for quick energy.

C. Use small samples from the material in the test tube to perform tests on the material for starch, glucose, fats, and proteins. (See Problem 20-1 if you need to refresh your memory on how to perform these tests.)

1. What foods contained the most fats?
2. What foods contained the most protein?
3. What foods contained the most starch?
4. What foods contained the most glucose sugar?
5. What foods contained proteins, starches, *and* fats?
6. Glucose, a simple sugar, is used by the body to provide quick energy for the cells. What foods would you eat if you wanted to get quick energy?

Any glucose that is not used by the body is changed into **glycogen** (an animal starch). Glycogen may be changed into fats and stored for later use. Proteins are used by the body for growth. If

7. Foods high in fats and starches contribute to weight gain, if eaten in excess. Such foods are butter, bacon, peanut, bread, and potato.

8. Protein.

other types of food are not available, proteins may be changed into sugar to release energy. No other food, however, can be converted into a protein. This is why proteins are so essential in your diet.

7. What foods would tend to cause you to become overweight if you ate large amounts of them?
8. What food nutrient should be eaten daily to ensure proper growth?

You should now be able to

Test foods for the presence of carbohydrates, fats, and proteins.

Estimate the relative amount of each basic nutrient present in a food item.

Determine which basic nutrient is essential for growth and repair of tissue.

Other basic food nutrients

In addition to carbohydrates, fats, and proteins, foods may also contain vitamins and minerals. Vitamins and minerals are required for the proper functioning of all living things. If they are lacking in the diet, the body will not be working at peak efficiency. A serious lack of vitamins may result in *deficiency diseases*, among which are beriberi and scurvy. Table 20-3 on the next page lists some of the essential vitamins.

Some foods have large amounts of vitamins. Those foods are recommended to prevent certain deficiency diseases. A chemical test may be used to detect the presence of vitamin C in fresh oranges. You will learn about this test in Problem 20-3.

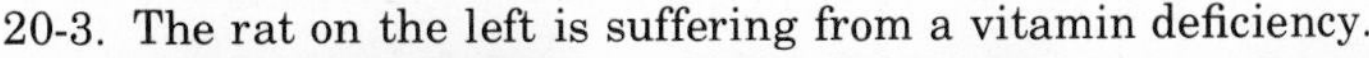

20-3. The rat on the left is suffering from a vitamin deficiency.

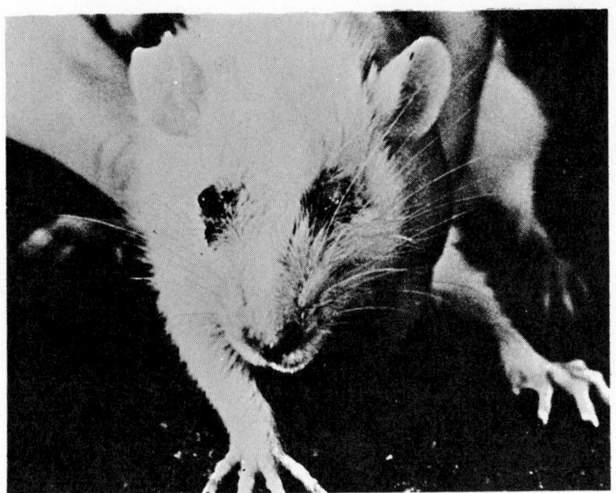

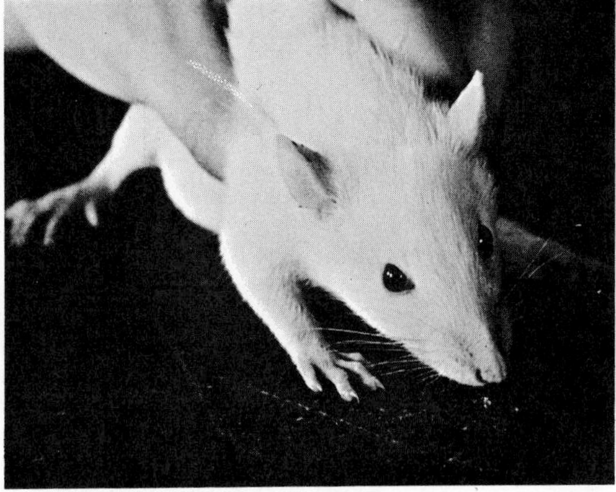

TABLE 20-3 SOME ESSENTIAL VITAMINS

Name of Vitamin	*Found In*	*Deficiency Condition*
Vitamin A	Yellow vegetables and leafy vegetables. Also found in fish liver oils, milk, egg yolk, and butter	Low resistance to infections. Night blindness
Vitamin B_1 (Thiamin)	Yeast, seafood, fruits, whole grain, leafy vegetables, egg, liver, butter, and milk	Poor growth Loss of weight Beriberi
Vitamin B_2 (Riboflavin)	Lean meat, soybeans, milk, fruit, eggs, liver, carrots	Poor growth Eye lesions Premature aging
Vitamin B_6 (Niacin)	Lean meat, green vegetables, whole grains, and liver	Skin diseases Nervous disorders Poor growth
Vitamin C	Citrus fruits, berries, leafy vegetables, and tomatoes	Scurvy
Vitamin D	Fish-liver oils, egg yolk, and fortified milk	Soft bones Teeth defects Poor growth

Problem 20-3 How can you test a food for the presence of vitamin C?

Purpose To test for the presence of vitamin C. To determine the effect of heating or cooling on vitamin C.

Materials

The iodine-starch mixture must be freshly prepared for each of the three trials.

- starch solution
- iodine solution
- orange, fresh
- Bunsen burner
- wire screen
- beakers, 250-ml (2)
- graduated cylinder
- test tubes (3)
- marking pen
- knife
- medicine droppers (3)
- ring stand and ring
- freezer
- test-tube rack

Procedure

A. Pour 10 ml of starch solution into a large test tube. Add 3 drops of iodine solution to produce the familiar blue-black color. This mixture will be used to test for vitamin C.

B. Add the juice from a fresh orange, one drop at a time, into the mixture in the test tube from Step A. Add drops and keep count until a color change occurs in the blue-black liquid.

1. How many drops were required to produce a color change?
2. What color is the liquid after adding orange juice with vitamin C?

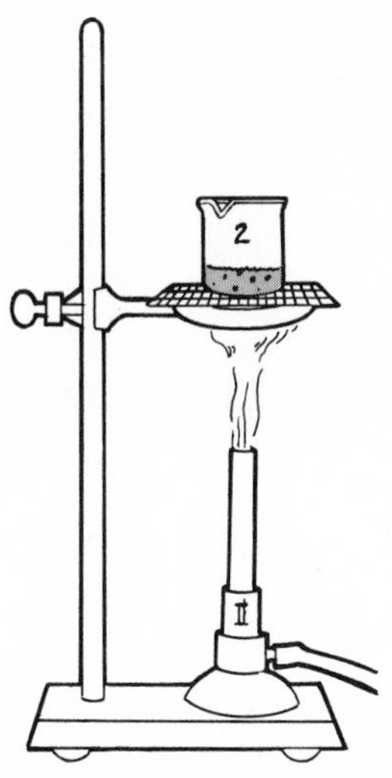

20-4. Place Beaker 2 over a burner and gently boil the juice for about 5 minutes. *Be careful not to evaporate all of the juice.*

C. Copy Table 20-4 into your notebook. Use your table to record the results of boiling and freezing vitamin C (Steps D, E, and F that follow).

D. Remove the juice from a fresh orange and divide the liquid equally into two beakers marked "1" and "2." Place Beaker 1 into the freezer compartment of a refrigerator. Leave it there until the liquid is frozen. Place Beaker 2 over a burner as shown in Figure 20-4. Gently boil the juice for about 5 minutes. Be careful not to evaporate all of the liquid.

E. Prepare two test tubes with the iodine-starch test liquid as described in Step A. Label the test tubes "1" and "2." Add frozen juice from Beaker 1 to Test Tube 1, one drop at a time, until the color change occurs.

3. How many drops of juice from Beaker 1 (frozen juice) needed to be added to produce a color change?

F. Add the boiled juice from Beaker 2 to Test Tube 2, one drop at a time, until a color change occurs.

1. The number of drops required will depend on the amount of vitamin C present (between 2 and 10 drops, usually).

2. Clear or colorless.

3. 2-15 drops, usually. (See Table 20-4.)

TABLE 20–4 THE EFFECT OF BOILING AND FREEZING ON VITAMIN C

Orange Juice	*Vitamin C Test Results*
Frozen	Color change with 2-15 drops.
Boiled	No color change even after 15-30 drops are added.

4. (See Table 20-4.) There may be no color change, since all the vitamin C may have been destroyed in boiling.

5. Freezing.

4. How many drops of juice from Beaker 2 (boiled juice) needed to be added to produce a color change?
5. Which treatment of the orange juice, freezing or boiling, preserves the most vitamin C?

G. Test other kinds of juices and drinks available and see how they respond to the vitamin C test.

You should now be able to

Test a food for the presence of vitamin C.

Describe the effect of freezing and boiling on vitamin C.

State which vitamin is needed to prevent a particular deficiency disease.

Discuss the need for vitamins in the daily diet.

Measuring food energy

Your body needs energy to maintain its life activities. The energy needed is released in the cells as part of the process of respiration. Fats and carbohydrates are oxidized in the cells, releasing the energy needed by the body. Some of this energy is used to maintain a constant body temperature.

A device called a calorimeter can be used to measure the energy value of a food. Food energy is usually listed in large Calories. Calorie charts show the energy values of various foods. You can find the total energy value of the food you eat in a day by adding up the Calories contained in each serving of food. Charts such as the sample one in Table 20-5 are available to the public, listing just about any food you might want to look up.

The average daily requirement of Calories varies with age, activity, and the efficiency with which the body operates. Table 20-6 lists some average daily Calorie requirements. When a person uses food energy at the same rate that he or she takes it in, the body weight will remain the same. However, some people use up far fewer Calories than they take in each day. The excess food is stored by the body in the form of fat. To maintain your body weight, you must match your food intake with the activity performed each day.

In Problem 20-4 you will see how a very simple calorimeter can be used to measure the fuel value of a food. In this problem a small piece

TABLE 20-5 CALORIE CHART OF SOME FOODS

Food	*Calories in an Average Serving*
Apple	90
Banana	100
Bread, wheat	60
Celery	5
Cola	145
Corn, small ear	70
Frankfurter	170
Hamburger on a bun	500
Ham sandwich	350
Ice cream, plain	200
Liver, beef, fried	130
Mango	65
Milk	140
Orange	80
Peanut-butter sandwich	370
Peanuts	60
Pie, apple	560
Pizza	185
Pork chop	260
Rice, white	185
Spaghetti	155
Tea or coffee, plain	0
Tea or coffee, with cream and sugar	90
Tortilla	50
Yogurt	150

TABLE 20–6 DAILY CALORIE NEEDS

Lumberjack	5,000
Teen (Active Boy)	4,000
Man	3,000
Teen (Active Girl)	2,500
Woman	2,000

of food is burned inside a can. The heat absorbed by water as a result is measured. The number of small calories absorbed by the water can be found by multiplying the volume of water in the test tube by the change in water temperature.

Problem 20-4 How do we measure the fuel value of a food?

Purpose To learn about the energy released in the oxidation of a food.

Materials None. You will be provided with the results of an experiment that has been previously completed.

Procedure A jockey wanted to find out how many sunflower seeds she could eat and still not be overweight for the next race. She and her friends devised a piece of apparatus to measure the energy released when one sunflower seed burned.

A. The steps the jockey and her friends followed are shown in Figures 20-5 and 20-6. The apparatus included a needle stuck in a cork to hold the burning sunflower seed under a test tube of water. A small can was used to support the test tube and to shield the flame of the burning seed.

B. The experimenters ran three trials, using three different sunflower seeds. The results are recorded in Table 20-7.

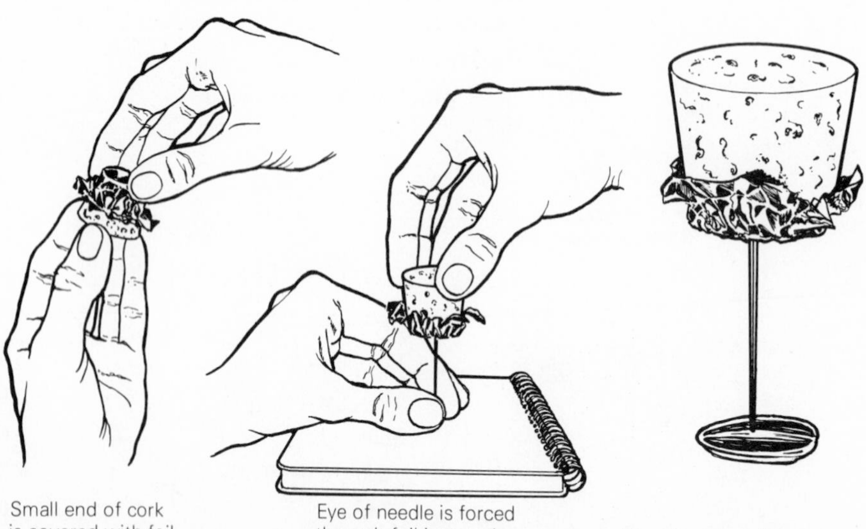

Small end of cork
is covered with foil.
Eye of needle is forced
through foil into cork.
The pinned sunflower seed

20-5. Preparing the cork and forcing the needle into a sunflower seed.

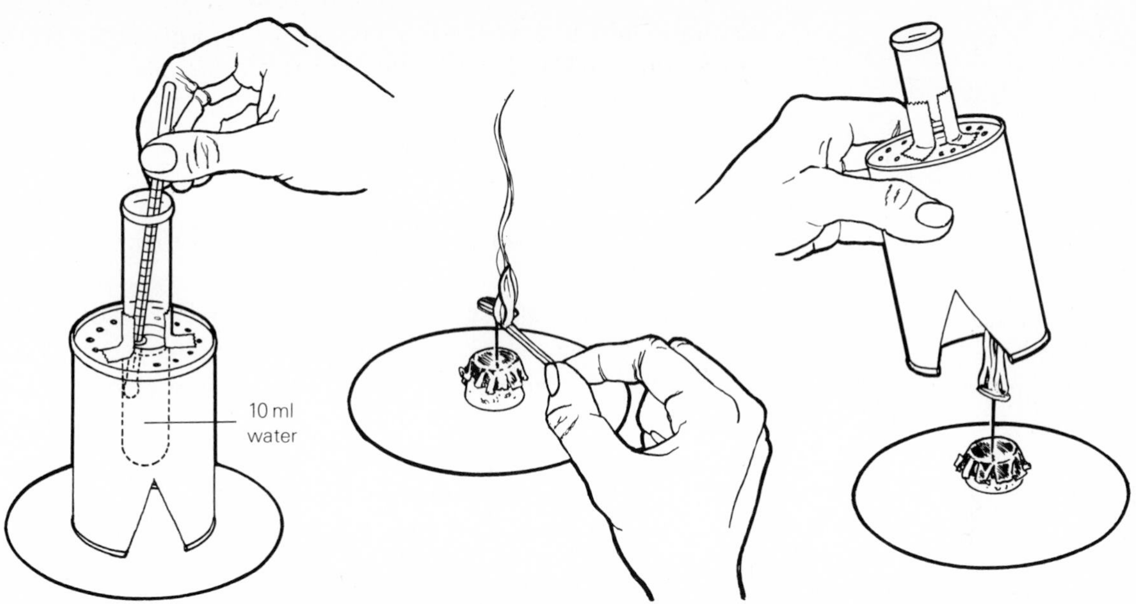

20-6. The original temperature of the water is measured. Then the seed is ignited and covered with the calorimeter so that the flame is directly under the test tube.

C. The data in Table 20-7 may be used to calculate the average number of small calories in one sunflower seed. You need to determine the number of small calories absorbed by the water in the test tube. To do this, multiply the temperature change in °C by the number of milliliters of water.

For example, if the temperature was 23°C before heating and 37°C after heating, the temperature change would be: 37°C − 23°C = 14°C. The volume of water in the test tube was 10 milliliters. So the amount of heat absorbed by the water (in small calo-

TABLE 20-7 RESULTS OF OXIDATION OF THREE DIFFERENT SUNFLOWER SEEDS

Food Material	*Water Temperature Before Heating*	*Water Temperature After Heating*	*Difference in Water Temperature*
Trial 1	23 °C	37 °C	14 °C
Trial 2	25 °C	45 °C	20 °C
Trial 3	27 °C	53 °C	26 °C

1. 10 x 14 = 140
10 x 20 = 200
10 x 20 = 260
600
600 ÷ 3 = 200
Answer = 200 calories

ries) is found by multiplying the temperature change in °C by the volume of water heated. (This relationship is true only when the liquid being warmed is water.)

14°C (temperature change) × 10 ml (volume) = 140 small calories

3. Different sizes of seeds, variations in room temperature, and other such variables could be mentioned.

4. $\frac{200}{1,000} = 0.2$
Answer = 0.2 large Calories were absorbed by the water.

6. The seed (because of its greater oil content).

7. Meals planned will vary, but should not exceed 1,500 large Calories and should include the four food groups. Students should refer to a calorie chart more comprehensive than the one on page 377.

1. What was the *average* number of small calories absorbed by the water in all three trials?
2. How did the three trials compare in terms of small calories released? 2. Fewest calories released in first trial; most calories released in last trial.
3. What could account for the difference in the number of calories in the three trials?
4. It takes 1,000 small calories to make one large Calorie. How many large Calories of heat energy were absorbed by the water? (Use the average of three trials for your calculations.)
5. If our jockey can have an intake of 1,500 large Calories and still maintain her weight, how many sunflower seeds could she eat per day and not gain weight? 5. $\frac{1,500}{0.2}$ = 7,500 seeds
6. If a sunflower seed and a sugar cube weighed the same, which would probably contain more energy?
7. Plan three meals for the jockey that would contain foods from the four basic food groups and would not exceed 1,500 large Calories. List the food types and amounts for each of the three meals.

You should now be able to

Define a large Calorie in terms of energy available in food.
State the approximate energy released in the burning of food.
Understand the relationship between temperature change and small calories for a given volume of water.
Plan a meal to be nutritional and limited in large Calories.

Science terms

balanced diet	fats	nutrients	sugars
carbohydrates	glycogen	proteins	vitamins
deficiency disease	large Calorie	small calorie	water
diet	minerals	starches	

Review questions

1. Carbohydrates, fats, proteins, minerals, vitamins, water.
2. A condition resulting from the lack of a certain vitamin.

1. List the six classes of food nutrients.
2. What is a vitamin deficiency disease?

3. One large Calorie equals 1,000 small calories.

4. For growth and tissue repair.

5. Carbohydrate starch.

6. Scurvy is a vitamin deficiency disease caused by the lack of vitamin C. This disease may be prevented by eating foods high in vitamin C, such as citrus fruits.

7. Simple sugar would cause a color change ranging from green to brick red. Starch will not cause any change in the blue color of Benedict's solution.

8. Simple sugar will cause no change in the golden-brown color of the iodine. Starch will cause the color to change to blue-black.

3. How does a large Calorie used by nutritionists compare to a small calorie?
4. What is the chief use of protein in the body?
5. Bread and potatoes contain large amounts of what nutrient?
6. What is the cause of scurvy? Explain how this disease may be prevented.
7. What color should you expect when Benedict's solution is used to test foods containing simple sugar? Containing starch?
8. What color should you expect when iodine solution is used to test foods containing simple sugar? Containing starch?

Check your understanding See Teacher's Guide section for answers to Questions 9-16.

9. Explain the difference between the words *food* and *nutrient*.
10. How are proteins, fats, and carbohydrates used in the body?
11. What is the chief use of sugar in the body?
12. Explain what is meant by a balanced diet.
13. Boiled orange juice contains less vitamin C than does frozen orange juice. Why?
14. Vitamin pills are unnecessary for most people if foods from the four food groups are eaten daily. Explain.
15. How is it possible for people to have a food deficiency and yet feel full after each meal?
16. Calculate the small calories absorbed by 100 grams of water as it is heated from 20°C to 40°C.

Chapter 21 **Pollution of the environment**

Chapter-opening photo of acid mine runoff provides a pretty picture of a not-so-pretty situation. You might tell the students also that some of the most beautiful sunsets are contributed to by pollutant particles in the atmosphere.

(*Above*) Acid runoff from a stripmine.

For many centuries people have slowly changed the environment by using up raw materials and throwing away wastes. The canopy of air above the earth was thought to be so large that people's activities on earth would not affect it. The oceans have been used as a handy dumping ground for liquid and solid wastes.

Unregulated industrial processes, careless use of resources, and an increasing population have taken their toll on the environment. Manufactured goods from factories have made our lives easier. But these goods have also caused an outpouring of waste products. The large quantities of wastes — sewage, garbage, trash, chemicals, gases — have begun to accumulate. The reservoir of clean air surrounding us has been contaminated by smoke and soot. Streams that were once clear have become dirtied with factory wastes. Dead or dying fish are symptoms of our mistreatment of the earth's waters.

This **pollution** of the air, water, and land has, in some cases, made them unfit for use. Major **pollutants**, or sources of environmental pollution, include industrial wastes, detergents, automobile exhaust, burning trash, radioactive fallout, reactor wastes, and insecticides. These pollutants affect the earth's water, air, and land.

Water pollution

At one time, liquid waste products from our cities and factories were simply dumped into nearby rivers and streams. The flowing rivers carried the wastes away from one place only to pollute the waters downstream. In time, people noticed the effects of this kind of pollution. Certain natural organisms disappeared. And other organisms appeared in their place.

Chemicals in wastes pollute water by the chemical reactions they bring about. Acids and certain salts can kill most of the living things in a stream or lake in a short time. Excess fertilizers washed downstream can cause algae to thrive and cover the surface of the water. This, in turn, interferes with swimming and boating and may even cause the fish to die. Rotting algae produce unpleasant odors, further polluting the area.

Still another water pollution problem is the result of drilling for oil. Breaks or bad connections in the pipelines of offshore oil wells may cause oil to leak into the ocean. Tankers carrying oil from dis-

21-1. Industrial wastes are sometimes dumped into nearby bodies of water.

21-2. When certain waste gases in the air are acted on by sunlight, smog can be formed.

tant parts of the world may become damaged and spill their cargo into the ocean. This leakage from tankers and offshore wells can cause *oil slicks* to form along the coast. These oil slicks ruin the shore for swimming and boating. More seriously, the oil may kill birds, fish, and plants that live along the coast.

Because of the activities of concerned citizens, the government has begun to take action. Stricter regulations are being written and enforced. But no law can bring a sea gull back to life. Much remains to be done to protect the natural world.

Air pollution

Pollution of the air is brought about by the discharge of wastes into the atmosphere. Wastes from furnaces, motor vehicles, and industries spew great amounts of gases and solid particles into the air. Most of the solid particles settle out of the atmosphere as dust. Such gases as carbon monoxide, sulfur dioxide, and nitrogen dioxide, which are given off when certain fuels are burned, are a big problem in some areas of the country.

Scientists now know that **smog**, such as is found around Los Angeles, is not caused solely by the initial air pollutants. It is formed when ultraviolet radiation from sunlight acts on the waste gases to form new compounds. These compounds include ozone, aldehydes, and other organic molecules. These compounds irritate the eyes and lungs, and are responsible for crop damage in some areas.

Every city with a sizable population has at least a potential smog problem. The problem stems mainly from automobile exhaust and the action of ultraviolet radiation upon it. It is a complex problem, but one that must be attended to before the city areas become unfit to live in.

Insecticides and detergents

Of all the creatures on earth, humans are the only ones that can plan the changes they make in their surroundings. Most of the changes result in more food, better shelter, and less sickness. But sometimes unforeseen effects accompany the changes. Such effects may not appear for several years, which was the case with the insecticide known as **DDT**.

In 1942, the chemical DDT was developed to kill disease-carrying insects such as flies, ticks, and lice. Later, the same chemical was used to control insects that destroy crops. Within five years after its development, DDT had reduced crop losses due to insects by 90%. The benefits seemed overwhelming.

Only after years of its use did people begin to realize that DDT killed other living things besides insects. DDT lasts up to 17 years

21-3. After years of using insecticides, people now realize that such chemicals damage living things besides the insects they were intended for.

21-4. People became concerned about detergent pollution as their streams and rivers became covered with suds.

before chemically breaking down. With its long life, DDT killed not only harmful insects but also the birds, fish, and other animals in the insects' food chain.

In 1969, the United States government enacted legislation that limited the use of DDT after 1973. Scientists have turned their attention to finding ways to control insect pests by natural means. Sometimes the natural enemies of insects can be used to control insect pests. Certain chemicals extracted from the bodies of the insects are another possibility for insect control.

Synthetic **detergents** were developed several years ago to replace soap. They had the advantage of cleaning clothes in "hard" water better than soap did. Where soap tended to leave a scum, the new synthetic detergents did not.

As a result of the improved effectiveness, the new detergents were used extensively. At the time, it was not apparent that the use of the detergents would have far-reaching biological effects. Soap molecules are broken down by the action of bacteria. But the synthetic detergent molecules were *not* broken down in this manner. People became concerned as their streams and rivers became covered with suds. Within a few years, detergent molecules began to appear in fresh-water supplies taken from deep wells. When the public became aware of these problems, the manufacturers responded. They changed the composition of the detergent molecules so that bacteria could break them down. Some detergents, however, still contain chemicals that may cause unwanted algae to grow in streams and lakes.

The balance of nature

All organisms on earth, including humans, must utilize the same air (**atmosphere**) and the same water (**hydrosphere**). It is everyone's concern that our one atmosphere and one hydrosphere not be contaminated with pollutants.

The plants and animals in a community influence the lives of other living things. Green plants are the "food factories" of the world, but they rely on other forms of life for the raw materials with which to form food. (See Figure 21-5.) There is a delicate balance among living things. And that **balance of nature** may be disturbed by new factors in the environment. Changes within one community may have far-reaching consequences. Without a doubt, the most serious threat to the balance of nature is the human population.

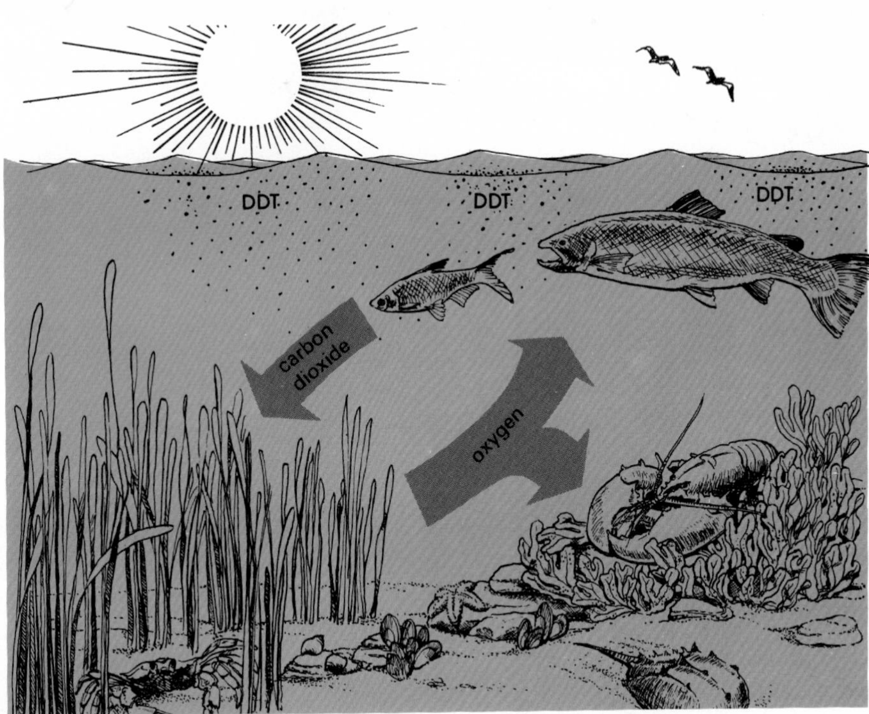

21-5. The delicate balance among living things may be disturbed by some new factor in the environment. What will the result be here?

Problem 21-1 How does detergent affect the activities of fish?

Purpose To determine the effect of various concentrations of detergent on the survival of fish.

Materials

Do not use biodegradable detergent for the stock solution.

distilled water	graduated cylinder
detergent, liquid	marking pen
medicine dropper	gallon jars (3)
small fish (6)	liter bottle

Procedure This problem should be done by large groups of students or as a class activity.

A. Obtain three wide-mouthed gallon jars. Label them "1", "2", and "3."

B. Fill each jar about three-fourths full with distilled water. Check to see that the water level in each jar is the same.

C. Place two small fish into each jar.

D. Prepare a detergent solution in the liter bottle. Add 25 drops of concentrated liquid detergent to one liter of distilled water. Label this jar "stock solution."

E. Each day for the next 8 to 10 days, add 5 ml of stock solution to Jar 1, 10 ml to Jar 2, and 15 ml to Jar 3.

1. Yes. The detergent is not broken down, and there is no way that the fish can escape.

1. Will the fish still be influenced by the polluted environment, even though no detergent is added on the weekend? Explain.

21-6. Creating a polluted environment.

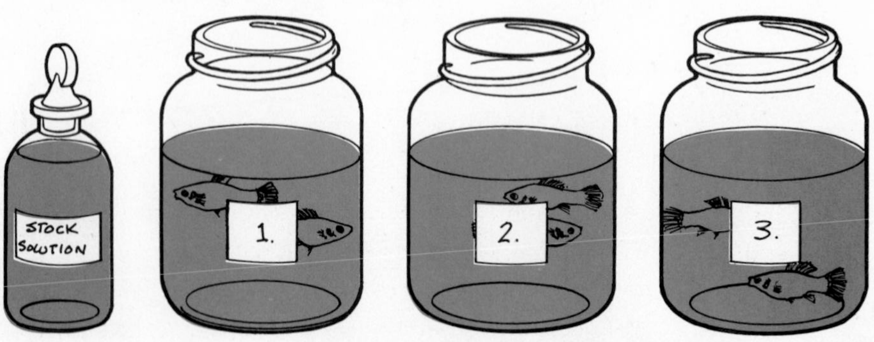

3. The fish should all be affected by the detergent, but those in Jar 3 should show the most effects. The fish in Jar 3 will begin to swim near the surface, erratically and fast. The fish in Jars 1 and 2 will take longer to show the same results, and may never show the erratic swimming patterns. The size and strength of the fish will influence the results of this experiment.

4. The gills usually enlarge. (This prevents oxygen in the water from coming into contact with the blood vessels, thus depriving the fish of oxygen.)

5. Some detergents cannot be broken down by organisms found in nature. Detergents can kill fish and other living organisms that live in water.

6. Put fish in a jar containing water without detergent. This would, in effect, serve as a control for this experiment.

TABLE 21–1 THE EFFECT OF DETERGENT ON FISH

Activities of Fish in Detergent								
	Day 1	Day 2	Day 3	Day 4	Day 5	Day 6	Day 7	Day 8
Jar 1								
Jar 2								
Jar 3								

F. Prepare a chart in your notebook similar to Table 21-1.

G. Observe and record the activities of the fish each day. Notice the levels at which the fish swim in the jar, the rates at which they swim, and the positions of their gill covers.

2. In which container was the detergent most concentrated? 2. In Jar 3.
3. How did the different amounts of detergent affect the behavior of the fish?
4. How were the gills of the fish affected by the detergent?
5. Why should detergents be considered dangerous as water pollutants?
6. How would you change this experiment to prove that the fish did not die of natural causes?

You should now be able to

Determine the effect of detergent on the survival of fish.

Observe changes in the gills of fish in different water-and-detergent samples.

Relate concentration of detergent in water to fish survival.

Suggest a plan to prevent the harmful effect of detergent on fish.

Investigating problems in our environment

Chemical pollutants, even in low concentrations, may produce serious results. The presence of even a couple of milliliters of certain materials in a water supply may cause millions of liters of water to taste bad. Often, as with the detergents, it may be years before the real problem is evident. In the meantime, the problem may have grown so large that many years will be needed to remedy the ill effects. This is why it is so important to consider all effects of a process that could possibly affect human populations in the future.

Many people are concerned about the possible ill effects of using atomic fuel. Atomic fuel promises clean air and inexpensive electricity. But part of the process involves releasing warm water into nearby bodies of water. Adding heat to water may have serious effects on the animals and plants that live there. Increased heat may lengthen the growing season of some plants, producing an overgrowth of algae with its associated problems.

Another problem involved with any use of nuclear energy is what to do with the radioactive wastes. These and many other problems of our environment demand immediate attention. In Problem 21-2 you will study some samples of how people change the environment in which they live.

Problem 21-2 How do people change the environment in which they live?

Purpose To consider some of the results of polluting the air and water of our environment.

Procedure

Part One: Water pollution

A. Water is one of the world's best solvents. (A solvent is a substance in which other substances will dissolve.) For this reason, people have used rivers and lakes to remove many of the waste products of industrial processes. Because the water dissolved and carried away the waste so well, few people noticed the changes in the water.

As the human population continued to grow and industrial wastes increased, changes became more apparent. Still, because the changes were gradual, most people did not think there was a problem. These people felt that natural processes would take care of things. But the fish in polluted streams died in great numbers.

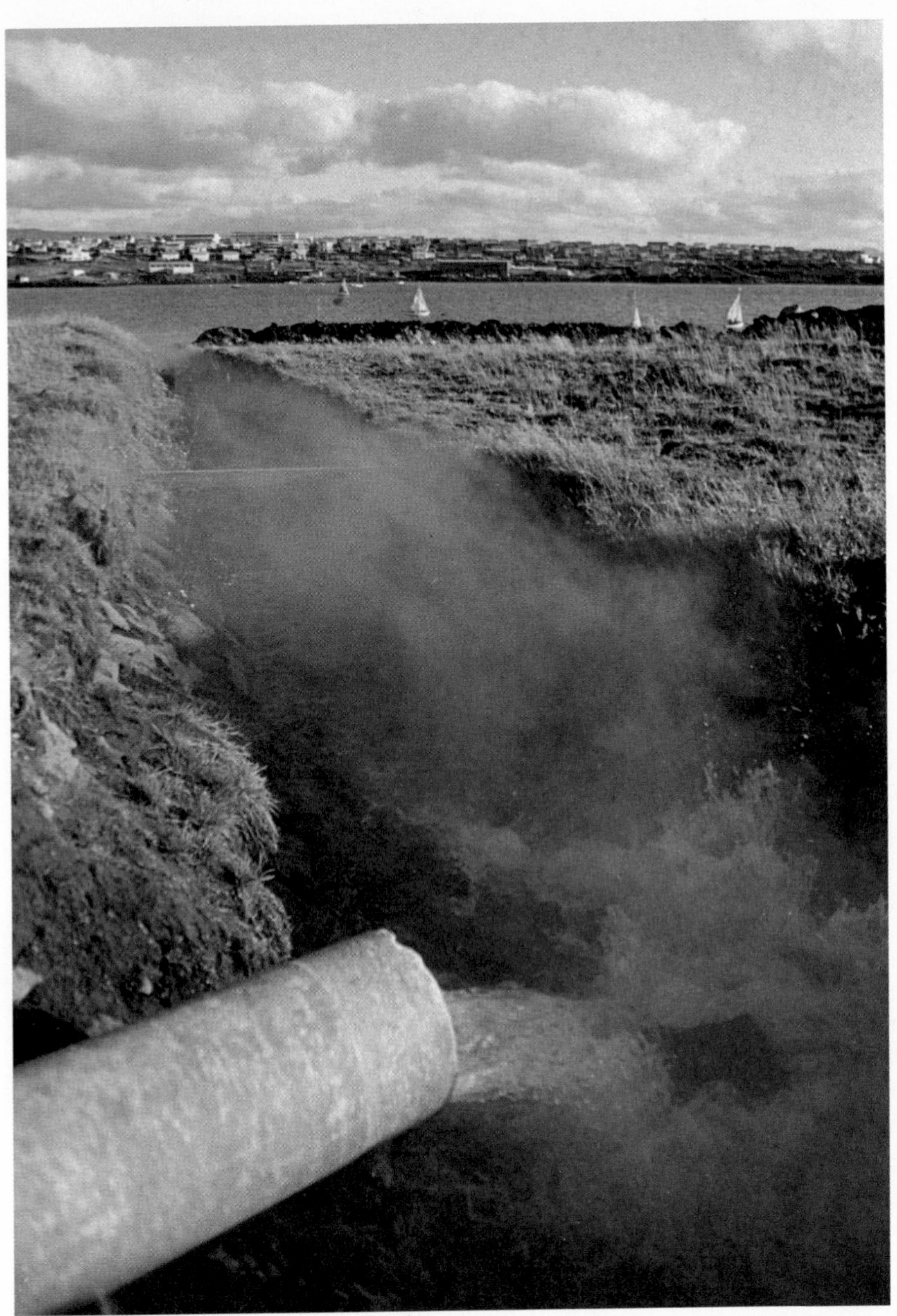

21-7. Adding heat from power plants to water may have serious effects on the fish and plants that live there.

Their oxygen supply had been lowered by the presence of decaying organic waste. The results were dramatic, as shown in Figure 21-8 on the next page.

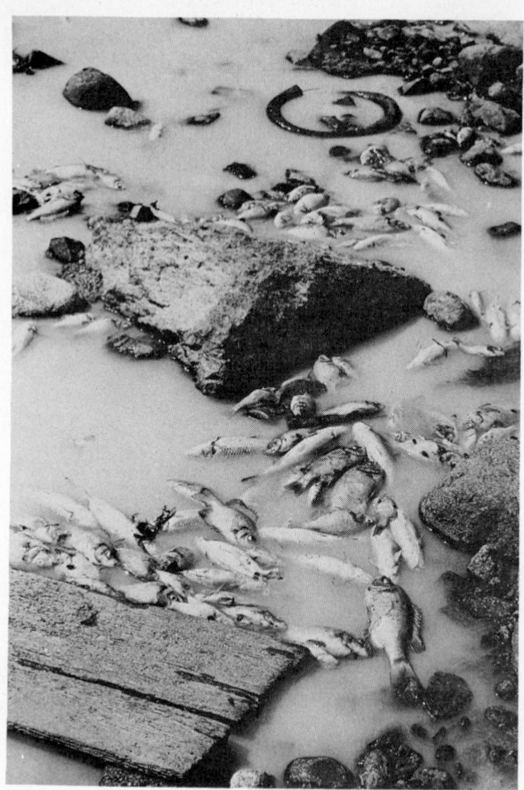

21-8. A lowered oxygen supply results in dead fish.

1. How do decaying fish affect the oxygen supply that is present in water?

1. They deplete the oxygen. The fish decay due to the action of microorganisms that use oxygen. The more decaying fish present, the more the microorganisms multiply, and thus the more oxygen used.

B. The materials from dead fish would also affect plant growth in the stream. The increased amount of nutrients in the stream caused algae to grow rapidly. After a period of time, algae covered the water's surface.

2. How might algae covering the surface of a stream affect plants that grow on the bottom?

2. The algae can block out sunlight and thus prevent bottom plants from carrying on photosynthesis, which they need to do in order to survive.

3. What would happen to fish that depend on plants growing on the bottom for their food supply?

3. The fish would either die or have to seek other sources of food.

C. The effects of pollution on the life in a stream are far-reaching. Each consumer organism depends on other organisms for the food that it needs. The quantity of nutrients in the water determines the number of producer organisms that grow.

D. All living things need water to maintain life. Humans are certainly no exception. Just think for a minute about all the ways you use water in a single day.

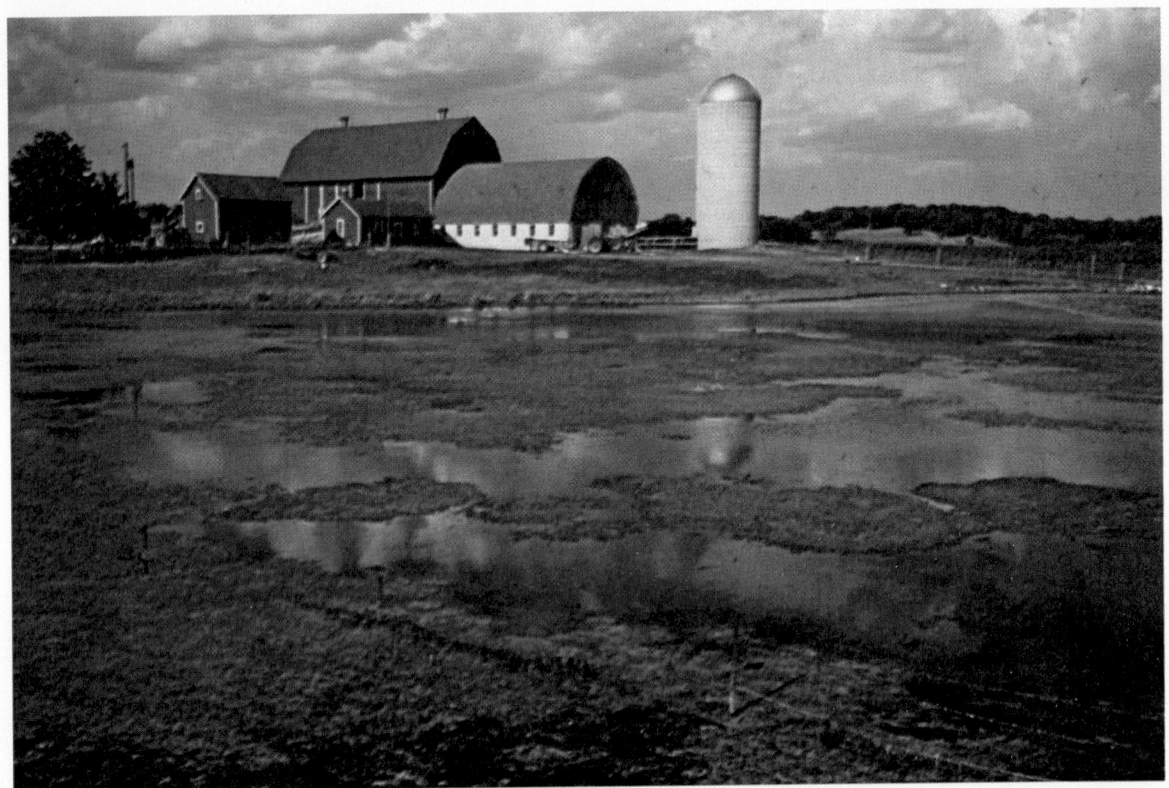

21-9. The excessive growth of algae covering the surface of this lake will eventually decay and pollute the water.

4. Rivers, streams, and lakes.
5. It must be aerated, filtered, and chemically purified.

4. Where do most of our cities get their water supply?
5. What must be done to the water before we can use it for drinking purposes?
6. What effect could insecticides have on the water supplies?

Part Two: Air pollution

6. They could cause higher expense in purification; if the insecticides could not be removed, they could make the water unfit to drink.

E. On the next page are photographs of three familiar sources of air pollution: industrial smokestacks, airplanes, and automobiles. The smoke, haze, and poor visibility evidenced in these pictures are the result of smoke particles, carbon dioxide, carbon monoxide, sulfur dioxide, hydrogen sulfide, and other air pollutants. These products are often found in the smog of large cities.

Besides reducing visibility and leaving a film of soot, the substances in polluted air can cause harm to the lungs, eyes, and skin. Cities are now trying to clean up their air so that scenes like those shown in the photographs will no longer be common.

Most of the gaseous pollutants in the air are released by transportation exhaust, while others come from industrial sources.

7. Answers depend on the area. Usually smoke and poor visibility are what one detects.

7. What evidences of air pollution can you detect in your own surroundings?
8. What are two of the main causes of air pollution in your area?
9. How could you show that some of the pollutants found in air are solid materials?
10. How could you show that air pollution is harmful to some kinds of plants?

Part Three: Fighting pollution

8. Automobiles and factories, usually. Other possibilities: airport, trash burning, mining operations.

9. A sheet of white paper or a strip of cellophane tape could be placed on a roof top or other open area to collect particles.

10. Plants could be grown in an environment containing high concentrations of such pollutants as smoke and carbon monoxide. Plants would be observed for evidence of harmful effects.

So far you have read about some of the ways people have polluted their environment. But, recognizing the seriousness of the problem, people are seeking solutions. No one wants our air, water, and soil resources spoiled.

F. Different communities have different kinds of problems, and they are trying in different ways to solve them. Some problems are local in nature. They affect only a limited number of people or other living things. Other problems are nationwide. The combined efforts of millions of people are required to solve those problems.

In this part of the problem you, or a committee from your school, will try to find out what pollution problems exist in your city or state, and what efforts are being made to fight these sources of pollution.

G. It is suggested that a fact-finding committee be formed in your school to seek answers to the questions that follow (Step H). The answers to some of the questions will be found in articles in newspapers or magazines. You will need to question the local pollution control office in your city, if there is such an office. Perhaps a letter to the office in charge of pollution control in your state will be helpful in your search for information.

H. Answer the following questions about pollution in your area and what is being done about it.

What are the three most critical pollution problems in your city or area of the state?

What efforts have been or are being made to reduce the pollution in your community?

What efforts have been successful in reducing the amounts of solid pollutants put into the atmosphere from factories?

What efforts have been made by your city, town, or state to reduce pollution of water in lakes, streams, or the oceans?

What laws have been passed in your state regulating the amount and kinds of exhaust gases that can be given off by transportation vehicles, including cars, trucks, buses, and airplanes?

What studies of smog damage to plants and human health have been conducted by research groups in your state?

I. If possible, make arrangements to give a report to all science classes — or better still, the whole school — on the results of your study. The solution to these problems will have much to do with the quality of life in your region.

J. Pollution control, in the long run, is not only the responsibility of industry, the government, or scientists. It is also up to you. Keeping our planet a healthy and pleasant place to live is the job of every person. Any efforts on the part of government, industry, or scientists will be wasted if most people are apathetic about their environment.

How can you help? First of all, you can call attention to the problem. Talk with your family and friends about pollution, and discuss what can be done about it. If you see a motor vehicle discharging smoky exhaust fumes, report it to the local pollution control board or motor vehicle department. If there are any organizations in your area dedicated to fighting pollution, volunteer to work for them.

Most important of all, set an example for others. When you go to the beach or park for a picnic, pick up any trash before you leave. Try walking or bicycling to where you want to go, if possible, instead of asking someone to take you there in a car. As a class, why not form a committee to clean up a local river bank, recreation area, or business district? Your actions may cause other people to become interested in cleaning up the environment.

K. You have learned that all plants, animals, and protists face the same basic problems in their struggle to survive and carry on their species. Every organism depends on the environment for the raw materials that it uses to grow, move, breathe, and reproduce. It is essential that we respect and care for the environment on which all living things, including ourselves, depend.

You should now be able to

Describe some effects of pollution of a water environment.

Suggest methods of controlling pollution of our environment.

Discuss the effect of accumulation of pollutants in the environment.

Identify the most critical pollution problems in your city, town, or state, and tell what measures are being taken to combat the pollution.

Volunteers help clean up a beach after an oil spill. Helping hands gently wash oil from a duck that was trapped in the polluted water. What have you done to help fight against pollution?

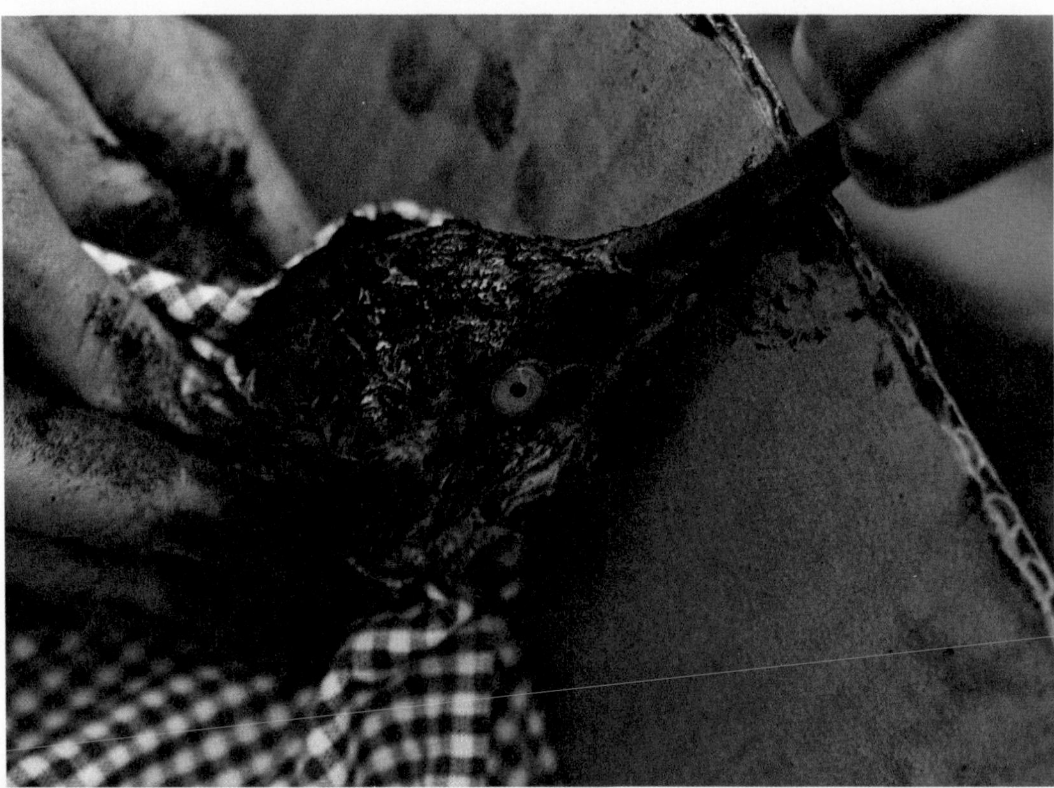

Science terms

atmosphere
balance of nature
DDT
detergent
hydrosphere
pollutants
pollution
smog

Review questions

1. What is pollution?
2. List five major sources of environmental pollution.
3. What are two methods used to reduce the amount of water pollution?
4. Name two gases that pollute our air.
5. Why was DDT developed?
6. Explain why synthetic detergents have caused so much concern to scientists.
7. What is the "balance of nature"?
8. How are radioactive wastes different from other kinds of wastes?

Check your understanding

See Teacher's Guide section for answers to Questions 9-19.

9. Why is pollution of any kind dangerous?
10. Why is water pollution such a serious problem?
11. Name two ways that water pollution may be costly to humans.
12. Why is air pollution so difficult to control?
13. What type of pollution can be decreased by the installation of a sewage disposal plant?
14. In what way is air pollution an even greater hazard than water pollution?
15. In what ways can the pollution of our hydrosphere and atmosphere be prevented?
16. How are humans dependent on their environment?
17. Discuss several ways that you, as an individual, can help to fight or eliminate pollution.
18. Suppose a housing development were to be built on the shores of a small lake. How would this be likely to affect the lake and the organisms in it? What could the builders and the residents of the housing development do to preserve the environment and do as little damage to it as possible?
19. One of the major sources of environmental pollution is the burning or discarding of trash and garbage. An obvious solution to this problem is to find ways to recycle some of this discarded trash. Can you think of any ways in which this might be done?

1. Pollution is the undesirable environmental condition created by the outpouring of waste products such as sewage, garbage, trash, chemicals, smoke, etc.

2. Sewage, garbage, chemical and industrial wastes, detergents, smoke, noise, automobile exhaust, etc.

3. Treating sewage, controlling industrial wastes, etc.

4. Carbon monoxide, sulfur dioxide, etc.

5. To kill harmful insects.

6. The molecules of certain detergents cannot be broken down by bacteria; thus, they accumulate and pollute the environment. (Many detergents used to contain phosphates, which caused the excessive growth of algae.)

7. When the living and nonliving factors in the environment exist in a delicate balance. Within a given area, producer and consumer populations tend to become stablilized, unless acted upon by some outside force.

8. They cannot be detected by any of our senses; they usually last a relatively long time.

Glossary/Index

This glossary/index provides brief definitions of science terms. The pronunciations of some of the words are shown in [brackets]. The syllable with the major accent is shown in CAPITAL LETTERS. The page numbers after the definitions show some of the places where the words are used in this book.

A

absorption [ab-ZORP-shun]: the passage of water and other fluids through cell membranes; 122, 335

adaptation [ad-ap-TAY-shun]: the act or process of adjusting to environmental conditions; (in frog) 305-306

agar [AHG-ahr]: a gelatinlike substance used for culturing molds and bacteria; 151, 158

alga [AL-guh]: a plantlike protist that contains chlorophyll but has no roots, leaves, or stem; pl. *algae;* 125-127; (and water pollution) 383, 392

amphibian [am-FIB-ee-un]: one of a large group of cold-blooded vertebrate animals that live in or near fresh water; 297-302

anatomy [uh-NAT-uh-me]: the structure of a living thing; 295

anterior: toward the front or near the head of an organism; 319

anther: small tip of the stamen that produces and contains the pollen; 279

antibiotic [ant-ih-by-AHT-ik]: a chemical produced from living organisms such as bacteria, fungi, and molds; when used as a medicine, it slows or destroys disease; penicillin is an example; 170

antiseptic [ant-ih-SEP-tik]: a substance that slows or stops the growth or action of microorganisms; iodine is an example; 177

anus [A-nuss]: opening at the posterior end of the digestive tract; 122, 336

Aristotle: scholar in early Greece; (and theory of plant growth) 257

artery: any blood vessel that carries blood away from the heart; 318, 329

asepsis [a-SEP-sis]: the process of ridding an area of most disease-causing microorganisms; 177

atmosphere [AT-muh-sfeer]: the gaseous layer covering the earth and containing gases essential for life on earth; 387

atrium [A-tree-um]: saclike section above the ventricle in the heart; pl. *atria;* 329, 331, 332

auxin [AWK-sin]: chemical substance in plants that functions somewhat as hormones do in animals; produced in the tips of stems and roots; 212, 220

axis: the horizontal or vertical line on a graph used to show a variable; 26, 30-31

B

bacillus [buh-SILL-us]: any rod-shaped bacterium; pl. *bacilli;* 174, 176

backbone: part of the skeletal system in all vertebrate animals; the dorsal bone composed of vertebrae; 323, 324

bacteriologist [bak-teer-ee-ALL-uh-jist]: a scientist who studies bacteria; 176

bacterium [bak-TEER-ee-um]: one-celled protist that cannot make its own food; three kinds of shapes — round (coccus), rodlike (bacillus), and spiral (spirillum); pl. *bacteria;* 167-170, 174-176, 180

balanced diet: a diet in which foods in proper proportion supply the body's needs; 367

balance of nature: an equilibrium established by the plant and animal populations in a given area; 387

bar graph: a type of graph usually comparing different objects or events; 26, 30-32, 34-36

beriberi [bare-ee-BARE-ee]: a deficiency disease resulting from a lack of vitamin B1 and characterized by gradual paralysis; 373, 374

bile: a fluid that helps to digest fats; secreted by the liver and stored in the gall bladder; 335

biomass [BY-oh-mass]: the combined mass of all living material, including both plants and animals, that a given area produces; 355

blood: substance that circulates in the heart, arteries, and veins of certain animals; carries oxygen and nutrients to body cells and carries waste materials away from the cells; 117, 118, 119, 318, 329, 331, 332

breathing rate: the rate of exchange of air into and out of the lungs; 306, 309, 313

budding: a form of asexual reproduction in yeast and hydra; also, the uniting of a bud with a stalk; 157

C

calorie [KAL-uh-ree]: unit of heat necessary to raise the temperature of one gram of water one degree Celsius; large Calorie of nutrition is equal to one thousand small calories; 367, 376, 377

calorimeter: device used to determine the energy or fuel value of foods; 376, 378-380

camouflage [KAM-uh-flahj]: the blending of an organism by color or pattern with its surroundings; 302

canine [KAY-nine] **tooth:** pointed tooth constructed to tear food into pieces; 317, 322

capillary [KAP-uh-lair-ee]: tiny blood vessel through which gases, foods, and wastes are exchanged between the blood and cells of the body; 318, 329

capillary action: the process in which water held in a narrow tube moves upward due to molecular attraction between the water and the tube; 252

carbohydrate [kar-bo-HY-drate]: chemical compound needed by the body and containing carbon, hydrogen, and oxygen atoms; sugars, starches, and cellulose are examples; 366, 367, 376; (test for sugar) 368; (test for starch) 368

carbon dioxide: colorless, odorless gas found in the air; gaseous waste product of internal respiration in plants and animals; (and air pollution) 393; (and photosynthesis) 113, 259-260, 266; (and respiration) 204; (test for) 156, 208

cell: the basic unit of all living things; 67, 88-94, 107; (cork) 101; (division and specialization) 107-111, 113-115, 127

cell membrane: thin, living, semipermeable layer that surrounds the materials of all cells; 93, 97, 107, 167

cellulose [SELL-yuh-lohs]: a carbohydrate that is the main part of the cell walls of plants; 93

cell wall: nonliving material that surrounds a plant cell; 93, 95, 96, 103, 107

centimeter (cm): 1/100 of a meter; approximately the length across the little finger at the fingernail; 8, 9, 80-81

characteristic: an identifying trait or feature; 46; (of living things) 54-56, 57-58, 60-61; (variations in) 341, 343-344, 349

chemotaxis [kem-oh-TAK-sis]: in freely moving protists or simple animals, a reaction or response to chemicals; 140

chemotropism [keh-MAH-truh-piz-um]: in plants, a response or reaction to chemicals; 215

chlorophyll [KLOR-uh-fill]: the green-colored material in some protists and in green plants that is necessary for photosynthesis; 93, 98, 114, 127, 259-260; (*a* and *b* pigments in) 275

chloroplast [KLOR-uh-plast]: small structure that contains chlorophyll and is found in the cytoplasm of certain protists and in the mesophyllic cells of green plants; 93, 99, 105, 114, 260, 272-273

chromatography [kro-muh-TAHG-ruh-fee]: a method of separating pigments based on their rates of solubility; 272-275

chromosome [KRO-muh-sohm]: one of the threadlike bodies composed of genes that control heredity; found in a cell's nucleus; 344

cilia [SILL-ee-uh]: tiny, hair-like structures used for locomotion by certain protists; sing. *cilium;* 131

circulatory system: the collection of blood vessels that carries blood to and from the body cells; 110, 318; (in earthworm) 117, 119; (in frog and human) 329-332

class: the division of plant and animal phyla that is further divided into orders; 55, 57, 58

classification key: the explanation of a system of grouping objects; 55-56, 60-61

classification system: any arrangement in categories according to relationships of varying degrees; with living things, a system that utilizes characteristics of organisms to classify them as similar or dissimilar to other organisms; 43-46; (for human) 58

classify: to sort out in a methodical manner; 42

cloaca [klo-A-kuh]: in certain vertebrates, the cavity below the large intestine into which the digestive tract, kidneys, bladder, and reproductive organs discharge their products; 336

closed community: environmental area where the populations cannot move outside that area easily; ponds are examples; 361

coccus [KAHK-us]: any round-shaped bacterium; pl. *cocci;* 174, 176

cold-blooded: term applied to fish, reptiles, and amphibians, whose body temperatures change with the outside temperature; 302

colony: a group of microorganisms that has grown from a single cell or small group of cells; 147-149, 158, 163, 169, 174, 175

community: all the populations, plant and animal, found in a given area; 354-358, 360-361

complete flower: any flower that contains all four structures — sepals, petals, stamens, and pistil; 279

compound microscope: a microscope that contains two lenses or two sets of lenses; 70, 72

concentration: a measure of how closely packed objects are in a given area, such as molecules in a liquid, gas, or solid; 235, 237, 242, 244 .

consumer: an organism that depends on producers or other organisms for its food; 356-358

control factor: condition in an experiment that is unchanged, providing a standard for comparison when analyzing experimental results; 19, 22

control group: the group in an experiment that exhibits the unchanged factors; 22

cotyledon [kaht-ul-EED-un]: the portion of a seed that contains the stored food; 195

crop: in certain animals, enlarged portion of the digestive tract that is specialized for temporary storage of the food; 121, 122

cross-pollination: the transfer of pollen grains from the anther of one flower to the pistil (stigma) of another flower; 281

cross section: section cut at a right angle to the length of an object; 113

culture: the growth of microorganisms or cells in a prepared nutrient medium such as agar; (medium for) 151, 158, 181; (pure) 158, 161

cyst [SIST]: in protists, a hard covering around the living material that resists extreme temperatures and strong chemicals, allowing the organism to survive unfavorable conditions; 132

cytoplasm [SITE-uh-plaz-um]: granular liquid material between the nucleus and outside boundary of all cells; 93, 105, 131

D

data [DATE-uh]: information collected from an experiment; sing. *datum;* (collecting and recording) 9-11; (graphing) 26-38; (storing) 12-13

DDT: a chemical developed in 1942 to kill disease-carrying insects such as flies, ticks, and lice; letters stand for **d**ichloro-**d**iphenyl-**t**richloroethane; 385-386

deficiency [dih-FISH-un-see] **disease:** a condition resulting from the lack of one or more vitamins; 373, 374

deoxyribonucleic [dee-ahk-see-RYE-bo-new-klee-ik] **acid (DNA):** a chemical believed to be responsible for the passing on of features from generation to generation; 344

dependent variable: the experimental factor that depends on, or changes because of, the independent variable; 26

detergent: synthetic substance developed to take the place of soaps; 386-387

dichotomous [dye-KAHT-uh-mus]: refers to an "either-or" type of classifying objects into groups; 62

dicotyledon [dye-kaht-ul-EED-un]: any seed plant that has two seed leaves, or cotyledons; also called a *dicot;* 193, 197, 233

diet: daily food intake; 365-367

diffusion [dif-YU-zhun]: the movement of particles, such as molecules, from an area of high concentration to an area of lower concentration; 235, 237

digestion: the process of breaking down complex foods into simpler compounds; 317-318, 333

digestive system: the organ system that works to break down foods into substances the organism can use; (in earthworm) 120-122; (in frog and human) 317-318, 333-336

dominant trait: one of a pair of different characteristics that is stronger than, or masks, the other in the pair; 344

dormant: term applied to organisms such as seeds in a state of inactivity, or dormancy; 193, 200

dorsal: refers to the back, or top side, of an organism; 319

E

ear: sensory organ of the nervous system that permits hearing; (in frog) 303; (in human) 316

ecology [ih-KAHL-uh-jee]: the study of the relationships among living things and their environment; 361

egg cell: female reproductive cell; the ovule in a seed plant; 280, 281, 283

electron microscope: microscope in which a beam of electrons functions in a way similar to rays of light in a light microscope; magnetic coils focus the beam of electrons; 104

embryo [EM-bree-oh]: a developing organism; (in plants) 193-194, 283, 289-290

endosperm [EN-duh-sperm]: the tissue in some seeds that contains stored foods; 196, 283

environment [en-VY-run-ment]: the living and nonliving surroundings of an organism; 339-340, 354-355, 360-361; (pollution of) 382-387, 390-396

enzyme [EN-zime]: a catalyst produced by living cells that aids a chemical reaction within the organism; 241-242; (and digestion) 333, 334, 335

epidermis [ep-ih-DER-miss]: the outer tissue of a root, stem, leaf, and other plant parts; also, the outer layer of the skin in animals; (in plants) 110-111, 113; (in human) 316

epiglottis [ep-ih-GLAHT-iss]: the flap of muscle that partially covers the opening to the trachea during swallowing; 317, 320

esophagus [ee-SAHF-uh-gus]: the food tube, or gullet, that connects the mouth and the stomach; 121, 321, 335

eustachian [yoo-STAY-shun] **tube:** the tube connecting the pharynx with the middle ear; 316, 321

experimental group: the group in an experiment that exhibits the only factor changed in the experiment; 22

eye: sensory organ of the nervous system that permits sight; (in frog) 303, 304; (in human) 129, 316

eyepiece lens: microscope lens that, when used with the objective lens, gives the microscope its total magnification; the lens closest to the user's eye; also called the *ocular lens;* 73, 74

eye spot: in some protists, a primitive form of eye capable of distinguishing light and dark; 127, 128, 129

F

family: the division of plant and animal orders that is further divided into genera (pl. of genus); 57, 58

fats: chemical compound needed by the body and used by body cells to produce energy; 366, 376; (test for) 369

fertilization [fert-ul-uh-ZAY-shun]: the joining of an egg cell with a sperm cell; (in plants) 281

field of view: the lighted circular area seen through a microscope; 76; (measuring) 81-82

filament: in a flower, the stalk of the stamen; 279

fission [FISH-un]: method of reproduction in which one cell divides into two cells about the same size as the original cell; 127

flagellum [flah-JEL-um]: in certain protists, the whiplike projection of cytoplasm used for locomotion; pl. *flagella;* 131, 174

flaming: process of placing the end of an inoculating loop into a flame, heating until it is red hot, and then not allowing the loop to touch another surface while it cools; the flamed loop is used to transfer bacteria; 171

flower: the part of certain plants that contains the reproductive organs; 277-281, 286-287

focus: to bring into clear view; (with microscope) 76-78

food chain: the food relationship between producers and consumers, and in which, generally, the larger organisms eat the smaller organisms for food; 129, 130, 356; (and DDT) 386, 387

food group: one of four groups of food that a balanced diet should include each day; the four food groups are milk, meat, bread-cereal, and vegetable-fruit; 367

fruit: the edible, fleshy part of a plant that develops from the ovary of the flower; 278, 289-290

function: the task or job something performs; an object's function is usually closely related to its structure; 88, 108-111, 114-115, 295

fungicide [FUN-jih-side]: a chemical used to stop mold growth; 151

G

gall bladder: small sac attached to the liver and small intestine, used to store the bile produced by the liver; 335

gene [JEEN]: part of a chromosome that carries one inherited trait; 344

genetics [juh-NET-iks]: the study of heredity; 344

genus [JEE-nus]: the division of plant and animal families that is further divided into species; pl. *genera;* 57, 58

geotaxis [jee-oh-TAK-sis]: in freely moving protists or simple animals, a response or reaction to gravity; 144

geotropism [jee-AH-truh-piz-um]: in plants, a response or reaction to gravity; 216, 219

germicide [JER-mih-side]: a chemical used to kill microorganisms; 180

germination [jer-mih-NAY-shun]: sprouting of the seed when conditions are favorable; 192, 193, 200; (calculating percentage of) 198

gibberellic [jib-uh-REL-ik] **acid:** a plant growth hormone; 224, 225-229

gizzard [GIZ-erd]: in earthworms, insects, and birds, the muscular organ used for grinding food; 121

glottis [GLAHT-us]: the opening in the back of the throat that leads to the trachea in the frog and also to the esophagus in the human; 317, 320, 321

glucose [GLUE-kos]: a simple sugar used by cells for energy; also, a product of photosynthesis; 113, 114, 260, 333; (test for) 239-240, 368

glycogen [GLY-kuh-jin]: an animal starch, stored in the liver and muscles; 372

graph: a picturelike way of showing information, useful for analyzing data for patterns or relationships; 26-28, 34-36

guard cell: one of two epidermal cells that surround a stoma and regulate the gases entering and leaving the leaf; 110, 111

gullet: food tube or opening to esophagus; also, passageway to food vacuole in paramecium; 129, 320, 321

H

habitat [HAB-ih-tat]: the physical environment in which an organism lives; 299

heart: muscular organ of the circulatory system that pumps the blood; (in earthworm) 117; (in frog) 329, 330-331; (in human) 329, 332

Helmont, Jan van: Belgian scientist who, in the 1800s, conducted an experiment to see if plants use soil for food; 257-259

heredity: the inherited traits of an organism; 344

hibernation [hy-ber-NAY-shun]: in certain animals, the spending of winter months in an inactive condition; 302

histogram [HISS-tuh-gram]: a type of bar graph that relates information about a population; 342-343

Hooke, Robert: English scientist (1635-1703) credited with inventing the compound microscope and, viewing a thin slice of cork, to be the first to use the term "cells"; 72, 88, 89

horizontal axis: on a graph, the axis that runs along the bottom of the graph and on which, usually, is charted the independent variable; also called the x-axis; 26, 27, 30, 31

hormone: chemical produced by living cells that affects certain cellular activities in an organism; plant hormones are called *auxins;* 220, 224

hydrosphere [HY-druh-sfeer]: the earth's waters (the oceans, rivers, lakes, etc.); 387

hydrotropism [hy-DRAH-truh-piz-um]: the response or reaction of roots to water; 215

I, J

image [IM-ij]: the likeness of an object as seen through a microscope; 74

imperfect flower: one that contains only male parts or only female parts; 286

impermeable [im-PUR-me-uh-bul]: allowing no substances to pass through, as in an *impermeable membrane;* 237

incisor [in-SY-zer] **tooth:** one of the front teeth adapted for biting or cutting food; 317, 322

incubate [IN-kyu-bate]: to provide ideal conditions (usually warmth) for growth and development, as in the incubation of eggs or bacteria; 165, 181

independent variable: the factor in an experiment that is determined in advance as the one that will be changed; 26

inoculating [in-AHK-yuh-late-ing] **loop:** wire loop used to transfer bacteria; 171

insecticide [in-SEK-tih-side]: a chemical used to kill insects; DDT is an example; 385-386

interdependence [int-er-dih-PEN-dents]: a state in which cells or organisms depend on other cells or organisms for complete functioning; (within a community) 360-361

internal respiration: respiration at a cellular level; 318

interpretation: the answer to a question about why something has happened; 4, 22

intestine: tubular organ of the digestive system through which most of the absorption of food materials into the bloodstream occurs; (in earthworm) 122; (in frog and human) 317-318, 327, 328, 333-336

K

kidney: bean-shaped organ that filters waste products out of the blood; 316, 318

kingdom: the largest division in the classification of living things, further divided into phyla; 57, 58

L

leaf: growing from a stem, the plant organ that makes sugar by photosynthesis and through which respiration occurs; 110-111, 113-115, 259-260; (pigments in) 273

Leeuwenhoek, Anton van: Dutch naturalist (1632-1723) known for his skillful grinding of lenses and careful observations of microorganisms; 71-72, 129, 167

life processes: activities characteristic of living things, such as motion, food intake and use, reproduction, and reaction to stimuli; 54-55

line graph: connected data points, resulting in a line that shows a comparison between two variables; 26-28, 32-33, 34-36

line of best fit: on a graph, smooth line showing the general pattern of the data, though it may not pass directly through all the plot points; 35

Lister, Lord Joseph: English surgeon (1827-1912) who developed the aseptic technique; 176-177

liver: organ in the digestive system that produces digestive enzymes such as bile; 317, 327, 328, 334

lung: saclike organ in the respiratory system; (in frog) 306, 307, 309, 323, 327, 328; (in human) 316, 324, 327

M

mammal: one of a large group of warm-blooded, vertebrate animals that have fur or hair on their bodies, feed their young with milk, and have four-chambered hearts; 58, 61

medium: material such as agar on which molds and other microorganisms are grown; also, material such as water used in preparing wet mount slides; (for cultures) 151, 158; (for mounting) 75

membrane: a thin layer of living or nonliving material; in cells, the living, outside boundary; (in cells) 92, 93, 242; (and diffusion) 237-238

mesophyll [MEZ-uh-fill]: leaf tissue made up of a palisade layer and a spongy layer, and separating the upper and lower epidermis; 113-114, 116

metabolism [meh-TAB-uh-liz-um]: the total chemical processes of the body; 318

metamorphosis [met-uh-MOR-fuh-siss]: a change, as from egg to larva to adult insect or from egg to tadpole to adult frog; 297, 299

meter (m): basic unit of length in the metric system; equivalent to 39.37 inches in the English system; 8, 9, 80-81

metric system: a worldwide system of measurement that is based on multiples of 10 and uses the meter (length), gram (mass), and liter (volume) as basic units; 8, 9, 80-81

micron: 1/1,000 of a millimeter, or one-millionth of a meter; symbol μ [myu]; 80-81

microorganism [my-kro-OR-guh-niz-um]: tiny living thing so small that it can be seen only through a microscope; 68, 128

microscope: basic research tool that uses sets of lenses or other means to magnify tiny objects invisible to the unaided eye; 69-87, 104

millimeter (mm): 1/1,000 of a meter; about the thickness of a dime; 8, 9, 80-81

mineral: a chemical element or compound that is important to life and occurs naturally in the earth's crust; 366, 367, 373

mitosis [my-TOE-sis]: in complex organisms, the process by which a cell and its nucleus divide in two; 108, 195

molar tooth: tooth with large, irregular surface used for grinding food; 317, 322

mold: a fuzzy-looking, nongreen protist that is either a parasite or a saprophyte; 147-151, 158-163

molecule [MAHL-ih-kyul]: the smallest particle of any substance that still has the properties of that substance; 235

monocotyledon [mahn-uh-kaht-ul-EED-un]: any seed plant that has only one seed leaf, or cotyledon; also called a *monocot;* 193, 197, 233

muscle: a tissue in many animals that contracts to produce movement; (in earthworm) 118-119

mutation: a permanent change in a gene; 170, 185

N

nectar: sweet liquid secreted by certain plants; chief raw material of honey; 286

negative taxis: in freely moving protists or simple animals, a response or reaction away from a stimulus; 140, 142

nervous system: the collection of nerve cells and sense organs that supply an organism with information about its surroundings; 316, 318-319; (nerve cell) 91, 109

nonviable [nahn-VY-uh-bul]: term applied to any seed that is not able to germinate because the embryo is not alive or is poorly formed; 193

normal curve: the bell-shaped graph line of a normal distribution, showing a small number of individuals or scores at the extreme ends and an increasing number toward the middle of the range; 343, 348

nucleus [NOO-klee-us]: the round body in the cytoplasm of most plant and animal cells that controls the activities of the cell; pl. *nuclei;* 92, 93, 105; (mitosis in) 108

nutrient [NOO-tree-ent]: nourishment, or food; 151, 158, 365-367, 373-374; (testing for) 368-369

O

objective lens: the lens of a microscope that is nearest the object being observed; most compound microscopes have a low-power and a high-power objective; 73-74

observation: the careful inspection of some object or event; also, a statement that describes something experienced or measured; 4, 22

ocular lens: the eyepiece lens on a microscope; 73, 74

open community: environmental area in which the populations may come and go; a prairie is an example; 361

order: the division of plant and animal classes that is further divided into families; 57, 58; (of mammals) 61

organ: a combination of different tissues that work together to perform a particular function; examples of organs include leaves, stems, stomachs, and brains; 68, 109, 189, 191, 295

organic [or-GAN-ik] **matter:** material that is or once was alive; 147

organism [OR-guh-niz-um]: an individual living protist, plant, or animal; 67

organization: arrangement in a logical manner; 11-2, 9-10, 42-46

organ system: a combination of different organs that work together to perform certain functions; 68, 110; (in earthworm) 117-122; (in frog and human) 315-336

osmosis [ahz-MO-siss]: process by which water passes through a living membrane from an area of high concentration to an area of lower concentration; 233, 238, 241-242, 244

ovary [OVE-uh-ree]: the female organ of reproduction that contains the egg cells; (in flowers) 280, 283, 285, 290; (in frog) 336

ovule [AWV-yule]: in seed plants, the egg cell formed in the ovary of the female flower; 280, 281, 283

oxygen [AWK-sih-jin]: colorless, odorless gas found in the air; necessary for respiration and a product of photosynthesis; (and blood) 332; (and photosynthesis) 114, 259-260, 266; (and respiration) 204; (test for) 207-208, 272

P, Q

palisade [pal-uh-SADE] **layer:** the dense portion of the mesophyllic tissue in green leaves, consisting of one or more rows of chlorophyll-containing palisade cells; 113, 114, 260

pancreas [PAN-kree-us]: organ of the digestive system, located behind the stomach, that produces digestive enzymes; 327, 335

parasite [PAIR-uh-site]: any organism that takes its nourishment from a living plant or animal; 147

pasteurization [pass-chuh-rih-ZAY-shun]: the process of heating and then cooling milk to kill or retard the growth of bacteria; 169-170

pelvic girdle: the group of bones that protect the intestine and reproductive organs; 324

penicillin [pen-uh-SILL-in]: antibiotic developed from the blue-green mold *Penicillium;* 151, 170

perfect flower: one that contains both stamens and pistil, though some other parts may be missing; 286

permeable [PUR-me-uh-bul]: allowing substances to pass through, as in a *permeable membrane;* 237

petal: one of the usually colored parts of a flower; 279

pharynx [FAIR-inks]: part of the digestive tract between the mouth cavity and the esophagus; 120, 317, 320, 321

phloem [FLO-um]: the tissue in roots and stems that conducts dissolved food substances downward; 114, 116, 233, 249, 252

photosynthesis [fote-un-SIN-thuh-siss]: process by which glucose sugar is made in the cells of green plants; 113-114, 259-261, 266, 269

phototaxis [fote-uh-TAK-siss]: in freely moving protists or simple animals, a response or reaction to light; 140, 142

phototropism [fo-TAH-truh-piz-um]: in plants, a response or reaction to light; 219

phylum [FY-lum]: the division of plant and animal kingdoms that is further divided into classes; pl. *phyla;* 57, 58

physiology [fizz-ee-AHL-uh-jee]: the study of how tissues and organs function; 295

pigment: a distinctive or hidden color in leaves and other plant organs; 273, 275

pistil: the female reproductive system in a flower, consisting of the ovary, style, and stigma; 279, 280, 284-285

plasmolysis [plaz-MAHL-ih-siss]: the shrinking of cytoplasm in a cell due to a loss of water; 244

plot point: a data point marked on a graph to show the values of the independent variable and the dependent variable at a given time; 28

pollen grain: male reproductive structure in flowers that contains sperm cells and is formed in the anther; 279, 281, 283

pollen tube: the structure that develops from a pollen grain after landing on the stigma of a pistil, providing a pathway for the sperm nuclei to travel to the ovules; 283, 285

pollination: the transfer of pollen from stamen (anther) to pistil (stigma); 281

pollution: a condition brought about by an overabundance of undesirable materials; 340, 382-383; (of water) 383-384, 386-387, 390-393; (of air) 384-385, 393-395

population: the living organisms of one kind that live in a given area at a given time; 341, 354-355, 358; (variations in) 342-344, 349

positive taxis: in freely moving protists or simple animals, a response or reaction toward a stimulus; 140, 142

posterior: toward the rear of an organism; 319

producer: any green plant or protist; the starting link in any food chain; 356-358

protein: chemical compound needed by the body, supplying the materials the body needs for growth and repair; 366, 372-373; (test for) 368-369

protist: a microorganism that possesses certain simple characteristics of both plants and animals; examples are algae, protozoa, molds, and bacteria; 125-132, 135-136

protozoan [prote-uh-ZOH-un]: a one-celled protist capable of locomotion; examples include vorticella, paramecium, ameba, stentor, euglena, and chlamydomonas; pl. *protozoa;* 125, 131

pseudopod [SUED-uh-pod]: a "false foot", as in an ameba, used for food-getting and locomotion; 131

pure culture: a mold or bacterial growth containing only one type of colony; 158, 161

R

random sample: the process of selecting by chance, as the drawing of numbers from a hat: 343

receptacle [rih-SEP-tih-kul]: the enlarged base of a flower that connects it to the stem and bears the reproductive structures; 284

recessive trait: one of a pair of different characteristics that is weaker than, or "hidden by", the other in the pair; 344

reproduction: the process of giving rise to offspring and thus continuing a species; (in mold) 147-148, 161-162; (in plants) 281-283; (in protozoa) 127; (in yeast) 157

reproductive system: the organ system that works to ensure the continuation of the species by producing sperm cells or egg cells and usually providing protection for developing embryos; 279-283, 324, 326

respiration [res-puh-RAY-shun]: in all living cells, the process that combines oxygen and food molecules to release energy; carbon dioxide and water are waste products of the process; also called *internal* respiration; 204, 318

response: the reaction to a stimulus; 140, 211-212

root: the organ of a plant that holds the plant in the soil and absorbs water and minerals into the plant; 212, 213, 215, 232, 233, 244

root hair: a projection of an epidermal cell of a young root; 215, 232

S

sampling: a process that uses random selection to obtain a general, or overall, picture of a large area; 355, 358

saprophyte [SAP-ruh-fite]: any plant that lives on dead organic matter; 147

scarifying [SCAR-ih-fy-ing]: the process by which seeds are scratched in order to hasten germination; 200

Schleiden, Matthias: German biologist (1804-1881) credited, with Schwann,. for the cell theory; 88, 90

Schwann, Theodor: German biologist (1810-1882) credited, with Schleiden, for the cell theory; 88, 90

scurvy: a deficiency disease resulting from a lack of vitamin C and characterized by bleeding gums, loosened teeth, and roughened skin; 373, 374

seed: the fertilized, ripened ovule of a flowering plant, containing an embryo and stored food and protected by a seed coat; 192-193, 197, 204, 281-283, 289-290

seed coat: the hard covering that protects a seed; 193, 194

seedling: a small or young plant grown from a seed; 193

self-pollination: the transfer of pollen from anther to stigma in the same flower or with another flower on the same plant; 281

semipermeable [sem-ih-PUR-me-uh-bul]: allowing different substances to pass through in different amounts, as in a *semipermeable membrane;* 238

sepal [SEEP-ul]: the leaflike, usually green, outermost part of a flower that serves to protect the parts of the flower in the bud; not involved in the reproductive process; 279

serial [SEER-ee-ul] **dilution:** the process of making progressively diluted suspensions of microorganisms in order to count or isolate cells; 182

sex-linked trait: term applied to any hereditary trait that is passed on by males only or by females only; 344

simple microscope: a microscope that contains only one lens; a magnifying glass is an example; 70-72

skeletal system: the organ system in advanced animals that serves to protect and support the internal organs of the animal; (in frog) 323, 324; (in human) 324

skull: the bone in the head that protects the brain; 323, 324

slope line: on a line graph, the smooth line that connects all the plot points; 28

smog: a condition brought about by the action of ultraviolet radiation from sunlight on waste gases in the atmosphere; 384-385

species [SPEE-sheez]: the smallest division in the classification of living things; the subdivision of a genus; 57, 58

spectrum: rainbow of colors produced when white light is passed through a prism; also occurs when sunlight passes through raindrops; 269

sperm cell: male reproductive cell; in flowers, contained in a pollen grain; 279, 281, 283

spirillum [spy-RILL-um]: any spiral-shaped bacterium; pl. *spirilla;* 174, 176

spongy layer: the less-dense layer of mesophyllic tissue in a leaf, consisting of loosely packed, chlorophyll-containing spongy cells; 113, 114, 260

spore: protected reproductive cell of a mold or bacterium, capable of producing a complete new colony when conditions are favorable; 147-149, 151, 161, 163

spore case: thick structure that holds mold spores; 160, 161

stamen [STAY-min]: the male reproductive structure in a flower, consisting of a filament and an anther; 279, 280, 281, 283

starch: a carbohydrate food form; the form in which food is stored in green plants; 195, 263, 266, 366; (test for) 195, 264-265, 368

sterilize: to kill all microorganisms in an area, in a substance, or on an object; 151, 158; (sterile technique) 161-162

sternum: the flat bone, or breastbone, in the center of the chest; 324

stigma: the sticky top of the pistil that receives pollen grains; 280, 281, 283

stimulus [STIM-yuh-lus]: a condition that brings about a reaction; pl. *stimuli;* 139-140, 211-213, 215-216, 219

stoma [STO-mah]: pore in a leaf through which water vapor and other gases travel in and out; pl. *stomata;* 110-111, 113, 114, 231, 235

stomach: in many animals, pouchlike organ of the digestive system; 317, 327, 328, 333, 334, 335

style: the stalk of the pistil of a flower; 281

sugar: a carbohydrate food form; in glucose form, a product of photosynthesis; 114, 260, 333, 366; (test for glucose) 239-240, 368

T

tadpole: the larval stage of a frog or toad; 297, 299, 300

taxis: in freely moving protists or simple animals, a response involving locomotion or movement of the entire organism; 140, 142

theory: an explanation of relationships among observed facts or phenomena; (cell theory) 88-89

thermotaxis [thur-muh-TAK-siss]: in freely moving protists or simple animals, a reaction to heat or cold; 140, 143

thigmotaxis [thig-muh-TAK-siss]: in freely moving protists or simple animals, a response to touch or contact; 140

tissue: a group of cells similar in structure and function; 68, 109, 113-115, 118

tongue [TUNG]: muscular organ of the digestive system; (in frog) 304, 305, 317, 320, 321; (in human) 317

trachea [TRAY-kee-uh]: tubular organ of the respiratory system between the pharynx and the lungs; 316, 317

trait: characteristic; (inherited) 344

transpiration [trans-puh-RAY-shun]: the loss of water

through the leaves of plants; 232, 252

tropism: a growth response by a plant to a stimulus; 140, 211

turgor [TUR-gur] **pressure:** the stiffness of plant cells due to the presence of water; 243

U

ultraviolet light: radiation in sunlight; used to slow the growth of microorganisms; 149, 170, 180

V

vacuole [VAK-yu-wole]: a clear area in the cytoplasm of a cell; 92, 93

variable factor: the single factor in an experiment that is changed between the experimental and control groups; 22

vascular bundle: the conducting and supporting tissue of a plant, composed mainly of xylem and phloem cells; 114, 116, 233

vein: in a leaf, the vascular tissue; in an animal, any blood vessel that carries blood toward the heart; (in leaf) 114, 235; (in animal) 329

ventral: refers to the underside of an organism; 319

ventricle: the thick-walled pumping section of the heart; 329, 331, 332

vertebra [VERT-ih-brah]: a bone of the spinal column in vertebrates; pl. *vertebrae;* 323, 324

vertebrate: any animal that has a spine or vertebral column (backbone); 55, 296

vertical axis: on a graph, the up-and-down axis on which, usually, is charted the dependent variable; also called the *y*-axis; 26, 27, 30, 31

Vesalius, Andreas: Belgian anatomist and artist (1514-1564); 296

viable [VY-uh-bul]: term applied to any plant embryo that is alive and capable of germinating; 193, 197

virus: a noncellular "organism" composed of a nucleic acid core and a protein shell; may or may not be living, as it can reproduce only within a living cell; 1-2, 57, 127

vitamin: a nutrient essential for normal body activities; 366, 367, 373, 374

W

warm-blooded: term applied to birds and mammals, whose body temperatures remain fairly constant regardless of the outside temperature; 309

water: the most widely distributed compound known; essential to life; (in plants) 231-235, 244, 249, 252, 266; (in photosynthesis) 259-260; (human consumption of) 366, 392

wet mount slide: microscope slide preparation that entails adding a drop of water to the object to be viewed so it appears more natural and without distortion; 75-76

X, Y, Z

x-**axis:** the horizontal axis on a graph, usually containing the independent variable; 26, 27, 30, 31

xylem [ZY-lum]: the thick-walled, large-diameter tube cells in roots and stems that conduct water and dissolved minerals upward; 114, 116, 233, 249, 252

y-**axis:** the vertical axis on a graph, usually containing the dependent variable; 26, 27, 30, 31

yeast: a nongreen protist that forms spores and reproduces by budding; 147-157

ABCDEFGHIJ 08543210798
Printed in the United States of America